MONOGRAPHS IN STATISTICAL PHYSICS AND THERMODYNAMICS

Volume 1
Non-Equilibrium Statistical Mechanics
by I. PRIGOGINE

Volume 2
Thermodynamics
With quantum statistical illustrations
by P. T. LANDSBERG

Volume 3
Ionic Solution Theory
Based on cluster expansion methods
by HAROLD L. FRIEDMAN

Volume 4
Statistical Mechanics of Charged Particles
by R. BALESCU

Volume 5
Order-Disorder Phenomena
by H. S. GREEN and C. A. HURST

Volume 6
Theory of Spin Relaxation
by W. J. CASPERS

Volume 7
Ergodic Theory in Statistical Mechanics
by I. E. FARQUHAR

Volume 8
The Statistical Mechanics of Simple Liquids
by STUART A. RICE and PETER GRAY

MONOGRAPHS IN STATISTICAL PHYSICS AND THERMODYNAMICS

Editor: I. PRIGOGINE
Professor of Physical Chemistry and of Theoretical Physics
Université Libre, Brussels, Belgium

VOLUME 8

WR Lu

THE STATISTICAL MECHANICS OF SIMPLE LIQUIDS

An Introduction to the Theory of Equilibrium and Non-Equilibrium Phenomena

STUART A. RICE

The University of Chicago

PETER GRAY

University of Newcastle-upon-Tyne

INTERSCIENCE PUBLISHERS 1965

a division of John Wiley & Sons, Inc., New York · London · Sydney

Library of Congress Catalog Card Number 65-14731

PRINTED IN THE UNITED STATES OF AMERICA

To our families:

Marian, Barbara, and Janet Rice

Barbara, Alexander, and Simon Gray

Preface

The liquid state has long been regarded as presenting the least tractable of all problems in the field of classical statistical mechanics. Indeed, the view is often expressed that although the statistical mechanics of the gaseous and crystalline states is, in principle, well understood, there is no acceptable theory of the liquid state. It is the purpose of this book to show that this view is obsolescent.

The first attempts to develop a theory of the equilibrium properties of liquids based solely on the principles of statistical mechanics, without the use of simplified models, are now almost thirty years old. From these early researches two different approaches to the classical many body problem have developed: systematic cluster (density) expansions, following from the analysis of Mayer, and the integral equation formalism defining the relationship between the distribution functions for subsets of molecules and the intermolecular potential, following from the work of Kirkwood and Yvon. Contemporary studies of the theory of liquids ordinarily fall into one or other of these categories and still owe much to the original analyses. Disregarding model calculations, the evolution of techniques permitting quantitative prediction of the equilibrium properties of a simple dense fluid has been slow. The work of the late 1930's and early 1940's was devoted primarily to extensions and improvements of the cluster expansion formalism, to the qualitative discussion of critical phenomena, to the attempt to obtain qualitatively correct radial distribution functions from approximate integral equations, and to the development of theories of dielectric phenomena, fusion, etc. Since 1946 the theory of the equilibrium properties of liquids has developed rapidly, stimulated both by advances in analysis and by the availability of high-speed computing machinery. As described in this book, it is now possible to make accurate calculations of the equilibrium properties of a fluid at densities as large as one-third to one-half of normal liquid densities. At higher densities the agreement between theory and experiment falls off, but nowhere is theory qualitatively incorrect, except in the study of the critical region and phase changes.

The history of the theory of non-equilibrium processes in liquids is shorter. Indeed, except for the work of Enskog in 1922, it was not until 1946 that serious attempts were made to develop a statistical mechanical theory of transport suitable for the description of processes in dense fluids. Of those concerned with the theory at its inception the names Kirkwood, Born and Green, Bogolubov, and Yvon are foremost. It was through the work of Kirkwood and collaborators that a theory of transport processes, specifically applicable to liquids, was developed. The theory dealt only with quasi-steady phenomena, which can be treated in terms of random processes of the Markov type. Owing to the complexity of the strong interactions present in a liquid, the theory had a large intuitive content. In the early work, only order of magnitude agreement between theory and experiment was obtained, but with the refinements of the last four years, significant improvements in the accuracy of calculated transport coefficients have been achieved. At present, the agreement between theory and experiment is quantitative, but limited by the accuracy of the available equilibrium distribution functions.

In this book we are concerned primarily with the theory of transport in simple liquids. However, since the theory of transport draws heavily on the theory of the equilibrium properties, we have also developed the equilibrium theory extensively. In addition to developing the theory in detail, an attempt has been made to compare theory and experiment wherever possible, and to confront the reader with a description of the level and sophistication of the current understanding of the properties of liquids. We have attempted, therefore, to attain three goals:

(*1*) The provision of a systematic and coherent description of the theory of liquids, as it now stands, emphasizing the analysis and assessment of the approximations made and the relationship between theory and experiment,

(*2*) The encouragement of further study, by exposing the theory in a manner which directs attention to the fundamental problems,

(*3*) The provision of an account of the theory suitable as an introduction to research.

The philosophy of our analysis cannot be better expressed than in the words of Lord Kelvin:

"Where you can measure what you are speaking about and express it in numbers, you know something about it, and when you cannot measure it, when you cannot express it in numbers, your knowledge is of a meagre and unsatisfactory kind. It may be the beginning of knowledge, but you have scarcely in your thought advanced to the stage of a science."

It is our belief that the kinetic theory of liquids presented in this book is at a stage of development analogous to that of the mean free path theory of gases in relation to the more modern theories of, for instance, Enskog or Bogoliubov. That is, we believe that all the important qualitative features of the physical problem are incorporated, and that the good agreement between theory and experiment is meaningful. We offer no excuse for presenting a theory which has some rather crude features: indeed, we feel that a candid review of the overall situation at the present time may lead to significant advances in the near future.

There remains only the pleasant task of thanking our many friends and collaborators. Our debt of gratitude to the late Professor J. G. Kirkwood cannot be overstated. Both through his papers and personal contact (with S.A.R.) he has stimulated much of the work reported here. It is also a pleasure to acknowledge the contributions to this subject of Dr. A. R. Allnatt, Dr. B. J. Berne, Professor H. T. Davis, Professor R. A. Harris, Dr. L. D. Ikenberry, Dr. B. A. Lowry, and Dr. J. Naghizadeh. During the period in which this book was written we derived great benefit from lively discussions with Dr. B. J. Berne and our colleagues at the University of Chicago, and are most grateful to Professor J. W. Stout for his critical reading of the manuscript.

Professor P. Resibois and Dr. G. Severne of the University of Brussels provided valuable criticisms of Chapter 7, for which we wish to thank them.

Several of the diagrams used in this book have been reproduced from the original publications. We are grateful to the *Journal of Chemical Physics*, the University of Chicago Press, the *Physics of Fluids*, the *Physical Review*, and the editors and authors concerned for permission to use these figures. A large fraction of Chapter 2 was used by the authors as a supplement to the book by I. Z. Fisher, *Statistical Theory of Liquids*, University of Chicago Press (1964).

Much of the research reported in this book was supported by the Directorate of Chemical Sciences of the Air Force Office of Scientific Research, by the Petroleum Research Fund of the American Chemical Society, and by the Alfred P. Sloan Foundation. One of us (P.G.) is greatly indebted to Professor G. S. Rushbrooke and the Senate of the University of Newcastle-upon-Tyne for a year's leave of absence, during which this book was written, and to the United States Educational Commission for a Fulbright Travel Grant. Finally, we wish to acknowledge the skill and patience Mrs. Ruth Patterson has shown in deciphering our handwriting, and to thank her for preparing the typescript and putting up with the almost endless stream of changes in the draft manuscript.

Department of Chemistry and
Institute for the Study of Metals,
The University of Chicago, Chicago

STUART A. RICE

Department of Physics,
University of Newcastle-upon-Tyne,
Newcastle-upon-Tyne, England

PETER GRAY

Contents

CHAPTER 1

Introduction

The liquid phase generically defines a state of matter which is stable at densities and temperatures intermediate between the regions of stability of the solid and gaseous states. Exceptions to this rule occur in a few cases; for instance, water is most dense at 4°C, and is there denser than ice at 0°C. Compression of a liquid eventually causes it to solidify. Compression of a gas always causes it to condense, if the temperature is below the critical temperature. Both liquids and gases can be included in a wider class, called fluids; that is, substances that flow. Thus, fluids deform continuously under an applied shear stress. Solids, on the other hand, adopt a constant deformation (unless the applied stress is large enough to cause fracture or the time scale long enough to allow creep deformation). Liquids and gases may be distinguished by the difference in typical densities and compressibilities, except near the critical point, where these and other properties merge. Thus, the density of a liquid is of the same order as that of its parent solid, while that of the derived gas may be one thousand times less, at atmospheric pressure. At high pressures, however, the density of the gaseous phase may be raised to the same order as that of the liquid phase, since the gas is much more compressible at low pressures than is the liquid. In a highly compressed state, then, the gas phase may not be clearly distinguishable from the liquid phase by its density or compressibility. However, at all densities, liquids and gases differ by the former's ability to form a free surface.

The liquid state is therefore similar to the solid state, and differs from the gaseous state, in respect of its high density, low compressibility, and ability to form a free surface. It is similar to the gaseous state in respect of its fluidity. These properties of the three phases can be understood qualitatively at a microscopic level in terms of the interplay between the thermal motion of the molecules and the intermolecular spacing. The main points are these: the molecules of a solid occupy sites on a lattice, containing basic geometrical units repeated regularly over large distances on a microscopic scale. Thermal motion takes the form of small vibrations about the lattice sites. The molecules of a liquid, on the other hand, do not occupy lattice sites, but the linear extent of their thermal motion is limited by the proximity of neighboring molecules. Thus, while solids possess a long range order by virtue of their lattice structure, liquids possess only a short range order, which is imposed by purely geometric considerations concerned with molecular packing, i.e., determined by the relative volume of the molecules and of the space available for them to move in. The low compressibility of both solid and liquid is explained by the near close-packing of the two phases. The difference in response to shear stress arises simply because in the solid phase molecules do not have enough thermal energy to leave lattice sites, so that the lattice structure resists shear, while in the liquid phase there is no lattice structure and the liquid deforms continuously. If, however, a shear is applied to a liquid very rapidly, the liquid may respond elastically because it has not had time to flow. We may consider this dynamical response from another point of view. The motion of a molecule in a liquid is very disordered or chaotic compared to the motion in a solid. Molecules of a liquid are continually changing position and moving through the body of the liquid. This process is called diffusion, and a study of the mathematical model of diffusion, or random walk, shows that the extent of diffusion can be measured by the mean-square distance that a molecule is displaced in unit time. If the stress is applied so quickly that a molecule has not time to diffuse out of its local cell of nearest neighbors, then the local structure is preserved during the application of the stress, and the liquid behaves like a solid, i.e., elastically. Most simple liquids have diffusion coefficients of the order of 10^{-5} cm.^{2} sec.$^{-1}$, and intermolecular separations of the order of 3–4 A., so that the time τ for the relaxation of local structure, given by

$$\tau \approx \sigma^2/6D,$$

is $\tau \sim 10^{-11}$ sec.

The important differences between a gas and a liquid may be understood in terms of the difference in density. Clearly, a gas is more compressible than a liquid because it is less dense. That is, there is much more space between the molecules in a gas, which may be taken up by compression, than in a liquid. A second consequence of the low density is that a molecule may travel many times the average molecular separation without coming into collision with another molecule. The situation in a liquid is just the opposite; the high density implies that there is not sufficient space, on average, for a molecule to pass between two others. It can only do so when a space appears as a result of thermal motion. Thus, we see that in a gas the intermolecular interactions are much less important than is the thermal energy in determining molecular motion. On the other hand, in a solid, the thermal energy is a small perturbation on the intermolecular interactions which determine the lattice structure. A liquid is intermediate between these two cases: thermal energy and intermolecular interactions are equally important. The thermal motion of the molecules is chaotic, as in a gas, but each molecule is in simultaneous interaction with a number of other molecules.

It is this combination of chaotic motion and strong interactions which make the development of the theory of liquids such a challenging problem. By contrast, the theory of the solid state may be simplified in most cases by taking the lattice structure as fixed, and discussing, say, anharmonic corrections to the harmonic thermal vibrations of the molecules about their lattice sites. The theory of gases can be developed in terms of modifications to free particle motion imposed by collisions between two, three, four, $\cdots$ particles.

The difficulties inherent in the theory of liquids have so far prevented its development and application to any but the most simple substances. In this book we therefore restrict attention to the simplest possible classical models in which molecules interact by pairwise superposable spherically symmetric potentials of the Lennard-Jones type; numerical calculations and comparison with experiment are applied almost always to liquid argon.

The calculations to which the theory leads are often tedious and complex. It is inevitable that some errors remain; we hope that they are few, and that there are none of consequence. Some of the material in this book has not been previously published; we particularly draw the reader's attention to the following:

(*a*) The derivation of the cluster expansion for the three body correlation function, and the subsequent use of that expansion to improve the theory of the equation of state of the rigid sphere fluid (Chapter 2).

(*b*) The discussion of Markov processes for the case that two independent randomizing mechanisms exist (Chapter 4).

(*c*) An improved derivation of the fundamental equations of the Rice-Allnatt theory (Chapter 5).

(*d*) A simplified derivation of the autocorrelation function relations defining transport coefficients (Chapter 7).

It is hoped that this new material enhances the clarity of the presentation of the theory.

The text of this book has been divided into seven chapters.

Chapter 2 is devoted exclusively to the equilibrium theory of liquids. It is intended that this chapter should provide both a comprehensive survey of the theory and a basis for the later calculations of the transport coefficients. Initially, the theory is presented from the two differing viewpoints of cluster expansions and distribution functions. These are combined in the discussion of the various approximate integral equations for determining the radial distribution function. All the theories are discussed for which comparison with experiment has been made.

In Chapter 3, the problem of formulating a theory of irreversible processes from (reversible) classical mechanics is discussed. Attention is drawn to time reversibility, the recurrence time paradox, and other notable examples of the fundamental difficulties encountered. The classical resolutions of these problems are discussed; in particular, the meaning of irreversibility as an observable phenomenon, and the means by which kinetic equations (that is, equations describing the evolution of distribution functions and exhibiting an approach to equilibrium) may be derived from the equations of mechanics.

Some properties of random processes are discussed in Chapter 4. Particular emphasis is laid upon the application of the theory of continuous Markov processes to Brownian motion. Familiarity with the intuitive basis of this problem, and with the techniques, is essential to the understanding of kinetic theory.

In Chapters 5 and 6 we develop, and apply, a kinetic theory for simple dense fluids. Chapter 5 begins with a discussion of time coarse graining as a means of introducing a suitable probability ansatz into the equations of mechanics, whence are obtained the kinetic equations. The method of solution of these equations, due to Enskog and Hilbert, is discussed and used to perform a check on the validity of the probability ansatz. Approximate, though accurate, solutions of the kinetic equations are then obtained. Chapter 6 deals with detailed applications of the kinetic theory developed in the previous chapter. The equations of hydrodynamics are discussed first, from both a macroscopic and a microscopic viewpoint, thereby leading to the identification of the stress tensor and heat flux with certain microscopic expressions. Using these relations, the shear and bulk viscosities and thermal conductivity are calculated for liquid argon. These are followed by discussions of ion mobility, diffusion, and some related topics. Wherever possible, detailed comparisons with experiment are made.

Chapter 7 is intended to serve as a bridge between the kinetic theory specifically applied to liquids in Chapters 5 and 6, and the general theories which have not yet been developed to the point where they can be applied to liquids. We give first an account of the essential features of the rigorous kinetic theory of Prigogine and co-workers. This is followed by a review of the correlation function theory of transport coefficients, and a discussion of the relations between these theories and that of the preceding two chapters.

CHAPTER 2

Theory of the Equilibrium Properties of Fluids

2.1. INTRODUCTION (1,2)

In a liquid or dense fluid every molecule is in continuous interaction with a number of other molecules. This interaction is of dual origin: direct and indirect. In spite of the high density, the limited range of the intermolecular potential restricts the direct (energetic) interactions to those between a molecule and about its ten nearest neighbors. In addition, the strongly repulsive interactions between molecules at small separations (which can be adequately represented as "hard core" interactions for many purposes) impose density-dependent (entropic) constraints on the statistical geometry of the molecular packing. Consequently, there are strong indirect correlations between molecules extending to several times the nearest neighbor separation. Because of these interactions, liquids exhibit a local ordering. Any theory of liquids must describe, or attempt to describe, the dynamics of a sufficient number of molecules to account for this ordering.

The problem of constructing a theory is conveniently approached from two standpoints. The theory of imperfect gases develops what are known as cluster expansions (in increasing powers of the density), and here the emphasis is laid on mathematical rigor (1,2). The expansions can only be evaluated exactly for low orders in the density, and thus only dilute systems are described with complete rigor. The expansions can, however, be extended to higher orders, and, therefore, to the description of more dense systems, if rigor is sacrificed to some form of approximation. Recent developments (3–8) succeed in evaluating some of the contributions from every order, and, while they do not give quantitative agreement with experiment at liquid densities, they nevertheless do describe dense gases quite well. On the other hand, one can obtain a hierarchy of integral equations for the many-particle correlation functions which can be truncated by a number of different assumptions (9–13), each of which represents some features of the intuitive pictures of liquid structure described. This method also gives qualitative agreement with experiment for dense systems, but generally it is not possible to say which assumption is preferable, except on the basis of the agreement. The situation may be summarized by the statement that both approaches are incomplete: the well-defined mathematical approximations of the cluster theory do not, so far, give a quantitative account of the properties of liquids, and the physical assumptions of the integral equation theory often cannot be assessed in terms of the mathematical approximation involved.

2.2. SUMMARY OF THE ENSEMBLES (1,2)

2.2.A. *General Remarks*

It is convenient at the outset to introduce the most general ensemble with which we shall be dealing. By an ensemble is meant a collection of replica systems so large that the proportion of all replica systems in each state available to the particular system under discussion may be identified with the probability of finding the particular system in that state at an arbitrary instant. The most general ensemble used herein is known as the Grand Canonical Ensemble (G.C.E.). It is supposed to consist of a large number M of systems, each of volume V, and each separated from the other systems by membranes permeable to energy and matter. The state of each system is specified by its volume V (which is fixed), its composition $\mathbf{N}$, and its energy E_k. The composition $\mathbf{N}$ is the set of numbers $(N_1, \cdots, N_i, \cdots)$ of molecules of type $1, \cdots,$ type $i, \cdots,$ respectively, in the volume V. For each composition $\mathbf{N}$ a certain set of energy states is available to the system, and these are imagined grouped into levels of width ΔE, such that $E \leqslant E_k \leqslant E + \Delta E$ contains ω_k states. We have, of course,

$$\left.\begin{aligned} E_k &= E_k(\mathbf{N}) \\ \omega_k &= \omega_k(\mathbf{N}) \end{aligned}\right\}. \tag{2.2.1}$$

Following Mayer (14), we suppose that, of the M systems, m are in the kth energy level for a particular composition $\mathbf{N}$. The number of ways this can arise is denoted by $\Omega(m)$, and is given by

$$\Omega(m) = \binom{M}{m} \omega_k{}^m \Omega_r(M - m). \tag{2.2.2}$$

Here, $\binom{M}{m}$ is the number of ways m systems may be chosen from M, $\omega_k{}^m$ is the number of ways the m systems may be distributed among the ω_k states if the states have equal weight, and $\Omega_r(M - m)$ is the number of states available to the remaining (M-m) systems. $\Omega_r(M - m)$ must be evaluated subject to the constraints that the total energy and the total number of molecules of each type in the ensemble is constant. It is, of course, possible that $m \gtrless \omega_k$ in equation (2.2.2). We can define an entropy for the ensemble, for this arrangement, by

$$S(m) = k \ln \Omega(m). \tag{2.2.3}$$

Since the equilibrium configuration is defined as that for which the entropy is a maximum under conditions of constant energy and volume, the value which m must assume in equilibrium is that for which

$$\Delta S(m) = S(m) - S(m - 1) = 0 \tag{2.2.4}$$

or

$$k \ln \left(\frac{\omega}{m}(M - m + 1)\right) = -(S_r(M - m) - S_r(M - m + 1)), \tag{2.2.5}$$

where

$$S_r = k \ln \Omega_r. \tag{2.2.6}$$

The change from $(m - 1)$ to m in the number of systems in the ω_k states in the kth level involves, in the rest of the ensemble, a *decrease* of V in the volume, a *decrease* of $\mathbf{N}$ in the number of molecules, and a decrease E_k in the energy. If $M \gg m \gg 1$ and M approaches infinity, in conformity with the initial definition of the ensemble, S_r may be equated with the entropy of the system, so that

$$S_r(M - m) - S_r(M - m + 1) = -V\left(\frac{\partial S_r}{\partial V}\right)_{\mathbf{N},E} - \mathbf{N}\cdot\left(\frac{\partial S_r}{\partial \mathbf{N}}\right)_{V,E} - E_k\left(\frac{\partial S_r}{\partial E}\right)_{V,\mathbf{N}}$$
$$= k\beta(-pV + \mathbf{N}\cdot\boldsymbol{\mu} - E_k), \tag{2.2.7}$$

where k is Boltzmann's constant, $\beta \left(=\frac{1}{kT}\right)$ the inverse temperature in energy units, p is the pressure, and $\boldsymbol{\mu} = (\mu_1, \cdots, \mu_i, \cdots)$ are the chemical potentials per molecule of the various species. From equations

(2.2.5) and (2.2.7), in the limit of large M, we obtain

$$\frac{m}{M\omega_k} = \exp\,[\beta(-pV + \mathbf{N}\cdot\boldsymbol{\mu} - E_k)], \tag{2.2.8}$$

which can be interpreted as the probability that a system will, for given pressure, volume, temperature, and composition, occupy a given state of energy E_k. After multiplication by the degeneracy ω_k, it is also the probability that, in an infinitely large system of known pressure, temperature, and composition, an arbitrary volume V will be found to have a composition $\mathbf{N}$ and an energy E_k. Defining this probability by $P(E_k,\mathbf{N},V)$, we have

$$\begin{aligned}\frac{m}{M} &= P(E_k,\mathbf{N},V)\\ &= \omega_k \exp\,[\beta(-pV + \mathbf{N}\cdot\boldsymbol{\mu} - E_k)].\end{aligned} \tag{2.2.9}$$

Since we shall have occasion to deal only with one-component systems, the vector notation for $\mathbf{N}$ and $\boldsymbol{\mu}$ will be dropped from now on.

It is now convenient to introduce the Grand Partition Function (G.P.F.) by

$$\Xi = \sum_{k,N} \omega_k \exp\,[\beta(N\mu - E_k)]. \tag{2.2.10}$$

Since, by definition,

$$\sum_{k,N} P(E_k,N,V) = 1,$$

we have, from equation (2.2.9),

$$\Xi = \exp\,(\beta pV), \tag{2.2.11}$$

whereupon

$$P(E_k,N,V) = \Xi^{-1}\omega_k \exp\,[\beta(N\mu - E_k)]; \quad \text{G.C.E.} \tag{2.2.12}$$

One can now write down expressions for the entropy, mean energy, and composition according to the G.C.E.:

$$S = -k\sum_{k,\mathbf{N}} P(E_k,N,V)\ln P(E_k,N,V) + \text{constant} \tag{2.2.13}$$

$$\langle E\rangle = \sum_{k,\mathbf{N}} E_k P(E_k,N,V) \tag{2.2.14}$$

$$\langle N\rangle = \sum_{k,N} N P(E_k,N,V). \tag{2.2.15}$$

The constant term in equation (2.2.13) represents the somewhat arbitrary nature of the grouping of states into levels performed earlier.

Let us now consider the special case in which the members of the ensemble are constrained to have the same number of molecules. Such an ensemble is called the Canonical Ensemble (C.E.). The sum over N disappears and equation (2.2.12) becomes

$$P(E_k,N,V) = Q_N^{-1}\omega_k \exp(-\beta E_k); \quad \text{C.E.}, \tag{2.2.16}$$

where

$$Q_N = \sum_k \omega_k \exp(-\beta E_k). \tag{2.2.17}$$

If we further restrict the possible energies to one level E_k only, then the sum over k disappears, and we have the microcanonical ensemble, for which

$$P(E_k,N,V) = 1. \tag{2.2.18}$$

The probability of finding the system in one of the ω_k *states* of energy E_k is then ω_k^{-1} in the microcanonical ensemble.

2.2.B. *Transition to the Classical Phase Space Description* (1,2)

Hitherto, we have discussed the properties of the ensembles in terms of energy levels, a feature arising essentially from the necessity of describing microscopic phenomena in terms of quantum mechanics. In discussing the properties of liquids, such as argon, krypton, etc., whose important properties can be explained in classical terms, we shall find it more convenient to introduce the phase space description of the system. In this description we represent the state of the system by the set of momenta $\mathbf{p}^N = (\mathbf{p}_1, \mathbf{p}_2, \cdots, \mathbf{p}_N)$ and coordinates $\{N\} = (\mathbf{R}_1, \mathbf{R}_2, \cdots, \mathbf{R}_N)$ of its N constituent molecules. It is conventional to regard the state of a system as being represented by a single point $(\mathbf{p}^N,\{N\})$ in a 6 N-dimensional phase space. In this context we remark that the addition or removal of molecules to or from the system *changes the dimensionality of the phase space*, so that a phase space of a given dimensionally cannot describe the Grand Canonical Ensemble.

In setting up the classical equivalent of the canonical and microcanonical ensembles, we are led to the question: How precisely may we define the energy level in the continuous spectrum of states? According to the uncertainty principle, a point in the phase space of a particle constrained to one-dimensional motion cannot be located more closely than a "cell" of size h:

$$\Delta p\,\Delta R \sim h \tag{2.2.19}$$

and we suppose that the finest subdivision of phase space allowable in quantum mechanics is a cell of size h^{3N}. Classically, we can conceive of integrating over such a cell, but according to (2.2.19) we cannot distinguish any variation in a phase function. Turning to equation (2.2.17), we see that each term in the summation must correspond to the integral of $\exp[-\beta H(\mathbf{P}^N,\{N\})]$ over the region of the phase space for which the classical Hamiltonian $H(\mathbf{P}^N,\{N\}) = E_k$ and $E \leqslant E_k \leqslant E + \Delta E$, where ΔE is subject to equation (2.2.19). This region, or shell, has volume $N!\,h^{3N}$, because there are $N!$ permutations of the molecules among the momenta and positions for a single phase cell, for which the energy E_k is unchanged. In a rigorous treatment of the transition to a phase space description, the leading (classical) term is found to be independent of the symmetry of the molecular wave functions. Thus, the volume of the shell is *not* associated with the quantum mechanical permutation factor $(-)^P$, P being zero or unity according as the permutation is even or odd. The weighting factor ω_k, originally chosen to represent the number of quantum mechanically distinct states with energies in the interval $E \leqslant E_k \leqslant E + \Delta E$, is taken to be unity because ΔE is now the smallest distinguishable energy difference. As a result, for a single term in equation (2.2.17), we have

$$N!\,h^{3N}e^{-\beta E_k} = \int_{E\leqslant E_k\leqslant E+\Delta E}\!\!\cdots\int e^{-\beta H}\,d\mathbf{p}^N\,d\{N\} \tag{2.2.20}$$

and

$$Q_N = \frac{1}{N!\,h^{3N}}\int\cdots\int e^{-\beta H}\,d\mathbf{p}^N\,d\{N\}, \tag{2.2.21}$$

where the integral is now over the entire region of phase space accessible to the system.

If the Hamiltonian can be expressed in the form

$$H = (\mathbf{p}^N,\{N\}) = \sum_{i=1}^{N}\frac{1}{2m}\,p_i^{\,2} + U(\{N\}) \tag{2.2.22}$$

where $U(\{N\})$ is the potential energy of the system and is assumed to depend only on the coordinates of the N molecules, then

$$Q_1 = V\left(\frac{2\pi m}{\beta h^2}\right)^{3/2}$$

and

$$Q_N = \frac{1}{N!}\left(\frac{Q_1}{V}\right)^N \int \cdots \int_V e^{-\beta U(\{N\})}\, d\{N\}, \tag{2.2.23}$$

where, as before, V is the volume of the system.

2.3. THEORY OF IMPERFECT GASES (1,2)

The theory of imperfect gases has played an important role in the development of our general understanding of the properties of systems of interacting molecules. In addition, the formal structure of the theory is fundamental to the derivation of some of the most recent liquid theories. For these reasons we shall examine the statistical mechanics of imperfect gases in some detail. However, no attention will be devoted herein to the study of critical phenomena and the problems attendant thereto; we confine our discussion solely to the behavior of one phase fluid systems.

2.3.A. *A Preliminary Study*

From equations (2.2.11) and (2.2.17) we see that the Grand Canonical and Canonical Ensembles are related to each other by

$$\Xi = \sum_N Q_N(N,\beta,V) \exp(\beta N\mu). \tag{2.3.1}$$

Consider now new quantities, λ (absolute activity) and z (fugacity), defined by

$$\lambda = \exp(\beta\mu)$$
$$z = \frac{Q_1}{V}\lambda.$$

In these variables equations (2.3.1) may be written

$$\Xi = 1 + Q_1\lambda + Q_2\lambda^2 + \cdots$$
$$= \sum_{N\geqslant 0} \frac{Z_N z^N}{N!}, \tag{2.3.2}$$

where Z_N is the configurational partition function which will be discussed in detail in Section 2.4.A. By comparison of equations (2.3.1) and (2.3.2),

$$Z_N = \left(\frac{V}{Q_1}\right)^N N!\, Q_N, \tag{2.3.3}$$

using the fact that $Q_0 = 1$.

The pressure can be related to the configurational partition functions by means of equations (2.2.11), (2.3.2), and (2.3.3). We have

$$\beta p V = \ln\left(\sum_{N\geqslant 0} \frac{Z_N z^N}{N!}\right), \tag{2.3.4}$$

so that if the right side of equation (2.3.4) is expanded in a power series in z,

$$\beta p = \sum_{j\geqslant 1} b_j z^j. \tag{2.3.5}$$

The quantities $j!\, b_j V$ are well known in statistics as the semi-invariants of Thiele (15), or cumulants. They are closely related to the cumulant functions discussed in Section 2.3.C and are given in terms of the partition function by

$$j!\, b_j V = j! \sum_{\mathbf{n}} (-)^q q! \prod_i \left[\frac{1}{n_i!}\left(\frac{Z_i}{i!}\right)^{n_i}\right], \tag{2.3.6}$$

where $q = \sum_i n_i - 1$ and $\sum_{\mathbf{n}}$ is the sum over all positive or zero integers such that $\sum_i i n_i = j$. The first few terms are

$$\begin{aligned} b_1 V &= Z_1\ (= V) \\ b_2 V &= \tfrac{1}{2}(Z_2 - Z_1^2) \\ b_3 V &= \tfrac{1}{6}(Z_3 - 3Z_1 Z_2 + 2Z_1^3). \\ &\cdots \end{aligned} \tag{2.3.7}$$

It is seen from the form of equation (2.3.7) that the semi-invariant of order j is expressed in terms of a set of configurational partition functions of order not greater than j. Equation (2.3.5) is therefore an expansion in terms of the properties of clusters of molecules of increasing size, and the quantities b_j are called the cluster integrals. Z_N may also be expressed in terms of these cluster integrals as follows: Substitution of equation (2.3.5) in equation (2.2.11) gives

$$\begin{aligned} \exp(\beta p V) &= \prod_{j\geqslant 1} \exp(b_j V z^j) \\ &= \prod_{j\geqslant 1}\left[\sum_{m_j\geqslant 0} \frac{1}{m_j!}(b_j V)^{m_j} z^{j m_j}\right] \\ &= \sum_{N\geqslant 0}\sum_{\mathbf{m}}\left[\prod_{j=1}^{N} \frac{(b_j V)^{m_j}}{m_j!}\right] z^N \end{aligned} \tag{2.3.8}$$

so that, by comparison with equation (2.3.2),

$$Z_N = N! \sum_{\mathbf{m}} \left[\prod_{j=1}^{N} \frac{(b_j V)^{m_j}}{m_j!} \right], \tag{2.3.9}$$

where $\sum_{\mathbf{m}}$ means the summation over all sets of $m_1, m_2, \cdots, m_j \cdots$ compatible with $\sum_j jm_j = N$. Equation (2.3.9) is an expression for the configurational partition function for N molecules in terms of the cluster integrals for smaller numbers of molecules.

The derivation given is rigorous and valid for quantum-mechanical systems insofar as the expansion of (2.3.4) is valid. This is generally accepted to be the case if the expansion is applied to an imperfect gas, but difficulties with convergence are encountered when one attempts to apply the expression to the study of condensation phenomena, critical phenomena, and the liquid phase. The derivation does not depend upon pairwise additivity for the intermolecular potentials, or any other property, so that it is very general. However, the generality of the formalism hides many interesting details and much of the physics. For this reason we next consider a much more detailed derivation of the expansion (2.3.9). In particular, the relation between the cluster integrals, b_j, the intermolecular potential, and the character of the simultaneous interactions of j molecules will be displayed. A great simplification will be obtained by the introduction of certain "irreducible" cluster integrals.

It is convenient here to assume, as we do throughout the rest of the book, that the total potential energy of interaction is pairwise decomposable,

$$U(\{N\}) = \sum_{i>j} u(i,j),$$

whereupon

$$\exp(-\beta U(\{N\})) = \prod_{i>j} \exp[-\beta u(i,j)]$$
$$= \prod_{i>j} (1 + f_{ij}) \tag{2.3.10}$$

and

$$f_{ij} = \exp[-\beta u(i,j)] - 1. \tag{2.3.11}$$

This technique, which enables the exponential function of N coordinates to be separated into the sum of products of functions of smaller numbers of coordinates, is due to Mayer (16). A one to one correspondence (mapping) between the terms in equations (2.3.10) and a set of graphs may be established. The graphs are defined by stating that a point defines a molecule and a line between points i and j represents the factor f_{ij}. For example, the figure shown in (2.3.11a)

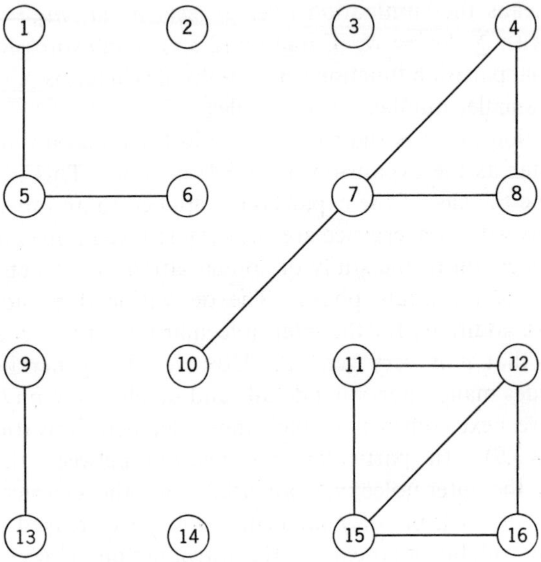

(2.3.11a)

is a mapping of the product

$$f_{1,5}f_{5,6}f_{4,7}f_{4,8}f_{7,8}f_{7,10}f_{9,13}f_{11,12}f_{11,15}f_{12,15}f_{12,16}f_{15,16} = (f_{1,5}f_{5,6})(f_{4,7}f_{4,8}f_{7,8}f_{7,10})(f_{9,13})(f_{11,12}f_{11,15}f_{12,15}f_{12,16}f_{15,16}).$$

An irreducible cluster is defined by a mapping in which each point (molecule) is connected by a bond (f_{ij}) to at least two other points. For completeness, the exceptional case of two interacting molecules is included as the lowest irreducible cluster. In this classical case, the cluster integrals, b_j, are related to the cluster mappings by

$$b_j = \frac{1}{j!V}\int S_{1,2,\cdots,j}\, d\{j\}, \qquad (2.3.12)$$

where $S_{1,2,\cdots,j}$ is the sum of all terms which connect in a cluster molecules $1, 2, \cdots, j$, no other molecules being connected. For example,

$$b_3 = \frac{1}{6V}\int S_{1,2,3}\, d\{3\}$$

$$= \frac{1}{6V}\int [f_{3,1}f_{2,1} + f_{3,2}f_{3,1} + f_{3,2}f_{2,1} + f_{3,1}f_{3,2}f_{2,1}]\, d\{3\}$$

$$= \tfrac{1}{2}\beta_1^{\,2} + \tfrac{1}{3}\beta_2. \tag{2.3.13}$$

Equation (2.3.13) is arrived at in the following way. Each of the products of two f_{ij} factors may be represented graphically by, for instance,

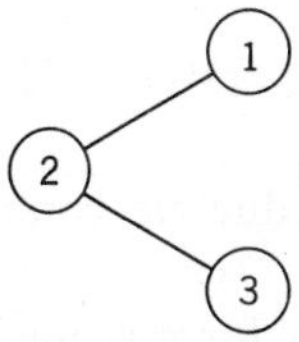

$$\equiv \int f_{1,2}f_{2,3}\, d\{3\}, \tag{2.3.14}$$

since the numbering of the molecules is immaterial. Now, $f_{1,2}$ and $f_{2,3}$ depend on $\mathbf{R}_{12} = \mathbf{R}_2 - \mathbf{R}_1$ and $\mathbf{R}_{23}$, respectively. The integration, which is over the space of $\mathbf{R}_1$, $\mathbf{R}_2$, $\mathbf{R}_3$, may be changed to an integration over $\mathbf{R}_{12}$, $\mathbf{R}_{23}$, $\mathbf{R}(= \frac{1}{3}[\mathbf{R}_1 + \mathbf{R}_2 + \mathbf{R}_3])$. Consequently, (2.3.14) contains the product of two integrals of the type

$$\int f_{ij}\, d\mathbf{R}_{ij} = \beta_1 \tag{2.3.15}$$

and one of the type

$$\int d\mathbf{R} = V. \tag{2.3.16}$$

The three terms of the general form of equation (2.3.14), therefore, give rise to the term $\frac{1}{2}\beta_1^{\,2}$, where β_1 is the irreducible cluster integral for two molecules. The remaining term in the integrand $f_{1,2}f_{1,3}f_{2,3}$ is the most highly connected arrangement of factors for three molecules and gives rise to the irreducible cluster β_2. Quite generally, the largest irreducible cluster for a group of n molecules is of order $(n - 1)$, since the last variable of integration ($\mathbf{R}_{23}$ in the 3-molecule case) is always expressible in terms of the other variables, (e.g., $\mathbf{R}_{23} = \mathbf{R}_{13} - \mathbf{R}_{12}$). Hence, the final integration is an unweighted integral over the center of mass, giving rise to a factor V. In the case of four molecules, we have, according to the definition of irreducible clusters, three types of integrals contributing. These are shown in (2.3.16*a*).

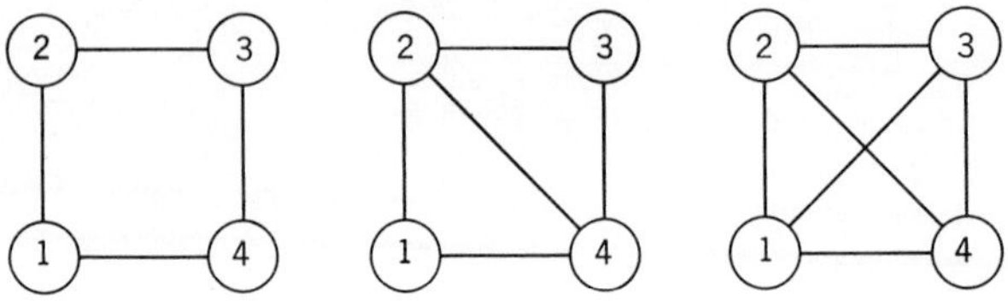

(2.3.16*a*)

For different orderings of the molecules, there can be seen to arise three distinct graphs of the first kind, six of the second, and one of the third. Finally, we remark that the irreducible cluster integrals are defined in an analogous way to the b_j; namely

$$\beta_j = \frac{1}{j!\,V} \int \mathscr{S}_{1,2,\cdots,j+1}\, d\{j+1\}, \tag{2.3.17}$$

where $\mathscr{S}_{1,2,\cdots,j}$ is the sum of all irreducible connections between j molecules.

It is clear that the irreducible clusters form a much smaller set than do the reducible (general) clusters. Indeed, it can be shown that the equation of state of the imperfect gas is

$$pV = NkT\left(1 - \sum_{k=1}^{N} \frac{k}{k+1}\, \beta_k \rho^k\right), \tag{2.3.18}$$

where ρ is the density N/V, and T is the temperature.

2.3.B. *A Different Expansion* (17–19)

The expansion (2.3.18) of the equation of state in powers of the density is equivalent to that given earlier in powers of the activity, equation (2.3.5), since, in the limit of low density the activity tends to the density. In this section we sketch a different method of expansion which does not require the assumption of pairwise additive potentials. Indeed, this method is also valid for quantum mechanical systems, and provides a bridge between the Mayer f-function expansion and the simple evaluation of the Grand Partition Function outlined in the first discussion of the imperfect gas.

We begin by defining a set of probability distributions $W(\{k\})$ by

$$W(\{k\}) = \prod_{i<j=2}^{k} (1 + f_{ij}) = \sum_{(G_k)} \prod^{(k)} f_{ij}, \tag{2.3.19}$$

the sum going over *all* graphs G_k of k labeled points. The W_k are normalized in such a way that they approach unity when the k molecules become distant from one another. We next define a class of related functions, the Ursell cluster functions (20,1,2), or $\mathscr{U}$ functions, by

$$\mathscr{U}(\{k\}) = \sum_{(C_k)} \prod^{(k)} f_{ij}, \tag{2.3.20}$$

the sum going over all *connected* graphs of k labeled points C_k. From equation (2.3.20) we have, for example,

$$\begin{aligned}
\mathscr{U}(\{1\}) &= 1 \\
\mathscr{U}(\{2\}) &= f_{1,2} \\
\mathscr{U}(\{3\}) &= f_{1,2}f_{1,3} + f_{1,3}f_{2,3} + f_{1,2}f_{2,3} + f_{1,2}f_{1,3}f_{2,3}. \qquad (2.3.21)\\
&\cdots
\end{aligned}$$

It is seen that the last displayed member of equation (2.3.21) is identical with the integrand of b_3 in equation (2.3.13), and so forth.

The relation between the $\{W\}$ and the $\{\mathscr{U}\}$ is called the Ursell development:

$$\begin{aligned}
\mathscr{U}(\{1\}) &= W(\{1\}) \\
\mathscr{U}(\{2\}) &= W(\{2\}) - W(1)W(2) \\
\mathscr{U}(\{3\}) &= W(\{3\}) - W(1,2)W(3) - W(2,3)W(1) \\
&\quad - W(1,3)W(2) + 2W(1)W(2)W(3), \qquad (2.3.22)\\
&\cdots
\end{aligned}$$

where we have used the notation (i) to represent the coordinates of the ith labeled point (while retaining the notation $\{i\}$ to represent the set of coordinates of all i labeled points). The coefficients of the terms are $(-)^{n-1}(n-1)!$, where n is the number of W factors in the term. In the absence of an external field we can choose the energy zero such that $W(\{1\}) = 1$. Equation (2.3.22) then may be inverted to give

$$\begin{aligned}
W(\{1\}) &= \mathscr{U}(\{1\}) = 1 \\
W(\{2\}) &= \mathscr{U}(1)\mathscr{U}(2) + \mathscr{U}(\{2\}) \\
W(\{3\}) &= \mathscr{U}(1)\mathscr{U}(2)\mathscr{U}(3) + \mathscr{U}(1,2)\mathscr{U}(3) + \mathscr{U}(1,3)\mathscr{U}(2) \\
&\quad + \mathscr{U}(2,3)\mathscr{U}(1) + \mathscr{U}(\{3\}). \qquad (2.3.23)\\
&\cdots
\end{aligned}$$

The coefficients before all terms in this expression are $+1$. What we have achieved, formally, is a representation of the Boltzmann factor for N molecules, $W(\{N\})$, as a sum of products of $\mathscr{U}$-functions. Suppose that any of these products contains m_1 groups of 1 molecule, m_2 groups of 2 molecules, $\cdots m_l$ of l molecules, subject to the conservation condition: $\sum_l lm_l = N$. We now note the following:

The function $\mathscr{U}(\{l\})$ is zero for separated configurations; i.e., for all configurations wherein the l molecules are separated into two or more groups at such distances that no interaction exists between the molecules of the several groups.

The proof of this theorem is based on the product property of exponentials. For a separated configuration of molecules in sets $\{i\}$, $\{j\}$, $\{k\}$, etc., we have

$$e^{-\beta U(\{N\})} = e^{-\beta U(\{i\})}e^{-\beta U(\{j\})}e^{-\beta U(\{k\})}\cdots. \tag{2.3.24}$$

Let the theorem be proved for all functions for which $k < l$. Both sides of equation (2.3.24) are now expressed in terms of $\mathscr{U}$-functions. On the right-hand side no terms appear containing $\mathscr{U}$-functions sharing molecules of different groups. The sum of such terms, *which must occur on the left-hand side*, is therefore zero. This sum contains a large number of terms containing $\mathscr{U}$-functions with $k < l$ which were assumed to be zero, and therefore the term $\mathscr{U}(\{l\})$, which occurs once, must be zero also. The theorem can be immediately verified for the special cases $\mathscr{U}(\{2\})$ and $\mathscr{U}(\{3\})$, and the general proof follows by induction. The theorem is also valid in quantum statistics where the W functions are now Slater sums (18). The product property used for the exponentials also holds for Slater sums because for a separated configuration the Hamiltonian operator separates into a sum and the wave function factorizes into a product. The proof then goes through as in the classical case.

Having expressed the Boltzmann factor for the system of N molecules as the sum of products of $\mathscr{U}$-functions, we may now formally integrate the configurational partition function. From equation (2.3.20), we have

$$b_l = \frac{1}{l!\,V}\int \mathscr{U}(\{l\})\,d\{l\}. \tag{2.3.25}$$

The general expression for any product of $\mathscr{U}$ terms is then

$$(1!\,b_1V)^{m_1}(2!\,b_2V)^{m_2}\cdots(l!\,b_lV)^{m_l} = \prod_j (j!\,b_jV)^{m_j}, \tag{2.3.26}$$

where there are m_j clusters (nonseparated groups) of j molecules in the product of $\mathscr{U}$-functions. The constraint is, again, $\sum_j jm_j = N$. Other terms can be obtained by permutation of molecules, except those within a subgroup, and also by permutation of groups of unequal size. The total number of these terms is

$$N! \prod_{j=1}^{N} \frac{1}{(j!)^{m_j} m_j!}, \tag{2.3.27}$$

whereupon

$$Z_N = N! \sum_{(\sum_j jm_j = N)} \prod_{j=1}^{N} \frac{(Vb_j)^{m_j}}{m_j!}, \tag{2.3.28}$$

which is, again, the same as equation (2.2.32).

Alternatively, the terms in the development of $W(\{N\})$, equation (2.3.23), may be reordered in the following way. First, all terms are collected in which molecule 1 occurs in a group by itself, i.e., which contain the factor $\mathscr{U}(1)$; the coefficient of this term is $W(2, \cdots, N)$. Next, all terms in which molecule 1 occurs in a group with one other molecule $[\mathscr{U}(1,2)]$ are collected; the coefficient of each one is $W(3, \cdots, N)$, and so on. We finally obtain

$$W(\{N\}) = \mathscr{U}(1)W(\{N-1\}) + \sum_P \mathscr{U}(1,i)W(\{N-2\}) + \cdots, \tag{2.3.29}$$

where $\sum_P$ means the sum over all ways of choosing molecule i, molecules i and j, etc. Equation (2.3.29) is now integrated over $\{N\}$, and from the definition of the cluster integrals (2.3.25) we find

$$Z_N = \sum_{j=1} \binom{N-1}{j-1} (j!\, b_j V) Z_{N-j}. \tag{2.3.30}$$

Thus, there is achieved a decomposition of Z_N into sums of products of disjoint clusters of j molecules, and systems of $N - j$ molecules. The first few terms of the decomposition may be understood in the following way: Since

$$W(\{N\}) = \prod_{i<j=2}^{N} (1 + f_{ij})$$

the product may be separated into

$$W(\{N\}) = \prod_{\substack{i<j=3 \\ (\text{not } 1)}}^{N} (1 + f_{ij}) \prod_{k=2}^{N} (1 + f_{1k}), \tag{2.3.31}$$

where the condition (not 1) on the first product means that all terms in which molecule 1 appears are put into the second product. On expanding the second product, equation (2.3.31) becomes

$$W(\{N\}) = \prod_{\substack{i<j=3\\(\text{not }1)}}^{N} (1 + f_{ij})\left(1 + \sum_{k=2}^{N} f_{1k} + \sum_{k<l=2}^{N}\sum^{N} f_{1k}f_{1l} + \cdots\right)$$

$$= W(\{N-1\}) + \prod_{\substack{i<j=3\\(\text{not }1)}}^{N} (1 + f_{ij})\left(\sum_{k=2}^{N} f_{1k} + \cdots\right). \quad (2.3.32)$$

In the second term of equation (2.3.32) we have a sum of terms

$$f_{1k} \prod_{\substack{i<j=3\\(\text{not }1)}}^{N} (1 + f_{ij}), \qquad k = 2, \cdots, N,$$

and each may be separated into

$$f_{1k} \prod_{\substack{i<j\\(\text{not }1,k)}}^{N} (1 + f_{ij}) \prod_{m=2}^{N} (1 + f_{km})$$

$$= f_{1k}W(2, \cdots (k-1), (k+1), \cdots N)$$

$$+ f_{1k} \prod_{\substack{i<j\\(\text{not }1,k)}}^{N} (1 + f_{ij})\left(\sum_{m=2}^{N} f_{km} + \cdots\right).$$

As there are $(N-1)$ terms of this type, equation (2.3.31) may be written

$$W(\{N\}) = W(\{N-1\})$$

$$+ \sum_{k=2}^{N} f_{1k}W(2, \cdots (k-1), (k+1), \cdots N) + \cdots$$

$$= W(\{N-1\}) + (N-1)\mathscr{U}(1,2)W(3, \cdots N) + \cdots,$$

as before.

2.3.C. *The Method of Cumulants* (21)

General Formulation. In the preceding sections we have demonstrated the relationship between the equation of state of a fluid and a set of irreducible integrals. These irreducible integrals have a graphical representation (in the classical case) in which each point (molecule) is connected by a bond (f_{ij}) to at least two other points. By the introduction of irreducible integrals a great economy is achieved in accounting for all possible molecular interactions. In this section we consider in greater detail the meaning of the graphical representation and its connection to the invariant expansion of equation (2.3.6). To establish this connection we must examine the properties of cumulants.

Given a random variable X, the moments and cumulants (semi-invariants), of X are defined by the moment generating function, $M(\xi)$, and the cumulant function, $K(\xi)$. These are:

$$M(\xi) \equiv \langle e^{\xi X} \rangle = \sum_{n=0}^{\infty} \frac{\xi^n}{n!} \mu_n$$

$$= \exp\left[\sum_{n=1}^{\infty} \frac{\xi^n}{n!} \varkappa_n\right] \equiv \exp K(\xi). \qquad (2.3.33)$$

Equation (2.3.6) follows directly from (2.3.33). As usual, the bracket indicates the expectation value of the variable and μ_n and $\varkappa_n$ are defined to be the nth moment and nth cumulant, respectively. For the case of N random variables, $X_1, \ldots, X_N$, we have by analogy:

$$M(\xi_1, \cdots, \xi_N) \equiv \left\langle \exp\left[\sum_{j=1}^{N} \xi_j X_j\right]\right\rangle = \sum_{\nu_1=0}^{\infty} \cdots \sum_{\nu_N=0}^{\infty} \left(\prod_j \frac{\xi_j^{\nu_j}}{\nu_j!}\right) \mu(\nu_1, \cdots, \nu_N)$$

$$= \exp\left[\sum_{\nu_1, \cdots, \nu_N}' \left(\prod_j \frac{\xi_j^{\nu_j}}{\nu_j!}\right) \varkappa(\nu_1, \cdots, \nu_N)\right]$$

$$\equiv \exp K(\nu_1, \cdots, \nu_N), \qquad (2.3.34)$$

where the prime on the summation indicates that the summation is carried over all values of $\nu_1, \cdots, \nu_N$, except the single term $\nu_1 = \nu_2 = \cdots = \nu_N = 0$. It will be convenient to use the notation

$$\mu(\boldsymbol{\nu}) \equiv \mu(\nu_1, \cdots, \nu_N) \equiv \mu(X_1^{\nu_1}, \cdots, X_N^{\nu_N}) \equiv \langle X_1^{\nu_1}, \cdots, X_N^{\nu_N} \rangle$$

$$\varkappa(\boldsymbol{\nu}) \equiv \varkappa(\nu_1, \cdots, \nu_N) \equiv \varkappa(X_1^{\nu_1}, \cdots, X_N^{\nu_N}) \equiv \langle X_1^{\nu_1}, \cdots, X_N^{\nu_N} \rangle_c, \qquad (2.3.35)$$

where the subscript c indicates "connected" in the graphical sense already introduced. More generally, the subscript c indicates a *cumulant average*, which is not a simple average. For example,

$$\langle x_1 x_2 \rangle_c = \langle x_1 x_2 \rangle - \langle x_1 \rangle \langle x_2 \rangle. \qquad (2.3.36)$$

Using equation (2.3.35), equation (2.3.34) may be rewritten in the form

$$\left\langle \exp\left[\sum_{j=1}^{N} \xi_j X_j\right]\right\rangle = \sum_{\nu_1=0}^{\infty} \cdots \sum_{\nu_N=0}^{\infty} \left(\prod_j \frac{\xi^{\nu_j}}{\nu_j!}\right) \langle X_1^{\nu_1} \cdots X_N^{\nu_N}\rangle$$
$$= \exp\left[\sum_{\nu_1}' \cdots \sum_{\nu_N}' \left(\prod_j \frac{\xi_j^{\nu_j}}{\nu_j!}\right) \langle X_1^{\nu_1} \cdots X_N^{\nu_N}\rangle_c\right]. \tag{2.3.37}$$

We can also write, by summation of equation (2.3.37),

$$\left\langle \exp\left[\sum_{j=1}^{N} \xi_j X_j\right]\right\rangle = \exp\left\langle \exp\left[\sum_{j=1}^{N} \xi_j X_j\right] - 1\right\rangle_c. \tag{2.3.38}$$

An important property of cumulants which makes them useful in the treatment of interacting systems is the following: a cumulant can be explicitly represented only by the lower (*not higher*) moments, and vice versa. Equation (2.3.34) can be inverted to read

$$\varkappa(\boldsymbol{\nu}) = -\left(\prod_{j=1}^{N} \nu_j!\right) \sum_{\{\mathbf{m}_i\}} \left(\sum_{i=1}^{\infty} k_i - 1\right)! \, (-)^{\sum_{i=1}^{\infty} k_i} \prod_{i=1}^{\infty} \frac{1}{k_i!} \left[\frac{\mu(\mathbf{m}_i)}{\prod_{j=1}^{N} m_{ij}!}\right]^{k_i}. \tag{2.3.39}$$

$$\left(\sum_{i=1}^{\infty} k_i m_{ij} = \nu_j\right)$$

Equation (2.3.39) is seen to be a generalization of equation (2.3.6). As displayed, equation (2.3.39) is a relation for $\varkappa(\boldsymbol{\nu})$ in terms of moments $\mu(\boldsymbol{\omega})$ for each of which $\omega_i \leqslant \nu_i$ for all i. That this is so is implied by the restriction

$$\sum_{i=1}^{\infty} k_i m_{ij} = \nu_j$$

on the sum over all sets of moments $\mu(\mathbf{m}_i)$. If, for any i, $m_{ij} > \nu_j$ then the restriction implies that $k_i = 0$, so that the corresponding term in the product $\prod_{i=1}^{\infty}$ is unity. Also, of course, while the product $\prod_{j=1}^{N} \nu_j!$ includes every variable formally, any $\nu_j = 0$ gives a factor unity.

Equation (2.3.39) is of sufficient importance that we digress to discuss its derivation. Consider first the case of a single variable. Equation (2.3.33) can be rearranged to read

$$\sum_{n=1}^{\infty} \frac{\xi^n}{n!} \varkappa_n = \ln(1 + X), \tag{2.3.40}$$

where

$$X = \sum_{m=1}^{\infty} \frac{\xi^m}{m!} \mu_m. \tag{2.3.41}$$

Since ξ is arbitrary, the right-hand side of equation (2.3.40) may always be expanded in a nondivergent series

$$\ln(1 + X) = X - \frac{X^2}{2} + \frac{X^3}{3} - \cdots$$

$$= \sum_{l=1}^{\infty} (-)^{l-1} \frac{X^l}{l} \tag{2.3.42}$$

for some ξ. Since, in a multinomial expansion of

$$X^l = \left(\sum_{i=1}^{\infty} x_i\right)^l,$$

the general term is

$$l! \prod_{i=1}^{\infty} \frac{x_i^{n_i}}{n_i!}; \qquad \sum_{i=1}^{\infty} n_i = l$$

the coefficient of ξ^m in the nth term of equation (2.3.42) is

$$\frac{(-)^{n-1}}{n} n! \prod_{i=1}^{\infty} \frac{1}{n_i.} \left(\frac{\mu_i}{i!}\right)^{n_i}; \qquad \sum_{i=1}^{\infty} i n_i = m, \qquad \sum_{i=1}^{\infty} n_i = n$$

and, from equation (2.3.40), we find

$$\varkappa_m = -m! \sum_{\mathbf{n}} (-)^{\sum_{i=1}^{\infty} n_i} \left(\sum_{i=1}^{\infty} n_i - 1\right)! \prod_{i=1}^{\infty} \frac{1}{n_i!} \left(\frac{\mu_i}{i!}\right)^{n_i}.$$

$$\left(\sum_{i=1}^{\infty} i n_i = m\right). \tag{2.3.43}$$

Again, because of the restriction on the summation over sets $\mathbf{n}$, no μ_i $(i > m)$ appears on the right-hand side.

We now derive equation (2.3.39) following Meeron (5). In the notation

$$\boldsymbol{\nu}! = \prod_{i=1}^{N} \nu_i!$$

$$\boldsymbol{\xi}^{\boldsymbol{\nu}} = \prod_{i=1}^{N} \xi_i^{\nu_i}$$

$$\left(\frac{\partial}{\partial \boldsymbol{\xi}}\right)^{\boldsymbol{\nu}} = \prod_{i=1}^{N} \left(\frac{\partial}{\partial \xi_i}\right)^{\nu_i},$$

equation (2.3.41) may be written

$$\phi(\boldsymbol{\xi}) = \exp \gamma(\boldsymbol{\xi}), \tag{2.3.44}$$

where

$$\phi(\boldsymbol{\xi}) = \sum_{\boldsymbol{\nu} \geqslant \mathbf{0}} \frac{\boldsymbol{\xi}^{\boldsymbol{\nu}}}{\boldsymbol{\nu}!} \mu(\boldsymbol{\nu}) \tag{2.3.45}$$

and

$$\gamma(\boldsymbol{\xi}) = \sum_{\boldsymbol{\nu} > \mathbf{0}} \frac{\boldsymbol{\xi}^{\boldsymbol{\nu}}}{\boldsymbol{\nu}!} \varkappa(\boldsymbol{\nu}), \tag{2.3.46}$$

where $\boldsymbol{\nu} > \mathbf{0}$ means that the summation includes all vectors $\boldsymbol{\nu}$ with *at least* one element different from zero. By differentiation,

$$\left[\left(\frac{\partial}{\partial \boldsymbol{\xi}}\right)^{\boldsymbol{\nu}} \phi(\boldsymbol{\xi})\right]_{\boldsymbol{\xi}=\mathbf{0}} = \mu(\boldsymbol{\nu}); \qquad \boldsymbol{\nu} \geqslant \mathbf{0} \tag{2.3.47}$$

$$\left[\left(\frac{\partial}{\partial \boldsymbol{\xi}}\right)^{\boldsymbol{\nu}} \gamma(\boldsymbol{\xi})\right]_{\boldsymbol{\xi}=\mathbf{0}} = \varkappa(\boldsymbol{\nu}); \qquad \boldsymbol{\nu} > \mathbf{0}. \tag{2.3.48}$$

We now seek a formula for the $\boldsymbol{\nu}$th derivative of an exponential function. This is

$$\left(\frac{\partial}{\partial \mathbf{x}}\right)^{\boldsymbol{\nu}} e^{g(\mathbf{x})} = e^{g(\mathbf{x})} \boldsymbol{\nu}! \sum \prod_i \frac{1}{k_i!} \left[\frac{1}{\mathbf{m}_i!} \left(\frac{\partial}{\partial \mathbf{x}}\right)^{\mathbf{m}_i} g(\mathbf{x})\right]^{k_i}$$

$$\left(\sum_i k_i \mathbf{m}_i = \boldsymbol{\nu}\right) \tag{2.3.49}$$

which may be verified when x is the only variable and proved in general by induction. The function $\phi(\boldsymbol{\xi})$ may now be differentiated $\boldsymbol{\nu}$ times with respect to $\boldsymbol{\xi}$. If $\boldsymbol{\xi}$ is then set equal to zero and equations (2.3.47–48) used, we find

$$\mu(\boldsymbol{\nu}) = \boldsymbol{\nu}! \sum_{\{\mathbf{m}_i\}} \prod_{i=1}^{\infty} \frac{1}{k_i!} \left(\frac{\varkappa(\mathbf{m}_i)}{\mathbf{m}_i!}\right)^{k_i}$$

$$\left(\sum_{i=1}^{\infty} k_i \mathbf{m}_i = \boldsymbol{\nu}\right). \tag{2.3.50}$$

It is now necessary to invert equation (2.3.49) to read

$$\left(\frac{\partial}{\partial \mathbf{x}}\right)^{\boldsymbol{\nu}} \ln f(\mathbf{x}) = -\boldsymbol{\nu}! \sum_{\{\mathbf{m}_i\}} \left(\sum_{i=1}^{\infty} k_i - 1\right)! \prod_{i=1}^{\infty} \frac{1}{k_i!} \left[\frac{(-)}{\mathbf{m}_i! f(\mathbf{x})} \left(\frac{\partial}{\partial \mathbf{x}}\right)^{\mathbf{m}_i} f(\mathbf{x})\right]^{k_i}.$$

$$\left(\sum_{i=1}^{\infty} k_i \mathbf{m}_i = \boldsymbol{\nu}\right) \tag{2.3.51}$$

When equation (2.3.51) is used to differentiate the inverse of equation (2.3.50) we find

$$\varkappa(\boldsymbol{\nu}) = -\boldsymbol{\nu}! \sum_{\{\mathbf{m}_j\}} \left(\sum_{i=1}^{\infty} k_i - 1\right)! \prod_{i=1}^{\infty} \frac{1}{k_i!}\left[-\frac{\mu(\mathbf{m}_i)}{\mathbf{m}_i!}\right]^{k_i}.$$

$$\left(\sum_{i=1}^{\infty} k_i \mathbf{m}_i = \boldsymbol{\nu}\right) \tag{2.3.52}$$

The most important property of cumulants (for our present purposes) is the following: a cumulant, $\varkappa(X_i X_j \cdots)$, is zero if the elements $X_i, X_j, \cdots$ may be divided into groups which are statistically independent. As a corollary, we note that a cumulant is zero if one of the variables in it is independent of the others. Conversely, a cumulant is non-zero *if and only if* the variables in it are statistically connected.

Let the variables $(X_i, X_j, \cdots)$ be divided into two groups

$$\{X\} = \{X'\} + \{X''\}, \tag{2.3.53}$$

which are statistically independent. Then,

$$\langle \exp (\sum \xi X)\rangle = \langle \exp (\sum \xi' X')\rangle\langle \exp (\sum \xi'' X'')\rangle \tag{2.3.54}$$

because of the assumed independence. Further, using equations (2.3.34),

$$K\{\xi\} = K'\{\xi'\} + K''\{\xi''\}, \tag{2.3.55}$$

so that powers of ξ' and ξ'' never mix. Thus, any cumulant in which variables from the two groups do appear must vanish.

The important simplification brought about by the use of cumulants is in the explicit recognition of the kind of averages which are used in Statistical Mechanics. To establish a deeper connection we now consider a rearrangement of the cumulant expansion into a cluster expansion. Define

$$K(\xi_1, \cdots, \xi_N) = \sum{}' \prod_{i=1}^{N} \frac{\xi_i^{\nu_i}}{\nu_i!} \varkappa(\boldsymbol{\nu}) = \sum_l K_l. \tag{2.3.56}$$

First, collect all the terms in the cumulant series which contain the particular variable X_i. This term, denoted by $K_1(X_i)$, is given by the moment generating function of the single variable, $M_1(X_i)$,

$$M_1(X_i) \equiv \langle \exp (\xi_i X_i)\rangle = \exp [K_1(X_i)] \tag{2.3.57}$$

and, therefore, the first term in the expansion $K = \sum_l K_l$ may be chosen to be

$$K_1 = \sum_i K_1(X_i). \tag{2.3.58}$$

The next term, K_2, will be of the form

$$K_2 = \sum_{i,j} K_2(X_i, X_j), \tag{2.3.59}$$

where $K_2(X_i, X_j)$ is the collection of all terms in the cumulant series that contain two variables, X_i and X_j. Now the two variable moment generating function can be written in the form

$$\begin{aligned} M_2(X_i, X_j) &= \langle \exp(\xi_i X_i + \xi_j X_j) \rangle \\ &= \exp[K_1(X_i) + K_1(X_j) + K_2(X_i, X_j)], \end{aligned} \tag{2.3.60}$$

and, therefore,

$$\exp[K_2(X_i, X_j)] = \frac{M_2(X_i, X_j)}{M_1(X_i) M_1(X_j)}. \tag{2.3.61}$$

Let $\{n\}_N$ denote a set of n variables selected from N variables $X_1, \cdots, X_N$. Then we may proceed as outlined to obtain the expansion

$$K = \sum_{n=1}^{N} \sum_{\{n\}_N} K_n(\{n\}_N), \tag{2.3.62}$$

where $K_n(\{n\}_N)$ is the collection of all terms involving the cumulants which contain any of the variables $\{n\}_N \equiv (X_{i_1}, \cdots, X_{i_n})$ at least once. The series (2.3.62) converges since N is finite and the convergence of the moments is assured. The same principle of rearrangement also applies to more complex cases where we have a hierarchy of functions $U(\{n\}_N)$ which are functions of n variables, $\{n\}_N = (X_{i_1}, \cdots, X_{in})$, selected from a given set of N variables, $\{N\} = (X_1, \cdots, X_N)$. The analogs of the relations given are:

$$M_n(\{n\}_N) = \langle \exp[U(\{n\}_N)] \rangle \tag{2.3.63}$$

$$M(\{N\}) = \langle \exp[U(\{N\})] \rangle = \exp[K(\{N\})] \tag{2.3.64}$$

$$K(\{N\}) = \sum_{n=1}^{N} \sum_{\{n\}_N} K_n(\{n\}_N). \tag{2.3.65}$$

We now seek to show that in the cluster expansion of a cumulant function, $K(\{N\})$, the cluster cumulant function, $K_n(\{n\}_N)$, for a set of n variables is given explicitly by

$$K_n(\{n\}_N) = \sum_{l=1}^{N} (-)^{n-l} \sum_{\{l\}_n} \ln M_l(\{l\}_N), \tag{2.3.66}$$

or

$$\exp\,(K_n(\{n\}_N)) = \frac{M_n(\{n\}_N)\prod M_{n-2}(\{n-2)_N)\cdots\prod\limits_{i<j} M_2(i,j)}{\prod M_{n-1}(\{n-1\}_N)\cdots\prod\limits_i M_1(i)}, \tag{2.3.67}$$

if n is even, and if n is odd,

$$\exp\,[K_n(\{n\}_N)] = M_n(\{n\}_N)\frac{\prod M_{n-2}(\{n-2\}_N)\cdots\prod\limits_i M_1(i)}{\prod M_{n-1}(\{n-1\}_N)\cdots\prod\limits_{i<j} M_2(i,j)}. \tag{2.3.68}$$

In conformity with the notation introduced, $\{l\}_n$ is a set of l variables selected from the set $\{n\}_N$. To prove this, consider a set of variables $\{n+1\}_N$. From the definition of K_n,

$$\begin{aligned}\ln M_{n+1}(\{n+1\}_N) &= \sum_{m=1}^{n+1}\sum_{\{m\}_{n+1}} K_m(\{m\}_N)\\ &= \sum_{m=1}^{n}\sum_{\{m\}_{n+1}} K_m(\{m\}_N) + K_{n+1}(\{n+1\}_N).\end{aligned} \tag{2.3.69}$$

Substitute equation (2.3.66) into equation (2.3.67) to give

$$\begin{aligned}K_{n+1}(\{n+1\}_N) = -\sum_{m=1}^{n}\sum_{\{m\}_{n+1}}\sum_{l=1}^{m}(-)^{m-l}\times\\ \sum_{\{l\}_n}\ln M_l(\{l\}_N) + \ln M_{n+1}(\{n+1\}_N).\end{aligned} \tag{2.3.70}$$

On the right-hand side, collecting terms, the coefficient of $\ln M_l(\{l\}_N)$ is found to be

$$\begin{aligned}1 - \binom{n-l+1}{1} + \binom{n-l+1}{2} + \cdots + (-)^{n-l}\binom{n-l+1}{n-l}\\ = (1-1)^{n-l+1} - (-)^{n-l+1}\\ = (-)^{n-l},\end{aligned} \tag{2.3.71}$$

which verifies equation (2.3.66).

An important property of cumulants can be demonstrated by considering the case where the set $\{n\}_N$ is divided into two independent sets, $\{n'\}_N$ and $\{n''\}_N$ such that

$$\{n\}_N = \{n'\}_N + \{n''\}_N. \tag{2.3.72}$$

Then it is clear that [cf. equation (2.3.54)]

$$M_n(\{n\}_N) = M_{n'}(\{n'\}_N)M_{n''}(\{n''\}_N), \tag{2.3.73}$$

whereupon

$$K_n(\{n\}_N) \equiv K_{n'+n''}(\{n' + n''\}_N) = 0, \tag{2.3.74}$$

and even more generally

$$K_{n'+m''}(\{m'\}_{n'} + \{m''\}_{n''}) = 0, \tag{2.3.75}$$

provided that neither $\{m'\}_{n'}$ nor $\{m''\}_{n''}$ is empty. The demonstration that equation (2.3.74) is valid follows directly from

$$M_{n'+n''}(\{n\}_N) = \exp\left[\sum_{m=1}^{n} \sum_{\{m'\}_{n'}} \sum_{\{m''\}_{n''}} K_{m=m'+m''}(\{m'\}_{n'} + \{m''\}_{n''})\right]$$

$$M_{n'}(\{n'\}_N)M_{n''}(\{n''\}_N) = \exp\left[\sum_{m'=1}^{n'} \sum_{\{m'\}_{n'}} K_{m'}(\{m'\}_{n'})\right] \times$$

$$\exp\left[\sum_{m''=1}^{n''} \sum_{\{m''\}_{n''}} K_{m''}(\{m''\}_{n''})\right]. \tag{2.3.76}$$

The sum over m in the first line of equation (2.3.76) contains contributions in which $\{m'\}_{n'}$ and $\{m''\}_{n''}$ may be empty, while in the second line we see that only terms for which neither $\{m'\}_{n'}$ nor $\{m''\}_{n''}$ are empty contribute. Equation (2.3.75) follows then from a comparison with equation (2.3.73).

The Mayer Cluster Theory. In general, a set of variables $\{n\}$ is called connected if there is no way of dividing it into two or more subsets $\{n'\}$, $\{n''\}$ such that equation (2.3.73) is satisfied; otherwise, it is called unconnected. The importance of the cumulant cluster expansion is that it consists only of connected cluster cumulant functions, since the unconnected ones vanish. This is the clearest demonstration of the physical content of the elaborate algebraic techniques used in the original derivation by Mayer. It is in the nature of the averaging process that unconnected clusters do not appear and it is only because the older methods do not take advantage of this fact that elaborate analysis is required to establish it.

To demonstrate how the virial expansion follows easily from the cumulant averaging it is convenient to introduce a generalized exponential function. We define

$$\begin{aligned}\exp_L\left(\sum_{i=1}^{N} X_i\right) &= \sum_{n=0}^{\infty} \frac{1}{n!} L\left(\sum_{i=1}^{N} X_i\right)^n \\ &= 1 + \sum_i X_i + \sum_{i<j} X_i X_j + \cdots + \sum_{\{n\}_N} X_{i_1} \cdots X_{i_n} + \cdots \\ &= \prod_{i=1}^{N} (1 + X_i).\end{aligned} \tag{2.3.77}$$

The operation L is called leveling (and $\exp_L(\Sigma X_i)$ is called a leveled exponential) because, by definition, it levels off a product of X_i's by erasing those terms in which any X's appear with a power greater than unity. Obviously,

$$\exp_L\left(\sum_{i=1}^{N} X_i + \sum_{j=1}^{M} Y_j\right) = \exp_L\left(\sum_{i=1}^{N} X_i\right) \exp_L\left(\sum_{j=1}^{M} Y_j\right)$$
$$= \prod_{i=1}^{N} (1 + X_i) \prod_{j=1}^{M} (1 + Y_j). \qquad (2.3.78)$$

We also have the following example:

$$\left\langle \exp_L\left(\sum_{i=1}^{N} \xi_i X_i\right)\right\rangle = \exp\left\langle \exp_L\left(\sum_{i=1}^{N} \xi_i X_i\right) - 1\right\rangle_c, \qquad (2.3.79)$$

using equation (2.3.38). But

$$\left\langle \exp_L\left(\sum_{i=1}^{N} \xi_i X_i\right)\right\rangle = \exp[K(\xi)], \qquad (2.3.80)$$

whereupon

$$K(\xi) = \sum_{\nu_1}{}' \cdots \sum_{\nu_N}{}' \prod \frac{\xi_i^{\nu_i}}{\nu_i!} \langle L X_1^{\nu_1} \cdots X_N^{\nu_N} \rangle_c, \qquad (2.3.81)$$

which leads to the explicit forms:

$$\begin{aligned} \langle L X_i \rangle_c &= \langle X_i \rangle \\ \langle L X_i^2 \rangle_c &= \langle L X_i^2 \rangle - \langle L X_i \rangle^2 = -\langle X_i \rangle^2 \\ \langle L X_i^3 \rangle_c &= \langle L X_i^3 \rangle - 3\langle L X_i^2 \rangle \langle L X_i \rangle + 2\langle L X_i \rangle^3 \\ &= 2\langle X_i \rangle^3. \end{aligned} \qquad (2.3.82)$$

In terms of the cluster cumulants,

$$\exp_L\left(\sum_{i=1}^{N} \xi_i X_i\right) = \prod_{i=1}^{N} \exp_L(\xi_i X_i)$$
$$= \prod_{i=1}^{N} (1 + \xi_i X_i), \qquad (2.3.83)$$

and so

$$M_n(\{n\}_N) = \left\langle \prod_{\{n\}_N} (1 + \xi_i X_i) \right\rangle. \qquad (2.3.84)$$

Introducing equation (2.3.66),

$$\left\langle \exp_L\left(\sum_{i=1}^{N} \xi_i X_i\right)\right\rangle = \exp[K_N] = \exp\left(\sum_{n=1}^{N} \sum_{\{n\}_N} K_n\right), \qquad (2.3.85)$$

where

$$K_1 = \sum_{j=1}^{N} \ln M_1(X_j) = \sum_{j=1}^{N} \ln(1 + \xi_j\langle X_j\rangle)$$
$$= \sum_{j=1}^{N}\sum_{r=1}^{\infty} (-)^{r-1}\xi_j{}^r \frac{\langle X_j\rangle^r}{r}$$
$$K_2 = \sum_{i,j=1}^{N} \ln [M_2(X_i,X_j)/M_1(X_i)M_1(X_j)] \tag{2.3.86}$$
$$= \sum_{i,j=1}^{N} \ln \left(1 + \frac{\xi_i\xi_j\langle X_iX_j\rangle}{(1 + \xi_i\langle X_i\rangle)(1 + \xi_j\langle X_j\rangle)}\right),$$

and so forth.

We are now ready to study the imperfect gas, once again. Consider the classical case for which we write (pairwise additive potentials)

$$\exp(-\beta U(\{N\})) = \exp\left[-\beta \sum_{i<j} u(i,j)\right]$$
$$= \prod_{i<j=2}^{N} (1 + f_{ij})$$
$$= \exp_L\left(\sum_{i<j=2}^{N} f_{ij}\right). \tag{2.3.87}$$

The interaction contribution to the configurational free energy, A_N', is then, by equation (2.3.79), just

$$-\beta A_N' = \ln \langle \exp [-\beta U(\{N\})]\rangle$$
$$= \ln \exp \left\langle \exp_L\left(\sum_{i<j=2}^{N} f_{ij}\right) - 1\right\rangle_c$$
$$= \left\langle \exp_L\left(\sum_{i<j=2}^{N} f_{ij}\right) - 1\right\rangle_c . \tag{2.3.88}$$

It should be noted that an average does not change the dimensions of the quantity averaged. In the case of the first member of equation (2.3.88), the average is defined as

$$\langle\cdots\rangle = V^{-N}\int d\{N\} \cdots .$$

The general term of the expansion has the form

$$\left\langle \prod_{i<j=2}^{(n)} f_{ij}\right\rangle_c$$

with the product over a specified set of bonds. The set of these bonds must be connected or the term vanishes [see equations (2.3.73–74)]. Now the set of bonds is unconnected unless the bonds connect all of the particles involved. What about the set of connected bonds? If n molecules are involved in the set of bonds,

$$\begin{aligned}\left\langle \prod_{i<j=2}^{(n)} f_{ij} \right\rangle_c &= V^{-N} \int \cdots \int \left(\prod^{(n)} f_{ij} \right)_c d\{N\} \\ &= V^{-n} \int \cdots \int \left(\prod^{(n)} f_{ij} \right)_c d\{n\} \\ &= V^{-n+1} \int \cdots \int \left(\prod^{(n)} f_{ij} \right)_c d\{n-1\}, \end{aligned} \tag{2.3.89}$$

where we have introduced the definition of the average, and in the last term changed to relative coordinates and integrated over the volume V. Equations (2.3.88) and (2.3.89) lead to

$$\begin{aligned}-\beta A_N' &= \sum_{n=1}^{N-1} \binom{N}{n+1} \sum_{(C_{n+1})} \left\langle \prod^{(n+1)} f_{ij} \right\rangle_c \\ &= \sum_{n=1}^{N-1} \binom{N}{n+1} \sum_{(C_{n+1})} \left\langle \prod^{(n+1)} f_{ij} \right\rangle, \end{aligned} \tag{2.3.90}$$

where $\binom{N}{n+1}$ is the number of arrangements of N molecules in groups of $(n + 1)$, and the sum is over all graphs of $(n + 1)$ labeled points, each of which is connected to at least two others. The fact that the graphs are fully connected in this way arises because, as was shown in equation (2.3.75), the cumulant average for a graph which is not fully connected vanishes. The replacement of the cumulant average by the ordinary average: $\langle \cdots \rangle_c \to \langle \cdots \rangle$, is valid for large systems. That is, the other terms in the expansion of the cumulant average [e.g., equation (2.3.36)] contain a higher negative power of V, and are therefore negligible. Taking the limit $N \to \infty$, $V \to \infty$, $(N/V) = \rho =$ constant, we have

$$-\beta A_N' = N \sum_{n=1} \frac{\beta_n}{n+1} \rho^n, \tag{2.3.91}$$

where the irreducible cluster integral β_n is defined by [c.f. equation (2.3.17)]

$$\sum_{(C_{n+1})} \left\langle \prod^{(n+1)} f_{ij} \right\rangle_c = \frac{n!}{V^n} \beta_n. \tag{2.3.92}$$

With the usual thermodynamic relation between p' and A_N', it is found that

$$p' = -\left(\frac{\partial A_N'}{\partial V}\right)_{N,T} = -\rho kT \sum_{n=1} \frac{n}{n+1} \beta_n \rho^n, \qquad (2.3.93)$$

which is in agreement with equation (2.3.18).

2.3.D. *Some Topological Arguments* (22)

In previous sections we have established a relationship between the thermodynamic properties of a fluid and a set of defined irreducible integrals. For the classical case where the total intermolecular potential is pairwise decomposable and there is a one to one mapping of the various interaction terms we have seen that

$$\beta p V = \left[Vz + \sum_{N=2}^{\infty} \frac{z^N}{N!} \left(\sum_{\substack{\text{all clusters} \\ \text{of } n \text{ molecules}}} \int \cdots \int \prod f_{ij} \, d\{N\} \right) \right] \qquad (2.3.94)$$

where the second summation on the right is over all products Πf_{ij} whose corresponding graph is a cluster, i.e., a connected graph in which no pair of points is joined by more than one line. We now wish to consider the topological properties of these clusters and examine how they may be reduced to the irreducible clusters. This argument is inserted here because of its role in the method of summation of infinite subclasses of terms in series defined by diagrams. It is just these summation techniques that have proven very useful in recent theories of the liquid state.

To proceed we must introduce some definitions and concepts from the theory of linear graphs. Consider the graphs shown in (2.3.95), on facing page.

(1) Points such as 10 in equation (2.3.95*a*) are called articulation points. The removal of 10 and all lines connected to it severs the graph into two disjoint parts. Note that this is not true of 12, which is therefore not an articulation point.

(2) A connected graph without articulation points is called a star (e.g., the groups (10–12) or (4,5), considered as isolated from the other points).

(3) An arbitrary cluster is divided by its articulation points into a collection of stars. For example, in equation (2.3.95*b*) the articulation

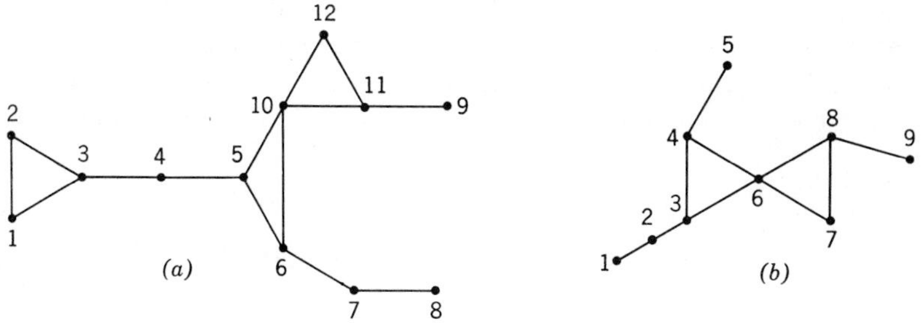

(2.3.95)

points are 2, 3, 4, 6, and 8. These divide the diagram into the stars (1,2), (2,3), (3,4,6), (4,5), (6,7,8), and (8,9).

(4) Because of 3 any cluster can be considered to be a collection of stars joined together at articulation points. From this point of view the cluster is called a star tree. A star tree with some point singled out is called a rooted star tree, and the cited point is called the root. A star tree may have a number of disjoint branches except for the root. In equation (2.3.95*b*) if 3 is designated as the root, we obtain a rooted tree with the branches (1,2,3) and (3,4,5,6,7,8,9).

A cluster may be subdivided in a number of different ways into stars, rooted star trees, and branches at articulation points. For each such subdivision the corresponding integral can be written as a product of integrals referring to the component stars, rooted star trees, and branches. The integral over the integrand represented by (2.3.95*b*) is then

$$\int f_{12}f_{23}f_{34}f_{36}f_{45}f_{46}f_{67}f_{68}f_{78}f_{89}\, d\{9\} =$$

$$V\int d(1) f_{12}\int d(2) f_{23}\int d(5) f_{45}\int d(9) f_{89} \times$$

$$\int d(3)\, d(4) f_{34}f_{36}f_{46}\int d(7)\, d(8) f_{67}f_{68}f_{78},$$

with the factor V arising from $d(6)$. Alternatively, this same integral may be written as the product of an integral referring to one of the stars and integrals referring to each one of the rooted star trees which are attached to this star through articulation points. For example,

$$\int f_{12}f_{23}f_{34}f_{36}f_{45}f_{46}f_{67}f_{68}f_{78}f_{89}\, d\{9\} =$$

$$V\int d(1)\, d(2) f_{12}f_{23} \int d(5) f_{45} \int d(3)\, d(4) f_{34}f_{36}f_{46} \times$$

$$\int d(7)\, d(8)\, d(9) f_{67}f_{68}f_{78}f_{89},$$

where, again, the factor V arises from $d(6)$.

What we shall now prove is that it is possible to express pV in terms of integrals referring only to stars.

Consider equation (2.3.95*b*). The three stars (8,9), (4,5) and (1,2) are attached to the remainder of the graph by only one articulation point. If these stars are removed, we obtain equation (2.3.95*c*). Now equation (2.3.95*c*) has two stars [(2,3) and (6,7,8)] each attached by only one articulation point. Removing these stars leads to the graphs of equation (2.3.95*d*). Thus, equation (2.3.95*b*) can be considered to be constructed from the fundamental star (3,4,6) by the attachment of the rooted trees (*3*,2,1) (*4*,5) and (*6*,7,8,9) where the italicized point is the root. The process of successive removal of all stars attached at only one point is called the reduction process. All stars containing a single articulation point must be completed before the new graph is examined and the reduction process repeated. The application of the reduction process to equation (2.3.95*a*) yields, not a fundamental star, but rather a fundamental point, which in this case is 5. It is easily seen that the application of the reduction process to an arbitrary cluster will yield after a finite number of steps either a fundamental star or a fundamental point. Any graph can, therefore, be considered to be built of a fundamental star with a number of attached rooted trees, or of a number of branches joined at a fundamental point.

What distinguishes a fundamental star or a fundamental point from all other stars and points in the graph? Define the order of a rooted star tree as follows: The order of a rooted star tree is the number of steps in the reduction process required to reduce it to a point. Then the following theorem is easily proved:

All clusters can be divided into two disjoint classes: Those with a unique fundamental point and those with a unique fundamental star.

If a graph has a fundamental point, no branch attached to this point has an order greater than the rest. If a graph has a fundamental star, no rooted star tree attached to this star has an order greater than the rest.

The theorem is proved by assuming a violation and deducing a contradiction. Suppose, for example, that a graph with a fundamental star has an attached rooted star tree, of order n, greater than the order of all the others. After $n - 1$ steps in the reduction process, all the other rooted star trees will have been reduced to points, while the given one will have been reduced to one or more stars attached to the fundamental star at one point. If this is so, however, one further application of the reduction process should result in a point. This contradicts the hypothesis that the graph has a fundamental star. A similar argument applies to the case of the fundamental point.

We can now proceed to examine the connected diagrams of the integrand of equation (2.3.94). Consider some cluster term which has a fundamental star σ and attached rooted star trees, $\tau_1, \cdots, \tau_r$. Let m be the number of points in σ and let $m_1, \cdots, m_r$ be the number of points besides the root in $\tau_1, \cdots, \tau_r$. The total number of points is $N = m + m_1 + \cdots + m_r$. Of course, there are a number of clusters which differ from the selected cluster only in the labeling. All of these clusters make the same contribution to pV, and we compute the contribution of all clusters identical except for labeling.

Let the fundamental star be labeled $1, 2, \cdots, m$, and let $\tau_1, \cdots, \tau_r$ be labeled with integers from the sets $\{m_1\}, \cdots, \{m_r\}$. The sum over all labelings of the selected graph is the sum over all labelings which do not interchange labels among σ and $\tau_1, \cdots, \tau_r$, multiplied by the number of ways of choosing sets of $m, m_1, \cdots\ m_r$ integers out of N integers. Thus, the total contribution of this cluster is

$$\frac{z^N}{N!}\frac{N!}{m!\,m_1!\cdots m_r!}\sum_{\substack{\text{(all labelings of }\sigma\\ \text{with integers from}\\ 1\cdots m)}}\int\prod f_{ij}\,d\{m\}\times$$

$$\prod_{s=1}^{r}\sum_{\substack{\text{(all labelings of }\tau_s\\ \text{with integers from}\\ 1\cdots m_s)}}\int\prod f_{ij}\,d\{m_s\}. \qquad (2.3.96)$$

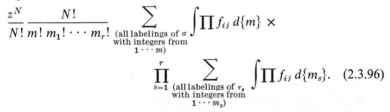

There are, of course, $N!$ different labelings of any particular N-point graph. Equation (2.3.96) represents the decomposition for a graph of the structure described. Consider now all clusters which have the same fundamental star. All such clusters can be built up by attaching various collections of trees to the points of the star, but the way in which the trees are added is restricted by the requirement that at any stage at least two must be of the same order. Consider now the *definition*

$$\rho = z + \sum_{N\geqslant 1} \frac{z^{N+1}}{N!} \sum_{\substack{\text{(all rooted star trees}\\ \text{with root 1 from points}\\ 2\cdots N+1)}} \int \prod f_{ij}\, d(2)\cdots d(N+1), \tag{2.3.97}$$

where z arises for the case that no rooted star tree is attached to σ. We now define a quantity Σ by

$$V\Sigma = \sum_{m=2}^{\infty} \frac{\rho^m}{m!} \sum_{\substack{\text{(all stars of}\\ m \text{ points)}}} \int \prod f_{ij}\, d\{m\}. \tag{2.3.98}$$

Σ contains all possible clusters built up by adding m rooted star trees of any order to fundamental stars of order m. For all terms in which the highest order rooted star tree occurs only once, the requirement of dependence cited is violated; in other words such terms refer to *different* fundamental stars. Consequently, Σ contains many clusters more than once. Since we have added trees independently, the sum of products in equation (2.3.98) is equal to the product of the sums. Now there is a one to one correspondence between labeled rooted star trees with root one formed from $N + 1$ points and labeled clusters formed from $N + 1$ points. From the definition of the grand partition function equations (2.2.15) and (2.3.2), we have

$$\begin{aligned}\langle N\rangle &= \frac{\partial \ln \Xi}{\partial \ln z}\\ &= V\left[z + \sum_{N\geqslant 1} \frac{z^{N+1}}{N!} \sum_{\substack{\text{(all clusters of}\\ N+1 \text{ molecules)}}} \int \prod f_{ij}\, d(2)\cdots d(N+1)\right],\end{aligned} \tag{2.3.99}$$

and, therefore, from equations (2.3.97) and (2.3.99)

$$\rho = \frac{\langle N\rangle}{V}, \tag{2.3.100}$$

so that ρ is just the average density.

We now must examine the overcounted terms. The contributions to be subtracted are those from clusters formed from σ (now no longer the fundamental star of the cluster) by attaching a number of rooted star trees, one of which has greater order than the rest. If s is the articulation point at which the tree of largest order (τ_s) is attached to σ, the remaining trees τ_i ($i \neq s$) together with σ form a branch β. The contributions to be subtracted are from those clusters formed by joining a branch of order p to a rooted star tree of order q, with $p \leqslant q$.

Consider now the contribution to pV from clusters with fundamental points. These are formed by attaching a number of branches at a point, taking care that at least two branches have orders greater than the rest (and equal to each other). The contribution of all clusters constructed from a fundamental point without the above restriction is

$$z + \sum_{N\geqslant 1} \frac{z^{N+1}}{N!} \sum_{\substack{\text{(All clusters}\\ \text{constructed by}\\ \text{adding branches}\\ \text{to one point)}}} \int \prod f_{ij}\, d(2) \cdots d(N+1), \quad (2.3.101)$$

which, by virtue of equation (2.3.97) is just ρ.

The contribution to be subtracted (the overcounted terms) is just that from clusters formed by joining one or more branches, $\beta_1, \beta_2, \cdots, \beta_s$, to a common root such that one, say β_s, has order p greater than the rest. The remaining branches, β_i ($i \neq s$), form a tree of order q, with $q < p$. The case when β_s is the only tree must also be included. If we call a point a tree of order zero, the overcounted contributions arise from joining a rooted star tree of order q and a branch of order p with $p > q \geqslant 0$. The overcounted configurations from both types of clusters comprise contributions from all graphs formed by joining a branch and a tree to a common root with no restriction on the order of the branch or the rooted tree. A given cluster appears in this collection as many times as the number of ways it can be constructed by attaching a tree and a branch at a common root.

Consider a particular cluster formed by joining a particular branch β, with a root 1 and remaining points labeled $2, \cdots, N+1$, and a particular tree τ, with a root 1 and remaining points labeled $N+2, \cdots, N+M+1$. The contribution of this cluster together with all distinct clusters formed by permutation of labels among points within the rooted star tree and branch may be written

$$V \sum_{\substack{\text{(All labelings of } \beta\\ \text{with integers } 2 \cdots N+1)}} \int \prod f_{ij}\, d(2) \cdots d(N+1) \times$$
$$\sum_{\substack{\text{(All labelings of}\\ \tau \text{ with integers}\\ N+2 \cdots N+M+1)}} \int \prod f_{ij}\, d(N+2) \cdots d(N+M+1). \quad (2.3.102)$$

(Note that integration over $d(1)$ leads to the factor V). Multiply by the number of ways of choosing N integers to label the points of the branch, M integers to label the points of the rooted star tree, and one integer to label the common root; sum over all branches and rooted star trees. The result is

$$V\sum_{N\geq 1}^{\infty}\frac{z^N}{N!}\sum_{\substack{\text{(All}\\ \text{branches)}}}\int\prod f_{ij}\,d(2)\cdots d(N+1)\times$$
$$\left(z+\sum_{M\geq 1}^{\infty}\frac{z^{M+1}}{M!}\sum_{\substack{\text{(All rooted star}\\ \text{trees with root 1}\\ \text{and other points}\\ N+2\cdots N+M+1)}}\int\prod f_{ij}\,d(N+2)\cdots d(N+M+1)\right). \tag{2.3.103}$$

Note that the term z comes from the rooted star trees of order zero, and the factorials from the combinatorial factors. Now, every branch can be represented in one and only one way as a rooted star with a number of rooted star trees attached at points other than the root. Therefore, the first factor in (2.3.103) is seen to be equivalent to the series

$$\sum_{N\geq 1}^{\infty}\frac{\rho^N}{N!}\sum_{\substack{\text{(All rooted stars}\\ \text{with root 1 and}\\ \text{points }2\cdots N+1)}}\int\prod f_{ij}\,d(2)\cdots d(N+1), \tag{2.3.104}$$

whereas the second factor is just ρ by equation (2.3.97). Noting the change in summation, equation (2.3.104) is seen to be the derivative of equation (2.3.98) with respect to ρ. Setting equation (2.3.98) equal to $V\Sigma$ we finally have for the equation of state,

$$\beta pV = V\left(\Sigma+\rho-\rho\frac{\partial\Sigma}{\partial\rho}\right). \tag{2.3.105}$$

By noting that

$$-\rho^2\frac{\partial}{\partial\rho}\left(\frac{\Sigma}{\rho}\right)=\Sigma-\rho\frac{\partial\Sigma}{\partial\rho}, \tag{2.3.106}$$

we return to the familiar relationship

$$\beta p=\rho-\frac{1}{V}\sum_{m=2}^{\infty}\frac{m-1}{m!}\rho^m\sum_{\substack{\text{(All stars}\\ \text{with }m\\ \text{points)}}}\int\prod f_{ij}\,d\{m\}. \tag{2.3.107}$$

The relabeling $\nu = m - 1$, and the definition

$$\beta_\nu = \frac{1}{\nu!\, V} \int \sum_{\substack{\text{(Stars with} \\ \nu+1 \text{ points)}}} \prod f_{ij}\, d\{\nu + 1\} \tag{2.3.108}$$

leads to

$$\beta p = \rho - \rho \sum_{\nu=1}^{\infty} \frac{\nu}{\nu + 1} \beta_\nu \rho^\nu, \tag{2.3.109}$$

a form more familiar than equation (2.3.105).

2.4. DISTRIBUTION FUNCTIONS (2)

The goal of the statistical theory of matter is the formulation of relationships between the macroscopic properties of matter and the presumed known properties of the molecules composing the system. For the case of the imperfect gas we have shown how the equation of state can be represented in terms of the contributions from isolated molecules, isolated pairs of molecules, isolated triplets of molecules, etc. This sequential analysis of the effect of intermolecular interactions is best suited to the discussion of a dilute system (such as a gas) but becomes relatively intractable for dense systems. For this reason we now discuss an alternative representation of the molecular-statistical properties of matter. Instead of analyzing the equation of state in terms of the additive effects of groups of isolated molecules, we seek a description of the behavior of small groups of molecules which are in interaction with the remainder of the system. We are thereby led to the study of molecular distribution functions.

2.4.A. *Definitions*

Canonical Ensemble. Consider a closed system containing N molecules. We denote by $\rho_N^{(n)}(\{n\})\, d\{n\}$ the probability of finding a molecule in $d\mathbf{R}_1$ at $\mathbf{R}_1$, another in $d\mathbf{R}_2$ at $\mathbf{R}_2$, $\cdots$, and another in $d\mathbf{R}_n$ at $\mathbf{R}_n$, irrespective of where the remaining $N - n$ molecules are located. $\rho_N^{(n)}(\{n\})$ is defined by

$$\rho_N^{(n)}(\{n\}) = \frac{N!}{(N - n)!} \frac{\int \cdots \int e^{-\beta U(\{N\})}\, d\{N - n\}}{Z_N}, \tag{2.4.1}$$

where Z_N is given by equations (2.2.23) and (2.3.3):

$$Z_N = \int \cdots \int e^{-\beta U(\{N\})}\, d\{N\} \tag{2.4.2}$$

$(N!/(N-n)!) = \binom{N}{n} n!$ is the number of ways of placing n molecules selected from N in $d\{n\}$. $\rho_N^{(n)}$ is known as the generic probability density, or distribution function, the term generic implying that the molecules at the positions in the argument of $\rho_N^{(n)}$ are not specifically chosen. From equation (2.4.1) we have

$$\int \cdots \int \rho_N^{(n)}(\{n\})\, d\{n\} = \frac{N!}{(N-n)!}. \tag{2.4.3}$$

In particular,

$$\int \rho_N^{(1)}\, d(1) = N$$

$$\int \rho_N^{(2)}\, d(1)\, d(2) = N(N-1). \tag{2.4.4}$$

We may define a completely random distribution in the limit for which $T \to \infty$, or alternatively, in the limit in which the system is so dilute that the most likely configurations are those for which the molecules are widely enough separated that $\beta U(\{N\}) = 0$. For this case,

$$Z_N = V^N$$

so that

$$\rho_N^{(n)} = \frac{1}{V^n} \frac{N!}{(N-n)!} = \rho^n \frac{N!}{N^n (N-n)!} \tag{2.4.5}$$

with

$$\rho_N^{(1)} = \rho = \frac{N}{V}$$

$$\rho_N^{(2)} = \frac{N(N-1)}{V^2} = \rho^2 \left(1 - \frac{1}{N}\right). \tag{2.4.6}$$

Correlation Functions. Because of molecular interactions, no real system exhibits a random distribution in configuration space. We define $g_N^{(n)}$, the correlation function corresponding to an n-molecule generic distribution function, by

$$\rho_N^{(n)} = \left(\prod_{i=1}^{n} \rho_N^{(1)}(i)\right) g_N^{(n)}(\{n\}). \tag{2.4.7}$$

Clearly, these functions represent the extent to which the distributions of n molecules are not completely random. The normalization properties of $g_N^{(n)}$ are such that

$$\int \cdots \int g_N^{(n)}\, d\{n\} = \frac{V^n}{N^n} \frac{N!}{(N-n)!}$$
$$= V^n\left[1 + \mathcal{O}\left(\frac{1}{N}\right)\right]. \tag{2.4.8}$$

In particular,

$$g_N^{(1)} = 1. \tag{2.4.9}$$

From (2.4.4) we see that

$$\int g_N^{(2)}\, d(1)\, d(2) = V^2\left(1 - \frac{1}{N}\right). \tag{2.4.10}$$

For a fluid, the pair distribution is spherically symmetric, so that

$$\left.\begin{aligned} \rho_N^{(2)}(\mathbf{R}_1,\mathbf{R}_2) &= \rho_N^{(2)}(R_{12}) \\ g_N^{(2)}(\mathbf{R}_1,\mathbf{R}_2) &= g_N^{(2)}(R_{12}) \end{aligned}\right\}, \tag{2.4.11}$$

whereupon equation (2.4.10) may be integrated over $\mathbf{R}_1$, and over the angular part of $\mathbf{R}_{12}$, to give

$$4\pi\rho \int g_N^{(2)}(R_{12}) R_{12}{}^2\, dR_{12} = N - 1, \tag{2.4.12}$$

which shows that $g_N^{(2)}$ appears in the role of the experimental radial distribution function, $g(R_{12})$. For this reason we shall sometimes denote it without either the superscript or subscript.

Grand Canonical Ensemble. If the system is open, the generic distribution function for n molecules, $\rho^{(n)}$, is the average of equation (2.4.1) over systems containing n or more molecules. That is,

$$\rho^{(n)} = \sum_{N \geqslant n} \rho_N^{(n)} P_N(V,T), \tag{2.4.13}$$

where P_N is constrained by

$$\sum_{N \geqslant 0} P_N(V,T) = 1.$$

From Sections 2.2.A and 2.2.B we see that

$$P_N(V,T) = \sum_k P(E_k,V,N)$$
$$= \Xi^{-1}\left(\frac{Vz}{Q_1}\right)^N Q_N$$
$$= \frac{z^n Z_N}{\Xi N!}, \tag{2.4.14}$$

whence

$$\rho^{(n)} = \frac{1}{\Xi}\sum_{N\geqslant n}\frac{z^N}{(N-n)!}\int\cdots\int e^{-\beta U(\{N\})}\,d\{N-n\}. \tag{2.4.15}$$

Equation (2.4.13), or (2.4.15), with equation (2.4.3), lead to the normalization relation

$$\int \rho^{(n)}\,d\{n\} = \sum_{N\geqslant n}\frac{N!}{(N-n)!}P_N$$
$$= \left\langle \frac{N!}{(N-n)!}\right\rangle. \tag{2.4.16}$$

Thus,

$$\int \rho^{(1)}\,d(1) = \langle N\rangle, \tag{2.4.17}$$

so that

$$\rho^{(1)} = \rho = \frac{\langle N\rangle}{V}. \tag{2.4.18}$$

Also,

$$\int \rho^{(2)}\,d(1)\,d(2) = \langle N^2\rangle - \langle N\rangle. \tag{2.4.19}$$

Equation (2.4.19) is important in the discussion of thermodynamic properties in the next section. Note the general differences between equations (2.4.16–19) and the corresponding equations for the canonical ensemble, in that the latter relations do not involve averages.

In the limit that the system becomes large with z and T fixed, that is $V\to\infty$, $\langle N\rangle\to\infty$, while $(\langle N\rangle/V) = \rho =$ constant, the two sets of equations become identical. This is because the probability distribution for N becomes very sharply peaked about $\langle N\rangle$ (it can be shown that the relative width $\propto \langle N\rangle^{-1}(\langle N^2\rangle - \langle N\rangle^2)^{1/2} \sim \langle N\rangle^{-1/2}$) so that effectively only one value of N, namely $\langle N \rangle$, is found. Then equation (2.4.16) may be written

$$\int \rho^{(n)}\, d\{n\} = \langle N^n \rangle \left(1 + \mathcal{O}\left(\frac{1}{\langle N \rangle}\right)\right). \tag{2.4.20}$$

For a completely random distribution, we may write $\beta U(\{N\}) = 0$, and find that

$$\rho^{(n)} = z^n = \rho^n. \tag{2.4.21}$$

This result differs from those for the canonical ensemble, equation (2.4.5–6), in that no terms of $\mathcal{O}\left(\frac{1}{\langle N \rangle}\right)$ appear.

Correlation Functions. The correlation function $g^{(n)}$ may be defined analogously to equation (2.4.7) by

$$\rho^{(n)} = \rho^n g^{(n)}, \tag{2.4.22}$$

so that

$$\int g^{(n)}\, d\{n\} = \frac{V^n}{\langle N \rangle^n} \left\langle \frac{N!}{(N-n)!} \right\rangle, \tag{2.4.23}$$

and in the limit $\langle N \rangle$, $V \to \infty$ while z and T remain constant,

$$\lim_{\langle N \rangle, V \to \infty} \int g^{(n)}\, d\{n\} = V^n. \tag{2.4.24}$$

If we rewrite equation (2.4.15) as

$$\begin{aligned} \rho^{(n)} &= \frac{z^n}{\Xi} \sum_{N \geqslant n} \frac{z^{N-n}}{(N-n)!} \int \cdots \int e^{-\beta U(\{N\})}\, d\{N-n\} \\ &= \frac{z^n}{\Xi} \sum_{m \geqslant 0} \frac{z^m}{m!} \int \cdots \int e^{-\beta U(\{n+m\})}\, d\{m\}, \end{aligned} \tag{2.4.25}$$

it is seen that, in the limit of infinite dilution, $z \to \rho \to 0$, and

$$\begin{aligned} \rho^{(n)} &= \rho^n e^{-\beta U(\{n\})} \\ g^{(n)} &= e^{-\beta U(\{n\})}. \end{aligned} \tag{2.4.26}$$

We shall have occasion to use these results later.

2.4.B. *The Thermodynamic Properties of a Fluid* (2)

We shall now examine the representation of the thermodynamic properties of a fluid in terms of the molecular distribution functions.

This representation has a compact form and is an exact and rigorous alternative to the virial expansion formalism.

It is convenient to start with the normalization conditions, equation (2.4.19), written for the two-body distribution function. These are

$$\int \rho^{(2)}(1,2)\, d(1)\, d(2) = \langle N^2 \rangle - \langle N \rangle, \tag{2.4.27}$$

$$\int \rho^{(1)}(1)\rho^{(1)}(2)\, d(1)\, d(2) = \langle N \rangle^2. \tag{2.4.28}$$

The subtraction of equation (2.4.28) from equation (2.4.27) yields

$$\int [\rho^{(2)}(1,2) - \rho^{(1)}(1)\rho^{(1)}(2)]\, d(1)\, d(2) = \langle N^2 \rangle - \langle N \rangle^2 - \langle N \rangle. \tag{2.4.29}$$

To evaluate the right-hand side of equation (2.4.29) we return to the definition of the Grand Partition Function. It is easily seen from equation (2.3.2) that

$$\langle N \rangle = \frac{1}{\Xi} \sum_{N \geqslant 0} N \frac{z^N}{N!} Z_N = \frac{\partial \ln \Xi}{\partial \ln z} \tag{2.4.30}$$

$$\langle N^2 \rangle = \frac{1}{\Xi} \sum_{N \geqslant 0} N^2 \frac{z^N}{N!} Z_N = \frac{1}{\Xi} \frac{\partial^2}{\partial \ln z^2} \Xi. \tag{2.4.31}$$

Examination of equations (2.4.30) and (2.4.31) also shows that

$$\langle N^2 \rangle - \langle N \rangle^2 = \frac{\partial \langle N \rangle}{\partial \ln z} = kT \left(\frac{\partial \langle N \rangle}{\partial \mu} \right)_{T,V}, \tag{2.4.32}$$

where the last term on the right-hand side of equation (2.4.32) is obtained when it is noted that

$$\begin{aligned} \mu &= kT \ln z + \text{constant} \\ (d\mu)_{T,V} &= (kT\, d \ln z)_{T,V}. \end{aligned} \tag{2.4.33}$$

Now we note that, from equations (2.2.11) and (2.3.2),

$$\left(\frac{\partial p}{\partial \mu} \right)_{V,T} = \frac{kT}{V} \cdot \frac{1}{kT} \frac{\partial \ln \Xi}{\partial \ln z} = \frac{\langle N \rangle}{V} = \rho, \tag{2.4.34}$$

and thereby

$$\left(\frac{\partial^2 p}{\partial \mu^2} \right)_T = \left(\frac{\partial \rho}{\partial \mu} \right)_T = \left(\frac{\partial \rho}{\partial p} \right)_T \left(\frac{\partial p}{\partial \mu} \right)_T = \rho^2 \kappa, \tag{2.4.35}$$

where κ is the isothermal compressibility. From equations (2.4.30) and (2.4.31) we find

$$VkT \left(\frac{\partial^2 p}{\partial \mu^2} \right)_T = \langle N^2 \rangle - \langle N \rangle^2 = \rho^2 \kappa VkT. \tag{2.4.36}$$

Equation (2.4.31), when divided by $\langle N\rangle = \rho V$, gives

$$\frac{1}{\rho V}\int[\rho^{(2)} - \rho^{(1)2}]\, d(1)\, d(2) = \frac{\langle N^2\rangle - \langle N\rangle^2}{\langle N\rangle} - 1 = \rho\kappa kT - 1. \tag{2.4.37}$$

Equation (2.4.37) is an equation of state, i.e., a connection between p, V, T and the molecular distribution function. If we introduce the pair correlation function, $g^{(2)}$, one has

$$4\pi\rho\int_0^\infty [g^{(2)}(R) - 1]R^2\, dR = \rho\kappa kT - 1. \tag{2.4.38}$$

To compute the internal energy, $\langle U\rangle$, we use the thermodynamic relation

$$\begin{aligned}\langle U\rangle &= \langle N\rangle\mu + TS - pV\\ &= \langle N\rangle\mu + kT^2\left(\frac{\partial \ln \Xi}{\partial T}\right)_{V,\mu}.\end{aligned} \tag{2.4.39}$$

Straightforward evaluation of the derivative of Ξ leads to

$$\left(\frac{\partial \Xi}{\partial T}\right)_{V,\mu} = \frac{1}{kT^2}\sum_{N\geqslant 2}\frac{z^N}{N!}\int U(\{N\})e^{-\beta U(\{N\})}\, d\{N\} + \left(\frac{3\langle N\rangle}{2T} - \frac{\langle N\rangle\mu}{kT^2}\right), \tag{2.4.40}$$

where the first summation excludes $N = 0$, $N = 1$ because $U(\{N\}) = 0$ for $N = 0$, and $N = 1$. Since there are $\frac{1}{2}N(N-1)$ equivalent terms in the integral of equation (2.4.40),

$$\begin{aligned}kT^2\left(\frac{\partial \ln \Xi}{\partial T}\right)_{V,\mu} &= \frac{1}{\Xi}\int u(1,2)\\ &\times\left[\sum_{N\geqslant 2}\frac{z^N}{N!}\frac{N(N-1)}{2}\int e^{-\beta U(\{N\})}\, d\{N-2\}\right] d(1)\, d(2)\\ &\qquad + \tfrac{3}{2}\langle N\rangle kT - \langle N\rangle\mu.\end{aligned} \tag{2.4.41}$$

Using the definitions (2.4.15) and (2.4.22) easily leads to

$$\begin{aligned}\frac{\langle U\rangle}{\langle N\rangle kT} &= \frac{3}{2} + \frac{\rho}{2kT}\int u(R)g^{(2)}(R)\, d\mathbf{R}\\ &= \frac{3}{2} + \frac{2\pi\rho}{kT}\int_0^\infty u(R)g^{(2)}(R)R^2\, dR,\end{aligned} \tag{2.4.42}$$

expressing the internal energy in terms of the pair-correlation function. Although equation (2.4.37) is valid irrespective of the form of $U(\{N\})$, equation (2.4.42) depends on the assumption that $U(\{N\})$ may be represented as the sum of pairwise additive interaction potentials.

In order to obtain an expression for the pressure we use the relation

$$\left(\frac{\partial}{\partial V}(\beta p V)\right)_{z,T} = \left(\frac{\partial \ln \Xi}{\partial V}\right)_{z,T} = \beta p, \tag{2.4.43}$$

in which we have used

$$\left(\frac{\partial p}{\partial V}\right)_{z,T} = 0,$$

which follows because z, T are the two independent thermodynamic variables required to determine completely the state of a system. In differentiating Ξ the variation of the limits of the configuration integral Z_N must be treated carefully. If we are prepared to restrict our calculation to systems large enough that the pressure does not sensibly depend on the shape of the container (this is indeed a weak restriction for most purposes!), it may be assumed that the gas is enclosed in a cubical box of side $V^{1/3}$. It is then possible to render the variables of integration dimensionless by the substitution

$$\mathbf{R} = V^{1/3}\,\mathbf{R}',$$

where the range $\mathbf{R}'$ is $(0,0,0) \leqslant \mathbf{R}' \leqslant (1,1,1)$. The potential now depends explicitly on V, so that

$$Z_N = V^N \int_0^1 \cdots \int_0^1 e^{-\beta U(\{N\})}\, d\{N'\} \tag{2.4.44}$$

and

$$\left(\frac{\partial Z_N}{\partial V}\right)_{z,T} = \frac{N}{V} Z_N - \beta V^N \int_0^1 \cdots \int_0^1 \frac{\partial U}{\partial V} e^{-\beta U(\{N\})}\, d\{N'\}, \tag{2.4.45}$$

where

$$\{N'\} = (\mathbf{R}_1', \cdots, \mathbf{R}_N').$$

Since

$$\frac{\partial U}{\partial V} = \sum_{i=1}^{N} \frac{\partial \mathbf{R}_i}{\partial V} \cdot \nabla_i U = \frac{1}{3V} \sum_{i=1}^{N} \mathbf{R}_i \cdot \nabla_i U, \tag{2.4.46}$$

we now have, from equation (2.4.43),

$$\begin{aligned} \beta p &= \frac{1}{\Xi} \sum_{N \geqslant 0} \frac{z^N}{N!} \left(\frac{N Z_N}{V} - \frac{\beta}{3V} \sum_{i=1}^{N} \int \cdots \int (\mathbf{R}_i \cdot \nabla_i U) e^{-\beta U}\, d\{N\} \right) \\ &= \frac{\langle N \rangle}{V} - \frac{\beta}{3V} \left\langle \sum_{i=1}^{N} \mathbf{R}_i \cdot \nabla_i U \right\rangle_{\text{config}}. \end{aligned} \tag{2.4.47}$$

The average used in the second term of equation (2.4.47) is seen from the previous line to be a combination of a configurational average and an average in the Grand Canonical Ensemble. If the potential is pairwise decomposable, equation (2.4.46) gives rise to $\frac{1}{2}N(N-1)$ similar terms of the form

$$\frac{\beta}{3V}\mathbf{R}_i \cdot \nabla_i u(i,j),$$

so that

$$\frac{\beta}{3V\Xi}\sum_{N\geqslant 0}\frac{z^N}{N!}\sum_{i=1}^{N}\int\cdots\int(\mathbf{R}_i\cdot\nabla_i U)e^{-\beta U}\,d\{N\}$$

$$=\frac{\beta}{6V}\iint Ru'(R)\left[\frac{1}{\Xi}\sum_{N\geqslant 0}\frac{z^N}{N!}N(N-1)\int\cdots\int e^{-\beta U}\,d\{N-2\}\right]d(1)\,d(2)$$

$$=\frac{2\pi\beta\rho^2}{3}\int_0^\infty u'(R)g^{(2)}(R)R^3\,dR. \qquad (2.4.48)$$

Finally, from equations (2.4.47–48), we have

$$p=\rho kT-\frac{2\pi\rho^2}{3}\int_0^\infty u'(R)g^{(2)}(R)R^3\,dR. \qquad (2.4.49)$$

This form of the equation of state will prove very useful in our later analysis.

2.4.C. *A Relationship Between the Pair Distribution Function and the Free Energy* (23)

There is an interesting relationship between the pair distribution function and the free energy which will be of use in our later analysis. To develop this relationship we need to consider the notion of functional differentiation (24). Consider the following definitions:

(*a*) z is a functional of the function $x(t)$ in the interval (a,b) when it depends on all the values taken by $x(t)$ when t varies in the interval (a,b); or alternatively, when a relation is given by which to every function, $x(t)$, defined on the interval (a,b), there can be made to correspond one and only one quantity z, completely determined. A convenient notation is

$$z=F\left[\begin{matrix} b \\ x(t) \\ a\end{matrix}\right]. \qquad (2.4.50)$$

It is clear that this definition is easily extended to the cases that the function x depends on more than one variable, and also to the case where z depends on several functions $x(t)$, $y(t)$, $\cdots$.

(*b*) A functional, $F[x(t)]$, of the function $x(t)$ will be defined in general only when $x(t)$ varies within a determinate field of functions. For example,

$$F[x(t)] = \int_a^b x(t)\, dt \tag{2.4.51}$$

exists (is definable) only for functions $x(t)$ which are integrable.

(*c*) A functional $U[A]$ is continuous at an element A if

$$\lim_{n\to\infty} U[A_n] = U[A], \tag{2.4.52}$$

where A is the limiting element of the aggregate within which U is defined. A functional is uniformly continuous if for arbitrary $\epsilon > 0$, there is an $\eta > 0$ such that

$$|U[A] - U[A']| < \epsilon \tag{2.4.53}$$

for $(A,A') < \eta$, whatever A and A' may be.

(*d*) The first derivative of the functional F with respect to the function $y(t)$ at the point ξ is denoted $F'[y(t),\xi]$ and exists if:

(*1*) The ratio $\dfrac{\delta F}{\epsilon h} < M$ with M a finite number and $\delta y(t) = \theta(t)$, $|\theta(t)| < \epsilon$, $\theta(t) = 0$ outside an interval (m,n) of (a,b) of amplitude h and containing ξ in its interior;

(*2*) Putting $\sigma = \displaystyle\int_m^n \theta(t)\, dt$, there exists a determinate and finite limit of $\dfrac{\delta F}{\sigma}$ when $\epsilon \to 0$ and $h \to 0$, subject to the condition that ξ is always interior to (m,n);

(*3*) That $\dfrac{\delta F}{\sigma}$ tends to its limit uniformly with respect to all possible functions $y(t)$ and to all points ξ.

Other higher order and mixed derivatives, differentials, etc., can be similarly defined.

As an example, consider the functional

$$F[y(t)] = k_0 + \sum_{i=1}^{n} \int_a^b \cdots \int_a^b k_i(t_1, \cdots, t_i) y(t_1) \cdots y(t_i)\, dt_1 \cdots dt_i, \tag{2.4.54}$$

where k_0 is a constant. Then the variation δF corresponding to the increment $\delta y(t)$ is

$$\delta F = \sum_{i=1}^{n} i \int_a^b \delta y(\xi)\, d\xi \int_a^b \cdots \int_a^b k_i(t_1, \cdots, t_{i-1}, \xi) \times y(t_1) \cdots y(t_{i-1})\, dt_1 \cdots dt_{i-1}, \quad (2.4.55)$$

and, therefore, the first derivative of F at ξ is

$$F'[y(t),\xi] = k_1(\xi) + \sum_{i=2}^{n} i \int_a^b \cdots \int_a^b k_i(t_1, \cdots, t_{i-1}, \xi) \times y(t_1) \cdots y(t_{i-1})\, dt_1 \cdots dt_{i-1}. \quad (2.4.56)$$

Note the factor i arising from the fact that there are i functions which can provide the variation δy.

We now consider the Helmholtz free energy to be a functional of the system Hamiltonian. To determine the variation of free energy with Hamiltonian we add to the Hamiltonian an arbitrary function. Since we are interested in distribution functions for small number of molecules we choose the test function to be of the form

$$\sum_{i_1 \neq i_2 \neq \cdots \neq i_s} \phi^{(s)}(i_1, \cdots, i_s).$$

Now

$$-\beta A_N = \ln Q_N = \ln \left[\frac{1}{h^{3N} N!} \int e^{-\beta H(\mathbf{p}^N, \{N\})}\, e^{-\beta \Sigma \phi^{(s)}}\, d\mathbf{p}^N\, d\{N\} \right], \quad (2.4.57)$$

whereupon

$$-\delta(\beta A_N) = h^{3N} N!\, \frac{1}{Q_N} \int \left[-\beta(\Sigma\, \delta\phi^{(s)}) e^{-\beta\Sigma\phi^{(s)}} \times \int e^{-\beta H(\mathbf{p}^N, \{N\})}\, d\mathbf{p}^{N-s}\, d\{N-s\} \right] d\mathbf{p}^s\, d\{s\}. \quad (2.4.58)$$

From the definition of $\rho^{(s)}$ in the canonical ensemble we easily find

$$\rho^{(s)} = \frac{\delta A_N}{\delta \phi^{(s)}}, \quad (2.4.59)$$

and in particular

$$\rho^{(2)} = \frac{\delta A_N}{\delta \phi^{(2)}}, \quad (2.4.60)$$

where $\phi^{(2)}$ is now considered to be an arbitrary potential depending on the coordinates (1) and (2). This is the desired relationship between the free energy and the distribution function.

The advantage of expressing the functions $\rho^{(s)}$ in the form cited is easily demonstrated when we consider the asymptotic properties of the distribution function. In a large system, for which N, $V \to \infty$, at constant ρ, the Grand Partition Function is given approximately by one term which is large compared to all the rest. Then the average number of molecules $\langle N \rangle$ may be replaced by the number N corresponding to this term, so that, from equation (2.3.2),

$$\Xi \simeq Q_N \left(\frac{Vz}{Q_1}\right)^N. \tag{2.4.61}$$

The free energy A_N, calculated in this approximation, is given by

$$-\beta A_N^{(0)} = \ln \Xi - N \ln z + N \ln \left(\frac{Q_1}{V}\right). \tag{2.4.62}$$

We therefore have

$$\beta\left(\frac{\partial^2 A_N^{(0)}}{\partial N^2}\right)_{V,T} = \frac{\partial \ln z}{\partial N}. \tag{2.4.63}$$

Again ignoring the difference between N and $\langle N \rangle$, we may write

$$\frac{\partial}{\partial N}\left(\frac{\partial \ln \Xi}{\partial \ln z}\right) = 1, \tag{2.4.64}$$

since

$$N \simeq \langle N \rangle = \frac{\partial \ln \Xi}{\partial \ln z}, \tag{2.4.65}$$

as is easily seen from equation (2.3.2). Now, writing equation (2.4.64) as

$$\left(\frac{\partial \ln z}{\partial N}\right)\left(\frac{\partial^2 \ln \Xi}{\partial \ln z^2}\right) = 1,$$

equation (2.4.63) becomes

$$\beta\left(\frac{\partial^2 A_N^{(0)}}{\partial N^2}\right)_{V,T} = \left(\frac{\partial^2 \ln \Xi}{\partial \ln z^2}\right)^{-1}. \tag{2.4.66}$$

A more exact evaluation of Ξ may be obtained by the method of steepest descents. This leads to

$$\Xi = \left(2\pi\left(\frac{\partial^2 \ln \Xi}{\partial \ln z^2}\right)\right)^{1/2} Q_N\left(\frac{Vz}{Q_1}\right)^N \tag{2.4.67}$$

so that a next approximation to A_N is given by

$$\beta A_N = \beta A_N^{(0)} - \tfrac{1}{2} \ln \left(\beta \frac{\partial^2 A_N^{(0)}}{\partial N^2} \right)_{V,T} + \tfrac{1}{2} \ln 2\pi, \tag{2.4.68}$$

where we have used equations (2.4.62) and (2.4.66). It is easily seen that this extra factor in equation (2.4.67) as compared to equation (2.4.61) is related to the variance $\langle (N - \langle N \rangle)^2 \rangle$ of the number-probability distribution, $P_N(V,T)$. Now consider the isothermal compressibility κ; we have

$$\kappa^{-1} = -V \left(\frac{\partial p}{\partial V} \right)_{N,T} = V \left(\frac{\partial^2 A_N}{\partial V^2} \right)_{N,T}. \tag{2.4.69}$$

Since our zeroth order of approximation is that of identifying Ξ with its maximum term, we may change the variable in equation (2.4.69) from V to N via the density $\rho = N/V$, and we thereby obtain

$$(\kappa^{(0)})^{-1} = \left(\rho N \frac{\partial^2 A_N}{\partial N^2} \right)_{T,V}. \tag{2.4.70}$$

We now take a variation of equation (2.4.68), and obtain

$$\delta A_N = \delta A_N^{(0)} - \frac{\rho^3 \kappa^{(0)}}{2N\beta} \frac{\partial^2}{\partial \rho^2} (\delta A_N^{(0)}), \tag{2.4.71}$$

where equation (2.4.70) has been used and the derivative of $\delta A_N^{(0)}$ expressed in terms of ρ. Equation (2.4.71) may be combined with equation (2.4.60) to give

$$\rho^{(s)} = \rho^{(s),(0)} - \frac{\rho^3 \kappa}{2N\beta} \frac{\partial^2}{\partial \rho^2} \rho^{(s),(0)}, \tag{2.4.72}$$

where, in the second term, the difference between κ and $\kappa^{(0)}$ has been ignored. For the case $s = 2$, in the limit of large separations, $\rho^{(2),(0)} \to \rho^2$, and equation (2.4.72) becomes

$$\lim_{R_{12} \to \infty} (\rho^{(2)} - \rho^2) = -\frac{\rho^3 \kappa}{N\beta}, \tag{2.4.73}$$

a result complementary to equation (2.4.37).

2.5. SERIES EXPANSIONS FOR THE PAIR DISTRIBUTION FUNCTION (18,25)

In the introduction to Section 2.4 it was pointed out that distribution functions allow a more economical approach to the calculation of, for instance, the equation of state of a dense fluid, than do the virial expansions discussed in Section 2.3. However, this is not to be taken as implying that the two methods are mutually exclusive. Indeed, they are complementary, and equivalent, so long as a virial expansion converges. Before going on to discuss the methods of calculation of distribution functions particularly suited to dense fluids, we give here two different virial expansions.

2.5.A. *The $\mathscr{U}$-Function Method*

The definition of the radial distribution function with which we start is

$$g_N^{(2)}(1,2) = \frac{V^2}{Z_N} \int \cdots \int W(\{N\})\, d\{N-2\}, \tag{2.5.1}$$

where $W(\{N\})$ is defined by equation (2.3.19). Here, we have singled out two molecules, 1 and 2, so that $\{N-2\} = (3, 4, \cdots, N)$ and $g_N^{(2)}(1,2)$ is the *specific* radial-distribution function. It is related to the generic radial-distribution function $g_N^{(2)}$ by [cf. equation (2.4.1)]

$$g_N^{(2)} = g^{(2)}(1,2) + \mathcal{O}(1/N). \tag{2.5.2}$$

Our procedure is to take equation (2.3.29) and study the various types of contribution which arise. We have

$$\begin{aligned} W(\{N\}) = {} & \mathscr{U}(1)W(2,\cdots,N) + \sum_P \mathscr{U}(1,i)W(2,\cdots,i-1,i+1,\cdots,N) \\ & + \cdots + \sum_P \mathscr{U}(1, i_1, \cdots, i_{n-1})W(2,\cdots,i_j-1,i_j+1,\cdots,N) \\ & \qquad\qquad\qquad\qquad\qquad\qquad (\text{all } j \in 1, \cdots, n-1) \\ & + \cdots. \end{aligned} \tag{2.5.3}$$

In the general term of order n two types of contributions may arise according as the set $(i_1, \cdots, i_{n-1})$ does, or does not, include 2. The total number of terms of this order is $\binom{N-1}{n-1}$, while if one $i_j = 2$ $(j \in 1, \cdots, n-1)$, there are $\binom{N-2}{n-2}$ terms. Consequently, the number of terms for which $i_j \neq 2$ $(j \in 1, \cdots, n-1)$ is

$$\binom{N-1}{n-1} - \binom{N-2}{n-2}.$$

Upon integrating both sides over $d\{N-2\}$, the terms of the first type are

$$\begin{aligned}\int\cdots\int \mathscr{U}(1, 2, i_1, \cdots, i_{n-2}) &W(\underset{(\text{all } j \in 1, \cdots, n-2)}{3, \cdots, i_{j-1}, i_{j+1}, \ldots, N})\, d\{N-2\} \\ &= \int \mathscr{U}(1, 2, i_1, \cdots, i_{n-2})\, d\{n-2\} \times \\ &\qquad \int W(\underset{(\text{all } j \in 1, \cdots, n-2)}{3, \cdots, i_{j-1}, i_{j+1}, \cdots, N})\, d\{N-n\} \\ &= (n-2)!\, \mathfrak{B}_n Z_{N-n},\end{aligned} \tag{2.5.4}$$

where

$$\{n-2\} = (i_1, \cdots, i_{n-2}) \quad \text{and} \quad \{N-n\} = (\underset{(\text{all } j \in 1, \cdots, n-2)}{3, \cdots, i_{j-1}, i_{j+1}, \cdots, N})$$

and we have defined

$$(n-2)!\, \mathfrak{B}_n = \int \mathscr{U}(1, 2, i_1, \cdots, i_{n-2})\, d\{n-2\}. \tag{2.5.5}$$

Terms of the second type are

$$\begin{aligned}\int \mathscr{U}(\underset{(i_j \neq 2,\, j \in 1, \cdots, n-1)}{1, i_1, \cdots, i_{n-1}}) &W(\underset{(\text{all } j \in 1, \cdots, n-1)}{2, \cdots, i_{j-1}, i_{j+1}, \cdots, N})\, d\{N-2\} \\ &= \int \mathscr{U}(\underset{(i_j \neq 2,\, j \in 1, \cdots, n-1)}{1, i_1, \cdots, i_{n-1}})\, d\{n-1\} \\ &\quad \times \int W(\underset{(\text{all } j \in 1, \cdots, n-1)}{2, \cdots, i_{j-1}, i_{j+1}, \cdots, N})\, d\{N-n-1\} \\ &= \frac{1}{V^2}(n!\, b_n V) Z_{N-n},\end{aligned} \tag{2.5.6}$$

where b_n is defined by equation (2.3.25). The result, (2.5.6), follows because the two integrals are each taken over the coordinates of one less molecule than are included in the argument. Since that molecule can be regarded as the origin of coordinates in each case, integration over the coordinates of these two molecules simply results in the factor V for each term, which is balanced by the factor V^{-2}. Substituting equations (2.5.4) and (2.5.6) in equations (2.5.1) with appropriate numerical factors, we obtain

$$g_N^{(2)}(1,2) = V^2 \sum_{n=2}^{N} \binom{N-2}{n-2} (n-2)!\, \mathfrak{B}_n \frac{Z_{N-n}}{Z_N} + \sum_{n=1}^{N} \binom{N-1}{n-1} n!\, b_n V \frac{Z_{N-n}}{Z_N} - \sum_{n=2}^{N} \binom{N-2}{n-2} n!\, b_n V \frac{Z_{N-n}}{Z_N}. \tag{2.5.7}$$

The second term is, from equation (2.3.30), just unity, so that

$$g_N^{(2)}(1,2) - 1 = V^2 \sum_{n=2}^{N} \binom{N-2}{n-2} (n-2)!\, \mathfrak{B}_n \frac{Z_{N-n}}{Z_N} - \sum_{n=2}^{N} \binom{N-2}{n-2} (n!\, b_n V) \frac{Z_{N-n}}{Z_N}. \tag{2.5.8}$$

Equation (2.5.8) is exact, but awkward. However, it can be developed into a simpler form by employing the steepest descent approximation (2.4.67) in a way which does not affect the final accuracy. Equation (2.4.67) may be written (2)

$$\frac{Z_N z^N}{N!} = \frac{\Xi}{(2\pi\langle(\Delta N)^2\rangle)^{1/2}}. \tag{2.5.9}$$

Since equation (2.5.9) is derived from a consideration of the shape of the peak of $P_N(V,T)$, expressing the contribution from the peak in terms of the value at the peak, we assume that equation (2.5.9) is true for a small number of different values $(N - n)$; $n \leqslant m$. By small is meant a number $m \ll N$. In fact, all that is required is that m, however small, is a monotonic increasing function of $\langle N \rangle$. Indeed, we have in mind a number of the order of the width of the peak $\langle(\Delta N)^2\rangle^{1/2} \sim N^{1/2}$. It is now possible to write

$$z^n = \frac{Z_{N-n} N!}{Z_N (N-n)!}, \tag{2.5.10}$$

and, provided the series converges quickly enough, equation (2.5.8) becomes

$$g_N^{(2)}(1,2) - 1 = \frac{V^2}{N(N-1)} \sum_{n=2}^{m(N)} \mathfrak{B}_n z^n - \frac{V}{N(N-1)} \sum_{n=2}^{m(N)} n(n-1) b_n z^n. \tag{2.5.11}$$

Upon recalling the cluster expansion,

$$\beta p = \sum_{n\geq 1} b_n(T)z^n, \tag{2.3.5}$$

we may write

$$\ln \Xi = V \sum_{n\geq 1} b_n z^n,$$

so that

$$N \simeq \langle N \rangle = V \sum_{n\geq 1} nb_n z^n \qquad \text{and} \qquad \rho = \sum_{n\geq 1} nb_n z^n. \tag{2.5.12}$$

It is, therefore, seen that

$$\sum_{n=2}^{m(N)} n(n-1)b_n z^n = \frac{\partial \rho}{\partial \ln z} - \rho, \tag{2.5.13}$$

and since

$$\frac{\partial \rho}{\partial \ln z} = \frac{\partial \rho}{\partial p}\frac{\partial p}{\partial \ln z} = \kappa \rho^2 kT, \tag{2.5.14}$$

equation (2.5.11) becomes

$$g_N^{(2)}(1,2) - 1 = \frac{1}{\rho^2}\sum_{n=2}^{m(N)} \mathfrak{B}_n z^n + \left(\frac{1}{N} - \frac{kT\kappa}{V}\right), \tag{2.5.15}$$

where we have ignored the difference in the upper limits of the summations in equations (2.5.11–12). It is easy to see that $g_N^{(2)}(1,2)$ has the correct limiting properties. In the limit of infinite dilution, $z \to \rho \to 0$, so that

$$g_N^{(2)}(1,2) - 1 \simeq \mathfrak{B}_2 = \exp[-\beta u(1,2)] - 1, \tag{2.5.16}$$

and in the limit of large separation $R_{12} \to \infty$,

$$\lim_{R_{12}\to\infty} [g_N^{(2)}(1,2) - 1] = \frac{1}{N} - \frac{kT\kappa}{V}, \tag{2.5.17}$$

showing proper normalization in the canonical ensemble. If we were to work in the Grand Canonical Ensemble and normalize such that

$$\lim_{R_{12}\to\infty} g^{(2)}(1,2) = 1 \qquad \text{(G.C.E)}, \tag{2.5.18}$$

our equation would be

$$g^{(2)}(1,2) - 1 = \frac{1}{\rho^2}\sum_{n=2}^{m(N)} \mathfrak{B}_n z^n, \tag{2.5.19}$$

and on integration over all space we would recover the compressibility equation (2.4.38). Equation (2.5.19) may be converted to a series in powers of the density, by substitution of the relation $z = z(\rho)$, but the series is not of any particular interest, and we leave this as an exercise.

2.5.B. *The Cumulant Method*

We begin again with the definition of $g_N^{(2)}(1,2)$, though in a slightly different form from equation (2.5.1):

$$g_N^{(2)}(1,2) = \frac{\langle e^{-\beta U(\{N\})}\rangle^{(1,2)}}{\langle e^{-\beta U(\{N\})}\rangle}, \tag{2.5.20}$$

where

$$\langle e^{-\beta U(\{N\})}\rangle^{(1,2)} = V^{2-N}\int\cdots\int e^{-\beta U(\{N\})}\, d\{N-2\}, \tag{2.5.21}$$

and, of course,

$$\langle e^{-\beta U(\{N\})}\rangle = V^{-N}Z_N. \tag{2.5.22}$$

Now, equation (2.5.21) may be rewritten as

$$\langle e^{-\beta U(\{N\})}\rangle^{(1,2)} = e^{-\beta u(1,2)}\langle e^{-\beta U'(\{N\})}\rangle^{(1,2)}, \tag{2.5.23}$$

where $U'(\{N\})$ is now the potential energy of N molecules less that of the pair already singled out. From equations (2.5.20) and (2.5.22–23) we obtain

$$\ln g_N^{(2)}(1,2) = -\beta u(1,2) + \ln\langle e^{-\beta U'}\rangle^{(1,2)} - \ln\langle e^{-\beta U}\rangle. \tag{2.5.24}$$

Following the procedure developed in Section 2.3.C, equation (2.5.24) may be written

$$\ln g_N^{(2)}(1,2) = -\beta u(1,2) + \left\langle \exp_L\left(\sum_{i<j}{}' f_{ij}\right) - 1\right\rangle_c^{(1,2)} - \left\langle \exp_L\left(\sum_{i<j} f_{ij}\right) - 1\right\rangle_c, \tag{2.5.25}$$

where Σ' does *not* include the term $i = 1, j = 2$. Consider the second term on the right-hand side of equation (2.5.25); three types of contribution may arise:

(*a*) Terms for n molecules $\left\langle \prod^{(n)} f_{ij}\right\rangle_c^{(1,2)}$ none of which is 1 or 2. Integration over $d\{N-2\}$ then includes the coordinates of all molecules appearing in the term, so that

$$\sum_{(C_n)} \left\langle \prod^{(n)} f_{ij} \right\rangle_c^{(1,2)} = \frac{(n-1)!\,\beta_{n-1}}{V^{n-1}}, \tag{2.5.26}$$

where β_n is defined by equation (2.3.17). The number of ways n molecules can be selected from $N-2$ is $\binom{N-2}{n}$ so that terms of this type contribute

$$\sum_{n=2}^{N-2} \binom{N-2}{n} \frac{(n-1)!\,\beta_{n-1}}{V^{n-1}} = \sum_{n=1}^{N-3} \binom{N-2}{n+1} \frac{n!\,\beta_n}{V^n}. \tag{2.5.27}$$

(*b*) Terms in which either molecule 1 or molecule 2 is included, but not both. Then,

$$\begin{aligned} \left\langle \prod^{(n-1/1)} f_{ij} \right\rangle_c^{(1,2)} &= \frac{1}{V^{N-2}} \int \cdots \int \prod^{(n-1/1)} f_{ij}\, d\{N-2\} \\ &= \frac{1}{V} \left\{ \frac{1}{V^{N-2}} \int \cdots \int \prod^{(n-1/1)} f_{ij}\, d\{N-2\} \right\} d(1), \end{aligned}$$

and

$$\sum_{(C_n)} \left\langle \prod^{(n-1/1)} f_{ij} \right\rangle_c^{(1,2)} = \frac{(n-1)!\,\beta_{n-1}}{V^{n-1}}. \tag{2.5.28}$$

Since there are two ways in which either molecule 1 or molecule 2 may appear in the cluster, the total contribution from terms of this type is

$$2\sum_{n=2}^{N-1} \binom{N-2}{n-1} \frac{(n-1)!\,\beta_{n-1}}{V^{n-1}} = 2\sum_{n=1}^{N-2} \binom{N-2}{n} \frac{n!\,\beta_n}{V^n}. \tag{2.5.29}$$

(*c*) Terms in which both molecules 1 and 2 appear. Here we define a new irreducible cluster integral γ_n in analogy with equation (2.5.5) by*

$$(n-2)!\,\gamma_n = \int \cdots \int \sum_{(C_n')} \prod^{(n-2/1,2)} f_{ij}\, d\{n-2\}, \tag{2.5.30}$$

so that

$$\sum_{(C_n')} \left\langle \prod^{(n-2/1,2)} f_{ij} \right\rangle_c^{(1,2)} = \frac{\gamma_n (n-2)!}{V^{n-2}}. \tag{2.5.31}$$

The total contribution from these terms is

$$\sum_{n=3}^{N} \binom{N-2}{n-2} \frac{(n-2)!\,\gamma_n}{V^{n-2}} \simeq \sum_{n=3}^{N} \rho^{n-2} \gamma_n, \tag{2.5.32}$$

* C_n' denotes all connected diagrams of n-labeled points excluding the bond f_{12}.

the term with $n = 2$ being the one already extracted in equation (2.5.23). The last term in equation (2.5.25) contributes [cf. equation (2.3.91)]

$$-\left\langle \exp_L\left(\sum_{i<j} f_{ij}\right) - 1 \right\rangle_c = -\sum_{n=1}^{N-1} \binom{N}{n+1} \frac{n!\,\beta_n}{V^n}. \tag{2.5.33}$$

The contributions from equations (2.5.27), (2.5.29), and (2.5.33) may be added to give

$$-\sum_{n=1} \frac{(N-2)!}{(N-2-(n+1))!\,(N-(n+1))(N-(n+2))} \frac{n\beta_n}{V^n}, \tag{2.5.34}$$

apart from small terms arising from the fact that the upper limits of the series are for $(N-3)$, $(N-2)$, and $(N-1)$, respectively. If we let $N, V \to \infty$, $\rho =$ constant, these terms may be entirely neglected, and equation (2.5.34) becomes

$$-\frac{1}{N} \sum_{n=1} n\beta_n \rho^n. \tag{2.5.35}$$

From equation (2.3.93) we have

$$p' = -kT \sum_{n=1} \frac{n}{n+1} \beta_n \rho^{n+1}, \tag{2.5.36}$$

so that equation (2.5.35) becomes

$$\begin{aligned} -\frac{1}{N} \sum_{n=1} n\beta_n \rho^n &= \frac{\beta}{N}\left(\frac{\partial p'}{\partial \rho}\right)_{T,N} \\ &= \frac{\beta}{N\rho\kappa'}, \end{aligned} \tag{2.5.37}$$

where κ' is the intermolecular interaction contribution to the compressibility. We now obtain, for equation (2.5.24), the final relation

$$\ln g_N^{(2)}(1,2) = -\beta n\,(1,2) + \sum_{n=3}^{\infty} \gamma_n \rho^{n-2} + \frac{\beta}{N\rho\kappa} - \frac{1}{N}, \tag{2.5.38}$$

where we have used the fact that

$$\kappa^{-1} = \beta^{-1}\rho + \kappa'^{-1}. \tag{2.5.39}$$

Let us compare equation (2.5.39) with equation (2.5.15). The main difference between them is due to the fact that the $\mathfrak{B}_n$ in (2.5.15) are not irreducible cluster integrals, because the $\mathscr{U}$-functions contain all connected diagrams, including those in which the coordinates of some molecules appear in only one bond, f_{ij}. The γ_n are, of course, irreducible, by virtue of the properties of cumulants demonstrated in Section 2.3.C. The fluctuation terms are similar, but not the same; in equation (2.5.15) the term is

$$\frac{1}{N}(1 - \rho kT\kappa),$$

while in equation (2.5.38) it is

$$\frac{1}{N}\left(\frac{1 - \rho kT\kappa}{\rho kT\kappa}\right).$$

This difference is an expression of the relation between the average value of a quantity and of its logarithm.

The γ_n cluster integrals are defined formally in equation (2.5.30), but the graphical representation of them is not immediately obvious. As with the version of the Mayer cluster theory discussed in Section 2.3.C, the γ_n graphs have the two general properties of cumulants. They are fully connected within their terms of reference. That is, the points representing molecules 1 and 2 are not required to be connected in the way that the other (field) points are. Since the f_{12} bond is in any case not present, examples of single connections between points 1 and 2 and the field points occur at all orders n. Also, the cumulant average is again equal to the ordinary average *for the connected graphs.*

The first of the cluster integrals, γ_3, has a single field point. The points 1 and 2 are not integrated over (fixed points) and are therefore distinguished by circles as opposed to dots. Thus,

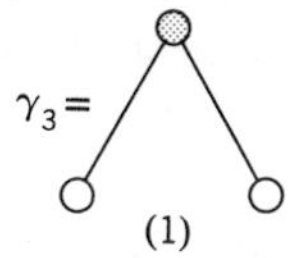

(2.5.40)

and there is only one diagram. At the next order we have three distinct four-point diagrams:

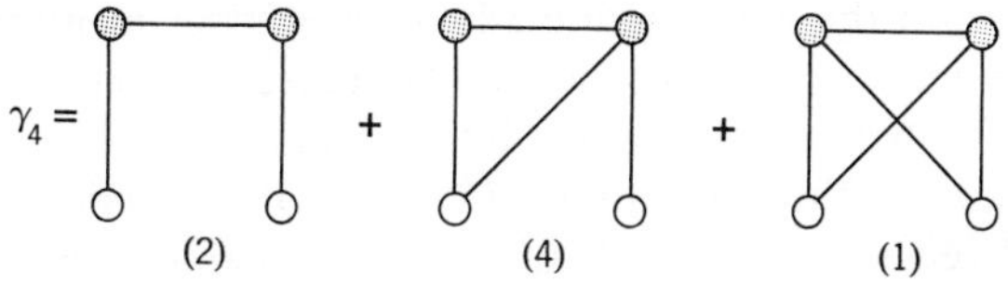

(2.5.41)

A general point to note, which is displayed by the γ_4 diagrams, is that each field point is connected to at least one other field point, apart from connections with the fixed points. This is a criterion of connectivity not made explicit previously. It follows that the diagram

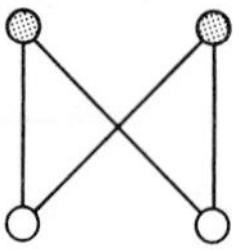

is not fully connected in the sense required, and indeed may be factorized into two γ_3 factors. The diagrams for all orders can be generated by inspection using these principles.

2.5.C. *A Perturbation Calculation of the Pair Correlation Function* (26,27)

Consider a pair potential of the form: $u(R) = 4\epsilon[(\sigma/R)^{12} - (\sigma/R)^6]$ where ϵ is an energy parameter and σ a range parameter. In the region where $(\epsilon/kT) \ll 1$ it might be anticipated that the effect of the attractive interaction is only a small perturbation to the properties of the fluid determined by the repulsive interaction. If the pair correlation function is known for a model fluid characterized by just the repulsive interaction, then it is possible to compute the change in $g^{(2)}(R)$ arising from the addition of a weak potential to the potential characterizing the model fluid.

Because we consider a perturbation analysis, the method described in this section has certain logical connections with the method of cluster expansions. However, insofar as we need the properties of the unperturbed fluid, particularly the pair correlation function for the reference fluid, it is necessary to refer the reader ahead to Sections 2.6.A–2.6.G and 2.7.B. Zwanzig (28) has developed a general perturbation theory applicable to problems of the type under consideration. The analysis proceeds by way of a semi-invariant expansion which is used to develop the perturbation as a power series in inverse powers of the temperature with coefficients determined by successively higher order (in number of molecules) interactions. Zwanzig applied the general theory to the calculation of the thermodynamic properties of pure fluids, regarding the Lennard-Jones interaction as a perturbation to the rigid-sphere interaction, and also to the study of polar fluids taking the Lennard-Jones potential as the reference interaction and the dipole–dipole (29) interaction as the perturbation.

It is convenient to place the following restrictions on the system studied:

(*a*) The perturbation energy is small relative to kT,

(*b*) The total potential energy can be separated into two contributions, $U_N = U_N^{(0)} + U_N^{(1)}$, where $U_N^{(0)}$ is the total potential energy of the unperturbed system and $U_N^{(1)}$ is the total perturbation. The first of these conditions is undoubtedly the more restrictive. There will be many conditions under which (*a*) is satisfied but each case must be carefully investigated.

To proceed, consider the pair correlation function, $g^{(2)}(R)$, defined by

$$g^{(2)}(R) = \frac{V^2 \int e^{-\beta[U_N^{(0)}+U_N^{(1)}]}\, d\{N-2\}}{\int e^{-\beta[U_N^{(0)}+U_N^{(1)}]}\, d\{N\}}. \tag{2.5.42}$$

The probability density of finding any particular configuration in the unperturbed system is

$$P_N^{(0)} = e^{\beta(A_N^{(0)}-U_N^{(0)})} \tag{2.5.43}$$

so that with the aid of the definition

$$\langle\alpha\rangle_0^{1,2,\cdots,n} = V^n \int P_N^{(0)}\alpha\, d\{N-n\}, \tag{2.5.44}$$

we may rewrite equation (2.5.42) in the form

$$g^{(2)}(R) = \frac{\langle\exp(-\beta U_N^{(1)})\rangle_0^{1,2}}{\langle\exp(-\beta U_N^{(1)})\rangle_0}. \tag{2.5.45}$$

As usual, $A_N^{(0)}$ is the configurational Helmholtz free energy and $Q_N^{(0)}$ the configurational partition function of the unperturbed system. If $\gamma \equiv U_N^{(1)} - u_p(1,2)$, with $u_p(1,2)$ the excess interaction potential between molecules one and two, expansion of the numerator of equation (2.5.45) yields

$$\langle\exp(-\beta U_N^{(1)})\rangle_0^{1,2} = \exp(-\beta u_p(1,2)) \sum_{k=0}^{\infty} \frac{(-\beta)^k}{k!} \langle\gamma^k\rangle_0^{1,2}. \tag{2.5.46}$$

In terms of Thiele semi-invariants, κ_n, defined by

$$\langle \exp(-\beta U_N^{(1)}) \rangle = \exp\left(\sum_{n=1}^{\infty} \frac{\kappa_n}{n!} (-\beta)^n \right) \tag{2.5.47}$$

and using the multinomial expansion theorem, the denominator of equation (2.5.45) becomes

$$\langle \exp(-\beta U_N^{(1)}) \rangle_0 = \sum_{s=0}^{\infty} (-\beta)^s \sum_{\substack{n_j \\ (\Sigma jn_j = s)}} \prod_{j=1}^{\infty} \frac{1}{n_j!} \left(\frac{\kappa_j}{j!} \right)^{n_j}$$

$$= \sum_{k=0}^{\infty} \frac{(-\beta)^k}{k!} \langle (U_N^{(1)})^k \rangle_0. \tag{2.5.48}$$

Equation (2.5.48) may now be used to express the κ_n in terms of averages of powers of $U_N^{(1)}$. The result obtained after these algebraic manipulations is

$$\kappa_j = j! \sum_{\substack{n_s \\ (\Sigma sn_s = j)}} (-)^{\Sigma n_s - 1} (\Sigma n_s - 1)! \prod_{s=1}^{\infty} \frac{1}{n_s!} \left(\frac{\langle (U_N^{(1)})^s \rangle_0}{s!} \right)^{n_s} \tag{2.5.49}$$

and by substitution

$$g^{(2)}(R) = e^{-\beta u_p(R)} \sum_{k=0}^{\infty} \frac{\langle \gamma^k \rangle_0^{1,2}}{k!} \sum_{s=0}^{\infty} (-\beta)^{s+k} \sum_{\substack{n_j \\ (\Sigma jn_j = s)}} \prod_{j=1}^{\infty} \frac{(-)^{n_j}}{n_j!} \left(\frac{\omega_j}{j!} \right)^{n_j}. \tag{2.5.50}$$

When the perturbation energy is small relative to kT only the first few terms of the series expansion need be retained. Including terms of order β^2, equation (2.5.50) reduces to

$$g^{(2)}(R) = e^{-\beta u_p(R)} \Big\{ g_0^{(2)}(R) + \beta (g_0^{(2)}(R) \langle U_N^{(1)} \rangle_0 - \langle \gamma \rangle_0^{1,2})$$

$$+ \frac{\beta^2}{2} (2 \langle U_N^{(1)} \rangle_0 \langle \gamma \rangle_0^{1,2} + 2 g_0^{(2)}(R) \langle U_N^{(1)} \rangle_0^2$$

$$- g_0^{(2)}(R) \langle (U_N^{(1)})^2 \rangle_0 + \langle \gamma^2 \rangle_0^{1,2}) \Big\}. \tag{2.5.51}$$

Consider that the pair potential between all the molecules is altered in the same way. Then it is readily shown that

$$\langle U_N^{(1)} \rangle_0 = \frac{\rho^2}{2} \int u_p(1,2) g_0^{(2)}(1,2)\, d(1)\, d(2)$$

$$\langle (U_N^{(1)})^2 \rangle_0 = \frac{\rho^4}{4} \int u_p(1,2) u_p(3,4) g_0^{(4)}(1,2,3,4)\, d(1)\, d(2)\, d(3)\, d(4)$$

$$+ \rho^3 \int u_p(1,2) u_p(2,3) g_0^{(3)}(1,2,3)\, d(1)\, d(2)\, d(3)$$

$$+ \frac{\rho^2}{2} \int [u_p(1,2)]^2 g_0^{(2)}(1,2)\, d(1)\, d(2)$$

$$\langle \gamma \rangle_0^{1,2} = 2\rho \int u_p(1,3) g_0^{(3)}(1,2,3)\, d(3)$$

$$+ \frac{\rho^2}{2} \int u_p(3,4) g_0^{(4)}(1,2,3,4)\, d(3)\, d(4). \qquad (2.5.52)$$

For practical computation it will be necessary to replace $g_0^{(k)}$ $(k > 2)$ by a product of pair functions using the scheme

$$W^{(n)} \equiv -kT \ln g_0^{(n)}$$

$$W^{(n)} \simeq \sum_{i>j}^{n} W^{(2)}(i,j). \qquad (2.5.53)$$

Since the perturbation to $g^{(2)}(R)$ is expected to be small, the use of the approximation embodied in equation (2.5.53) should introduce little error. We refer the reader to Section 2.6.D for a discussion of this approximation.

Consider now the calculation of the equation of state. Equation (2.5.47) will be recognized as an expansion of $\exp(-\beta A_N^{(1)})$, where $A_N^{(1)}$ is the perturbation to the Helmholtz free energy of the system. From equations (2.5.47) and (2.5.49) we find directly

$$A_N = A_N^{(0)} + \kappa_1 - \frac{\kappa_2}{kT} + \cdots$$

$$\kappa_1 = \langle U_N^{(1)} \rangle_0$$

$$\kappa_2 = \langle (U_N^{(1)})^2 \rangle_0 - \langle U_N^{(1)} \rangle_0^2, \qquad (2.5.54)$$

and the indicated averages are defined in equation (2.5.52). The equation of state is determined from (2.5.54) by differentiation of the free energy with respect to volume at constant temperature. To terms of order κ_1,

$$p = p_0 - \left(\frac{\partial \kappa_1}{\partial V}\right)_T, \tag{2.5.55}$$

where p_0 is the pressure of the unperturbed system. In reduced units, $\tilde{p} \equiv (\sigma^3/\epsilon)p$, $\tilde{T} \equiv (kT/\epsilon)T$, $\tilde{V} \equiv V/(N\sigma^3)$ and we have

$$\frac{p}{\rho kT} = \left(\frac{p_0}{\rho kT}\right) + \frac{\tilde{a}_1(\tilde{V})}{\tilde{T}}, \tag{2.5.56}$$

where $\tilde{a}_1$ is, by comparison of equations (2.5.56) and (2.5.55), just

$$\tilde{a}_1 = -\tilde{V}\frac{\partial}{\partial \tilde{V}}\left(\frac{\kappa_1}{N\epsilon}\right). \tag{2.5.57}$$

Before making any calculations, we see that if the reference fluid is taken to be the rigid sphere fluid, then the equation of state for small κ_1 is just

$$p - \epsilon\rho\tilde{a}_1(\tilde{V}) = \rho kT\left(1 + \frac{2\pi\rho\sigma^3 g^{(2)}(\sigma)}{3}\right), \tag{2.5.58}$$

and $\tilde{a}_1(\tilde{V})$ is *independent of temperature* because the average defining κ_1 is over the rigid sphere distribution function. We shall make use of this important result in the following.

Zwanzig has tested the adequacy of equation (2.5.58) and finds that at densities up to about half the normal liquid density, the accuracy in the predicted values of $(p/\rho kT)$ is at worst 10%, and is much better at the lower densities. Table 2.5.1 shows the calculated values of

TABLE 2.5.1

Values of $(p/\rho kT)_{HC}$ and $-\tilde{a}_1(\tilde{v})$. From the K and YBG Distribution Functions

	K		YBG	
$\tilde{\rho} = \tilde{v}^{-1}$	$(p/\rho kT)_{HC}$	$-\tilde{a}_1(\tilde{v})$	$(p/\rho kT)_{HC}$	$-\tilde{a}_1(\tilde{v})$
0.0	1.00	0	1.00	0
0.2	1.52	1.16	1.54	1.33
0.4	2.22	2.36	2.43	2.95
0.6	3.18	3.79	3.73	4.86
0.8	4.37	5.10	5.40	6.89

$\tilde{a}_1$ using the Kirkwood and Yvon-Born-Green hard sphere radial-distribution functions as reference (see Sections 2.6.2 and 2.7.2).

Figures 2.5.1–2.5.3 show the application of the theory to the case of argon. As can be seen from Figure 2.5.1, the equation of state, $(p/\rho kT)$, appears accurately linear in T^{-1} as required by (2.5.56).

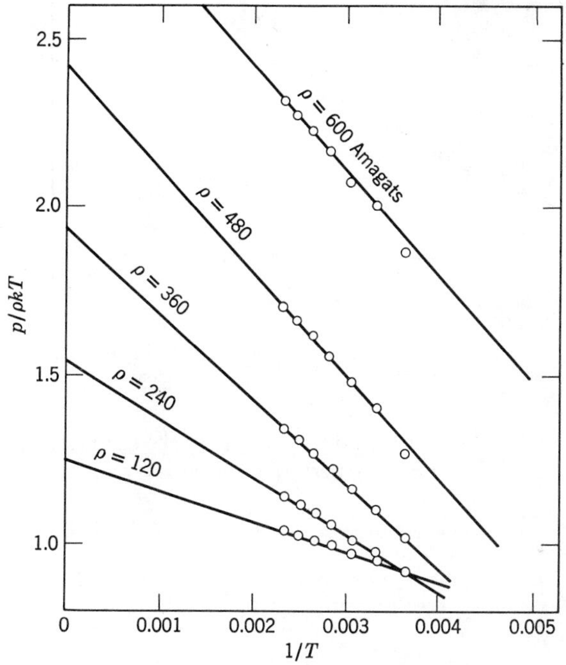

Fig. 2.5.1. Test of linearity of $(p/\rho kT)$ in $1/T$. Note that ρ is given in Amagat units.

From the limiting intercepts at $T^{-1} = 0$ is obtained, in principle, the equation of state of the rigid sphere fluid. The plot displayed in Figure 2.5.2 may be regarded as an experimental test of the theoretically predicted rigid sphere equation of state. Finally, in Figure 2.5.3 are compared the theoretical and experimental values of $\tilde{a}_1(\tilde{V})$. The parameter c scales the size of the hard sphere diameter. It is seen that, in general, the use of the first-order perturbation theory leads to good agreement with experiment, thereby verifying (2.5.58) for later use.

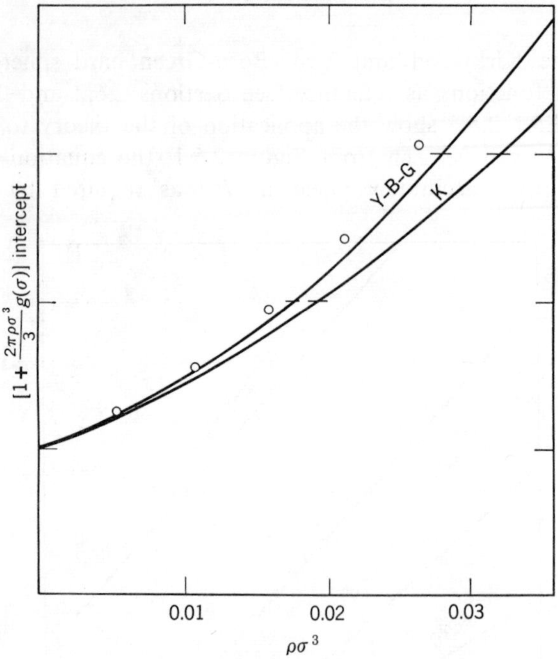

Fig. 2.5.2. Test of YBG and K approximations to the rigid sphere equation of state using perturbation theory.

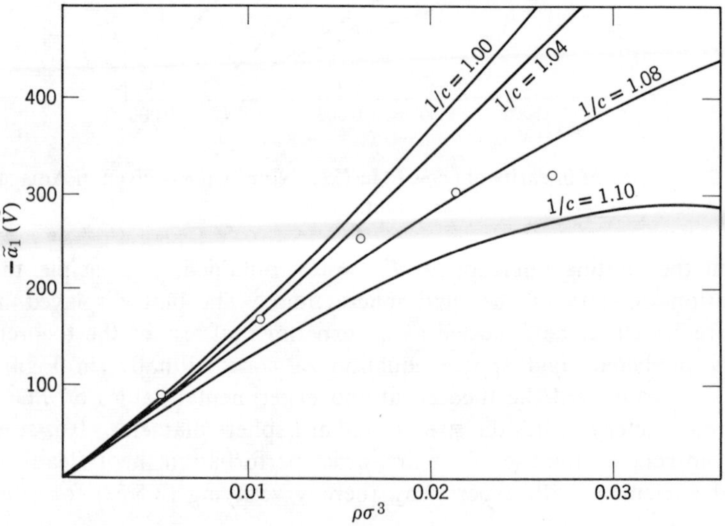

Fig. 2.5.3. Limiting slopes $\tilde{a}_1(\tilde{V})$ for Ar compared with YBG theory.

To complete this aside we now examine the change in $g^{(2)}(R)$ induced by the attractive field. For later use we examine the change in $g^{(2)}(R)$ about an isolated impurity due to the difference in potential between the impurity-host and host-host pairs. To answer this we rewrite equation (2.5.51) to terms of order β in the form

$$g^{(2)}(R) = g_0^{(2)}(R)e^{-\beta u_p(R)}\left[1 - \frac{\Phi}{R}\right]$$

$$\Phi = \frac{\pi\rho\beta}{V}\int\int u_p(s)g_0^{(2)}(s)[g_0^{(2)}(r) - 1]rs\,dr\,ds. \qquad (2.5.59)$$

In equation (2.5.59) cylindrical coordinates have been introduced. It is convenient to rewrite (2.5.59) in terms of the reduced variables

$$x = R/\sigma$$
$$y = s/\sigma$$
$$z = r/\sigma.$$

For an inverse power potential we put $u_p = \Delta\epsilon(\sigma/s)^n$ with σ the length parameter of the Lennard-Jones potential (or any other necessary length parameter if the cores of the solute and solvent differ appreciably). For any one inverse nth power perturbing potential,

$$\frac{\Phi(x)}{\sigma x} = \frac{\pi\rho\sigma^3\,\Delta\epsilon}{kTV}\,\Theta(n,x)$$

$$\Theta(n,x) = \frac{1}{x}\int_1^x z[g_0^{(2)}(z) - 1]\left\{\int_{|x-z|}^{x+z}\frac{g_0^{(2)}(y)}{y^{n-1}}\,dy\right\}dz. \qquad (2.5.60)$$

When the perturbation potential is a sum of several inverse power terms, a sum of functions $\Theta(n,x)$ is required for insertion in equation (2.5.60).

In order to examine the effects of various perturbation potentials we have evaluated (2.5.60) numerically for the inverse 4, 6, and 12 potentials, using as reference correlation functions those calculated by Kirkwood and co-workers. For a discussion of the origin of these correlation functions, we refer the reader ahead to Sections 2.6.2 and 2.7.2. For our purposes the choice of reference correlation function is not important, and the Kirkwood functions are readily available in numerical form whereas those deduced from other theories are not readily available. The results of some of these calculations are displayed in Figures 2.5.4–2.5.6 for liquid Ar at a density of 1.689×10^{22} cm.$^{-3}$

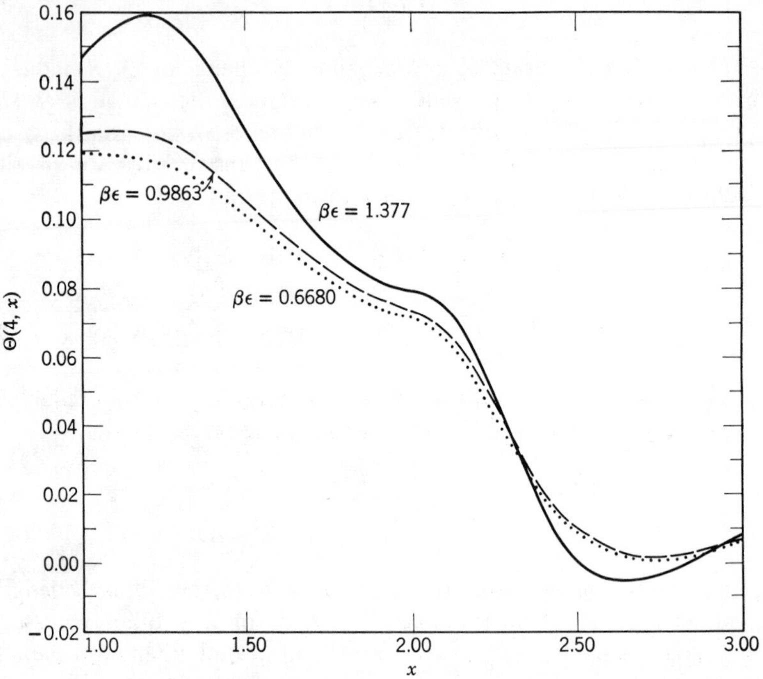

Fig. 2.5.4. The perturbation due to an inverse 4th power potential.

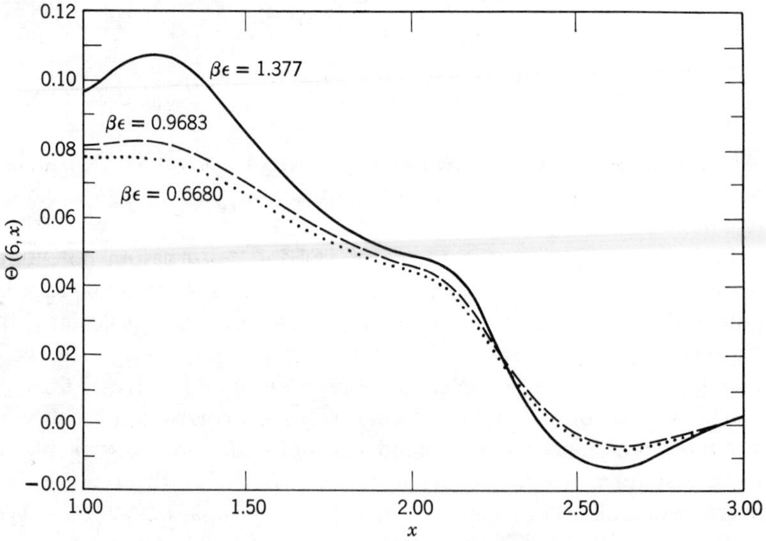

Fig. 2.5.5. The perturbation due to an inverse 6th power potential.

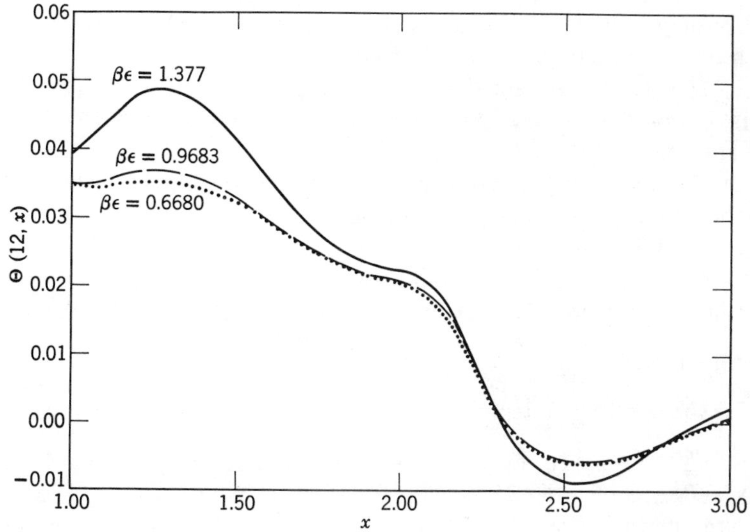

Fig. 2.5.6. The perturbation due to an inverse 12th power potential.

(1.12 gm. cm.$^{-3}$). The potential parameters chosen were $\sigma = 3.418 \times 10^{-8}$ cm. and $\epsilon = 171 \times 10^{-16}$ ergs. In the figures, the values of $\beta\epsilon$ cited correspond to temperatures of 90°K, 128°K, and 185.5°K. At the constant density cited, pressures are 50 and 500 atm., at 128°K and 185.5°K, respectively.

The integral $\Theta(n,x)$ is functionally similar for the several values of n investigated. At low temperature there is a maximum of $\Theta(n,x)$ close to the position of the first peak of $g^{(2)}(R)$. The secondary hump at about $x = 2$ occurs close to a point at which $g^{(2)}(R) = 1$. As the temperature is increased the first maximum diminishes in size. In general, the values of $\Theta(n,x)$ for $x > 2.00$ are only slightly different for the various temperatures considered, whereas for $1.00 < x < 2.00$, the differences are considerable. The reader should note that there is a crossing of curves at large x so that negative deviations at large x are largest for the lowest temperature, as expected.

It is also interesting to compare the values of $\Theta(n,x)$ for various n. In this case we see that $\Theta(12,x) < \Theta(6,x) < \Theta(4,x)$. It should not be concluded that this ordering will necessarily lead to a larger perturbation the smaller the value of n, since $\Theta(n,x)$ must be multiplied by $\Delta\epsilon$ to determine the correction to $g^{(2)}(R)$, and the magnitude of $\Delta\epsilon$ is fixed by other considerations.

Consider now the magnitude of the changes in $g^{(2)}(R)$. These can be conveniently described as arising from two sources:

(1) Due to the presence of the potential u_p there is a Boltzmann weighing of the particle separations leading to the term $e^{-\beta u_p(1,2)}$ in equation (2.5.59).

(2) Due to the presence of many interacting molecules in the vicinity of the impurity molecule, the Boltzmann weighing alone does not determine the density profile. Included in the work necessary to create a given density distribution is the entropy change on rearrangement and the change in interaction within the group of surrounding molecules. These interactions lead to the term $\left(1 - \frac{\Phi}{R}\right)$ of equation (2.5.59).

For the density and temperatures cited, if $\Delta\epsilon < \frac{\epsilon}{4}$ the contribution of Φ/R to $g^{(2)}(R)$ is only of order 0.2% or less, whereas the contribution of $\exp(-\beta u_p)$ is of order 25%. We, therefore, conclude that in the case that the perturbation potential is small relative to kT, the first-order changes in the pair correlation function are accurately given by

$$g^{(2)}(R) = g_0^{(2)}(R)e^{-\beta u_p(R)}.$$

When the perturbation potential is comparable to kT and many terms in the expansion (2.5.50) must be retained, this simplification is no longer valid.

The preceding analysis provides a justification for the simplest of procedures in calculating the change in pair correlation function in a very dilute solution when $\beta u_p < 1$. Even when $\frac{u_p}{kT} \sim 1$, only one higher order term (β^2) need be retained for moderate accuracy (10%). Thus, the expansion described should be useful for a wide variety of problems.

2.6. EQUATIONS FOR THE PAIR CORRELATION FUNCTION (3–13,30–37)

Exact equations for n-molecule correlation functions in terms of $(n + 1)$-molecule correlation functions may be obtained in several different ways. In order to calculate a correlation function of given order from these formalisms it is necessary to introduce some closure assumption to truncate the hierarchy of exact coupled equations. Without this closure, the calculation of the two-body correlation function cannot be divorced from the calculation of the three-body function, the three from the four, and so on. In this section we shall review the means by which various equations for the pair correlation function in particular are derived, and the meaning of the assumptions used to terminate the heirarchy.

2.6.A. *The Yvon-Born-Green Equation* (9,10)

Consider the defining equation for the n-molecule distribution function, equation (2.4.15). If we differentiate this equation with respect to the coordinates of one of the n molecules, say the molecule at $\mathbf{R}_1$, we obtain,

$$
\begin{aligned}
-kT\nabla_1\rho^{(n)} &= \frac{1}{\Xi}\sum_{N\geqslant n}\frac{z^N}{(N-n)!}\int e^{-\beta U}\nabla_1 U\, d\{N-n\} \\
&= \sum_{i=2}^{n}\nabla_1 u(1,i)\rho^{(n)} + \frac{1}{\Xi}\int \nabla_1 u(1, n+1) \\
&\quad \times \left[\int \sum_{N\geqslant n}\frac{(N-n)z^N}{(N-n)!}e^{-\beta U}\, d\{N-n-1\}\right] d(n+1) \\
&= \sum_{i=2}^{n}\nabla_1 u(1,i)\rho^{(n)} + \int \nabla_1 u(1, n+1)\rho^{(n+1)}\, d(n+1).
\end{aligned}
\tag{2.6.1}
$$

Thus, as forecast in the introduction, an exact equation for $\rho^{(n)}$ is obtained in terms of $\rho^{(n+1)}$. In order to truncate the heirarchy represented by equation (2.6.1), we introduce the concept of the potential of the mean force, $W^{(n)}$, by

$$W^{(n)} = -kT\ln g^{(n)}, \tag{2.6.2}$$

where, of course, $g^{(n)}$ is related to $\rho^{(n)}$ by equation (2.4.22). That $W^{(n)}$ is indeed the potential of the mean force field in which the n molecules are situated can be seen in the following way: equation (2.6.2) is differentiated with respect to the coordinates of one molecule, giving

$$-\nabla_1 W^{(n)} = \frac{kT\,\nabla_1 g^{(n)}}{g^{(n)}} = -\frac{\displaystyle\sum_{N\geqslant n} \frac{z^N}{(N-n)!} \int e^{-\beta U}\,\nabla_1 U\, d\{N-n\}}{\displaystyle\sum_{N\geqslant n} \frac{z^N}{(N-n)!} \int e^{-\beta U}\, d\{N-n\}}. \tag{2.6.3}$$

In equation (2.6.3) the factor $\rho^n \Xi^{-1}$ has cancelled out [cf. equation (2.4.22), defining $g^{(n)}$ in terms of $\rho^{(n)}$]. Equation (2.6.3) clearly has the form of a properly normalized average of the force on the molecule at $\mathbf{R}_1$, when the n molecules are held fixed at the locations $\{n\}$. In order to obtain an equation for $g^{(2)}$ we must, therefore, consider ways in which $W^{(3)}$ may be expressed in terms of $W^{(2)}$. As a first approximation, Kirkwood suggested that

$$W^{(3)}(1,2,3) = W^{(2)}(1,2) + W^{(2)}(1,3) + W^{(2)}(2,3), \tag{2.6.4}$$

or

$$g^{(2)}(1,2,3) = g^{(2)}(1,2)g^{(2)}(1,3)g^{(2)}(2,3). \tag{2.6.5}$$

The physical meaning of this assumption, called the superposition approximation, may be described qualitatively as follows: In evaluating $W^{(3)}$ we have neglected the effect of fixing a molecule at $\mathbf{R}_3$ on the distribution of the other $(N-3)$ molecules around the molecules fixed at $\mathbf{R}_1$ and $\mathbf{R}_2$. In Section 2.6.D we shall consider briefly the quantitative significance of this assumption; a detailed discussion of the decomposition of $W^{(n)}$ and the resulting relations between $W^{(n)}$ and the properties of smaller groups of molecules is presented in Appendix 2.A.

Substitution of equation (2.6.5) in equation (2.6.1) now leads to

$$-kT\,\nabla_1 \ln g^{(2)}(1,2) = \nabla_1 u(1,2) + \rho \int \nabla_1 u(1,3) g^{(2)}(1,3) g^{(2)}(2,3)\, d(3). \tag{2.6.6}$$

This nonlinear integral equation was first derived by Yvon, and later by Born and Green; it is to be solved subject to the boundary condition

$$g^{(2)}(1,2) \to 1; \qquad R_{12} \to \infty.$$

We refer to it later as the YBG equation.

2.6.B. *The Kirkwood Integral Equation* (11)

A slightly different integral equation for $g^{(2)}$ was derived by Kirkwood. Let the coupling between a selected molecule, say 1, and the rest of the fluid be imagined to be variable from zero to unity. As the interaction is "switched on" the structure of the fluid around molecule 1 changes. If the fractional interaction is denoted ξ, where $0 \leqslant \xi \leqslant 1$, then we obviously have

$$\Xi(\xi) = \sum_{N \geqslant 0} \frac{z^N}{N!} \int e^{-\beta U(\xi)} \, d\{N\} \tag{2.6.7}$$

$$U(\xi) = \xi \sum_{i=2}^{N} u(1,i) + \sum_{2 \leqslant i < j \leqslant N} u(i,j) \tag{2.6.8}$$

$$\rho^{(n)}(\{n\},\xi) = \frac{1}{\Xi(\xi)} \sum_{N \geqslant n} \frac{z^N}{(N-n)!} \int e^{-\beta U(\xi)} \, d\{N-n\}. \tag{2.6.9}$$

If we differentiate equation (2.6.9) with respect to ξ and collect equivalent terms

$$\Xi\left(\frac{\partial \rho^{(n)}}{\partial \xi}\right)_{z,V,T} - \frac{\rho^{(n)}}{kT} \int u(1,2) \times \left[\int \sum_{N \geqslant 2} \frac{z^N}{N!} (N-1) e^{-\beta U(\xi)} \, d\{N-2\}\right] d(1) \, d(2)$$
$$= -\frac{1}{kT} \sum_{N \geqslant 0} \frac{z^N}{(N-n)!} \left\{\sum_{i=2}^{n} u(1,i) \int e^{-\beta U(\xi)} \, d\{N-n\} + (N-n) \int u(1, n+1) \left[\int e^{-\beta U(\xi)} \, d\{N-n-1\}\right] d(n+1)\right\}. \tag{2.6.10}$$

Now, equation (2.6.10) is divided by $-\rho^{(n)}\Xi(\xi)/kT$ to yield

$$-kT\left(\frac{\partial \ln \rho^{(n)}}{\partial \xi}\right)_{z,V,T} + \frac{1}{\langle N \rangle} \int u(1,2) \rho^{(2)*}(1,2;\xi) \, d\{2\}$$
$$= \sum_{i=2}^{n} u(1,i) + \frac{1}{\rho^{(n)}} \int u(1, n+1) \rho^{(n+1)} \, d(n+1), \tag{2.6.11}$$

where $\rho^{(2)*}$ is defined by

$$\sum_{N\geq 2} \frac{z^N}{N!}(N-1)\int e^{-\beta U(\xi)}\,d\{N-2\} =$$
$$\sum_{N\geq 2} \frac{1}{N}\frac{z^N}{(N-2)!}\int e^{-\beta U(\xi)}\,d\{N-2\} = \frac{1}{\langle N\rangle}\rho^{(2)*}(1,2;\xi)\Xi. \quad (2.6.12)$$

If we allow $N,V \to \infty$, with ρ = constant, then it is seen that $\rho^{(2)*} \to \rho^{(2)}$, since the maximum term approximation to Ξ is valid and the factor N^{-1} may be replaced in the first member of equation (2.6.12) by $\langle N\rangle^{-1}$. For $n = 2$, using the superposition approximation, equation (2.6.4), we finally obtain

$$-kT \ln g^{(2)}(1,2;\xi) = \xi u(1,2) + \rho\int_0^\xi\int u(1,3)g^{(2)}(1,3;\xi) \times [g^{(2)}(2,3) - 1]\,d(3)\,d\xi, \quad (2.6.13)$$

where we have integrated over ξ. This equation was first obtained by Kirkwood.

Although equation (2.6.11) is exactly equivalent to equation (2.6.1), the superposition approximations are introduced in different ways, so that the final YBG and K equations are different. To see this, first write equation (2.6.6) in terms of an arbitrary coupling parameter, ξ.

$$-kT\,\nabla_1 \ln g^{(2)}(1,2;\xi) = \xi\,\nabla_1 u(1,2) + \rho\xi\int \nabla_1 u(1,3)g^{(2)}(1,3;\xi)g^{(2)}(2,3)\,d(3). \quad (2.6.14)$$

Now differentiate equations (2.6.13) with respect to $\mathbf{R}_1$ to obtain

$$-kT\,\nabla_1 \ln g^{(2)}(1,2;\xi) = \xi\,\nabla_1 u(1,2) + \rho\int_0^\xi\int \nabla_1[u(1,3)g^{(2)}(1,3;\xi)]g^{(2)}(2,3)\,d(3)\,d\xi, \quad (2.6.15)$$

where we have used the fact that

$$\nabla_1\int u(1,3)g^{(2)}(1,3;\xi)\,d(3) = 0. \quad (2.6.16)$$

It is seen immediately that, apart from the different way ξ appears in the integral terms of the two equations, equation (2.6.15) contains the extra term

$$\rho \int_0^{\xi} \int u(1,3)\, \nabla_1 g^{(2)}(1,3;\xi) g^{(2)}(2,3)\, d(3)\, d\xi.$$

2.6.C. *The Equations of Cole* (12) *and of Fisher* (13,34)

The superposition approximation, equations (2.6.4) and (2.6.5), is, as we shall see in Section 2.7, not entirely adequate to describe the thermodynamic properties of dense fluids. Consequently, a number of formal attempts have been made to improve upon it, and we review two of these here.

Suppose we form the tensor gradient of equation (2.6.1) with respect to $\mathbf{R}_1$,

$$-kT\nabla_1\nabla_1\rho^{(n)} = \sum_{i=2}^{n} \{\nabla_1 \nabla_1 u(1,i) + \nabla_1 u(1,i)\, \nabla_1 \rho^{(n)}\} + \int \nabla_1 \nabla_1 u(1, n+1)\rho^{(n+1)}\, d(n+1) + \int \nabla_1 u(1, n+1)\, \nabla_1 \rho^{(n+1)}\, d(n+1). \quad (2.6.17)$$

In equation (2.6.17) we now substitute for $\nabla_1 \rho^{(n+1)}$ from equation (2.6.1) with $(n + 1)$ replacing n there. The result is

$$-(kT)^2 \nabla_1 \nabla_1 g^{(n)} = g^{(n)}\left[\left(\sum_{i=2}^{n} \nabla_1 u(1,i)\right)\left(\sum_{i=2}^{n} \nabla_1 u(1,i)\right) + kT \sum_{i=1}^{n} \nabla_1 \nabla_1 u(1,i)\right] + 2kT\nabla_1 g^{(n)} \sum_{i=2}^{n} \nabla_1 u(1,i) + \rho \int [kT\nabla_1 \nabla_1 u(1, n+1) - \nabla_1 u(1, n+1)\, \nabla_1 u(1, n+1)] \times g^{(n+1)}\, d(n+1) - \rho^2 \iint \nabla_1 u(1, n+1)\, \nabla_1 u(1, n+2) g^{(n+2)}\, d(n+1)\, d(n+2). \quad (2.6.18)$$

The superposition approximation appropriate to a group of four molecules is obtained from the following recipe: select three molecules and express the correlation function as the product of that for the chosen three and the pair correlation functions for the fourth molecule and each of the chosen three separately. Thus,

$$g^{(4)}(\{4\}) = g^{(3)}(1,2,3)g^{(2)}(1,4)g^{(2)}(2,4)g^{(2)}(3,4). \qquad (2.6.19)$$

This formulation obviously has the effect of singling out molecule 4. Using equation (2.6.19), equation (2.6.18) may now be expressed in terms of $g^{(2)}$ only,

$$\frac{-(kT)^2}{g^{(2)}}\nabla_1\nabla_1 g^{(2)} = [\nabla_1 u(1,2)\nabla_1 u(1,2) + kT\nabla_1\nabla_1 u(1,2)] +$$

$$2kT\nabla_1 \ln g^{(2)}\nabla_1 u(1,2) +$$

$$\rho\int[kT\nabla_1\nabla_1 u(1,3) - \nabla_1 u(1,3)\nabla_1 u(1,3)]g^{(2)}(1,3)g^{(2)}(2,3)\,d(3) -$$

$$\rho^2\iint\nabla_1 u(1,3)\nabla_1 u(1,4)g^{(2)}(1,3)g^{(2)}(2,3)\times$$

$$g^{(2)}(1,4)g^{(2)}(2,4)g^{(2)}(3,4)\,d(3)\,d(4), \qquad (2.6.20)$$

an equation derived by Cole (12).

Alternatively we may refine the superposition approximation in a more direct way than equation (2.6.19) by applying the same *concept* as that expressed in equations (2.6.4–5) to $g^{(4)}$:

$$g^{(4)}(\{4\}) = g^{(3)}(1,2,3)g^{(3)}(1,2,4)g^{(3)}(1,3,4)g^{(3)}(2,3,4). \qquad (2.6.21)$$

If we now introduce a triplet indirect correlation function $h^{(3)}(1,2,3)$ by

$$g^{(3)}(\{3\}) = g^{(2)}(1,2)g^{(2)}(1,3)g^{(2)}(2,3)h^{(3)}(\{3\}), \qquad (2.6.22)$$

we may deduce two coupled vector equations by taking equation (2.6.1) for $n = 2,3$:

$$-kT\nabla_1 \ln g^{(2)}(1,2) = \nabla_1 u(1,2) +$$

$$\rho\int\nabla_1 u(1,3)g^{(2)}(1,3)g^{(2)}(2,3)h^{(3)}(\{3\})\,d(3) \qquad (2.6.23)$$

$$-kT\nabla_1 \ln h^{(3)}(1,2,3) = \rho\int\nabla_1 u(1,4)g^{(2)}(1,4)\times$$

$$[g^{(2)}(2,4)g^{(2)}(3,4)h^{(3)}(1,2,4)h^{(3)}(2,3,4)h^{(3)}(1,3,4) -$$

$$g^{(2)}(2,4)h^{(3)}(1,2,4) - g^{(2)}(3,4)h^{(3)}(1,3,4)]\,d(4). \qquad (2.6.24)$$

These equations should be solved subject to the conditions

$$\left.\begin{aligned} g^{(2)}(1,2) &\to 1 \\ h^{(3)}(1,2,3) &\to 1 \end{aligned}\right\} \quad \text{as any one of the molecules goes off to infinity,}$$

so that the proper normalization and physical significance of the correlation functions is preserved. The equations (2.6.23) and (2.6.24) were first derived by Fisher (13,34).

Equations (2.6.20) and (2.6.24) are enormously more difficult to solve than equations (2.6.6) and (2.6.13). No numerical solutions have, in fact, been obtained. Equation (2.6.20) has been used by Cole to estimate first-order corrections to the superposition approximation, equations (2.6.5), in a density expansion for dilute gases:

$$g^{(3)}(1,2,3) = g^{(2)}(1,2)g^{(2)}(1,3)g^{(2)}(2,3)(1 + \alpha\rho k^{(3)}(1,2,3) + \cdots), \tag{2.6.25}$$

where $k^{(3)}(1,2,3)$ is a known simple function of $\{3\}$ and α is the numerical factor which is determined by this procedure.

2.6.D. *The Meaning of the Superposition Approximation*

It follows from the definitions of $\rho_N^{(n)}$, $\rho^{(n)}$ and $g^{(n)}$ in Section 2.4 that, to terms of order N^{-1},

$$g^{(2)}(1,2) = \frac{1}{V}\int g^{(3)}(1,2,3)\, d(3). \tag{2.6.26}$$

Use of the superposition approximation, equation (2.6.5), then results in

$$\int g^{(2)}(2,3)g^{(2)}(1,3)\, d(3) = V, \tag{2.6.27}$$

which is clearly a contradictory result except in the limit of low density, since the left-hand side must depend upon $(\mathbf{R}_2 - \mathbf{R}_1)$. Thus, the superposition approximation has obvious shortcomings. However, this is not to say that it is not of use for calculating the thermodynamic functions of both gases and liquids. As we shall now show, the superposition approximation is a simple mathematical expression representing the sum of a class of diagrams (to all orders in the density) in a cluster expansion.

We recall the linked-cluster expansion derived in Section 2.5.B for $\ln g^{(2)}(1,2)$:

$$\ln g^{(2)}(1,2) = -\beta u(1,2) + \sum_{n=1}^{\infty} \gamma_{n+2}\rho^n + O(N^{-1}), \qquad (2.6.28)$$

where the residual $O(N^{-1})$ is the fluctuation term previously given explicitly, but in which we are not now interested. Consider now a similar evaluation of $g^{(3)}(1,2,3)$. The starting point is

$$\begin{aligned}\ln g^{(3)}(1,2,3) &= \ln \langle e^{-\beta U}\rangle^{(1,2,3)} - \ln \langle e^{-\beta U}\rangle \\ &= -\beta(u(1,2) + u(1,3) + u(2,3)) \\ &\quad + \left\langle \exp_L\left(\sum_{i<j}{}' f_{ij}\right) - 1\right\rangle_c^{(1,2,3)} - \ln \langle e^{-\beta U}\rangle, \qquad (2.6.29)\end{aligned}$$

where the prime on Σ' denotes the fact that the intermolecular potential terms for the specified group of molecules have been removed, and are displayed separately. Contributions to $\langle \exp_L (\sum'_{i<j} f_{ij}) - 1\rangle_c^{(1,2,3)}$ arise in four ways: terms for groups of n molecules including none, any one, any two, or all three, of molecules 1, 2, and 3. The first two types of terms are just those which combine with the last term on the right-hand side of equation (2.6.29) to give the fluctuation terms, and we henceforth ignore them. Consider all terms representing n molecules including a particular pair, say 1,2. We have

$$\sum_{(C_n')} \left\langle \prod^{(n-2/1,2)} f_{ij} \right\rangle_c^{(1,2,3)} = \frac{1}{V^{N-3}} \int \sum_{(C_n')} \prod^{(n-2/1,2)} f_{ij}\, d\{N-3\}. \qquad (2.6.30)$$

The set $\{N-3\}$ includes all of the $(n-2)$ molecules since this subgroup does not include molecule 3. Hence,

$$\begin{aligned}\sum_{(C_n')} \left\langle \prod^{(n-2/1,2)} f_{ij} \right\rangle_c^{(1,2,3)} &= \frac{1}{V^{n-2}} \int \sum_{(C_n')} \prod^{(n-2/1,2)} f_{ij}\, d\{n-2\} \\ &= (n-2)!\, \gamma_n(1,2) V^{2-n}, \qquad (2.6.31)\end{aligned}$$

where we have used the definition of γ_n in equation (2.5.30). There are two other series of this type, involving, respectively, $\gamma_n(1,3)$ and $\gamma_n(2,3)$.

A term of the third type for groups of n molecules is*

$$\sum_{(C_n'')} \left\langle \prod^{(n-3/1,2,3)} f_{ij} \right\rangle_c^{(1,2,3)} = \frac{1}{V^{N-3}} \int \sum_{(C_n'')} \prod^{(n-3/1,2,3)} f_{ij}\, d\{N-3\}$$
$$= \frac{1}{V^{n-3}} \int \sum_{(C_n'')} \prod^{(n-3/1,2,3)} f_{ij}\, d\{n-3\}$$
$$= (n-3)!\, \delta_n(1,2,3) V^{3-n}, \qquad (2.6.32)$$

where the last member of equation (2.6.32) defines the next higher order of irreducible cluster integral, $\delta_n(1,2,3)$, in which molecules 1, 2, and 3 are held fixed. The contribution of these terms is

$$\sum_{n=4}^{N} \binom{N-3}{n-3} \frac{(n-3)!\, \delta_n(1,2,3)}{V^{n-3}} = \sum_{n=4} \rho^{n-3}\, \delta_n(1,2,3), \qquad (2.6.33)$$

so that from equations (2.6.31 and 33), equation (2.6.29) becomes

$$\ln g^{(3)}(1,2,3) = \ln g^{(2)}(1,2) + \ln g^{(2)}(1,3) + \ln g^{(2)}(2,3) + \sum_{n=1}^{\infty} \rho^n\, \delta_{n+3}(1,2,3). \qquad (2.6.34)$$

We see immediately from equations (2.6.4–5) that the last term on the right-hand side of equations (2.6.34) is the one which is neglected in the superposition approximation. Also, equation (2.6.34) shows immediately that the superposition approximation sums a certain class of diagrams to all orders in the density, and therefore is possibly superior to an evaluation of individual virial coefficients for the description of a dense fluid because it represents an approximation to the asymptotic form of the *complete* virial series.

On the other hand, if the superposition approximation is used to calculate the virial coefficients for the equation of state of a dilute system, then it is easily shown that virial coefficients higher than the third are given incorrectly. To demonstrate this we include the correction term in equation (2.6.6), thus rendering it exact:

$$-kT\nabla_1 \ln g^{(2)}(1,2) = \nabla_1 u(1,2) + \rho \int \nabla_1 u(1,3) g^{(2)}(2,3) g^{(2)}(1,3) \exp\left(\sum_{n=1}^{\infty} \rho^n\, \delta_{n+3}\right) d(3). \qquad (2.6.35)$$

* C_n'' denotes all connected diagrams of n labeled points excluding the bonds f_{12}, f_{13}, f_{23}. These terms have also been derived by R. Abe, *Prog. Theor. Phys.*, **21**, 421 (1959) (see also Ref. (41)).

We now expand each $g^{(2)}$ in a power series in the density as

$$g^{(2)}(i,j) = e^{-\beta u(i,j)}\left(1 + \rho\gamma_3(i,j) + \rho^2\left(\frac{\gamma_3^{\,2}(i,j)}{2!} + \gamma_4(i,j)\right)\right). \quad (2.6.36)$$

After substituting equation (2.3.36) in equation (2.6.35) and equating coefficients of equal powers of the density, there is obtained a set of equations of which the first two are:

$$-kT\nabla_1\gamma_3(1,2) = \int \nabla_1 u(1,3)e^{-\beta(u(1,3)+u(2,3))}\, d(3)$$

$$-kT\nabla_1\gamma_4(1,2) = \int \nabla_1 u(1,3)e^{-\beta(u(1,3)+u(2,3))} \times (\gamma_3(1,3) + \gamma_3(2,3) + \delta_4(1,2,3))\, d(3). \quad (2.6.37)$$

[The reader should note that this procedure is valid because the irreducible integrals are defined in such a way that they are volume independent in a system large enough that surface effects are negligible.] Since the first of the set of terms (the δ_n) neglected in the superposition approximation appears in the *second* of equation (2.6.37), it follows that γ_3 is given correctly by the first equation, but that when δ_4 is neglected γ_4 is incorrect. Thus, $g^{(2)}$ is calculated correct only to terms of $O(\rho)$:

$$g^{(2)}(i,j) = e^{-\beta u(i,j)}(1 + \rho\gamma_3(i,j) + \cdots). \quad (2.6.38)$$

Recalling now the pressure equation (2.4.49),

$$\frac{\beta p}{\rho} = 1 - \frac{2\pi}{3}\rho\int_0^\infty u'(R)g^{(2)}(R)R^3\, dR, \quad (2.6.39)$$

we see that $(\beta p/\rho)$ is given correctly to terms of $O(\rho^2)$ by equation (2.6.38), i.e., up to the third virial coefficient.

It is informative to consider the reason that the neglect of a first-order term in the density for $g^{(3)}$ should lead to an incorrect evaluation of only the second order density term in $g^{(2)}$. This stepping down feature is easily traced to the factor ρ multiplying the integral term in equation (2.6.35). This results in equation (2.6.37) in γ_3 being expressed in terms of γ_2 [i.e., the "bare" potential $u(i,j)$], γ_4 being expressed in terms of γ_3, and so on. It follows that Fisher's use of the refined superposition approximation equation (2.6.21), which has the two coupled equations (2.6.23–24), results in two successive step-downs of the correction so that his theory predicts the fourth virial coefficient correctly, but not the fifth.

2.6.E. *An Extension of the* YBG *Equation* (35)*

We shall now consider an extension and improvement of one of the approaches to the equilibrium theory of dense fluids, namely that of Yvon, Born, and Green. The YBG integro-differential equation for the pair correlation function was derived in Section 2.6.A, on the assumption that the triplet correlation function $g^{(3)}(1,2,3)$ can be adequately represented by the Kirkwood product of pair correlation functions, i.e., $g^{(2)}(1,2)g^{(2)}(1,3)g^{(2)}(2,3)$. The equation resulting is

$$-kT\nabla_1 \ln g^{(2)}(1,2) = \nabla_1 u(1,2) + \rho \int d(3) g^{(2)}(1,3) g^{(2)}(2,3)\, \nabla_1 u(1,3), \tag{2.6.6}$$

and has been solved numerically, both for the hard sphere and for the Lennard-Jones potentials. The results are not as close to the molecular dynamics calculations (which form the "experimental" situation for these idealized potentials) as the HNC† values, and compare still worse with the PY‡ results (see Fig. 2.7.3 and the next several sections).

There is, however, one consideration which weighs strongly for the YBG and against the PY and HNC theories: the existence of a phase transition. Solution of the latter two equations for the hard sphere fluid shows that the pressure continues to be a smooth function of the density even into the (unphysical) region more dense than a system of close-packed spheres. The YBG equation, on the other hand, becomes divergent beyond a certain critical density, and Kirkwood has shown that this density corresponds to the onset of long-range order in the system. We may take this as indicating that the Yvon-Born-Green-Kirkwood approach is qualitatively sound, and that it can be made quantitatively correct by improvements on the superposition approximation.

Triplet Correlations and the Superposition Approximation (35). Two interesting studies of the superposition approximation for the triplet correlation function have recently been made. Alder (36) considered a dense fluid of hard spheres, and showed that at high densities the superposition approximation is surprisingly accurate (see Table 2.6.1).

* This section was written by Mr. J. Lekner.
† See Section 2.6.F.
‡ See Section 2.6.G.

TABLE 2.6.1
Test of Superposition Approximation for the Rigid Sphere Fluid, $\rho_0/\rho = 1.60$

$x = R/\sigma$	$g^{(2)}(x)$	$[g^{(3)}(x,x,x)]^{\frac{1}{3}}$
1.000	4.95	4.85[a]
1.088	2.72	2.72
1.253	1.12	1.18
1.399	0.73	0.74
1.531	0.64	0.61
1.652	0.71	0.69
1.764	0.88	0.94
1.870	1.08	1.15
1.970	1.24	1.24

[a] Extrapolated.

Rahman's (37) results for a liquid system interacting with a Lennard-Jones potential also indicate that what was formerly thought to be purely a low-density approximation may be quite satisfactory at liquid densities.

Now the first-order correction to the superposition approximation has been evaluated by Rowlinson (38) for hard spheres, and is negative, having a large magnitude in the contact configuration. Because of the aforementioned satisfactory nature of the superposition approximation at high densities, one surmises that there must be considerable cancellation among the first, second, and higher order corrections. It is further clear that some way of approximating the *entire* series of terms missing from the superposition product would be necessary for high-density applications. A method which has proved successful in approximating the behavior of a function from the first few terms of its series expansion is that of Padé approximants (39,40). To use such a Padé approximant we need at least one more term in the density series for the triplet correlation function. We shall consider this series in the next paragraph.

The Series for the Triplet Correlation Function. We recall from Section 2.6.D that the Kirkwood expression for the triplet correlation function contains approximations to the $\gamma_n(i,j)$ diagrams (two fixed points) to infinite order. To put this in more self-evident form, all *pair* correlations between (1,2), (1,3), and (2,3) entering into $g^{(3)}(1,2,3)$ are already included in the superposition product. In fact, the exact expression as derived by Salpeter (41) and, by a different method, in Section 2.6.D, is

$$g^{(3)}(1,2,3) = g^{(2)}(1,2)g^{(2)}(1,3)g^{(2)}(2,3) \exp\left[\sum_{n=1}^{\infty} \rho^n \,\delta_{n+3}(1,2,3)\right]. \qquad (2.6.40)$$

The coefficient of ρ^n, $\delta_{n+3}(1,2,3)$, gives the contribution to correlations between the fixed points 1, 2, and 3 due to the interaction of 1, 2, and 3 with n field points. These coefficients are called "simple 123 irreducible clusters" by Salpeter, and are defined as follows:

(*a*) Each pair of field points is connected by at least one continuous line which passes through neither 1, 2, nor 3.

(*b*) Each field point lies on at least one continuous line joining the points (1,2), as well as on a line joining (2,3) and one joining (1,3).

The following examples will fix the meaning better than further description. Consider the coefficient of ρ (one field point), given by

$$\delta_4(1,2,3) = \int d(4) f_{14} f_{24} f_{34} \equiv$$

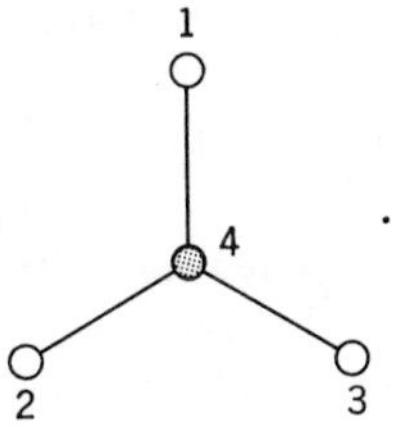

. (2.6.41)

There are no other diagrams in δ_4: interactions between pairs of the fixed points are already taken into account (cf. the factor $\exp[-\beta u(i,j)]$ in (2.6.28)); pair correlations are also included in the $g^{(2)}$'s, and hence, diagrams of the type

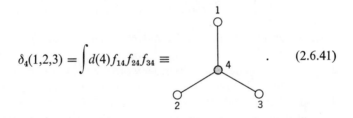

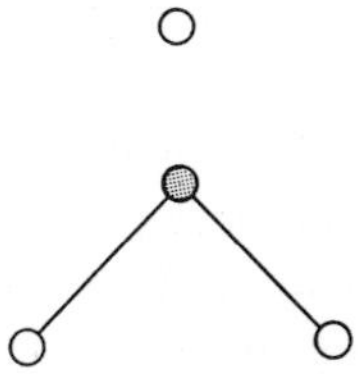

are redundant.

The coefficient of ρ^2 (two field points) is already rather complicated. The diagrams comprising this term (i.e., δ_5) are built up by putting additional f bonds onto the skeleton shown in (2.6.41a),

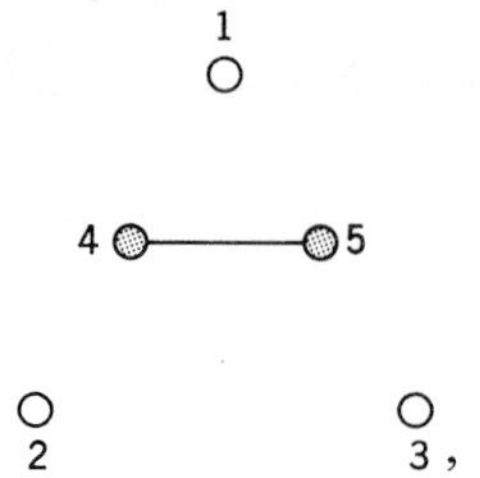

(2.6.41a)

according to condition (b). Condition (a) has already been satisfied by joining the field points 4 and 5. We find a set of 13 diagrams in Table 2.6.2.

The diagrams with 4, 5, and 6-bonds divide logically into 4 rows and 3 columns, as arranged in the table. The diagrams of a given row are obtained from each other by cyclic permutation of the indices 1, 2, and 3. For example, the first row diagrams sum to

$$\frac{1}{2!}\int d(4)\, d(5) f_{45}(f_{14}f_{24}f_{35} + f_{24}f_{34}f_{15} + f_{34}f_{14}f_{25}).$$

All diagrams except the 7-bond one *carry a weight of 2*, because interchange of the field points 4 and 5 gives a topologically distinct diagram *of the same value*. In order words, we have omitted from Table 2.6.2 all those diagrams with 4 to the right of 5, and let the existing diagrams have weight 2. The situation is different for the completely bonded diagram at the bottom of the table; here an interchange of 4 and 5 gives back a topologically identical diagram, and accordingly its weight is unity. The coefficient of ρ^2 in (1) is thus

$$\delta_5(1,2,3) = \frac{1}{2!}\int d(4)\, d(5) f_{45}(2f_{14}f_{24}f_{35} + 2f_{24}f_{34}f_{15} + \cdots + f_{14}f_{24}f_{34}f_{15}f_{25}f_{35}). \quad (2.6.42)$$

Evaluation of δ_4 and δ_5. Having defined δ_4 and δ_5, we shall now describe the essentially geometrical problem of evaluating these contributions to the triplet correlation function. In the process we hope to make their physical meaning more concrete. Consider, as a specific example, the hard sphere fluid, where the interparticle potential is infinite when the separation of the centers of two particles is less than the diameter of one, and zero for larger separations. The f bonds then

TABLE 2.6.2

4-bond:

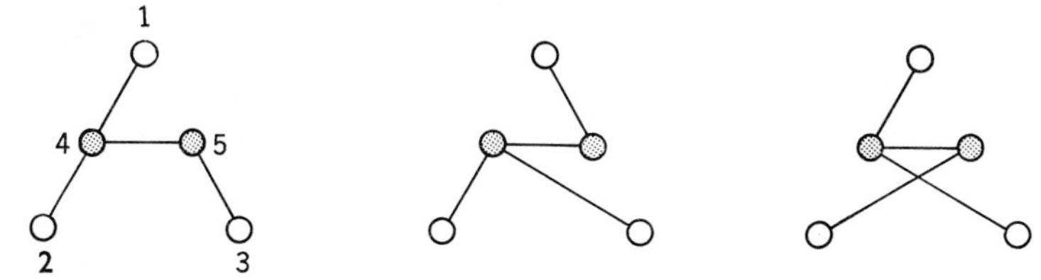

5-bond:

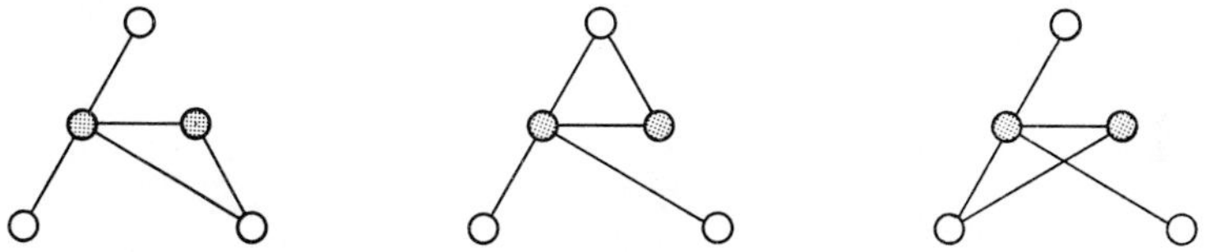

5-bond:

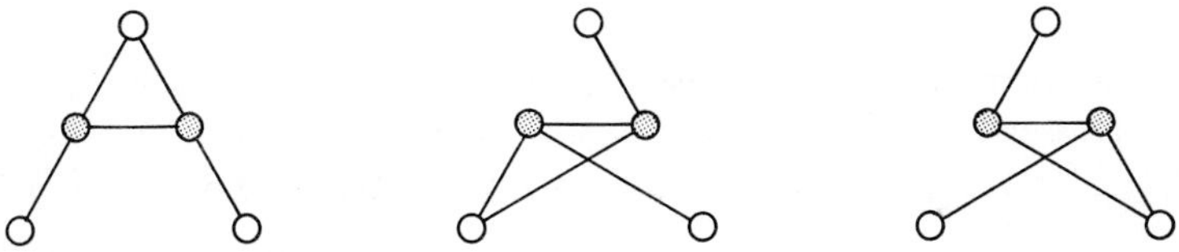

6-bond:

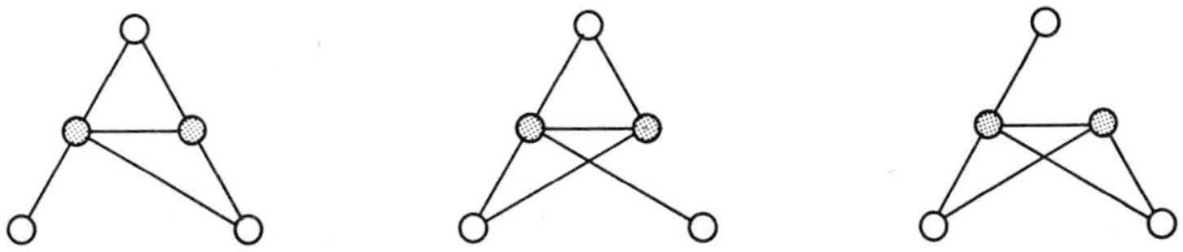

7-bond:

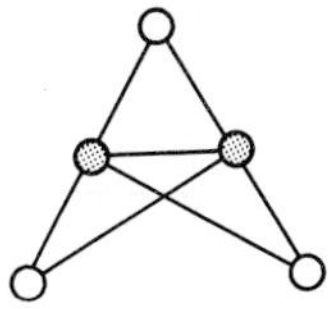

have the simple form shown in (2.6.43).

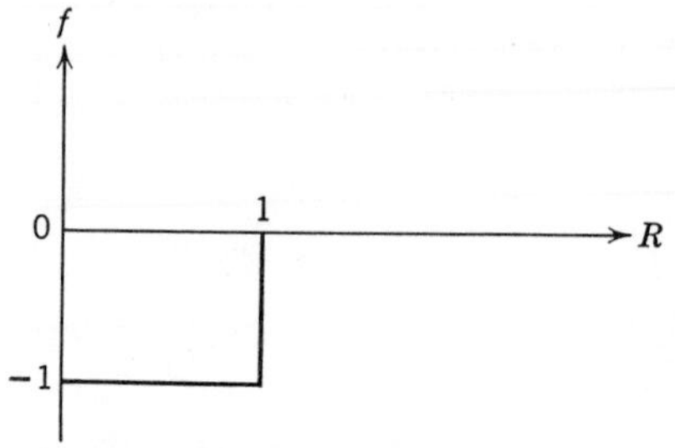

(2.6.43)

Let the sphere *diameter* be the unit of length.

Then $\delta_4(1,2,3)$ is given by (2.6.41)

$\delta_4(1,2,3) =$ 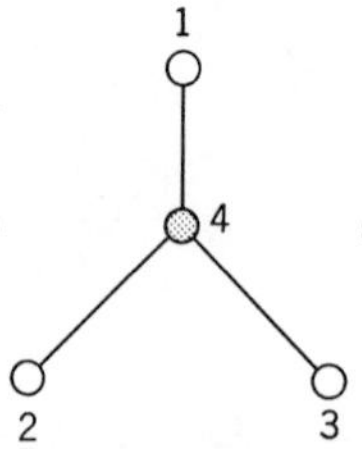

$= \int d(4) f_{14} f_{24} f_{34}.$

For the integrand to be nonzero it is necessary that all the f_{i4} be nonzero, i.e., particle 4 must be simultaneously within range of the potentials of 1, 2, and 3. If we treat 4 as a point, the range of the fixed points can be represented by enlarged spheres of unit *radius* centered at 1, 2, and 3. Hence, δ_4 is simply equal to *minus the volume common to the three enlarged spheres centered at the fixed points 1, 2, and 3.*

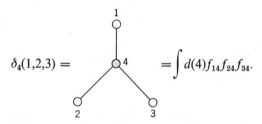

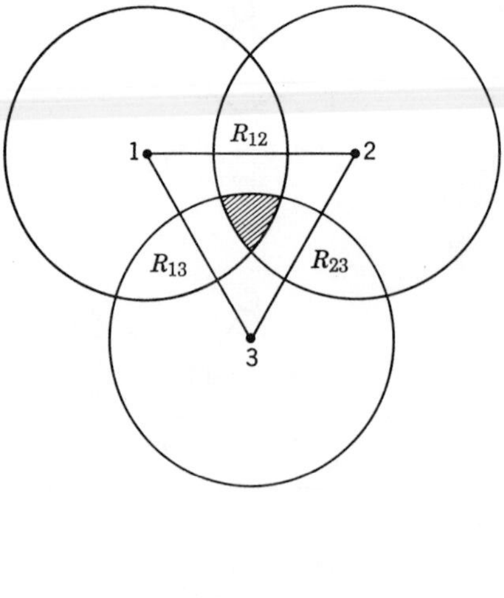

The diagram is intuitively obvious, since it is only when particle 4 is simultaneously in interaction with 1, 2, and 3 that it contributes to the triplet correlation of these particles.

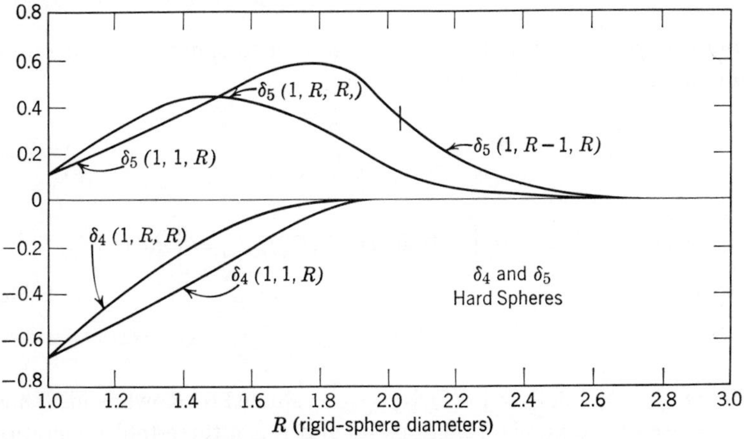

Fig. 2.6.1. Dependence of δ_4 and δ_5 on distance (units of hard sphere diameter) for some special configurations.

The evaluation, in analytic form, of the common volume for a general configuration of the triplet 1, 2, 3 has only recently been given by Rowlinson (38), and in a simpler form by Powell (42). The function $\delta_4(1,2,3) \equiv \delta_4(R_{12}, R_{13}, R_{23})$ is shown in Figure 2.6.1 for three special configurations of the triplet of particles.

The thirteen diagrams (Table 2.6.2) comprising δ_5 involve integration over two field points. Integration over one of the field points may, however, be carried out immediately, except in the case of the last (completely bonded) integral. For example,

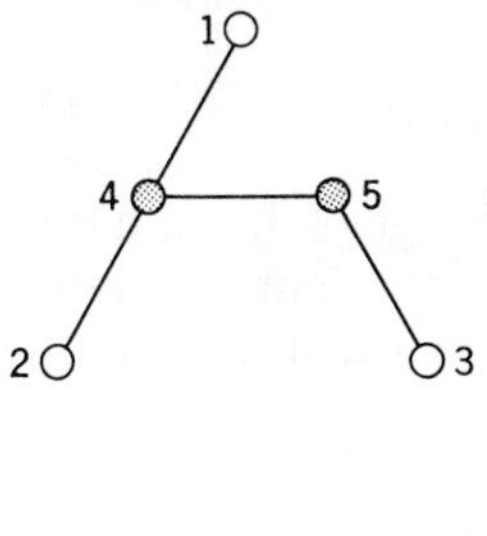

$$\equiv \int d(4)\, d(5) f_{14} f_{24} f_{35} f_{45} = \int d(4) f_{14} f_{24} p_{34}, \tag{2.6.44}$$

where

$$p_{34} = p(R_{34}) \equiv \int d(5) f_{35} f_{45} \equiv$$ 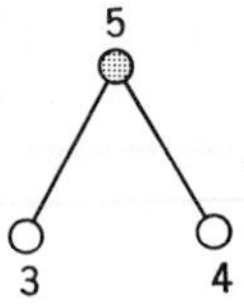

.

Note that p_{34} is simply the volume common to spheres of unit radius centered at 3 and 4. Similarly,

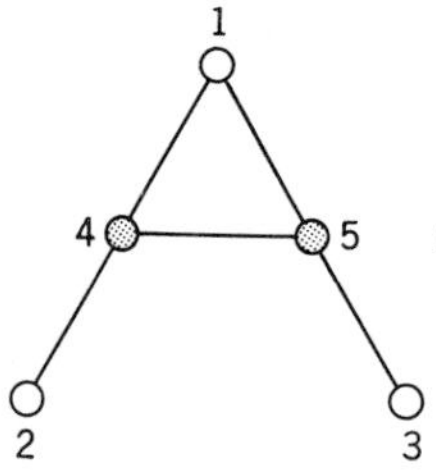

$$\equiv \int d(4)\, d(5) f_{14} f_{24} f_{15} f_{35} f_{45} = \int d(4) f_{14} f_{24} t_{134}, \tag{2.6.44a}$$

where $t_{134} \equiv \delta_4(1,3,4) = \int d(5) f_{15} f_{35} f_{45}$, evaluated by Rowlinson. Thus, by the use of the known functions p_{ij} and t_{ijk}, a three-fold integration can be carried out immediately, and we are left with a three-fold quadrature over the remaining field point 4.

Considering now the first *column* of the diagrams, we see that it consists of one 4-bond diagram, two 5-bond diagrams, and one 6-bond diagram. Since $f_{ij} = -1$ or 0, the 4- and 6-bond diagrams are positive, while the two 5-bond diagrams are negative. Hence, we expect extensive cancellation, and this is indeed the case. It is possible to avoid doing unnecessary integration over those volumes where cancellation occurs by combining each of the columns into one integral. For the first column there is obtained

$$\int d(4) f_{14} f_{24} p_{34} + \int d(4) f_{14} f_{24} f_{34} p_{34} + \int d(4) f_{14} f_{24} t_{134} + \int d(4) f_{14} f_{24} f_{34} t_{134}$$
$$= \int d(4) f_{14} f_{24} (p_{34} + t_{134})(1 + f_{34}) = \int d(4) f_{14} f_{24} (p_{34} + t_{134}) e_{34}$$
$$e_{ij} \equiv 1 + f_{ij} = \exp[-\beta u(i,j)]. \tag{2.6.45}$$

The function e_{34} is zero when 4 is within the range of 3, i.e., it excludes 4 from the enlarged sphere 3. In the sum of the four integrals, integration is restricted to the volume common to 1 and 2 but outside 3.

The volume available to 4 is shaded in the figure below:

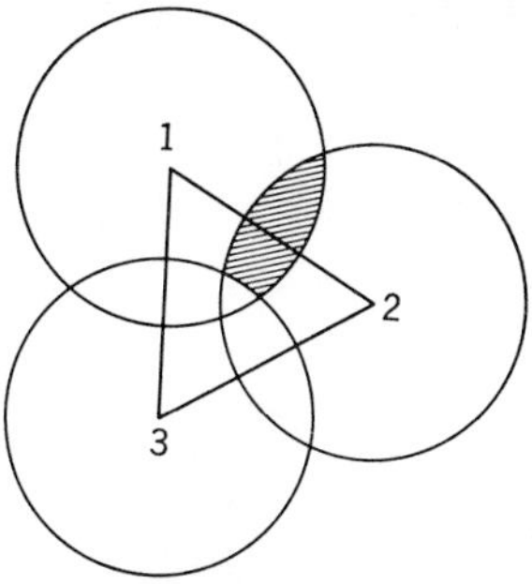

Further cancellation occurs because p_{34} and t_{134} are of opposite sign, but this cannot easily be made explicit. We give a numerical example for hard disks in contact:

$$\int d(4) f_{14} f_{24} p_{34} + \int d(4) f_{14} f_{24} f_{34} p_{34} = 0.4096\ (= 1.7643 - 1.3547)$$

$$\int d(4) f_{14} f_{24} t_{134} + \int d(4) f_{14} f_{24} f_{34} t_{134} = -0.3505.$$

Thus, the total for the first column is 0.0591, which is only 3% of the value of the first diagram! Clearly, it would be most inefficient to calculate each diagram separately.

The second and third columns are simply obtained by cyclic permutation of the fixed points 1, 2, and 3. Hence, the 4-, 5-, and 6-bond diagrams add to

$$\int d(4) f_{14} f_{24} (p_{34} + t_{134}) e_{34} + \int d(4) f_{24} f_{34} (p_{14} + t_{214}) e_{14} + \int d(4) f_{34} f_{14} (p_{24} + t_{234}) e_{24}. \quad (2.6.46)$$

From 12 six-fold integrals we have come to 3 three-fold integrals, at the price of more complicated limits, and of integrands which are functions instead of constants.

No immediate integration can be carried out on the completely bonded diagram

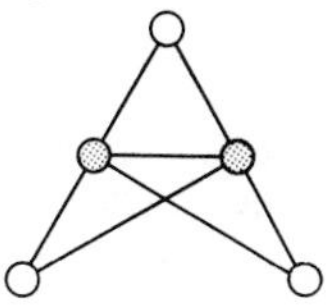

$$\equiv \int d(4)\, d(5) f_{14} f_{24} f_{34} \cdot f_{15} f_{25} f_{35} \cdot f_{45}. \quad (2.6.47)$$

We may, however, greatly reduce the six-dimensional volume of integration, simply by writing $f_{45} = e_{45} - 1$:

$$\int d(4)\, d(5) f_{14} f_{24} f_{34} \cdot f_{15} f_{25} f_{35} \cdot f_{45} = -\int d(4)\, d(5) f_{14} f_{24} f_{34} f_{15} f_{25} f_{35} + \int d(4)\, d(5) f_{14} f_{24} f_{34} \cdot f_{15} f_{25} f_{35} \cdot e_{45}$$

or

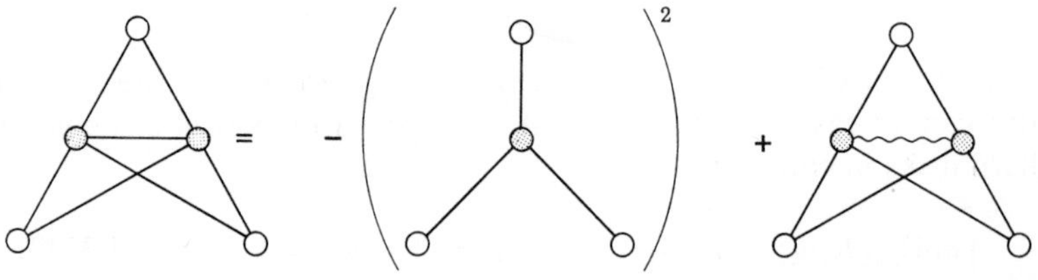

(2.6.48)

The wiggly bond denotes the *e* function. The first integral factorizes into a product of two triplet correlations (corresponding to 4 and 5 moving independently). The remaining integral is over the region of space where 4 and 5 are simultaneously interacting with the fixed points 1, 2, and 3, but are required to be distant by more than unity. This is a severe restriction, and in fact makes the second integral zero in the two-dimensional system of hard disks; for hard spheres the integral is 10% of the total δ_5 at contact, and decreases very rapidly. It is readily evaluated by Monte Carlo methods.

Behavior of δ_4 *and* δ_5. The functions δ_4 and δ_5 are shown in Figure 2.6.1 for three special configurations. The reader should note the following qualitative differences between the δ_4 and δ_5 contributions to the triplet distribution function:

(1) δ_4 is always negative, while δ_5 is entirely positive for spheres and largely so for discs.

(2) The magnitude of δ_4 decreases monotonically, while δ_5 has a maximum removed from the contact configuration.

(3) δ_5 has a range grəater than that of δ_4 by approximately one sphere diameter. It is interesting to look at these facts from the point of view of the *potential of mean force*, defined in Section 2.6.A. From the

definition we have

$$W^{(3)}(1,2,3) = -kT \ln g^{(3)}(1,2,3) = \sum_{i>j}^{3} W^{(2)}(i,j) - kT(\rho\, \delta_4(1,2,3) + \rho^2\, \delta_5(1,2,3) + \cdots). \tag{2.6.49}$$

Minus the gradient of $W^{(3)}(1,2,3)$ with respect to R_1, say, gives the average force acting on 1 when 1, 2, and 3 are held fixed in a given configuration, the ensemble average over the positions of all the remaining fluid particles being taken. From (2.6.49) we see that this potential is simply the sum of potentials averaged over configurations where only two particles are held fixed at a time, the $W^{(2)}(i,j)$, minus kT times the series $\rho\, \delta_4 + \rho^2\, \delta_5 + \cdots$. Now $-kT\rho\, \delta_4(1,2,3)$ is a monotonically decreasing positive term, and we conclude that, at low densities, the superposition approximation underestimates the effective repulsive potential between the triplet. At higher densities, however, especially when the interparticle distances are of the order of two diameters, the negative term $-kT\rho^2\, \delta_5(1,2,3)$ becomes dominant. This attractive potential contribution can be explained in terms of the shielding afforded the triplet 1, 2, 3 by the two field points 4 and 5 from collisions with other particles in the fluid.

The above discussion applies to a fluid with a purely repulsive pair interaction. When an attractive longer range potential is added, the f_{ij} becomes positive at larger distances, and the terms $\delta_{n+3}(1,2,3)$ vary rapidly with the range and strength of the attractive potential. For example, for the square well potential

$$u(R) = \begin{cases} +\infty & R \leqslant 1 \\ -\epsilon & 1 < R < 2 \\ 0 & \text{otherwise.} \end{cases} \tag{2.6.50}$$

δ_4 becomes a cubic in the parameter $f = e^{\beta\epsilon} - 1$. The contact value of δ_4 becomes zero when $\epsilon \sim kT$ (e.g., at $\epsilon = 2.0\, kT$ for disks), and thereafter rapidly becomes large and positive. Since for real fluids the attractive potentials are of this order of magnitude or greater, it is clear that one cannot readily draw general conclusions about the accuracy of the superposition approximation from hard sphere results. It is entirely possible that with realistic potentials and densities the cancellation among the terms correcting the superposition value of $g^{(3)}(1,2,3)$

may be almost complete, making the unmodified YBG equation quite satisfactory. This has indeed been strongly suggested by the results of Rahman.

2.6.F. *The Hypernetted Chain Equation* (3–8)

In this section, so far, we have described the derivations of some integral equations for the pair correlation function in which an assumption (the superposition approximation) has been introduced *ad hoc* to truncate the hierarchy of coupled equations (2.6.1). We *then* investigated the meaning of the assumption in terms of the classes of diagrams summed. The justification of this procedure is that one must find a tractable approximation in order to obtain numerical results, and having obtained the results one can then discuss the usefulness of the approximation. We now turn to the reverse procedure in which certain summable classes of diagrams are identified, other classes are ignored, and different corresponding integro-differential equations are obtained.

The diagrams described in Section 2.5.B for the γ_n cluster integrals may be separated into two topologically distinct classes in the following way. In any diagram a path or paths may be traced between the fixed points by passing along the f bonds. The diagrams

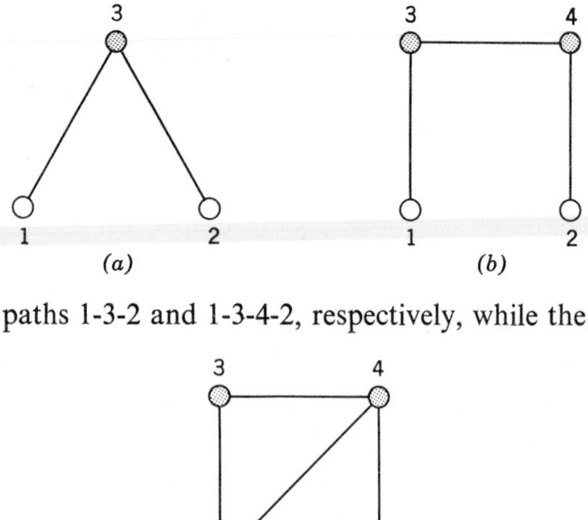

(2.6.51)

have single paths 1-3-2 and 1-3-4-2, respectively, while the diagram

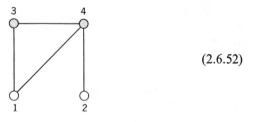

(2.6.52)

has two paths 1-3-4-2 and 1-4-2. Both the paths of diagram (2.6.52) pass through the point 4. Consider now the diagram

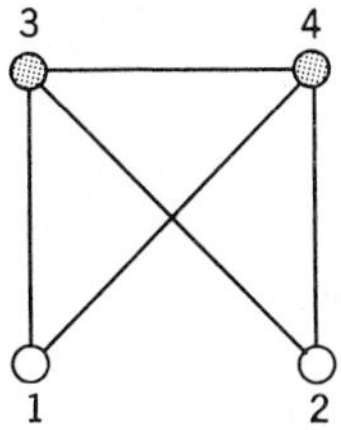

. (2.6.53)

There are several paths between 1 and 2 in this case. In particular, the paths 1-3-2, 1-4-2 have no field point in common, but are connected by the 3-4 bond. (The other two paths 1-3-4-2 and 1-4-3-2 cross each other at the 3-4 bond.) The diagrams (2.6.51) and (2.6.52) are topologically distinct from diagram (2.6.53) in that, in the former case, the paths from 1 to 2 pass through a common point, or node. We shall refer to the former type of diagram as a series diagram, and to the latter as a bridge diagram. In general, a series diagram may have any number of nodes, and may be represented as

. (2.6.54)

The 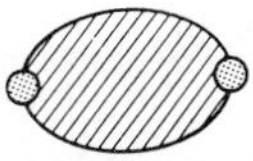 are diagrams which are not series diagrams. They include bridge diagrams, and diagrams of another type which we shall discuss later.

Consider now the series expansion (2.5.38) for $\ln g_N^{(2)}$. Denote the sum of all series diagrams by S. Thus,

$$S = \sum_{n=3}^{\infty} \gamma_n' \rho^{n-2}, \qquad (2.6.55)$$

where γ_n' is the contribution to γ_n of n-point series diagrams. Denote by B the sum of all bridge diagrams. Thus,

$$B = \sum_{n=3}^{\infty} \gamma_n'' \rho^{n-2}, \qquad (2.6.56)$$

where γ_n'' is the contribution to γ_n of n-point bridge diagrams. Obviously $\gamma_n = \gamma_n' + \gamma_n''$. It follows from equation (2.5.38) that

$$G_N(1,2) \equiv g_N^{(2)}(1,2) - 1 = \exp[-\beta u(1,2) + S + B] - 1. \qquad (2.6.57)$$

Expanding the exponential we find, with the definition (2.3.11) of f_{ij},

$$G_N(1,2) = (1 + f_{12})(1 + S + B + \tfrac{1}{2}(S + B)^2 + \tfrac{1}{6}(S + B)^3 + \cdots) - 1$$
$$= f_{12} + (1 + f_{12})(S + B + P_1). \qquad (2.6.58)$$

In equation (2.6.58) we have defined a new class of diagrams P_1, the *parallel* diagrams, which result from the product of S and B with themselves and each other at least once. Their structure is a number of sub-diagrams of the S or B type linked only at the fixed points 1 and 2; hence, the name parallel. The lowest order diagram in the set P_1 is obviously

$\gamma_3^2 =$ 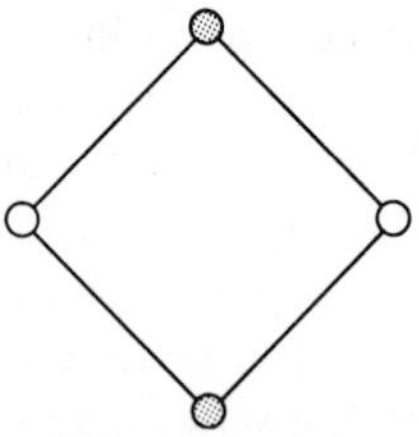 .

It is sometimes convenient to include the factor f_{12} directly in the diagrammatic mapping. Let $\Sigma^{(Q)}$ represent any of the operations $\Sigma^{(S)}$, $\Sigma^{(P_1)}$, $\Sigma^{(B)}$. The sums $(1 + f_{12})\Sigma^{(Q)}$ can be described by the terms originally in $\Sigma^{(Q)}$ (all of which come from the term unity) plus a set of parallel diagrams obtained by taking each diagram of $\Sigma^{(Q)}$ and adding a bond from 1 to 2 (from the factor f_{12}). The set of parallel diagrams defined by $(1 + f_{12})\Sigma^{(Q)}$ is denoted the augmented set of parallel diagrams. If we define a function $P(1,2)$ by the relation

$$P(1,2) = f_{12}[S(1,2) + B(1,2) + P_1(1,2)] + P_1(1,2), \qquad (2.6.59)$$

then

$$G_N(1,2) = f_{12} + S(1,2) + P(1,2) + B(1,2), \qquad (2.6.60)$$

which equation represents $G_N(1,2)$ as the sum of the single line, series, bridge, and augmented parallel diagrams. If $T(1,2)$ represents the sum of all non-series diagrams,

$$G_N(1,2) = T(1,2) + S(1,2) \qquad (2.6.61)$$

$$T(1,2) = f_{12} + P(1,2) + B(1,2). \qquad (2.6.62)$$

Then,

$$T(1,2) = \exp[-\beta u(1,2) + S(1,2) + B(1,2)] - S(1,2) - 1. \qquad (2.6.63)$$

Consider now a typical series diagram. These diagrams have at least one nodal point other than 1 or 2. The part of such a diagram contained between two nodal points at least one of which is neither 1 nor 2 can be any member of the augmented parallel or bridge classes. Let the nodal point nearest 1 be labeled 3 and designate the diagram between 3 and 2 the fixed diagram and that between 3 and 1 the variable diagram. Consider in $\Sigma^{(S)}$ the sum of all diagrams having the same fixed diagram between 3 and 2 but having any allowed diagram between 1 and 3. The sum will contain a common factor $[\alpha(3,2)]$ for the fixed portion of the total diagram. The variable portion, being a sum over all augmented parallel and bridge graphs and the line f_{12} gives just $T(1,3)$. A factor ρ is needed for the point 3 since it is a field point for the entire diagram which has been fixed for these subdiagrams. There also remains an integration over (3). From these considerations we find

$$S(1,2) = \rho \int T(1,3)\alpha(3,2)\, d(3). \tag{2.6.64}$$

But the diagrams connecting 3 with 2 can be any one of the G_N diagrams since they have not been specified (i.e., single line, series, augmented parallel or bridge types) so that the sum over all diagrams of $\Sigma^{(S)}$ yields

$$S(1,2) = \rho \int T(1,3)G_N(3,2)\, d(3) \tag{2.6.65}$$

$$\begin{aligned} G_N(1,2) &= T(1,2) + \rho \int T(1,3)G_N(3,2)\, d(3) \\ &= T(1,2) + \rho \int G_N(y)T(|\mathbf{R} - \mathbf{y}|)\, d\mathbf{y}, \end{aligned} \tag{2.6.66}$$

where $\mathbf{R} = \mathbf{R}_2 - \mathbf{R}_1$, and $\mathbf{y} = \mathbf{R}_2 - \mathbf{R}_3$, and the dependence is only upon magnitudes in a fluid. Equation (2.6.66) is the Ornstein-Zernicke equation relating the direct correlation function, $T(R)$, to the radial distribution function, $g_N^{(2)}(R)$. Since no diagrams have been omitted from the accounting, the equation can be seen to be exact.

We can perform the summation a different way. Let $S_m(1,2)$ be a series diagram with m nodes (apart from the points 1 and 2). If we treat each node as a fixed point and vary the diagrams connecting each node, a repetition of the previous argument shows that

$$S_m(1,2) = \rho^m \int T(1,3)T(3,4) \cdots T(m+2, 2)\, d(3) \cdots d(m+2). \tag{2.6.67}$$

But this diagram may be remapped onto a diagram in which each $T(i, j)$ is replaced by a line joining the nodes labeled i, j. Thus, the integrand maps into a chain diagram, and if we denote the Fourier transform of $T(R)$ by $\tilde{T}(\mathbf{k})$, then by the convolution theorem,

$$\tilde{S}_m(\mathbf{k}) = \rho^m \tilde{T}^{m+1}(\mathbf{k}), \tag{2.6.68}$$

since there are $(m + 1)$ links $T(R)$. Since

$$\sum_{m=0}^{\infty} S_m(R) = S(R), \tag{2.6.69}$$

$$\tilde{S}(\mathbf{k}) = \frac{\rho \tilde{T}^2(\mathbf{k})}{1 - \rho \tilde{T}(\mathbf{k})}, \tag{2.6.70}$$

which can be derived from equations (2.6.65–66) if it is assumed that $\rho \tilde{T}(\mathbf{k}) < 1$, so that the series converges.

Finally, we turn to an examination of the properties of bridge diagrams. It will be recalled that bridge diagrams are defined as those which have no nodal points other than 1 and 2, and for which 1 and 2 are not an articulation pair of points. Consider a typical bridge diagram. This will, in general, contain articulation pairs of points. Replace the (complex) diagrams between each such pairs of points by single line bonds. The resulting diagram is still a bridge diagram but has no articulation pairs of points. In general, replacing any line in a bridge diagram by some more complicated diagram does not remove that diagram from the class of bridge diagrams. Since the original diagram had no nodal point, there were at least two paths connecting 1 and 2. Replacing a line by a more complex graph does not connect these separate paths. Further, the original diagram cannot have two paths connecting 1 and 2 which are not themselves connected at some other point. Replacing a line by some other diagram cannot disconnect these paths. In view of these remarks we see that the replacement of complex diagrams between articulation pairs of points by lines between each pair of points removes the articulation pairs of points by denying the possibility of any pair of points being the sole connection between two subdiagrams. Bridge diagrams which do not have articulation pairs of points are denoted fundamental diagrams: any bridge diagram can be reduced to a fundamental diagram and, conversely, one can build up a unique set of bridge diagrams from a fundamental diagram. Thus, the set of all bridge diagrams can be generated from the set of all fundamental diagrams.

Consider some particular fundamental diagram which represents a mapping of the term

$$\rho^n \int \prod f_{ij}\, d(3) \cdots d(n+2).$$

Suppose there is a bond between 1 and 3, representing the factor f_{13} in the integrand. If f_{13} is replaced by any diagram of $G_N(1,2)$, then some member of the set of all bridge diagrams is produced. The sum of all such diagrams will include all the f_{ij} other than f_{13} of the original diagram but between 1 and 3 there will be a sum over all allowed diagrams of $G_N(1,2)$. The net effect is, then, that $G_N(1,3)$ replaces f_{13}. If the same procedure is followed for each f_{ij} there is obtained

$$\rho^n \sum_m \rho^{m+1} \int \prod G_N(i,j)\, d\{n\},$$

where the summation is over all fundamental diagrams of n field points, and m is the number of f_{ij} bonds in the diagram. The factor ρ^{m+1} appears because $m+1$ field points are held fixed while generating the successive subdiagrams. It is clear that the expression obtained by the preceding arguments can also be mapped into a bridge diagram, but in which the line bonds represent the functions $G_N(i,j)$. Such diagrams do not have articulation pairs of points. The entire set of bridge diagrams may now be generated by summing the new set of mappings over n from $n = 2$ to $n = \infty$. Finally,

$$B(1,2) = \sum_{n=2}^{\infty} \sum_m \rho^{n+m+1} \int \prod G_N(i,j)\, d\{n\}, \tag{2.6.71}$$

and the summations are over fundamental graphs only.

The original exact cluster expansion for $G_N(1,2)$ has now been replaced by a set of exact equations, each the result of a different summation procedure. To find $G_N(1,2)$ we must now solve simultaneously the set of equations:

$$T(R) = e^{-\beta u(R)}\, e^{S(R)+B(R)} - S(R) - 1 \tag{2.6.72}$$

$$\tilde{S}(\mathbf{k}) = \frac{\rho \tilde{T}^2(\mathbf{k})}{1 - \rho \tilde{T}(\mathbf{k})} \tag{2.6.73}$$

$$B(R) = \sum_{n=2}^{\infty} \sum_m \rho^{n+m+1} \int \prod G_N(i,j)\, d\{n\}, \tag{2.6.74}$$

where we have again written $R = |\mathbf{R}_2 - \mathbf{R}_1|$.

The approximation to $G_N(R)$ obtained if the set of equations (2.6.72–74) is solved with $B(R) = 0$, is called the hypernetted-chain (HNC) equation. We have:

$$G_N(R) = e^{-\beta u(R)+S(R)} - 1, \tag{2.6.75}$$

so that the potential of the mean force $W^{(2)}(R)$ is given by

$$W^{(2)}(R) = u(R) - kTS(R). \tag{2.6.76}$$

From equation (2.6.52) we, therefore, obtain

$$\begin{aligned} T(R) &= g_N^{(2)}(R) - S(R) - 1 \\ &= g_N^{(2)}(R) - 1 - \ln g_N^{(2)}(R) - \beta u(R), \end{aligned} \tag{2.6.77}$$

which is the desired result. It is thus clear that the HNC approximation consists in retaining the contributions from all series and parallel diagrams and neglecting the contributions from all bridge diagrams. Any improvement of the HNC approximation requires the enumeration of the set of fundamental bridge diagrams for n-field points. Partial enumeration of these sets has been made by Rushbrooke.

2.6.G. *The Percus-Yevick Equation* (30,31)

Another integral equation for the radial distribution function is that derived by Percus and Yevick. It yields a description of dense fluids of comparable accuracy to the other equations previously derived. The original derivation of this equation is long and difficult but, knowing the result in advance, it is possible to give a much simpler derivation. We give here the derivation due to Stell.

It should be clear to the reader, from a consideration of the previous section, that many rearrangements of the cluster expansion are possible. Therefore, by the use of different topological arguments many approximate integral equations can be generated. We define new cluster sums*

* Hereafter, in this section, the arguments R of all quantities, and the subscripts of f_{12} are omitted, without ambiguity.

$M(R)$, $Y(R)$ and $D(R)$ by

$$(G_N = S + T \qquad [\text{cf. Eq. (2.6.50)}]) \tag{2.6.78}$$

$$T = f(1 + S) + M \tag{2.6.79}$$

$$\begin{aligned} g_N^{(2)} &= e^{-\beta u}(1 + S) + M \\ &= e^{-\beta u} Y \end{aligned} \tag{2.6.80}$$

$$\begin{aligned} Y &= 1 + S + e^{\beta u} M \\ &= 1 + S + D \end{aligned} \tag{2.6.81}$$

$$T = fY + D, \tag{2.6.82}$$

where G_N, T are related by equation (2.6.66). If, for brevity, we introduce the notation

$$A(\mathbf{x}) * B(\mathbf{x}) = \rho \int A(\mathbf{x} - \mathbf{y}) B(\mathbf{y})\, d\mathbf{y}, \tag{2.6.83}$$

then it is seen that

$$S = T * G_N = T * (T + S), \tag{2.6.84}$$

and

$$Y = 1 + D + T * G_N. \tag{2.6.85}$$

In the approximation $M = 0$, which is the same as $D = 0$ for non-singular potentials, we find

$$Y = 1 + S, \tag{2.6.86}$$

$$T = fY, \tag{2.6.87}$$

and

$$Y = 1 + (fY) * G_N. \tag{2.6.88}$$

Equation (2.6.88) is the Percus-Yevick equation. We can now construct an iterative solution of equation (2.6.88). Because of the Fourier transform property of convoluted integrals [cf. Eq. (2.6.68)], equation (2.6.84) may be written

$$\begin{aligned} \tilde{S} &= \rho \tilde{T}(\tilde{T} + \tilde{S}) \\ &= \frac{\rho \tilde{T}^2}{1 - \rho \tilde{T}}, \end{aligned} \tag{2.6.89}$$

where $\tilde{S}$ is the Fourier transform of S, etc. Equation (2.6.89) may be expanded in a series in powers of $\rho\tilde{T}$. We assume that $\rho\tilde{T} < 1$, so that

$$\tilde{S} = \rho \tilde{T}^2 \sum_{m=0}^{\infty} (\rho \tilde{T})^m. \tag{2.6.90}$$

By retransforming equation (2.6.90) S is obtained as the sum of convolutions of T with itself; this is the reverse of the process leading from equation (2.6.67) to (2.6.70). The basic equations of the iterative scheme are equations (2.6.78) and (2.6.84) with equation (2.6.86):

$$S = T * T + T * S$$
$$T = f + fS$$
$$G_N = T + S,$$

so that, diagrammatically,

(2.6.91*a*)

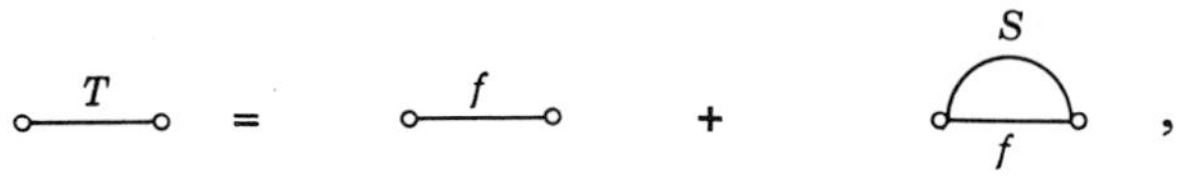

(2.6.91*b*)

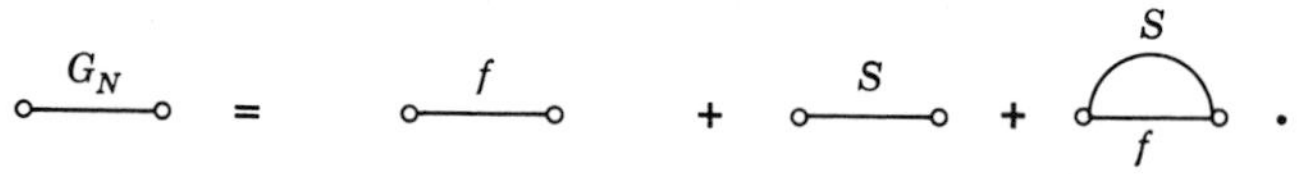

(2.6.91*c*)

The product fS in the expression for T in equation (2.6.91*b*) is represented by 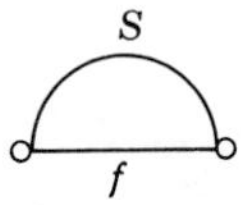 for the reason, given in Section 2.6.F, that the product of f with any diagram (i.e., cluster integral) with two fixed points turns that diagram into one of the parallel type. Thus, any diagram consisting of f bonds in the set giving G_N is either (*a*) the single f-bond, (*b*) a member of the set S, or (*c*) a member of the set formed by the union (product) of an f bond and the set S. Thus, equation (2.6.81*c*) for G_N is called the series–union expansion.

Suppose the iteration for G_N begins with $S_0 = 0$, so that $T_0 = f$ and $G_{N,0} = f$. We find

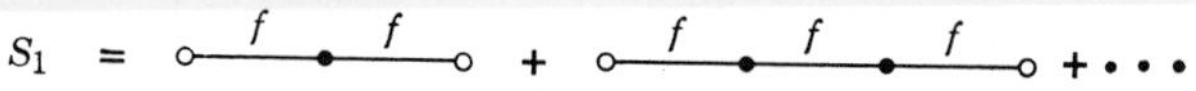

(2.6.92*a*)

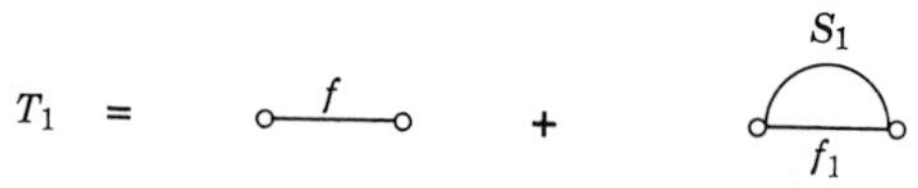

(2.6.92*b*)

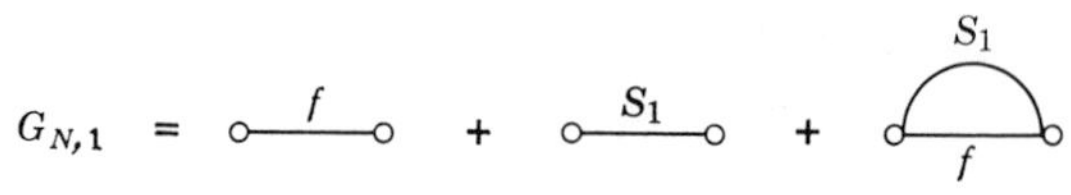

(2.6.92*c*)

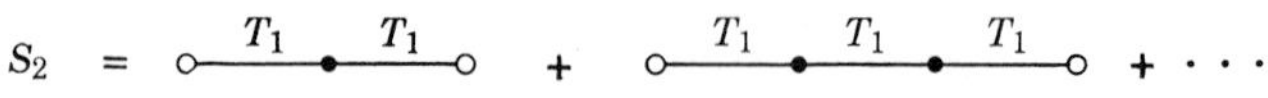

(2.6.92*d*)

and so on. S_n may be expressed in terms of f bonds only. For example, equation (2.6.92b) for T_1 may be written in terms of f bonds only as

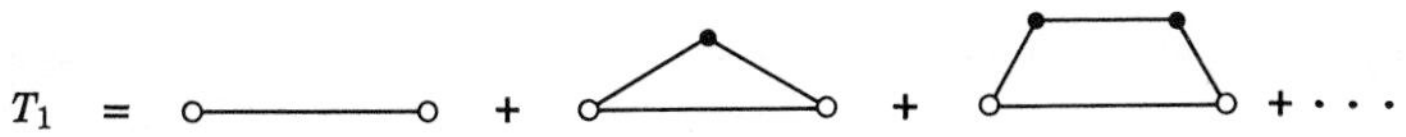

(2.6.93)

so that equation (2.6.92d) becomes

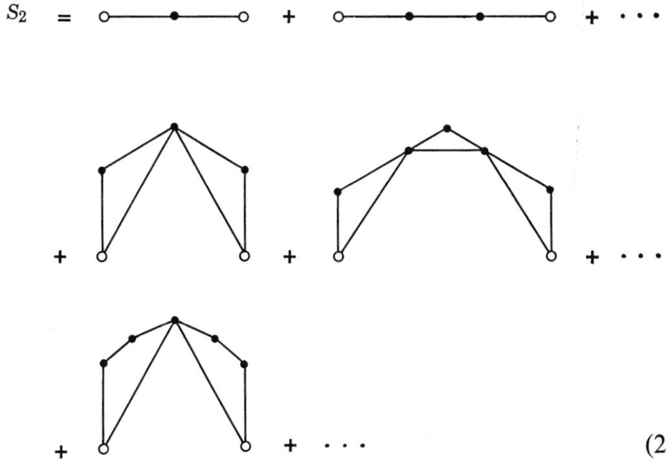

(2.6.94)

where the terms in the nth line come from equations (2.6.92d) and the nth term of equation (2.6.93). If $\lim_{n\to\infty} S_n = S$ exists, then diagrams appearing in the sum for S may be generated by the following prescription: For any convex polygon, label two adjacent vertices as the fixed points and delete the line joining them, and then add any number of non-intersecting straight lines (including zero) between the vertices in such a way that the final diagram may be divided into two topological mirror-images by a line passing between the two fixed points. The polygons are, of course, constrained to a plane during this construction. A prescription for the diagrams appearing in the sum for $G_N = \lim_{n\to\infty} G_{N,n}$ (if this exists) follows by a simple modification of the foregoing description according to equation (2.6.91c).

We see from equations (2.6.78–79) and (2.6.84) that the exact equation for the radial distribution function is

$$g_N^{(2)} - 1 = G_N = f(1 + S) + S + M, \qquad (2.6.95)$$

or

$G_N =$ 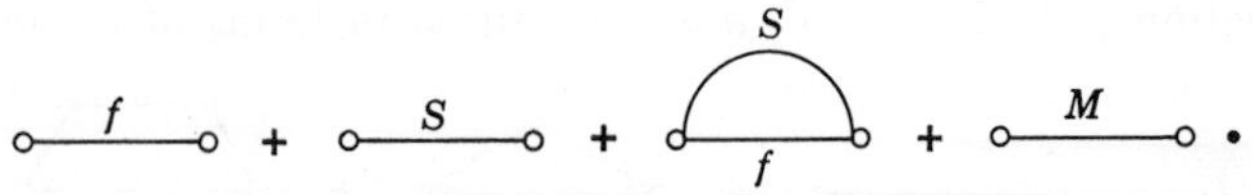

(2.6.96)

The Percus-Yevick approximation obtains when we set $M = 0$ for all R. By comparison of equations (2.6.59), (2.6.62), and (2.6.79) we see that

$$M = (B + P_1)(1 + f), \tag{2.6.97}$$

so that the Percus-Yevick approximation entails the neglect of all bridge and parallel diagrams without 1-2 bonds, and the parallel diagrams formed by inserting the 1-2 bonds in these diagrams; this is a much larger class than the class (bridge diagrams) neglected in the HNC approximation.

The HNC equation can be discussed in terms of an iterative scheme similar to that just described for the Percus-Yevick equation. If we introduce the approximation

$$M = e^{-\beta u}[e^S - 1 - S], \tag{2.6.98}$$

equations (2.6.78–79) give

$$S = \beta u + \ln g_N^{(2)}, \tag{2.6.99}$$

so that, since

$$T = G_N - S = g_N^{(2)} - 1 - \beta u - \ln g_N^{(2)},$$

$$S = T * G_N = \{g_N^{(2)} - 1 - \beta u - \ln g_N^{(2)}\} * \{g_N^{(2)} - 1\}. \tag{2.6.100}$$

Substitution of equation (2.6.100) in (2.6.99) gives the HNC equation in the form

$$\ln g_N^{(2)} = -\beta u + \{g_N^{(2)} - 1 - \beta u - \ln g_N^{(2)}\} * \{g_N^{(2)} - 1\}. \tag{2.6.101}$$

The equations linking S, T and G in this approximation may be written

$$S = T * T + T * S \tag{2.6.101a}$$

$$T = fe^S + e^S - 1 - S \tag{2.6.101b}$$

$$G_N = S + T. \tag{2.6.101c}$$

Equation (2.6.101a) may be expressed as a chain sum as in equation (2.6.91a). Equation (2.6.101b) may also be expressed as a chain sum when the exponentials are expanded. Thus, we have

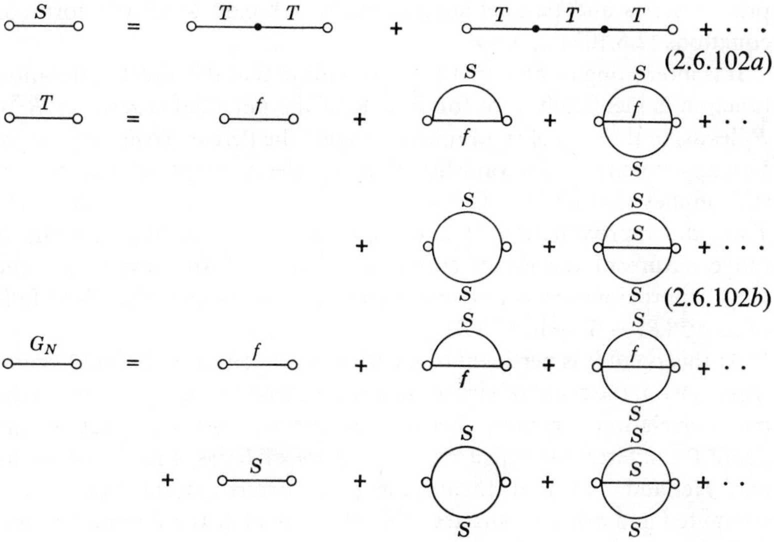

(2.6.102a)

(2.6.102b)

(2.6.102c)

The solution may be obtained by iteration in the following way. The initial choice of S is $S_0 = 0$. Then $T_0 = f$ and $G_{N,0} = f$, so that

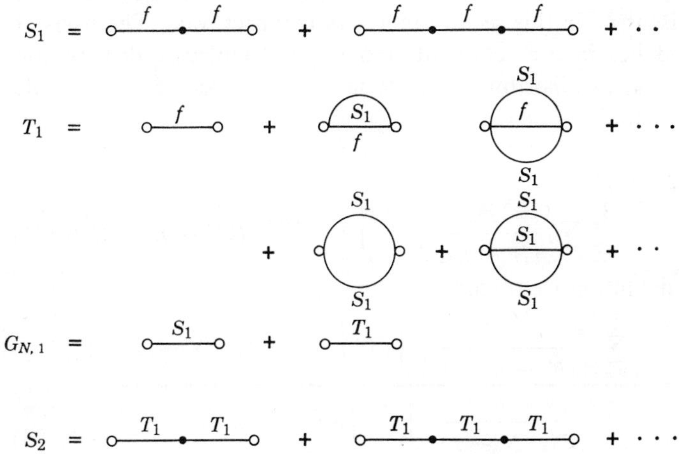

(2.6.103a)

(2.6.103b)

(2.6.103c)

(2.6.103d)

and so on. The limit $G_N = \lim_{n\to\infty} G_{N,n}$, if it exists, can be seen to comprise a series and parallel summation of f bonds, from the form of equations (2.6.103*a*,*b*,*c*).

It is interesting to note that the assumption that the direct correlation function is identically zero for $R > R_0$ if the potential is zero for $R > R_0$ leads, in the case of rigid spheres, to just the Percus-Yevick equation. For any potential that vanishes $R > R_0$, the assumption that $M \equiv 0$ still implies that $T(R) = 0$, but it does not completely specify $T(R)$. Thus, the approximation $M \equiv 0$ is an extreme statement on the short-range nature of the direct correlation function. In these terms, the HNC approximation is not so extreme since it assumes that $T(R)$ falls of as $g_N^{(2)}(R) - 1 - \ln g_N^{(2)}(R)$.

At this point it is pertinent to mention that interest in the equilibrium theory, from the point of view of transport theory, centers entirely on the pair correlation function. Because of this we shall not treat in any detail the interesting scaled particle theory of Reiss, Frisch, Lebowitz and Helfand. In that theory the pair correlation function is not computed and other means are utilized to calculate the thermodynamic properties of the liquid.

2.6.H. *The Method of Functional Differentiation* (23,32,33)

The method of functional differentiation described in Section 2.4.C can be used to derive the integral equations for the radial distribution function discussed in this section in a very compact way. The basis of this method lies in the representation of an n-molecule distribution function $\rho^{(n)}$ as the distribution function for one molecule in a suitable external potential.

The defining equation for $\rho^{(n)}$ in the Grand Canonical Ensemble is equation (2.4.15):

$$\rho^{(n)} = \frac{1}{\Xi} \sum_{N \geqslant n} \frac{z^N}{(N-n)!} \int \cdots \int e^{-\beta U(\{N\})}\, d\{N-n\}. \quad (2.6.104)$$

From this definition we obtain

$$\frac{\rho^{(n+1)}}{\rho^{(n)}} = \frac{\displaystyle\sum_{N \geqslant n+1} \frac{z^N}{(N-n-1)!} \int \cdots \int e^{-\beta U(\{N\})}\, d\{N-n-1\}}{\displaystyle\sum_{N \geqslant n} \frac{z^N}{(N-n)!} \int \cdots \int e^{-\beta U(\{N\})}\, d\{N-n\}}. \quad (2.6.105)$$

Now, it is always possible to represent the total potential energy of the system as the sum of the potential energies of two groups of n and $N - n$ molecules, and their respective interaction. In an obvious notation,

$$U(\{N\}) = U(\{n\}) + U(\{N - n\}) + U(\{n; N - n\}). \quad (2.6.106)$$

Upon changing the summation variable N to

$$N = M + n,$$

we obtain,

$$\frac{\rho^{(n+1)}}{\rho^{(n)}} = \frac{\sum_{M\geqslant 1} \frac{z^M}{(M-1)!} \int \cdots \int e^{-\beta[U(\{M\})+U(\{n;M\})]}\, d\{M-1\}}{\sum_{M\geqslant 0} \frac{z^M}{M!} \int \cdots \int e^{-\beta[U(\{M\})+U(\{n;M\})]}\, d\{M\}}. \quad (2.6.107)$$

Equation (2.6.107) defines a 1-molecule distribution function when the system is subjected to an external potential (due to the n fixed molecules). It is clear that the denominator of the right-hand side represents a generalization of the Grand Partition Function to this circumstance. The 1-molecule distribution function defined by equation (2.6.107) is a functional of the imposed potential, so that

$$\frac{\rho^{(n+1)}(1, \cdots, n, n+1)}{\rho^{(n)}(1, \cdots, n)} = \rho^{(1)}(n+1 \mid U(\{n\})), \quad (2.6.108$$

where the functional dependence upon the potential of the n-molecule group is represented by the symbol $U(\{n\})$ set off by a vertical bar. Consider the case that $n = 1$. Then

$$U(\{1;M\}) = \sum_{i=2}^{M+1} u(1,i), \quad (2.6.109)$$

where the M molecules of the system are labeled $2 \cdots M + 1$, and

$$U(1) = u(1,2). \quad (2.6.110)$$

Suppose that the strength of the interaction $u(1,i)$ between molecule 1 and M molecules of the system is varied in some way from u to u':

$$u'(1,i) = u(1,i) + \delta u(1,i). \quad (2.6.111)$$

After examining (2.6.111) it is pertinent to ask: What is the effect of this variation upon $\rho^{(1)}(2 \mid U(1))$? This effect can be calculated by taking the functional derivative of equation (2.6.107) with respect to

$u(1,i)$. First, we rewrite equation (2.6.107) in a slightly different form as

$$\rho^{(1)}(2 \mid U(1)) = \frac{1}{\Xi(U(1))} \sum_{M \geq 1} \frac{z^M}{(M-1)!} \times \int \cdots \int \exp\left(-\beta U(\{M\}) + \sum_{i=2}^{M+1} \beta u(1,i)\right) d\{M-1\}. \quad (2.6.112)$$

Upon varying $u(1,i)$ there is obtained the relation

$$\begin{aligned} -\delta\rho^{(1)}(2 \mid U(1)) = {} & \frac{\delta\beta u(1,2)}{\Xi(U(1))} \sum_{M \geq 1} \frac{z^M}{(M-1)!} \\ & \times \int \cdots \int \exp\left(-\beta U(\{M\}) + \sum_{i=2}^{M+1} \beta u(1,i)\right) d\{M-1\} \\ & + \frac{1}{\Xi(U(1))} \sum_{M \geq 1} \frac{z^M}{(M-1)!} \\ & \times \int \cdots \int \exp\left(-\beta U(\{M\}) + \sum_{i=2}^{M+1} \beta u(1,i)\right) \sum_{i=3}^{M+1} \beta\delta u(1,i)\, d\{M-1\} \\ & + \rho^{(1)}(2 \mid U(1)) \frac{\delta\Xi}{\Xi}. \end{aligned} \quad (2.6.113)$$

The second term on the right-hand side of equation (2.6.113) contains $(M-1)$ identical contributions so that the equation may be written

$$-\delta\rho^{(1)}(2 \mid U(1)) = \rho^{(1)}(2 \mid U(1))\, \delta\beta u(1,2) + \int \rho^{(2)}(2,3 \mid U(1))\, \delta\beta u(1,3)\, d(3) + \rho^{(1)}(2 \mid U(1)) \frac{\delta\Xi}{\Xi}. \quad (2.6.114)$$

The term $(\delta\Xi/\Xi)$ is determined by integrating equation (2.6.114) over (2). We have

$$\int \rho^{(1)}(2 \mid U(1))\, d(2) = \langle N \rangle$$

$$\int \rho^{(2)}(2,3 \mid U(1))\, d(2) = \langle N-1 \rangle \rho^{(1)}(3 \mid U(1))$$

$$\int \delta\rho^{(1)}(2 \mid U(1))\, d(2) = 0,$$

so that

$$-\frac{\delta\Xi}{\Xi} = \int \rho^{(1)}(3 \mid U(1))\, \delta\beta u(1,3)\, d(3). \quad (2.6.115)$$

Equation (2.6.114) now becomes

$$-\delta\rho^{(1)}(2 \mid U(1)) = \int \rho^{(1)}(2 \mid U(1))\, \delta(\mathbf{R}_3 - \mathbf{R}_2)\, \delta\beta u(1,3)\, d(3) + \int \rho^{(2)}(2,3 \mid U(1))\, \delta\beta u(1,3)\, d(3) - \rho^{(1)}(2 \mid U(1)) \int \rho^{(1)}(3 \mid U(1))\, \delta\beta u(1,3)\, d(3), \tag{2.6.116}$$

and the functional derivative of $\rho^{(1)}(2 \mid U(1))$ with respect to $\beta u(1,3)$ is, therefore,

$$-\frac{\delta\rho^{(1)}(2 \mid U(1))}{\delta\beta u(1,3)} = \rho^{(1)}(2 \mid U(1))\, \delta(\mathbf{R}_3 - \mathbf{R}_2) + \rho^{(2)}(2,3 \mid U(1)) - \rho^{(1)}(2 \mid U(1))\rho^{(1)}(3 \mid U(1)). \tag{2.6.117}$$

We are interested in the form taken by equation (2.6.117) when molecule 1 is far removed from molecules 2 and 3, i.e., in the limit $U(1) \to 0$. Equation (2.6.117) becomes

$$-\left.\frac{\delta\rho^{(1)}(2 \mid U(1))}{\delta\beta u(1,3)}\right|_{U(1)=0} = \rho^{(1)}(2)\, \delta(\mathbf{R}_3 - \mathbf{R}_2) + \rho^{(2)}(2,3) - \rho^{(1)}(2)\rho^{(1)}(3). \tag{2.6.118}$$

The functional inverse $A^{-1}(1,2)$ of a quantity $A(1,2)$ is defined by

$$\int A^{-1}(1,2)A(2,3)\, d(2) = \delta(\mathbf{R}_1 - \mathbf{R}_3), \tag{2.6.119}$$

so that if we *define* a quantity $T(2,3)$ by

$$-\left.\frac{\delta\beta u(1,2)}{\delta\rho^{(1)}(3 \mid U(1))}\right|_{U(1)=0} = \frac{\delta(\mathbf{R}_2 - \mathbf{R}_3)}{\rho^{(1)}(2)} - T(2,3), \tag{2.6.120}$$

then by equation (2.6.119) it follows that $T(2,3)$ is the direct correlation function given by [cf. Eq. (2.6.55)],

$$g^{(2)}(1,3) - 1 = T(1,3) + \rho^{(1)}(1) \int (g^{(2)}(1,2) - 1)T(2,3)\, d(2). \tag{2.6.121}$$

Any function $A(2 \mid U(1))$ may be regarded as a functional of a function $B(3 \mid U(1))$ and may be expanded in a functional Taylor expansion as

$$A(2 \mid U(1)) = A(2) + \int [B(3 \mid U(1)) - B(3)] \left[\frac{\delta A(2 \mid U(1))}{\delta B(3 \mid U(1))}\right]_{U(1)=0} d(3)$$
$$+ \frac{1}{2!} \int\int [B(3 \mid U(1)) - B(3)][B(4 \mid U(1)) - B(4)]$$
$$\times \left[\frac{\delta^2 A(2 \mid U(1))}{\delta B(3 \mid U(1))\, \delta B(4 \mid U(1))}\right]_{U(1)=0} d(3)\, d(4) + \cdots, \quad (2.6.122)$$

where

$$A(2) = A(2 \mid U(1) = 0), \qquad \text{etc.} \quad (2.6.123)$$

Now, it is evident from the derivation of equation (2.6.118) that the second derivative of $\rho^{(1)}(2 \mid U(1))$ will introduce the 3-molecule distribution function $\rho^{(3)}(2,3,4)$, and so on for higher derivatives. Since the integral equations previously discussed in this section involve 2-molecule distribution functions only, it follows that they correspond to truncating the expansion (2.6.122) after the first derivative. An alternative statement of this is that these equations are derived by choosing some functions $A(2 \mid U(1))$, $B(3 \mid U(1))$ and approximating A as a linear functional of B everywhere in the domain in which they are defined. Obviously, great physical insight is needed to make a good choice of A and B. If we choose $A = \rho^{(1)}(2 \mid U(1))e^{\beta u(1,2)}$ and $B = \rho^{(1)}(3 \mid U(1))$, then, by equation (2.6.120),

$$\frac{\delta[\rho^{(1)}(2 \mid U(1))e^{\beta u(1,2)}]}{\delta[\rho^{(1)}(3 \mid U(1)])} = \left[e^{\beta u(1,2)} \frac{\delta \rho^{(1)}(2 \mid U(1))}{\delta \rho^{(1)}(3 \mid U(1))}\right]_{U(1)=0}$$
$$+ \left[e^{\beta u(1,2)} \rho^{(1)}(2 \mid U(1)) \frac{\delta \beta u(1,2)}{\delta \rho^{(1)}(3 \mid U(1))}\right]_{U(1)=0}$$
$$= \delta(\mathbf{R}_2 - \mathbf{R}_3) + \rho^{(1)}(2)\left(T(2,3) - \frac{\delta(\mathbf{R}_2 - \mathbf{R}_3)}{\rho^{(1)}(2)}\right)$$
$$= \rho^{(1)}(2)T(2,3), \quad (2.6.124)$$

where the Dirac delta function arises because

$$\delta\rho^{(1)}(2 \mid U(1)) = \int \delta(\mathbf{R}_2 - \mathbf{R}_3)\, \delta\rho^{(1)}(3 \mid U(1))\, d(3). \quad (2.6.125)$$

Substitution of the given forms of A, B, and equation (2.6.124), in equation (2.6.122) yields the Percus-Yevick equation (2.6.88) in the form

$$\rho^{(2)}(1,2)[e^{\beta u(1,2)} - 1] = -\rho^{(1)}(1)\rho^{(1)}(2)T(1,2). \qquad (2.6.126)$$

Similarly, expansion of ln $[\rho^{(1)}(2 \mid U(1))e^{u(1,2)}]$ as a linear functional of $\rho^{(1)}(2 \mid U(1))$ yields the HNC equation, while the expansion of $\rho^{(1)}(2 \mid U(1)) \nabla\beta u(1,2)$ as a linear functional of ln $[\rho^{(1)}(2 \mid U(1))e^{\beta u(1,2)}]$ yields the Yvon-Born-Green equation.

It will be shown in Section 2.7 that the Percus-Yevick equation is superior to the others for hard sphere fluids. This is because the required relation between $\rho^{(1)}e^{\beta u}$ and $\rho^{(1)}$ is strictly obeyed even at the boundary of a hard sphere. Even for a more realistic model in which molecules interact with soft potentials of finite range the linear relationship is satisfied outside the range of the potential, and, in addition, continues its boundary value and slope for some distance inside the range. However, for separations of interest in calculating the pressure from equation (2.4.49), considerable deviations from linearity are bound to occur.

2.7. NUMERICAL SOLUTIONS OF THE INTEGRAL EQUATIONS (23–57)

The four approximate equations relating $g^{(2)}$ to u which we have derived in the previous section are the only ones with which sufficient work has been done to permit a comparison to be made between theory and experiment. As might be expected from their complexity, analytic solutions of the integral equations are not in general possible, at present, and numerical integration must be employed. However, an analytic solution to the Percus-Yevick equation has been found for the special case of hard spheres.

2.7.A. *Low Density Solutions* (43,44)

It has already been pointed out that if $g^{(2)}$ were known exactly the various forms of the equation of state, e.g., equations (2.4.38) and (2.4.49), would yield identical results. However, when approximations are introduced, consistency is destroyed, as was shown in Section 2.6.E, particularly equations (2.6.26,27). Consider now the low-density limit in which the virial expansion of the equation of state is valid. If we write the equation of state in the form

$$\frac{\beta p}{\rho} = 1 + B\rho + C\rho^2 + D\rho^3 + \cdots \qquad (2.7.1)$$

we can evaluate the coefficients B, C, $\cdots$ from either equation (2.4.38) or (2.4.49) and the various $g^{(2)}$ functions determined by equations (2.6.6, 13, 126 or 77). In practice, the exact values of B, C, $\cdots$ are known only for the special case of rigid spheres, so that our comparison is necessarily restricted to this example. The actual computation of the virial coefficients is tedious and we shall not consider the methods used herein. Using the superscripts p to refer to equation (2.4.49) and c to refer to equation (2.4.38) one finds the results displayed in Table 2.7.1.

TABLE 2.7.1

Virial Coefficients for the Rigid Sphere Fluid From the Several Approximate Theories[a]

	$B^p(b)$	$B^c(b)$	$C^p(b^2)$	$C^c(b^2)$	$D^p(b^3)$	$D^c(b^3)$	$E^p(b^4)$	$E^c(b^4)$
Exact:	1	1	$\frac{5}{8}$	$\frac{5}{8}$	0.2869	0.2869	0.1103	0.1103
YBG	1	1	$\frac{5}{8}$	$\frac{5}{8}$	0.2252	0.3424	0.0475	0.1335
K	1	1	$\frac{5}{8}$	$\frac{5}{8}$	0.1400	0.4418		
HNC	1	1	$\frac{5}{8}$	$\frac{5}{8}$	0.4453	0.2092	0.1447	0.0493
PY	1	1	$\frac{5}{8}$	$\frac{5}{8}$	0.2500	0.2969	0.0859	0.121

[a] The unit $b = \frac{2\pi\sigma^3}{3}$, where σ is the hard core diameter.

The first and most important observation to be made is that none of the approximate theories is consistent past the third virial coefficient. It is possible to develop procedures which insure consistency of all of the equations up to the fourth virial coefficient, but the fifth virial coefficient remains both inconsistent and incorrect. For example, when the coefficient D is made exact by extending the PY and HNC equations by the inclusion of extra terms neglected in equations (2.6.126) and (2.6.77) the fifth virial coefficient becomes $E^p_{\text{PY}} = 0.493b^4$ and $E^p_{\text{HNC}} = 0.398b^4$ (31). These values are even poorer than those obtained from the lower order PY and HNC equations. The values of the fifth virial coefficient from the extended Yvon-Born-Green or Kirkwood equations are not available, but there is no reason to believe they will be improved over the values obtained from the simple theory.

It is important to emphasize that the failure of the theories to reproduce the virial coefficients does not necessarily imply that the theories are useless in the liquid region. In each case, contributions from all orders of the density are included in the integral equation representation. We may therefore expect the equation of state to be superior to a four or five term virial expansion. Indeed, if the contributions of each order of the density are those most important in the liquid range (highly connected diagrams) the approximate theories might be quite good at high densities even if the virial coefficients are not exact. It is, therefore, important to examine other predictions of the various theories before deciding on their relative merits.

The inadequacy of using a comparison of approximate and exact virial coefficients as a criterion of excellence for a theory of liquids is clearly demonstrated by the work of Hoover and Poirier [*J. Chem. Phys.* **37,** 1041 (1962)] and of McQuarrie [*J. Chem. Phys.* **41,** 1197 (1964)]. Hoover and Poirier consider the rigid sphere potential and derive a new relationship between the potential of mean force and the excess chemical potential of the fluid. This relationship is then used to obtain virial coefficients, since the excess chemical potential is readily expressed in virial expansion form and the radial distribution function readily expressed as a density series. It is found that only the Kirkwood integral equation leads to the correct third virial coefficient. The results are: $C_{\mathrm{EXACT}} = \frac{5}{8}b^2$, $C_{\mathrm{K}} = \frac{5}{8}b^2$, $C_{\mathrm{PY}} = -\frac{1}{12}b^2$, $C_{\mathrm{HNC}} = \frac{5}{4}b^2$ and $C_{\mathrm{YBG}} = \frac{5}{6}b^2$. Similarly, the Kirkwood equation leads to the best value of the fourth virial coefficient, being in error by only 30%, whereas the PY and HNC equations lead in this case to values of D in error by a factor of three to four.

McQuarrie has studied the square well fluid, computing virial coefficients from a comparison of the virial equation of state and the density expansion for the internal energy of the fluid. The results are then compared with the known third and fourth virial coefficients of the square well fluid. It is found that the YBG and HNC equations give the least inconsistent results over most of the temperature range. This fact, together with the results of Hoover and Poirier and the observation that the PY equation leads to the best value of D from the compressibility equation and equation of state, clearly shows that the study of virial coefficients contributes little to our understanding of the theory of liquids.

2.7.B. *The High Density Solutions* (37–53)

The numerical solution of the various equations for the pair correlation function is a calculation of considerable magnitude. Nevertheless, we shall not concern ourselves with the details of the technique and will only examine the results of the calculations.

First consider the properties of a hypothetical rigid sphere fluid. For this case:

$$\begin{aligned} u(R) &= 0, \qquad R \geqslant \sigma \\ u(R) &= \infty \qquad R < \sigma, \end{aligned} \tag{2.7.2}$$

and all the properties of the liquid are determined by the statistical geometry of the packing of N spheres in a volume V. Since there is no real system which can be used as an experimental standard with which to compare theory, the approximate theories of the correlation function must be examined with different criteria.

Using high-speed digital computers (37,51) it is at present possible to solve, simultaneously, the equations of motion for a limited number of molecules. In three dimensions this number is of order 10^3, whereas in two dimensions it is larger. Alternatively, Monte Carlo methods can be used. The Monte Carlo method as used in statistical mechanics consists of the generation of a Markov chain of successive states of the system being studied. The successive states in the chain are generated in such a manner that a given state will occur with a frequency proportional to its probability in a given ensemble as the chain length is increased indefinitely. Thus, the method is just a means of directly averaging the properties of interest over the configuration space of the system, with each state receiving its correct weight according to a particular ensemble.

Calculations for the case of the hard sphere fluid have been made by both the method of molecular dynamics and by the Monte Carlo technique. The results are in agreement and will be considered herein to represent the "experimental" equation of state of the dense rigid sphere fluid.

For a rigid sphere fluid, the potential equation (2.7.2) when inserted into (2.4.49) leads to a simple equation of state

$$\frac{\beta p}{\rho} = 1 + \frac{2\pi\sigma^3}{3}\rho g^{(2)}(\sigma), \tag{2.7.3}$$

with $g^{(2)}(\sigma)$ the value of the pair correlation function when $R = \sigma$. Of course, $g^{(2)}(\sigma)$ is a function of the density, ρ, but because of the singular nature of the hard core potential, $g^{(2)}(\sigma)$ is not a function of the temperature (at ρ = constant).

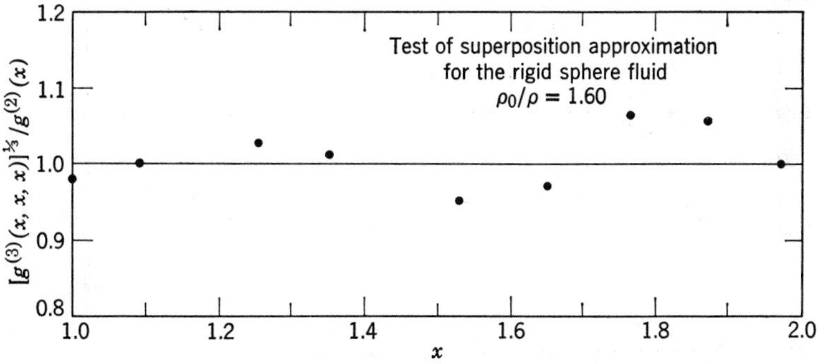

Fig. 2.7.1. A test of the superposition approximation for the dense rigid sphere fluid (see Ref. 36).

As a first example we consider the very recent work of Alder (36) and of Rahman (37). These investigators have examined the adequacy of the superposition approximation by direct comparison of the function $g^{(3)}$ computed from molecular dynamics with the corresponding computed superposition product. From the data plotted in Figures 2.7.1 and 2.7.2, the superposition approximation is seen to be remarkably accurate over most of the range of intermolecular separation. It is only at the smallest distances of approach that significant deviations occur, and it is to be anticipated, then, that the Rice-Lekner (35) modification of the YBG equation will lead to a significant improvement in the radial distribution function. For, by using a Padé approximant as an asymptotic approximation to the total sum (2.6.33), a finite range polynomial is used to represent a series with terms of longer range. Although this approximation will be inaccurate beyond the range of δ_4 and δ_5, it ought to be accurate within the domain over which δ_4 and δ_5 are defined. But, it is just this range in which the superposition product needs correction most. As will be seen shortly, the expected accuracy of the modified YBG equation is confirmed for the case of the rigid sphere fluid.

The results of calculations based on the various approximate theories of $g^{(2)}(\sigma)$ are displayed in Figures 2.7.3 and 2.7.4. For the case of the

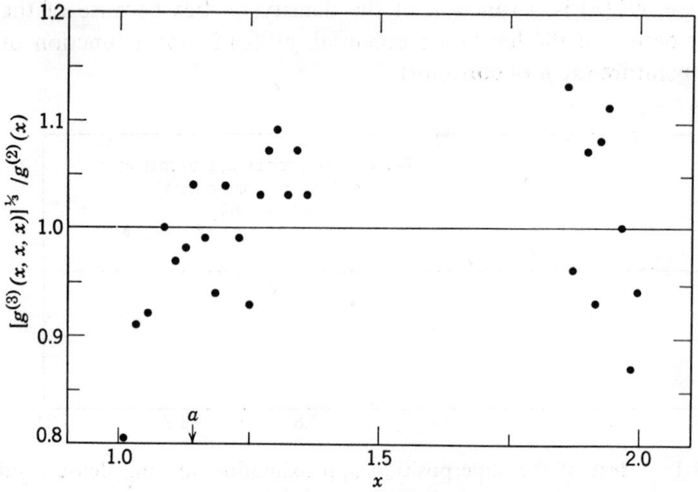

Fig. 2.7.2. A test of the superposition approximation for the dense Lennard-Jones fluid (see Ref. 37).

PY equation an analytic solution can be found (48). This solution leads to the two equations of state,

$$\left(\frac{\beta p}{\rho}\right)^p_{\mathrm{PY}} = \frac{1 + 2\left(\frac{\pi\rho\sigma^3}{6}\right) + 3\left(\frac{\pi\rho\sigma^3}{6}\right)^2}{\left(1 - \left(\frac{\pi\rho\sigma^3}{6}\right)\right)^2} \tag{2.7.4}$$

$$\left(\frac{\beta p}{\rho}\right)^c_{\mathrm{PY}} = \frac{1 + \left(\frac{\pi\rho\sigma^3}{6}\right) + \left(\frac{\pi\rho\sigma^3}{6}\right)^2}{\left(1 - \left(\frac{\pi\rho\sigma^3}{6}\right)\right)^3}. \tag{2.7.5}$$

It is even more remarkable that equation (2.7.5) is identical with an analysis of the dense rigid sphere fluid given by Reiss, Frisch, and

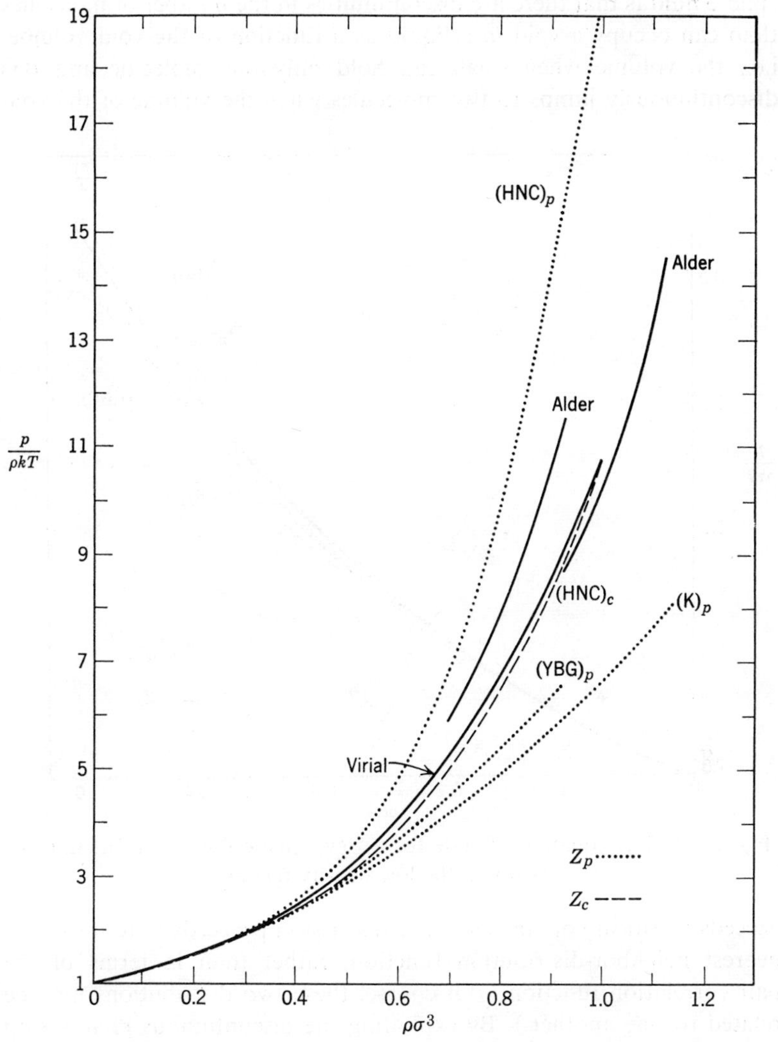

Fig. 2.7.3. The equation of state for a rigid sphere fluid as a function of density.

Lebowitz (50,58). The essential idea in the RFL theory of the rigid sphere fluid is that there are discontinuities in the number of molecules than can occupy a void in a liquid as a function of the void volume, i.e., the volume when small can hold only one molecule and this discontinuously jumps to two molecules when the volume of the void

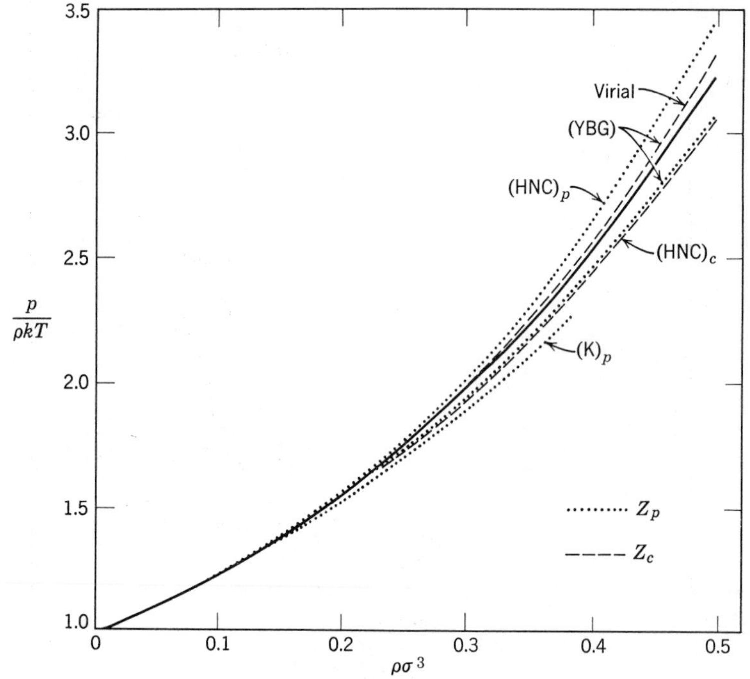

Fig. 2.7.4. The equation of state for a rigid sphere fluid as a function of density in the low-density region.

exceeds a critical volume, etc. The discussion proceeds in terms of the nearest neighbor-distribution function, rather than in terms of the pair correlation function. (Of course, these two distributions may be related to one another.) By exploiting the discontinuous relationship between particle occupation number and void volume, RFL are able to obtain an exact representation over a limited region of the conditional probability, $G^{(\mathrm{RFL})}(R)$, that the center of a molecule will be found within a spherical shell at R when the region enclosed by the shell is known to be free of molecular centers. When $R = \sigma$, the function

$G^{(\mathrm{RFL})}(\sigma)$ is equal to $g^{(2)}(\sigma)$, wherefrom the equation of state is determined. By use of an analytic polynomial approximation to $G^{(\mathrm{RFL})}(R)$ for R outside the range in which $G^{(\mathrm{RFL})}$ is known exactly, equation (2.7.5) is obtained. Although the theory has been generalized to the case of real potentials, no calculations have as yet been made and we therefore pursue this topic no further. The RFL analysis does appear to offer an alternative approach to those considered and is worthy of further intensive study.

An examination of Figure 2.7.3 shows that:

(*a*) The "experimental" equation of state displays a discontinuity corresponding to a phase transition.

(*b*) The various theories all reproduce the qualitative trend of the "data," but are not in quantitative agreement with the "data."

(*c*) There is a tendency for the two equations of state to bracket the correct isotherm. A more quantitative comparison of the agreement can be made by examination of Table 2.7.2.

The existence of a phase transition in a fluid of hard spheres is of great interest. It was first suggested by Kirkwood and Monroe (11) in 1942 and later by the numerical solution of the YBG and K equations: it is found that no solutions exist for which $R^2[g^{(2)}(R) - 1]$ is integrable if ρ exceeds a critical value. In the case of the YBG equation the critical density is $(\rho_0/\rho) = 1.48$, while for the K equation one finds $(\rho_0/\rho) = 1.24$, where $\rho_0\sigma^3 = \sqrt{2}$ corresponds to the closest packing density. It was suggested at that time that the lack of solutions probably represented the limit of stability of a fluid phase of rigid spheres. For greater densities a crystalline phase is presumably the stable phase. This interpretation has been strikingly confirmed by the numerical calculations of Alder and Wainwright (58).

It is also of interest to note that although the PY equation gives a superior representation of the equation of state to that derived from the YBG or K equations, it predicts that there is no phase change. Thus, alerted by this discrepancy, the reader should not be misled into believing that an approximate theory is equally good in predicting all phenomena. Although the YBG and K theories give poorer thermodynamic functions in the fluid phase than does the PY theory or the HNC theory, they are qualitatively correct (where the PY theory is qualitatively incorrect) in predicting a phase change.

The reader should also note that the radial distribution functions of a rigid sphere fluid show the characteristic features of the distribution

TABLE 2.7.2

Equation of State for the Dense Rigid Sphere Fluid[a,b,c]

	Virial Series			YBG		K	HNC		PY		"Expt"
$\rho\sigma^3$	z_3	z_4	z_5	z_p	z_c	z_c	z_p	z_c	z_p	z_c	z_p[d]
0.1	1.237	1.239	1.240	1.239	1.240	—	1.242	1.232	1.240	1.240	—
0.2	1.528	1.549	1.553	1.546	1.557	—	1.562	1.546	1.549	1.555	—
0.3	1.874	1.946	1.963	1.937	1.980	1.938	2.000	1.946	1.954	1.974	—
0.4	2.276	2.444	2.499	2.431	2.542	2.423	2.604	2.455	2.480	2.536	—
0.5	2.731	3.060	3.194	3.047	3.284	3.013	3.463	3.124	3.173	3.307	—
0.6	3.244	3.813	4.090	—	—	3.725	4.650	3.990	4.093	4.381	—
0.7	3.809	4.713	5.226	—	—	4.541	6.874	5.052	5.323	5.905	5.85
0.8	4.430	5.780	6.654	—	—	5.396	9.711	6.481	7.000	8.124	7.95
0.9	5.106	7.027	8.428	—	—	6.285	13.767	8.332	9.328	11.447	10.50
1.0	5.836	8.472	10.607	—	—	—	19.145	10.767	12.773	16.883	—

[a] $z_c = \left(\frac{p}{\rho kT}\right)^c$ $\quad z_4 = 1 + B\rho + C\rho^2 + D\rho^3.$

[b] $z_p = \left(\frac{p}{\rho kT}\right)^p$ $\quad z_5 = 1 + B\rho + C\rho^2 + D\rho^3 + E\rho^4.$

[c] $z_3 = 1 + B\rho + C\rho^2.$

[d] The entries labeled "experiment" are from the calculations by the molecular dynamics method. The figures listed have been obtained by graphical interpolation of the published results.

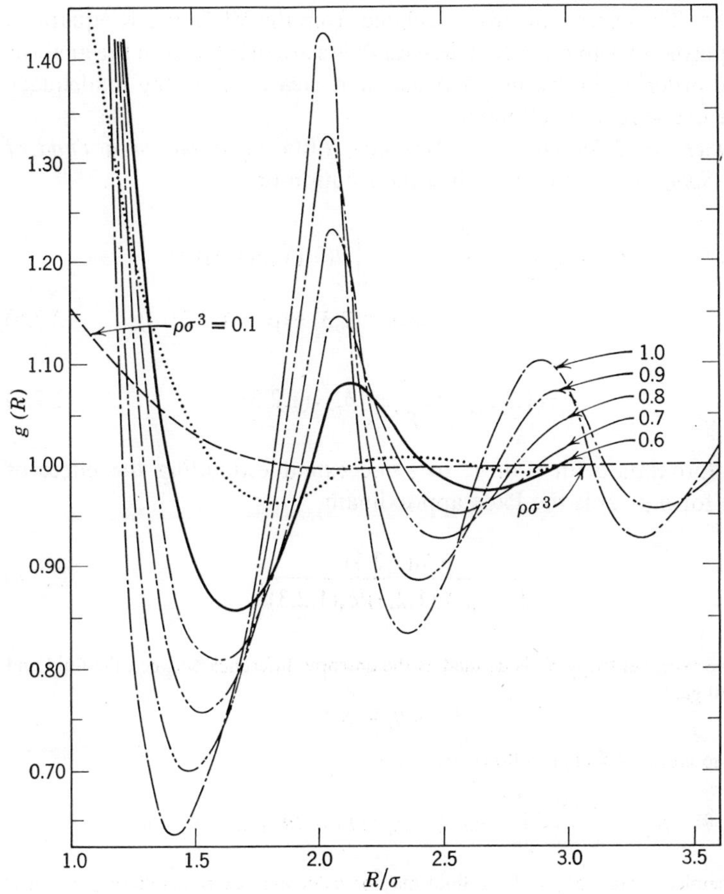

Fig. 2.7.5. The radial distribution function of a rigid sphere fluid as a function of intermolecular separation.

of matter in a real liquid. In Figure 2.7.5 are plotted some distribution functions for varying density. As $\rho\sigma^3$ increases towards $\sqrt{2}$, the ordering in the fluid extends to longer and longer distances from the origin (see Fig. 2.7.5). To the extent that the statistical geometry determined by the packing of rigid spheres is characteristic of real fluids, the excess entropy of the rigid sphere liquid should approximate that of a real liquid.* The excess entropy calculated from the YBG and K equations is displayed in Table 2.7.3. These numbers are of interest in the analysis of the ordering in the liquid phase, and clearly show the inadequacy of the over-ordered cell models.

Numerical Solution of the Modified YBG *Equation for a Fluid of Hard Spheres.* We now outline the solution of

$$-kT\nabla_1 \ln g^{(2)}(1,2) = \nabla_1 u(1,2) + \rho \int d(3)(\nabla_1 u(1,3)) \times g^{(2)}(1,3)g^{(2)}(2,3) \exp(\tau(1,2,3;\rho)), \tag{2.7.6}$$

where

$$\tau(1,2,3;\rho) \equiv \sum_{n=1}^{\infty} \rho^n \, \delta_{n+3}(1,2,3). \tag{2.7.7}$$

An approximate form of τ, to some extent estimating the effect of terms for $n > 2$, is the Padé approximant

$$\frac{\rho\, \delta_4(1,2,3)}{1 - \rho\, \delta_5(1,2,3)/\delta_4(1,2,3)}. \tag{2.7.8}$$

* The excess entropy S_E is defined as the entropy difference between the fluid and an ideal gas:

$$S_E = S_f - S_{ig}.$$

From equation (2.4.41) it follows that

$$S_E = \frac{2\pi}{3} \frac{\langle N \rangle \rho}{T} \int_0^{\infty} (Ru' + 3u) g^{(2)}(R) R^2 \, dR + \langle N \rangle (\mu_f - \mu_{ig}).$$

The chemical potential μ_f of the fluid may be calculated by remembering that it is the free energy change upon adding one molecule. We can do this conceptually by varying the coupling ξ between the molecule and the rest of the system (cf. Section 2.6.B). We then find

$$\frac{z}{\rho} = \frac{\Xi(\xi = 0)}{\Xi(\xi = 1)},$$

where the relation of z to μ_f is given in Section 2.3.A. It may then be shown that

$$\mu_f - \mu_{ig} = 4\pi\rho \int_0^1 \int_0^{\infty} u g^{(2)}(R,\xi) R^2 \, dR \, d\xi,$$

where

$$\mu_{ig} = kT \ln\left(\frac{\langle N \rangle}{Q_1}\right).$$

TABLE 2.7.3

The Excess Entropy of a Rigid Sphere Fluid

$\rho\sigma^3$	$(S^E/Nk)_K$	$(S^E/k)_{\text{YBG}}$
0.169	−0.03	−0.03
0.299	−0.12	−0.11
0.407	−0.24	−0.23
0.500	−0.39	−0.37
0.585	−0.55	−0.56
0.658	−0.73	−0.76
0.729	−0.92	−1.00
0.794	−1.14	−1.23
0.862	−1.37	−1.49
0.924	−1.60	−1.77
0.982	−1.80	—
1.032	−2.07	—
1.089	−2.32	—
1.141	−2.60	—

Writing $\exp \tau = 1 + [\exp \tau - 1]$, we see that the right-hand side of (2.7.6) will separate into the original YBG term of infinite range, *plus a term which has the range of* τ.

The mathematics by which (2.7.6) is reduced to a form suitable for numerical solution has been treated in detail by Kirkwood, Maun, and Alder (46) and reviewed by Hill (2). We state only the final result for hard spheres, modified by the addition of the triplet term:

$$R \ln g^{(2)}(R) = \frac{\lambda}{4}\left[\int_{R-1}^{R+1} dx\, x(g^{(2)}(x) - 1)([R - x]^2 - 1) - RT(R)\right]$$

$$T(R) \equiv \int_R^\infty \frac{dy}{y^2} \int_{y-1}^{y+1} dx\, x g^{(2)}(x)[\exp \tau(1,x,y) - 1](1 + y^2 - x^2)$$

$$\lambda \equiv 4\pi\rho g^{(2)}(1), \tag{2.7.9}$$

where we have used units in which the rigid sphere diameter is unity (equivalent to the conversion $R \to x = R/\sigma$). As pointed out by KMA, an attempt at solution of this integral solution by direct iteration will fail, i.e., it is of a divergent type. One need not perform the mathematical transformations used by KMA to avoid this difficulty, since a judicious mixture of input and output is found to give convergence.

Let $g_{in}{}^j$ and g_{out}^j be the jth iterate input and output values. Then the next iterate is taken as a linear combination of these, i.e.,

$$g_{in}^{j+1} = g_{in}^j + \alpha(g_{out}^j - g_{in}{}^j), \qquad 0 < \alpha \leqslant 1. \tag{2.7.10}$$

"Direct iteration" corresponds to $\alpha = 1$. Low values of α are needed for convergence of (2.7.9): typical satisfactory values of $\alpha = 0.25$ for $\lambda < 20$, $\alpha = 0.20$ for $20 \leqslant \lambda \leqslant 30$, and $\alpha = 0.1$ for $\lambda \geqslant 30$. The procedure for obtaining the radial distribution function is as follows:

(1) Choose a λ: This corresponds to a choice of $p/\rho kT$, because of the relation

$$\left(\frac{p}{\rho kT}\right) = 1 + \tfrac{2}{3}\pi\rho g^{(2)}(1) \equiv 1 + \frac{\lambda}{6}. \tag{2.7.11}$$

(2) Choose an initial iterate $g_{in}{}^1$. This choice is to a certain extent arbitrary, but of course the better it is, the more rapid will be the convergence of the iterative procedure.

(3) Choose an appropriate α, and begin iteration.

Note that the density is calculated anew after each iteration:

$$\rho^j = \frac{\lambda}{4\pi(g_{in}{}^j(1))}.$$

Thus, looked at from the point of view of the equation of state, the solution of the YBG equation is not a process obtaining the pressure as a function of density, but rather one which determines the density of a system as a function of $p/\rho kT$ or λ. According to the Kirkwood (11) theory of phase transformations, the critical value of λ, above which no fluid-type solutions exist, is given by the smallest real root of the equation

$$1 + \lambda_c \frac{j_1(x)}{x} = 0. \tag{2.7.12}$$

Here $j_1(x) = -\dfrac{d}{dx}\left(\dfrac{\sin x}{x}\right)$. This equation gives

$$\lambda_c = 34.8 \tag{2.7.13}$$

so that, on the Kirkwood theory, the transition from fluid to solid occurs when $(p/\rho kT) = 6.80$, and no solutions of (2.7.9) exist above this value of λ. The machine calculations of Alder and Wainwright, on the other hand, show a transition at $(p/\rho kT) \sim 9$. Up to this critical value of $(p/\rho kT)$, the YBG-Padé method gives better agreement with the molecular dynamics results than either the PY or HNC equations for the radial distribution function. The results are shown in Figures 2.7.6a and 2.7.6b and a few representative points are given in Table 2.7.4.

TABLE 2.7.4

λ	$p/\rho kT$	$\rho\sigma^3$	$g^{(2)}(\sigma)$
12	3	0.467	2.047
18	4	0.572	2.505
24	5	0.650	2.936
30	6	0.715	3.340
33	6.5	0.745	3.523

We now turn to an examination of the agreement between theory and experiment for the case of a realistic pair interaction potential. Almost all numerical calculations made have been for a potential of the form

$$u(R) = 4\epsilon\left[\left(\frac{\sigma}{R}\right)^{12} - \left(\frac{\sigma}{R}\right)^{6}\right], \tag{2.7.14}$$

or for a modified form of this potential in which equation (2.7.14) is maintained for $R \geqslant \sigma$ and a rigid core is used such that $u(R) = \infty$ for $R < \sigma$. The available experimental data do not permit the determination of the pair interaction potential with great accuracy. For example, the data of Michels (54) on argon permit the extreme parameter pairs for a potential of the form of equation (2.7.14) to be $(\epsilon/k) = 119.8°$, $\sigma = 3.401$ A. and $(\epsilon/k) = 115.4°$, $\sigma = 3.508$ A. The first pair of values fits the high temperature second virial coefficient best, while the second pair is a better fit to B at low temperatures. Moreover, the effective two body potential is likely to be a function of the density because of the interactions between induced moments in a dense system. Calculations by Kestner and Sinanoglu (56) suggest that this effect may reduce the attractive portion of the effective potential between two argon atoms by approximately 5%. Although these may seem to be small effects, they are of enormous importance when interactions in a dense system are studied. To demonstrate this sensitivity of $g^{(2)}(R)$ to $u(R)$, we have compared two potential energy curves in Figure 2.7.7 (55). If one assumes the YBG equation to be exact, and inverts the equation to determine $u(R)$ from the experimentally known $g^{(2)}(R)$, the derived potential is shockingly close to

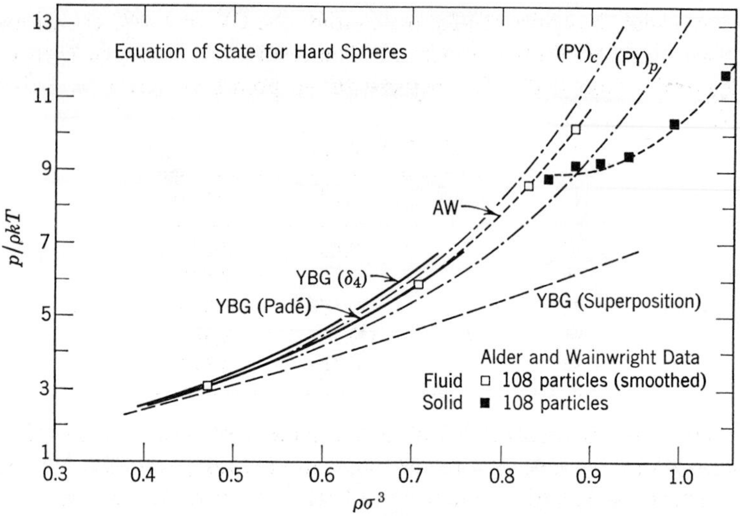

Fig. 2.7.6.a. A comparison of the Rice-Lekner modification of the YBG equation with other theories of the rigid sphere fluid.

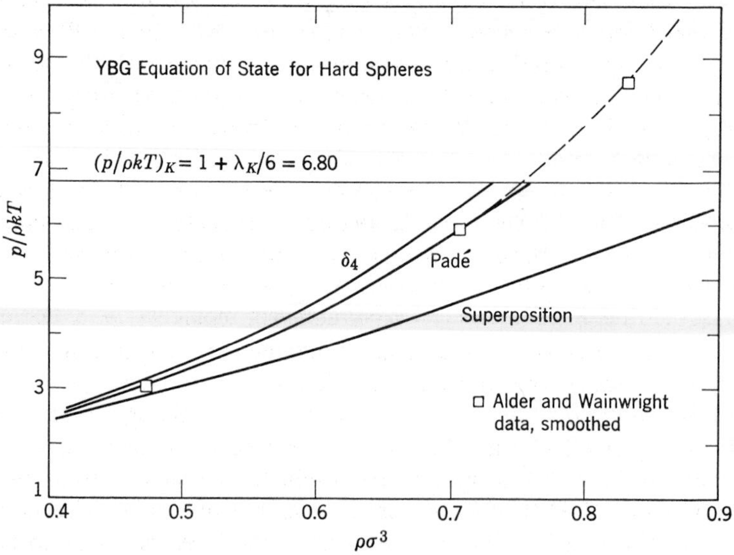

Fig. 2.7.6.b. Detailed comparison of the Rice-Lekner modification of the YBG equation and "experiment" for the rigid sphere fluid.

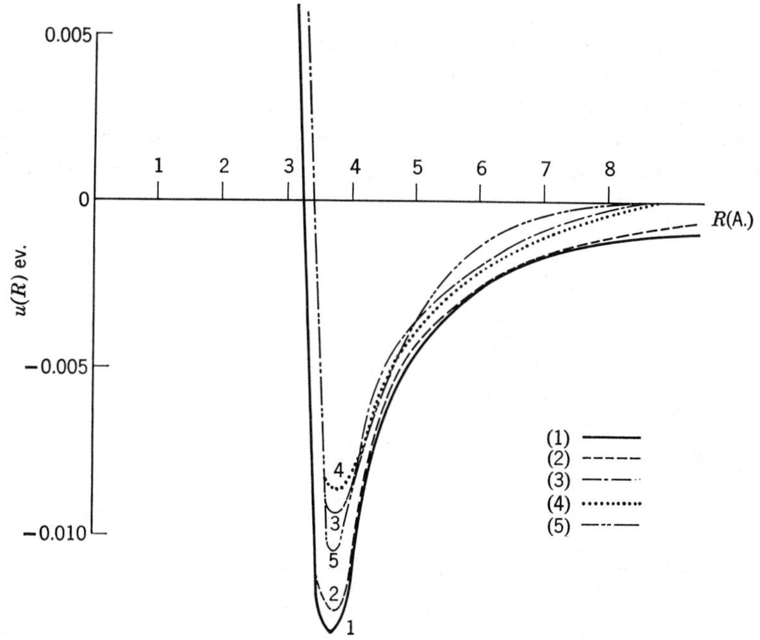

Fig. 2.7.7. The intermolecular pair potential deduced from gas-phase measurements and from inversion of the Born-Green equation and the experimental radial distribution function. Curve 1: Pair potential derived from YBG equation and 84°K $g^{(2)}(R)$. Curve 2: Pair potential derived from YBG equation and 149°K $g^{(2)}(R)$. Curve 3: Pair potential derived from PY equation and 84°K $g^{(2)}(R)$. Curve 4: Pair potential derived from PY equation and 149°K $g^{(2)}(R)$. Curve 5: LJ Potential for Ar.

that derived from other data. Nevertheless, the small differences displayed in Figure 2.7.7 are responsible for the deviation of the $g^{(2)}(R)$ calculated from the YBG equation and that observed for liquid argon.

Consider now the consistency of the various $g^{(2)}(R)$ determined by the several approximate integral equations. In Figure 2.7.8 is displayed $g^{(2)}(R)$ for $\rho\sigma^3 = 1.111$ and $kT/\epsilon = 2.74$. Although all curves have the same qualitative features, the quantitative discrepancies are large. As in the case of the rigid sphere fluid, we temporarily take as reference Monte Carlo calculations performed for a fluid of molecules interacting with a potential of the form equation (2.7.6).

The differences in $g^{(2)}(R)$ will, naturally, lead to differences in the predicted thermodynamic functions. A comparison of these predictions is made in Table 2.7.5.

Clearly, the agreement in calculation of the internal energy is better than that in the calculation of the pressure. Indeed, the pressure is so sensitive a function of the relative positions of the first maximum of

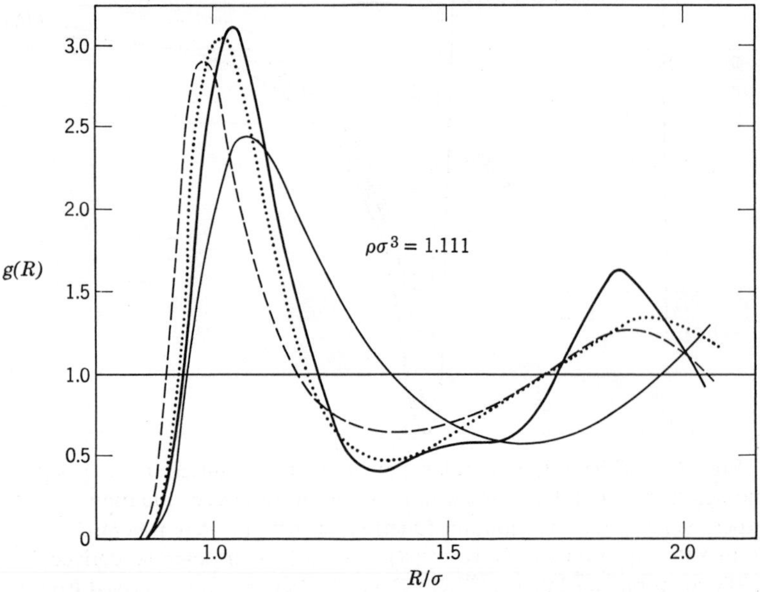

Fig. 2.7.8. The radial distribution function for a Lennard-Jones fluid as computed from the several theories discussed; .... PY, —— YBG, ---- HNC, —— MC.

$g^{(2)}(R)$ and the minimum of $u(R)$ that large discrepancies arise from minor errors in $g^{(2)}(R)$ and $u(R)$. In Figures 2.7.9 and 2.7.10 are plotted the internal energy and pressure as a function of $\rho\sigma^3$. For $\rho\sigma^3 < 0.7$ the theories are in good agreement with each other and the Monte Carlo calculations. For $\rho\sigma^3 > 0.7$, there are large discrepancies, although the computed pressures show almost parallel slopes as a function of $\rho\sigma^3$, indicating some consistency in the predicted values of the compressibility.

We now turn to a more detailed analysis of the fit between theory and experiment (49). In particular, we examine the agreement between the predicted and observed properties of argon. The reader should recall

TABLE 2.7.5

Comparison of Thermodynamic Functions from the YBG, HNC, PY, and MC Calculations

		$(p/\rho kT)^p$		
$\rho\sigma^3$	MC	PY	HNC	YBG
0.400	1.2–1.5	1.24	1.28	1.26
0.833	4.01	4.01	5.11	2.3
1.000	7.0	6.8	9.1	3.1
1.111	7.8	9.2	13.2	3.8

		$\langle U\rangle/NkT$		
$\rho\sigma^3$	MC	PY	HNC	YBG
0.400	−0.86	−0.865	−0.859	−0.85
0.833	−1.58	−1.61	−1.40	−1.8
1.000	−1.60	−1.67	−1.19	−2.2
1.111	−1.90	−1.59	−0.78	−2.6

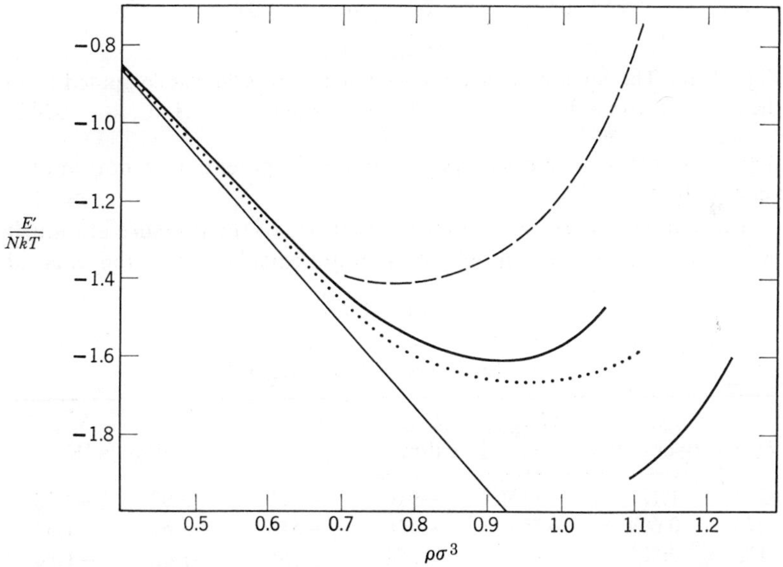

Figure 2.7.9. The internal energy of a Lennard-Jones fluid as computed from the several theories discussed; .... PY, —— YBG, – – – – HNC, —— MC.

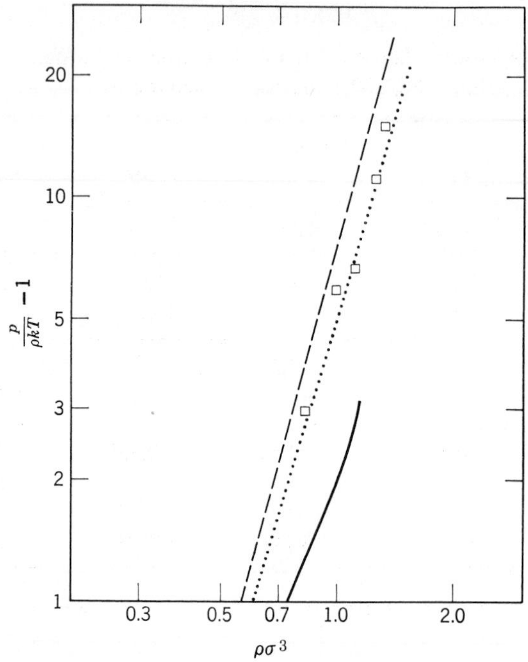

Fig. 2.7.10. The equation of state of a Lennard-Jones fluid as computed from the several theories discussed; .... PY, ——YBG, - - - - HNC, —— ΔMC.

that even for this simple system, the pair potential is not known accurately.

It has already been noted that calculations of the pressure are much more sensitive to errors in $g^{(2)}(R)$ than are calculations of the internal

TABLE 2.7.6

Comparison between Theoretical and Experimental Internal Energies and Entropies of Fluid Argon

T(°K)	ρ_m (g.cm.$^{-3}$)	$\langle U\rangle_K$	$\langle U\rangle_{HNC}$ cal/mole	$\langle U\rangle_{expt}$	S^E_{HNC} cal/mole °K	S^E_{expt}
273	1.12	−1155	−916	−911	−3.02	−3.38
273	0.609	−588	−536	−516	−1.61	−1.53
153	0.522	—	−554	−555	−1.82	−1.86
153	0.696	—	−693	−688	−2.31	−2.30
143	1.044	—	−996	−978	−3.90	−3.70

energy. We therefore examine first the agreement between theory and experiment for the internal energy and entropy. The results are displayed in Table 2.7.6, the potential parameters being: $(\epsilon/k) = 119.8°K$, $\sigma = 3.405$ A.

We again note the superiority of the HNC approximation to the YBGK approximation. For the cases cited in Table 2.7.6, the agreement is all that could be desired in view of the uncertainty in the pair potential.

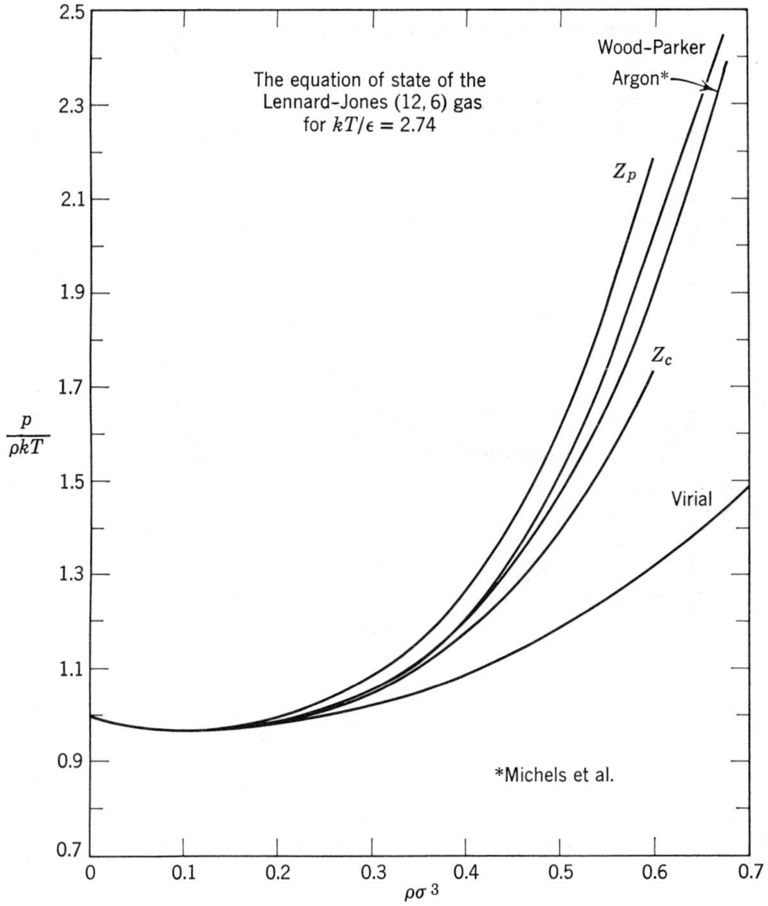

Fig. 2.7.11. A comparison of the theoretical and experimental equations of state of argon.

From equation (2.6.97) it is seen that one of the factors contributing to the accuracy of the PY equation is that all the terms neglected have as a multiplying factor $(1 + f)$. For any realistic physical interaction, f is small unless the molecules "overlap," and $1 + f$ is small if they do. Therefore, only a small contribution to the integrand is made by the neglected diagrams. Nevertheless, it is just this small contribution, summed to all orders, which prevents molecules from interpenetrating

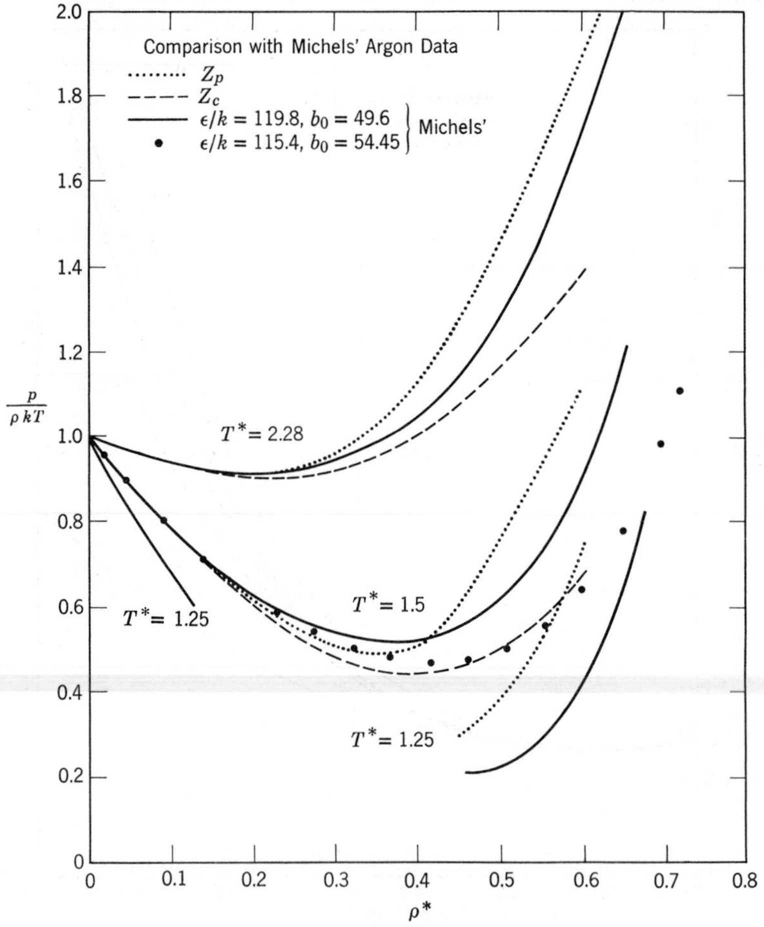

Fig. 2.7.12. The effect of changes in the intermolecular potential on the computed equation of state of argon [$T^* = kT/\epsilon$; $\rho^* = \rho\sigma^3$].

(which the PY approximation allows) and which leads to a phase transition which the PY equation does not predict.

When we consider the agreement between predicted and observed equations of state, the situation is less satisfactory, as shown in Figure 2.7.11. The effect of varying the pair potential between the limits defined by the second virial coefficient is shown in Figure 2.7.12, and the agreement between calculated and observed compressibilities in Figure 2.7.13. Again, the agreement between theory and experiment is qualitatively good, but only semiquantitative in detail.

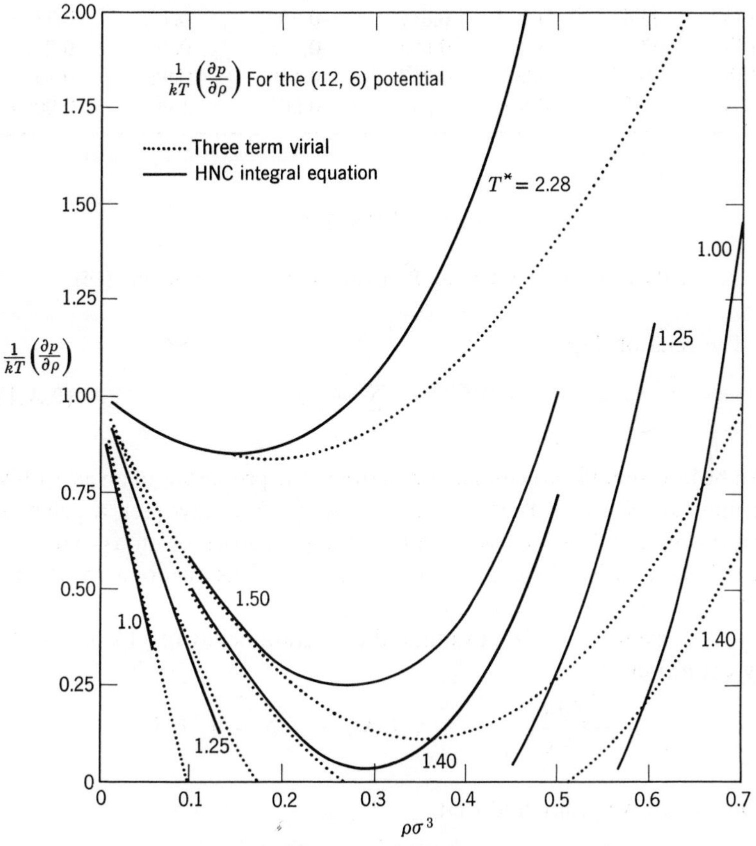

Fig. 2.7.13. A comparison of the theoretical and experimental compressibilities of argon.

Finally, we consider the coexistence curve between liquid and vapor. A comparison between theory and experiment is presented in Table 2.7.7. The agreement is seen to be very satisfactory.

TABLE 2.7.7

Boundary of the Two-Phase Region for Argon

T(°K)	p(HNC)	p(Expt) (atm.)	$\rho_{m,l}$(HNC)	$\rho_{m,g}$(HNC)	$\rho_{m,l}$(Expt) (g.cm.$^{-3}$)	$\rho_{m,g}$(Expt)
148	45.4	43.2	0.617	0.392	0.775	0.31
143	37	35.3	0.696	0.235	0.89	0.21
138	29	28.8	0.757	0.156	0.96	0.15
84	1.2	0.8	1.24	0.007	1.40	0.0049

APPENDIX 2.A

Extension of the Grand Partition Function Theorem (14)

The relationship

$$e^{pV/kT} = \sum_{N\geqslant 0} \frac{z^N}{N!} Z_N \tag{2.A.1}$$

can be interpreted as a connection between the properties of an assembly at any fugacity with those at zero fugacity. We now seek a generalization of (2.A.1) which will connect the properties of an assembly at one fugacity with those at another fugacity. The theorem to be discussed below was stated and proven by Mayer.

It is convenient to first examine the limiting behavior of z as $\rho \to 0$. By definition

$$\mu = \left(\frac{\partial A}{\partial N}\right)_{T,V} = A(N,T,V) - A(N-1,T,V), \tag{2.A.2}$$

from which we easily find that

$$-\frac{\mu}{kT} = \ln\frac{Z_N}{Z_{N-1}} - \ln N - \ln \Lambda^3, \qquad \Lambda = h(2\pi mkT)^{-\frac{1}{2}}. \tag{2.A.3}$$

We now may define z by

$$\frac{\mu}{kT} = \ln z + \ln \Lambda^3. \tag{2.A.4}$$

Then

$$z = N \frac{Z_{N-1}}{Z_N}. \tag{2.A.5}$$

In the limit as $\rho \to 0$, $Z_N \to V^N$ and, therefore,

$$\lim_{\rho \to 0} z = \frac{N}{V} = \rho, \tag{2.A.6}$$

which was the limit sought.

In the text of Chapter 2 we saw that the probability that there be exactly N molecules in the volume V and that this system be in the quantum state k is

$$P(N,V,E_k) = e^{(-pV+N\mu-E_k)/kT}, \tag{2.A.7}$$

where E_k is the energy corresponding to the quantum state k. The probability that these molecules (now for the moment numbered and collectively in the quantum state k) will occupy, respectively, the coordinates of configuration $\{N\}$ within the volume element $d\{N\}$ is $|\psi_k(\{N\})|^2\, d\{N\}$, where ψ_k is the normalized wave function of the system. Let $P_{NV}(\{N\})$ be defined by the statement that $P_{NV}(\{N\})\, d\{N\}$ is the probability that there are exactly N molecules in V and that these are located in the volume element $d\{N\}$ about the coordinates of configuration $\{N\}$ irrespective of the quantum state of the system. In terms of this definition,

$$P_{NV} = e^{(-pV+N\mu)/kT} \sum_k e^{-E_k/kT} |\psi_k(\{N\})|^2. \tag{2.A.8}$$

If the volume V is known to contain $N + n$ molecules, then the probability density that there be N molecules at the positions $\{N\}$ irrespective of the positions of the other n molecules in the volume V is

$$\int \frac{(N+n)!}{n!} P_{N+n,V}(\{N+n\})\, d\{n\}, \tag{2.A.9}$$

since any N of the $N + n$ molecules may fill the $\{N\}$ positions, and having chosen the particular N molecules, all permutations of the molecules among the positions are allowable. The summation of

(2.A.9) over all values of n, is the probability density that the configuration $\{N\}$ is occupied by the appropriate molecules at this temperature, T, and fugacity, z, namely

$$[\rho(z)]^N g^{(N)}(z,\{N\}) = e^{-pV/kT} \sum_{n\geq 0} e^{(N+n)\mu/kT} \frac{(N+n)!}{n!} \times \sum_k e^{-E_k/kT} \int |\psi_k(\{N+n\})|^2 \, d\{n\}. \quad (2.A.10)$$

An alternative view of this relation is as follows. Consider a system of volume V' composed of $V'\rho$ ($>N$) molecules. The probability of N specified molecules being in the volume element $d\{N\}$ at $\{N\}$ is

$$K\rho^N g^{(N)}(z,\{N\})\, d\{N\}, \quad (2.A.11)$$

where K is a constant of proportionality and z is the fugacity corresponding to the density ρ. The probability that the N molecules will be found somewhere in V' is unity so that

$$\int_{V'} \rho^N g^{(N)}(z,\{N\})\, d\{N\} = K^{-1} \quad (2.A.12)$$

$$K = (\rho V')^{-N}. \quad (2.A.13)$$

The probability of N unspecified molecules being located in $d\{N\}$ at $\{N\}$ is

$$\rho^N g^{(N)} \frac{(\rho V')!}{(\rho V' - N)!}\, d\{N\} = \frac{(N+n)!}{n!} \rho^{(N)} g^{(N)}(z,\{N\})\, d\{N\}. \quad (2.A.14)$$

This relation leads to equation (2.A.10) also; it will not be further pursued here.

The fugacity can be written in the form

$$z = \frac{Q_1}{V} e^{\mu/kT}, \quad (2.A.15)$$

with

$$\frac{Q_1}{V} = \lim_{\rho_0 \to 0} \rho_0 e^{-\mu_0/kT} \quad (2.A.16)$$

and μ_0 is the chemical potential of the system when the density is ρ_0. Equation (2.A.15) may be obtained by noting that the chemical potential per molecule for an ideal gas is

$$\mu = kT(\ln N - \ln Q_1). \quad (2.A.17)$$

Using (2.A.6),

$$\lim_{\rho_0\to 0}\frac{N_0}{Q_1}e^{-\mu_0/kT}=1=\frac{V}{Q_1}\lim_{\rho_0\to 0}(\rho_0 e^{-\mu_0/kT}),\qquad z=\frac{Q_1}{V}e^{\mu/kT}. \quad (2.A.18)$$

In the preceding equations, $Q_1 = \Lambda^{-3}(Z_N/Z_{N-1})$ is the partition function for the molecule.

Employing this definition of the fugacity,

$$\left(\frac{\rho(z)}{z}\right)^N g^{(N)}(z,\{N\}) = e^{-pV/kT}\sum_{n\geqslant 0}\frac{z^n}{n!}\int_V (N+n)!\left(\frac{V}{Q_1}\right)^{N+n}\times$$
$$\sum_k |\psi_k(\{N+n\})|^2 e^{-E_k/kT}\, d\{n\}. \quad (2.A.19)$$

Now, in the limit as z approaches zero, the only finite term remaining in the sum on the right of (2.A.19) is for $n = 0$; therefore,

$$g^{(N)}(0,\{N\}) = N!\left(\frac{V}{Q_1}\right)^N \sum_k |\psi_k(\{N\})|^2 e^{-E_k/kT}, \quad (2.A.20)$$

and (2.A.19) may be written

$$\left(\frac{\rho}{z}\right)^N g^{(N)}(z,\{N\}) = e^{-pV/kT}\sum_{n\geqslant 0}\frac{z^n}{n!}\int_V g^{(N+n)}(0,\{N+n\})\, d\{n\}. \quad (2.A.21)$$

An activity coefficient may be defined by

$$\gamma(z) = z/\rho(z). \quad (2.A.22)$$

When we set $p(0) = 0$ and $\gamma(0) = 1$,

$$e^{pV/kT}\frac{g^{(N)}(z,\{N\})}{[\gamma(z)]^N} = \sum_{n\geqslant 0}\frac{z!}{n!}\int_V e^{p(0)V/kT}\frac{g^{(N+n)}(0,\{N+n\})}{[\gamma(0)]^{N+n}}\, d\{n\}. \quad (2.A.23)$$

Consider the definition of the Grand Partition Function. For the case $N = 0$,

$$g^{(0)}(z,\{0\}) = 1, \quad (2.A.24)$$

which leads to a special case of (2.A.23):

$$e^{pV/kT} = \sum_{n\geqslant 0}\frac{z^n}{n!}\int g^{(n)}(0,\{n\})\, d\{n\}. \quad (2.A.25)$$

Now form the sum

$$I_N = \sum_{m\geqslant 0}\frac{(-z)^m}{m!}e^{p(z)V/kT}\int_V \frac{g^{(N+m)}(z,\{N+m\})}{[\gamma(z)]^{N+m}}\, d\{m\}. \quad (2.A.26)$$

Substituting (2.A.23) for the integrand, (2.A.26) becomes

$$I_N = \sum_{m\geqslant 0}\sum_{n\geqslant 0}(-)^m \frac{z^{m+n}}{m!\,n!}\int g^{(N+m+n)}(0,\{N+m+n\})\,d\{m+n\}. \tag{2.A.27}$$

Regrouping the terms and collecting those for which $m + n = j$

$$\begin{aligned} I_N &= \sum_{j\geqslant 0}\left[\sum_{i=0}^{j}\frac{(-)^i j!}{i!\,(j-i)!}\right]\frac{z!}{j!}\int g^{(N+j)}(0,\{N+j\})\,d\{j\} \\ &= \sum_{j\geqslant 0}(1-1)^j\frac{z^j}{j!}\int g^{(N+j)}(0,\{N+j\})\,d\{j\} \\ &= g^{(N)}(0,\{N\}). \end{aligned} \tag{2.A.28}$$

Therefore, I_N may be rewritten as

$$g^{(N)}(0,\{N\}) = \sum_{m\geqslant 0}\frac{(-z)^m}{m!}e^{pV/kT}\int \frac{g^{(N+m)}(z,\{N+m\})}{[\gamma(z)]^{N+m}}\,d\{m\}. \tag{2.A.29}$$

By rewriting (2.A.23) for the fugacity $z + y$, and employing (2.A.29) in the integrand we obtain

$$\exp\left(\frac{p(z+y)V}{kT}\right)\frac{g^{(N)}(z+y,\{N\})}{[\gamma(z+y)]^N} = \sum_{n\geqslant 0}\sum_{m\geqslant 0}\frac{(-)^m(z+y)^n z^m}{m!\,n!}e^{p(z)V/kT}\times \int\frac{g^{(N+m+n)}(z,\{N+m+n\})}{[\gamma(z)]^{N+m+n}}\,d\{m+n\}. \tag{2.A.30}$$

Again regrouping terms with $n + m = M$, and again using the multinomial theorem,

$$\exp\left(\frac{p(z+y)V}{kT}\right)\frac{g^{(N)}(z+y,\{N\})}{[\gamma(z+y)]^N} = \sum_{M\geqslant 0}\frac{y^M}{M!}e^{p(z)V/kT}\times \int\frac{g^{(N+M)}(z,\{N+M\})}{[\gamma(z)]^{N+M}}\,d\{M\}. \tag{2.A.31}$$

This relation allows, in principle, the calculation of the pressure $p(z + y)$, the activity coefficient $\gamma(z + y)$, and the distribution functions $g^{(N)}(z + y, \{N\})$ at any fugacity $z + y$ in terms of the pressure $p(z)$, activity coefficient $\gamma(z)$, and the distribution functions $g^{(N)}(z,\{N\})$ at any other value z of the fugacity.*

The equations derived are not restricted to any particular type of system. All the series converge because of the finite size and low compressibility of molecules, this being true even if the two fugacities z and $z + y$ refer to different phases. However, the series converge far too slowly to be of any use for numerical computations. The remainder of this appendix will be devoted to the transformation of these relations by the methods previously discussed so that the convergence of the series is made much more rapid.

The Potential of Mean Force. If the spacing of the energy levels of a system of N molecules in a volume V is small in comparison with kT, the probability density of finding the system in the configuration $\{N\}$ is

$$Q_N^{-1} \sum_k |\psi_k(\{N\})|^2 e^{-E_k/kT} = \frac{1}{h^f Q_N N!} \int e^{-\beta H_N}\, d\mathbf{p}^{(N)}\, d\{N\} \qquad (2.A.32)$$

in the semiclassical limit. Note that f is the total number of degrees of freedom of the system, and $H_N(\{N\},\mathbf{p}^{(N)})$ is the classical Hamiltonian which is a function of the momenta and coordinates:

$$H_N = \sum_j \frac{p_j^2}{2m} + U_N(\{N\}). \qquad (2.A.33)$$

After integration and use of the distribution functions at zero fugacity

$$g^{(N)}(0,\{N\}) = N! \frac{V}{Q_1} \sum_k |\psi_k(\{N\})|^2 e^{-E_k/kT}. \qquad (2.A.34)$$

Therefore, $g^{(N)}(0,\{N\})$ is proportional to $\exp(-U_N/kT)$ for all N, and by choosing the zero of energy properly

$$g^{(N)}(0,\{N\}) = e^{-\beta U_N(\{N\})}. \qquad (2.A.35)$$

* An easier way of going from (2.A.27) to (2.A.29) is to note that

$$\frac{(-z)^m(z)^n}{m!\,n!} = \frac{(m+n)!}{(m+n)!}\frac{(-z)^m(z)^n}{m!\,n!} = \text{one term in multinomial expansion.}$$

If $m + n = j$,

$$\frac{1}{(m+n)!} \sum_{\{m+n=j\}} \frac{(m+n)!}{m!\,n!}(-z)^m(z)^n = \frac{1}{(m+n)!}(z - z)^{m+n}.$$

Since only the term for which $m = n = 0$ survives, this reproduces (2.A.28).

Consider a system of $N + n$ molecules in a volume V. The force acting along the coordinate q of the molecule i occupying one of the N positions is given by

$$F_{qi}(\{n + N\}) = -\left(\frac{\partial U_{N+n}}{\partial q_i}\right)_{q_j}. \tag{2.A.36}$$

Now, the probability density that there be exactly $N + n$ molecules in V and that of these, n be located at the coordinates of configuration $\{n\}$ with the other N distributed in any way over the $\{N\}$ remaining coordinates is

$$\frac{(N + n)!}{n!} P_{N+n,V} = e^{-p(z)V/kT} \frac{z^{N+n}}{n!} g^{(N+n)}(0, \{N + n\}). \tag{2.A.37}$$

The average force $\langle F_{qi} \rangle$ averaged over all positions of the coordinates $\{n\}$ may be found by multiplying (2.A.36) and (2.A.37), followed by integration over the coordinates $\{n\}$, summation over all values of n, and then normalizing the result, i.e.,

$$\langle F_{qi} \rangle = \frac{\sum_{n\geqslant 0} \frac{z^n}{n!} \int \left(-\frac{\partial U_{N+n}}{\partial q_i}\right) e^{-\beta U_{N+n}}\, d\{n\}}{\sum_{n\geqslant 0} \frac{z^n}{n!} \int e^{-\beta U_{N+n}}\, d\{n\}} \tag{2.A.38}$$

or

$$\langle F_{qi} \rangle = \left(\frac{\partial}{\partial q_i} [kT \ln g^{(N)}(z,\{N\})]\right)_{qi}, \tag{2.A.39}$$

which shows that $W^{(N)} = -kT \ln g^{(N)}$ is, within an arbitrary constant, the potential of average force. In the limit of zero fugacity we have

$$W^{(N)}(0,\{N\}) = U_N(\{N\}). \tag{2.A.40}$$

Previously, it was convenient to consider the potential energy U_N to be a sum of component-pair potentials arising from the pairwise interactions of the molecules. If a similar breakdown is used for the potential of average force

$$W^{(N)}(z,\{N\}) = \sum_{\{n\}_N} w_n(z,\{n\}_N), \tag{2.A.41}$$

where $\{n\}_N$ denotes a subset (consisting of the coordinates of n molecules) of the set of coordinates $\{N\}$ of N molecules. Note that the sum is taken over all possible subsets and the terms w_n with $n > 2$ may be thought of as corrections for the deviation of $W^{(N)}$ from a sum of pair terms only. The inverse of (2.A.41) can be shown to be

$$w_n(z,\{n\}) = \sum_{\{N\}_n} (-)^{n-N} W^{(N)}(z,\{N\}_n)$$

$$1 \leqslant N \leqslant n. \qquad (2.A.42)$$

Expansion of the Distribution Functions. If, of a system of M molecules, m are far away from the remaining $M - m$, the distribution function may be written

$$g^{(M)}(z,\{M\}) = g^{(m)}(z,\{m\}_M)g^{(M-m)}(z, \{M - m\}_M). \qquad (2.A.43)$$

This condition arises from the fact that the $g^{(N)}$ are probabilities: when the subset m is far from the rest of the molecules, it does not interact with and is therefore independent of the remaining $M - m$ molecules of the entire system. Therefore, the probability of this configuration is the product of the probabilities for the two sets alone. Because of this property it will be possible to write $g^{(M)}$ as a sum of products of functions each of a smaller number of coordinates. That is, the distribution function may be regarded as unity plus a series of correction terms corresponding to the presence of pairs, triples, etc., of molecules close to one another. These correction terms are zero unless the configuration they describe exists. Thus, when there is one close pair of molecules, and all other molecules are distant from each other, the value unity is corrected by adding a term for the pair. If there are two pairs, in addition to the correction for the second pair, there must also be added a term which accounts for there being *simultaneously* two pairs present. This is obviously the product of the two pair correction terms. If a triple were present, there would be a term for the triple and also for all the possible pairs that can be formed from the triple. Thus, the distribution function contains not only the correction for a given aggregate, but also for all smaller aggregates which can be formed by its dissociation. If we begin with all molecules far apart, the function $g^{(M)}$ starts with unity and is corrected first for pairs, triples, etc., until the desired state of aggregation is reached.

The preceding discussion suggests that $g^{(M)}$ be expanded into the form

$$g^{(M)}(z,\{M\}) = \sum_{\{k\{m_i\}_M\}_u} \prod_{i=1}^{k} C_m(z,\{m_i\}_M), \qquad (2.A.44)$$

where the sum is over all complete sets of k unconnected (i.e., mutually exclusive) subsets $\{m_i\}_M$ $(1 \leqslant i \leqslant k)$ of the set M. This is denoted by the symbol $\{k\{m_i\}_M\}_u$ with the restriction

$$\sum_{i=1}^{k} m_i = M. \tag{2.A.45}$$

Note that two subsets of identical size are different if they do not contain the same particular molecules. $C_m(z,\{m_i\}_M)$ is the correction term at fugacity z for $\{m_i\}_M$ proximate molecules. Some examples of this expansion are

$$\begin{aligned} g^{(1)}(z,(i)) &= C_1(z,(i)) \\ g^{(2)}(z,(i),(j)) &= C_1(z,(i))C_1(z,(j)) + C_2(z,(i),(j)) \\ g^{(3)}(z,(i),(j),(k)) &= C_1(z,(i))C_1(z,(j))C_1(z,(k)) + C_2(z,(i),(j))C_1(z,(k)) \\ &\quad + C_2(z,(i),(k))C_1(z,(j)) + C_2(z,(j),(k))C_1(z,(i)) \\ &\quad + C_3(z,(i),(j),(k)). \end{aligned} \tag{2.A.46}$$

Consider now the function $g^{(N+M)}$. If the coordinates $\{N + M\}$ are such that $\{N\}$ and $\{M\}$ fall naturally into two exclusive groups,

$$\begin{aligned} g^{(N+M)}(z,\{N + M\}) &= g^{(N)}(z,\{N\})g^{(M)}(z,\{M\}) \\ &= g^{(N)}(z,\{N\}) \sum_{\{k\{m_i\}_M\}_u} \prod_{i=1}^{k} C_m(z,\{m_i\}_M). \end{aligned} \tag{2.A.47}$$

However, if some of the N molecules are close to some of the M, we need additional corrections. These corrections may be written

$$C_m(z,\{m_i\}_M) + \sum_{\{n\}_N} C_{nm}(z,\{n\}_N,\{m_i\}_M), \tag{2.A.48}$$

and the complete expansion becomes

$$g^{(N+M)}(z,\{N + M\}) = g^{(N)}(z,\{N\}) \times$$

$$\sum_{\{k\{m_i\}_M\}_u} \prod_{i=1}^{k} \left[C_m(z,\{m_i\}_M) + \sum_{\{n\}_N} C_{nm}(z,\{n\}_N, \{m_i\}_M) \right]. \tag{2.A.49}$$

If we now integrate (2.A.49) over all values of the coordinates $\{M\}$, two kinds of integrals are found,

$$Vm!\, b_m(z) = \int_V C_m(z,\{m_i\}_M)\, d\{m\}_M \tag{2.A.50}$$

$$m!\, b_{nm}(z,\{n\}_N) = \int_V C_{nm}(z,\{n\}_N\{m_i\}_M)\, d\{m\}_M, \tag{2.A.51}$$

which depend only upon the numerical value of the m_i and not upon which of the M molecules constitute the m_i. If the interaction forces drop to zero sufficiently rapidly with distance, the cluster integrals (2.A.50) and (2.A.51) are independent of the volume of the system.

We may subdivide the $\{M\}$ coordinates into μ_m subsets of size m in $\left(M!/\prod_m (m!)^{\mu_m}\mu_m!\right)$ different ways, all of which appear in the sum (2.A.49). Integration over M thus leads to the equations

$$\int_V g^{(N+M)}(z, \{N+M\})\, d\{M\} = g^{(N)}(z,\{N\}) \times$$

$$\sum_{\{k\{m_i\}_M\}_u} \prod_{i=1}^{k} \int \left(C_m(z,\{m_i\}_M) + \sum_{\{n\}_N} C_{nm}(z,\{n\}_N,\{m_i\}_M) \right) d\{m_i\}_M$$

$$= g^{(N)}(z,\{N\}) M! \sum_{\mu_m} \prod_m \frac{[Vb_m(z) + \sum b_{nm}(z,\{n\}_N]^{\mu_m}}{\mu_m!}, \quad (2.A.52)$$

in which the sum over μ_m is subject to the restriction

$$\sum_m m\mu_m = M. \quad (2.A.53)$$

By substitution of (2.A.52) into (2.A.30)

$$\frac{e^{p(z+y)V/kT} g^{(N)}(z+y, \{N\})}{[\gamma(z+y)]^N} = e^{p(z)V/kT} g^{(N)}(z,\{N\})[\gamma(z)]^{-N} \times$$

$$\sum_{M \geqslant 0} \sum_{\mu_m} \prod_m \frac{1}{\mu_m!} \left[Vb_m(z)\left(\frac{y}{\gamma(z)}\right)^m + \sum_{\{n\}_N} b_{nm}(z)\left(\frac{y}{\gamma(z)}\right)^m \right]^{\mu_m}. \quad (2.A.54)$$

Recognizing the exponential expansion in (2.A.54),

$$\frac{e^{p(z+y)V/kT} g^{(N)}(z+y, \{N\})}{[\gamma(z+y)]^N} = e^{p(z)V/kT} g^{(N)}(z,\{N\})[\gamma(z)]^{-N} \times$$

$$\exp\left(\sum_{m \geqslant 0} \left[Vb_m(z)\left(\frac{y}{\gamma(z)}\right)^m + \sum_{\{n\}_N} b_{nm}(z)\left(\frac{y}{\gamma(z)}\right)^m \right] \right), \quad (2.A.55)$$

for all values of the fugacity y which are smaller than the radius of convergence of the series in (2.A.55). Taking the logarithms of both sides,

$$\frac{p(z+y)V}{kT} - \frac{1}{kT}\sum_{\{n\}_N} w_n(z+y,\{n\}_N) - N\ln\gamma(z+y) =$$
$$\frac{p(z)V}{kT} - \frac{1}{kT}\sum_{\{n\}_N} w_n(z,\{n\}_N) - N\ln\gamma(z) + \sum_{m\geqslant 1} Vb_m(z)\left(\frac{y}{\gamma(z)}\right)^m +$$
$$\sum_{\{n\}_N}\sum_{m\geqslant 1} b_{nm}(z,\{n\}_N)\left(\frac{y}{\gamma(z)}\right)^m, \quad (2.A.56)$$

and equating the coefficients of like powers of V

$$p(z+y) - p(z) = kT\sum_{m\geqslant 1} b_m(z)\left(\frac{y}{\gamma(z)}\right)^m \quad (2.A.57)$$

and

$$w_1(z+y,(i)) + kT\ln\gamma(z+y) = w_1(z,(i)) + kT\ln\gamma(z) -$$
$$kT\sum_{m\geqslant 1} b_{1m}(z,(i))\left(\frac{y}{\gamma(z)}\right)^m, \quad (2.A.58)$$

where the subscript 1, m of b in the sum (2.A.58) means that all b_{nm} are zero except for $n = 1$.

Equation (2.A.57) expresses the difference in pressure corresponding to a difference in fugacity. In particular, when $z = 0$, it is found that

$$p(y) = kT\sum_{m\geqslant 1} b_m(0)y^m. \quad (2.A.59)$$

When (2.A.57) is differentiated h times with respect to y and we set $y = 0$, there is obtained the relation

$$\left(\frac{\partial^h p(z)}{\partial z^h}\right)_T = kTh!\, b_h(z)\left(\frac{1}{\gamma(z)}\right)^h, \quad (2.A.60)$$

which becomes, for $h = 1$,

$$\left(\frac{\partial p(z)}{\partial z}\right)_T = \frac{kT}{\gamma(z)}. \quad (2.A.61)$$

If instead, we put $y + z$ for z, there is obtained the relation

$$b_h(y+z)\left(\frac{y}{\gamma(z+y)}\right)^h = \sum_{m\geqslant 1}\frac{m!}{(m-h)!\,h!}\, b_m(z)\left(\frac{y}{\gamma(z)}\right)^m, \quad (2.A.62)$$

and again for $h = 1$,

$$\frac{y}{\gamma(z+y)} = \sum_{m\geqslant 1} mb_m(z)\left(\frac{y}{\gamma(z)}\right)^m. \quad (2.A.63)$$

Extension of the Virial Expansion. In this section we shall develop the difference of pressures (2.A.57) in a power series of $y/\gamma(z + y)$. Consider a simple integral $B_m(z)$ defined in terms of $b_m(z)$ by the relation

$$b_m(z) = \frac{1}{m^2} \sum \prod_{k \geq 2} \frac{(n_k B_k(z))^{n_k}}{n_k!}, \tag{2.A.64}$$

with the restriction

$$\sum_{k \geq 2} (k - 1)n_k = m - 1. \tag{2.A.65}$$

Equation (2.A.64) can be inverted to yield the relation

$$B_m(z) = \sum (-)^{\Sigma n_k - 1} \frac{(m - 2 + \sum n_k)!}{m!} \prod_{k \geq 2} \frac{(kb_k)^{n_k}}{n_k!}, \tag{2.A.66}$$

again with the restriction

$$\sum_{k \geq 2} (k - 1)n_k = m - 1. \tag{2.A.67}$$

This inversion can be obtained as follows. Define B_k' as

$$\sum_{k \geq 2} k(k-1)B_k' x^{k-1} = -\frac{1}{2\pi i} \oint \frac{1}{y} \sum_{h \geq 1} x^h \left[\sum_{m \geq 1} m b_m y^m \right]^{-h} dy$$

$$= \frac{1}{2\pi i} \oint \frac{x\,dy}{y(x - \sum m b_m y^m)} . \tag{2.A.68}$$

For $|x|$ sufficiently small,

$$|x| < |\sum m b_m y^m|, \tag{2.A.69}$$

and if y_0 is defined by

$$x = \sum m b_m y_0{}^m, \tag{2.A.70}$$

then (2.A.68) becomes

$$\sum_{k \geq 2} k(k-1)B_k' x^{k-1} = 1 - \frac{x}{\sum m^2 b_m y_0{}^m} . \tag{2.A.71}$$

Multiplying by dx/x and integrating

$$dx = (\sum m^2 b_m y_0{}^m)\, dy_0/y_0$$

$$y_0 = \exp\left(-\sum_{k \geq 2} k B_k' x^{k-1}\right). \tag{2.A.72}$$

Equating the coefficients of x^{k-1} in (2.A.68) we obtain

$$k(k-1)B_k' = -\frac{1}{2\pi i} \oint \frac{1}{y} \left(\frac{1}{\sum_{m \geq 1} m b_m y^m} \right)^{k-1} dy, \tag{2.A.73}$$

and since b_1 is unity,

$$-\frac{1}{2\pi i}\oint\frac{1}{y}\left(\frac{1}{\sum_{m\geqslant 1} mb_m y^m}\right)^{k-1} dy = -\frac{1}{2\pi i}\oint\frac{1}{y}\left(\frac{1}{1+\sum_{m\geqslant 2} mb_m y^m}\right)^{k-1} dy. \tag{2.A.74}$$

Now, $-k(k-1)B_K'$ is equal to the coefficient of y^{k-1} in the expansion of

$$\left(1+\sum_{m\geqslant 2} mb_m y^{m-1}\right)^{-k+1}. \tag{2.A.75}$$

Also, if the coefficient of

$$y_1^{h_1} y_2^{h_2}\cdots \tag{2.A.76}$$

in $(1+y_1+y_2+\cdots)^{-h}$ is $c(h_1, h_2, \cdots)$, then

$$\left[\frac{\partial^{\Sigma h_i}(1+y_1+y_2+\cdots)^{-h}}{\partial y_1^{h_1}\partial y_2^{h_2}\cdots}\right]_{y_1=0} = \prod_i h_i!\, c(h_1, h_2, \cdots). \tag{2.A.77}$$

Therefore,

$$(-)^{\Sigma h_i}\frac{[(h-1)+\sum h_i]!}{(h-1)!\prod_i h_i!} = c(h_1, h_2, \cdots), \tag{2.A.78}$$

and accordingly

$$\left(1+\sum_{m\geqslant 2} mb_m y^{m-1}\right)^{-k+1} = \sum_{\{h_i\}}(-)^{\Sigma h_i}\frac{[(k-2)+\sum h_i]!}{(k-2)!}\times \prod_{i\geqslant 1}\frac{[(i+1)b_{i+1}y^i]^{h_i}}{h_i!}, \tag{2.A.79}$$

so that finally

$$k(k-1)B_k' = \sum_k (-)^{\Sigma h_i - 1}\frac{[k-2+\sum h_i]!}{(k-2)!}\prod_{i\geqslant 1}\frac{[(i+1)b_{i+1}]^{h_i}}{h_i!} \tag{2.A.80}$$

with the restriction

$$\sum ih_i = k-1, \tag{2.A.81}$$

which proves (2.A.66). Note that B_k' is the same as B_k.

Let us now define another function $h_{n,m}(z,\{n\})$ by

$$b_{nm}(z,\{n\}) = mb_m(z)h_{n,1}(z,\{n\}) + \sum_{k\geqslant 2}^{m} h_{n,k}(z,\{n\})\left(\frac{\partial b_n(z)}{\partial B_k(z)}\right). \tag{2.A.82}$$

From (2.A.70) and (2.A.72)

$$\sum b_m y_0{}^m = x - \sum (k-1)B_k x^k. \tag{2.A.83}$$

Noting the similarity between (2.A.72) and (2.A.63)

$$\sum b_m(z)\left(\frac{y}{\gamma(z)}\right)^m = \frac{y}{\gamma(z+y)} - \sum (k-1)B_k(z)\left(\frac{y}{\gamma(z+y)}\right)^k \tag{2.A.84}$$

and

$$p(z+y) - p(z) = kT\left[\frac{y}{\gamma(z+y)} - \sum (k-1)B_k(z)\left(\frac{y}{\gamma(z+y)}\right)^k\right]. \tag{2.A.85}$$

Consider now the case $z = 0$, whereupon (2.A.85) reduces to the virial expansion for the gas phase. Differentiating with respect to B_k,

$$\sum_m \frac{\partial b_m}{\partial B_k} y_0{}^m = -(k-1)x^k - \sum_m m b_m y_0{}^m \frac{\partial \ln y_0}{\partial B_k}, \tag{2.A.86}$$

and from (2.A.72)

$$\frac{\partial \ln y_0}{\partial B_k} = -kx^{k-1}, \tag{2.A.87}$$

so that

$$\sum_m \frac{\partial b_m}{\partial B_k} y_0{}^m = x^k. \tag{2.A.88}$$

Using (2.A.83) to change the variables, (2.A.88) becomes

$$\sum_m \frac{\partial b_m(z)}{\partial B_k(z)}\left[\frac{y}{\gamma(z)}\right]^m = \left[\frac{y}{\gamma(z+y)}\right]^k. \tag{2.A.89}$$

Therefore,

$$\begin{aligned}\sum_m b_{nm}(z,\{n\})\left[\frac{y}{\gamma(z)}\right]^m &= h_{n,1}(z,\{n\})\sum_m m b_m(z)\left[\frac{y}{\gamma(z)}\right]^m \\ &\quad + \sum_{k,m} h_{n,k}(z,\{n\})\frac{\partial b_m}{\partial B_k}\left[\frac{y}{\gamma(z)}\right]^m \\ &= h_{n,1}(z,\{n\})\frac{y}{\gamma(y+z)} \\ &\quad + \sum_{k\geqslant 2} h_{n,k}(z,\{n\})\left[\frac{y}{\gamma(z+y)}\right]^k,\end{aligned} \tag{2.A.90}$$

and

$$w_1[z + y, (i)] + kT \ln \gamma(z + y) = w_1(z,(i)) + kT \ln \gamma(z) - kT \sum_{m\geq 1} h_{1,m}[z,(i)]\left[\frac{y}{\gamma(z + y)}\right]^m$$

$$w_n(z + y, \{n\}) - w_n(z,\{n\}) = -kT \sum_{m\geq 1} h_{n,m}(z,\{n\})\left[\frac{y}{\gamma(z + y)}\right]^m. \tag{2.A.91}$$

The relationship with the gas theory previously discussed is most easily established by noting that

$$g^{(N)}(0,\{N\}) = e^{-\beta U_N}, \tag{2.A.92}$$

so that $b_m(0)$ is the same as the cluster integrals previously defined and B_k is related to the irreducible integrals by

$$B_k = \frac{1}{k}\,\beta_{k-1}. \tag{2.A.93}$$

There is also obtained the relation, valid at zero fugacity,

$$C_m(\{m\}) = \sum_{m\geq i>j\geq 1}^{\text{cluster}} \prod f_{ij} \tag{2.A.94}$$

A Comment on the Equation of State. An interesting and novel form of the equation of state that holds for any condensed phase is easily derived from the preceding considerations. From

$$\langle N\rangle = \frac{\partial \ln \Xi}{\partial \ln z} = z\frac{\partial}{\partial z}\left(\frac{pV}{kT}\right) \tag{2.A.95}$$

we find

$$\frac{dp}{dz} = \frac{\rho kT}{z}, \tag{2.A.96}$$

which is another form of equation (2.A.61). Now, from (2.A.60) for the cases $h = 1$ and $h = 2$ we find

$$\left(\frac{\partial p}{\partial z}\right)_T = \frac{kT}{\gamma}\,b_1(z) \tag{2.A.97}$$

$$\left(\frac{\partial^2 p}{\partial z^2}\right)_T = \frac{2kT}{\gamma^2}\,b_2(z). \tag{2.A.98}$$

By elimination of $\gamma = z/\rho$ and use of (2.A.96), equation (2.A.98) takes the form

$$\frac{\partial}{\partial z}\left(\frac{\rho kT}{z}\right)_T = \frac{2kT\rho^2}{z^2}\, b_2(z). \tag{2.A.99}$$

A combination of (2.A.96) and (2.A.99) now gives

$$\frac{\partial}{\partial p}\left(\frac{\rho kT}{z}\right)_T = \frac{2\rho}{z}\, b_2(z) = \frac{kT}{z^2}\left(z\left(\frac{\partial \rho}{\partial p}\right)_T - \rho\left(\frac{\partial z}{\partial p}\right)_T\right). \tag{2.A.100}$$

When equation (2.A.96) is again used to eliminate $(\partial z/\partial p)$ there is obtained the relation

$$kT\left(\frac{\partial \rho}{\partial p}\right)_T = 1 + 2\rho b_2(z), \tag{2.A.101}$$

which is an equation giving the compressibility only in terms of the pair integral (instead of the whole series of cluster integrals). Actually, $b_2(z)$ involves consideration of all other molecules in the system because the integral is defined at the fugacity z. Indeed, the use of equations (2.A.50) and (2.A.46) shows that the form (2.A.101) is just the compressibility equation derived by other means in the text of Chapter 2.

Fluctuation Terms. It is pertinent, at this point, to remark on the difference in fluctuation terms in the Canonical Ensemble and Grand Ensemble. For large systems, the thermodynamic functions predicted using either ensemble are the same. However, in a closed system,

$$\int \rho_N^{(n)}(\{n\})\, d\{n\} = \frac{N!}{(N-n)!}, \tag{2.A.102}$$

and, therefore,

$$\int (\rho_N^{(2)} - \rho_N^{(1)}\rho_N^{(1)})\, d(1)\, d(2) = N^2 - N - N^2 = -N. \tag{2.A.103}$$

Proceeding through the same steps as lead to the compressibility equation, it is found that

$$2\rho b_2 = -1 \qquad \text{(closed system)}. \tag{2.A.104}$$

Now in each case one has

$$\rho^{(2)} \to \rho^2; \qquad R_{12} \gg R_0, \tag{2.A.105}$$

where R_0 is of the order of the range of intermolecular forces. In the open system, $\rho^{(2)} \to \rho^2$ exactly when $R_{12} \gg R_0$, but in a closed system

$$\rho^{(2)} \to \rho^2 + \mathcal{O}\left(\frac{1}{N}\right) \qquad \text{(Closed system)}, \qquad (2.A.106)$$

and the function C_2 thus approaches zero only to order N^{-1} for large values of R_{12}. Then the integral $b_2 = 2\pi \int R_{12}{}^2 C_2 \, dR_{12}$ has an added contribution of order ρ^{-1} not present in the case of the open system. Similar terms appear when higher order distribution functions are studied.

The origin of the difference arises from the following: $\rho^{(2)}(1,2)/\rho^{(1)}(1)$ is the probability that there be a molecule at (2) if it is known that there is a molecule at (1). In a closed system, the knowledge that there is a molecule at (1) has two effects. First, there are left only $N - 1$ molecules and second, the available volume is reduced by something of the order of a molecular volume. It is easy to see that the effective density then differs from $\rho = N/V$ by terms of order N^{-1}. This effect does not exist in an open system since molecules are free to move through the "walls" of the fixed volume. The average density at (2) in the case discussed is independent of whether or not one or many molecules are known to be fixed at positions far from (2) since the normal flow through the walls adjusts ρ to be just $\langle N \rangle / V$ under the equilibrium conditions specified by V, z, and T.

APPENDIX 2.B

The Asymptotic Radial Form of $\rho^{(n)}(\{n\})$ (23)

In the text of Chapter 2 we considered the asymptotic dependence of $\rho^{(n)} \to \rho^{(m)}\rho^{(l)}$ (when $n = m + l$) on the fluctuations in the medium. We now examine the asymptotic dependence of the distribution function in the limit $R \to \infty$.

If a molecule is fixed at a given point in a liquid, the density of the surrounding fluid is altered from its value when the molecule is free to move, because the fixed molecule exerts a force on the surrounding medium. In this sense, fixing a molecule at a point is analogous to applying an external field. Let the Hamiltonian of our system be

$$H_N = \sum_i^N \frac{p_i{}^2}{2m} + \sum_{i<j} u_{ij}(R_{ij}) + \sum_i \phi(\mathbf{R}_i), \qquad (2.B.1)$$

where $\phi(\mathbf{R}_i)$ is an external potential. The Grand Ensemble phase space density is

$$f_N^{(N)} = h^{-3N} \frac{\lambda^N}{N!\,\Xi} e^{-\beta H_N} = W(N) \frac{e^{-\beta H_N}}{N!\,Q_N}, \tag{2.B.2}$$

where

$$W(N) = h^{-3N} \frac{\lambda^N Q_N}{\Xi},$$
$$W(N) = P_N(V,T)\, h^{-3N}. \tag{2.B.3}$$

The reader should note that the density defined by (2.B.2) includes the momentum dependence characteristic of the complete phase space. If we now introduce the definition

$$\gamma(\mathbf{R}) = \nu + \beta\mu - \beta\phi(\mathbf{R}),$$
$$\nu = \ln \Lambda^{-3} = \frac{3}{2} \ln \left(\frac{2\pi mkT}{h^2}\right), \tag{2.B.4}$$

then it is seen that

$$\lambda^N e^{\nu N} Q_N = \frac{1}{N!} \int \exp\left[\sum_{i=1}^{N} (\gamma(\mathbf{R}_i) - \beta \sum_{i>j} u_{ij}(R_{ij})\right] d\{N\}. \tag{2.B.5}$$

From the definition of $\rho^{(n)}$,

$$f^{(n)}(\{n\},\mathbf{p}^{(n)}) = \sum_{N\geqslant n}^{\infty} W(N) \frac{N!}{(N-n)!} \int f_N^{(N)}\, d\{N-n\}\, d\mathbf{p}_{n+1} \cdots d\mathbf{p}_N$$
$$= \rho^{(n)} \prod_{i=1}^{n} \left[\left(\frac{2\pi mkT}{h^2}\right)^{-3/2} e^{-\beta p_i^2/2m}\right], \tag{2.B.6}$$

$$\rho^{(n)} = \sum_{N\geqslant 0} W(N) \rho_N^{(n)}$$
$$= \frac{1}{\Xi} \sum_{N\geqslant n} \frac{1}{(N-n)!} \int \exp\left[\sum_{i=1}^{N} (\gamma(\mathbf{R}_i) - \beta \sum_{i>j} u_{ij}(R_{ij})\right] d\{N-n\}, \tag{2.B.7}$$

and where (2.B.4) has been used to eliminate $\phi(\mathbf{R})$ from the integrand of (2.B.7), replacing it with $\gamma(\mathbf{R})$ and appropriate factors of λ and ν. We now regard $\ln \Xi$ as a generating functional for $\rho^{(n)}$, i.e., $\rho^{(n)}$ is considered a functional of the potential energy defined by (2.B.7). Thus,

$$\delta \ln \Xi = \frac{1}{\Xi} \sum_{N\geqslant 0} \frac{N}{N!} \int \delta\gamma(\mathbf{R}_1) e^{\gamma(\mathbf{R}_1)}\, d(1) \times$$
$$\int \exp\left[\sum_{i=2}^{N} \left(\gamma(\mathbf{R}_i) - \beta \sum_{i>j} u_{ij}\right)\right] d\{N-1\} \tag{2.B.8}$$

using (2.B.5). By the definition of functional derivative,

$$\frac{\delta \ln \Xi}{\delta \gamma(\mathbf{R}_1)} = \rho^{(1)}(\mathbf{R}_1) \tag{2.B.9}$$

using (2.B.7). In a similar way, higher derivatives yield higher order distribution functions. In fact,

$$\frac{\delta \rho^{(1)}(\mathbf{R}_1)}{\delta \gamma(\mathbf{R}_2)} = \rho^{(2)}(\mathbf{R}_1,\mathbf{R}_2) - \rho^{(1)}(\mathbf{R}_1)\rho^{(1)}(\mathbf{R}_2) + \rho^{(1)}(\mathbf{R}_1)\,\delta(\mathbf{R}_{12}) \tag{2.B.10}$$

$$\frac{\delta \rho^{(n)}(\{n\})}{\delta \gamma(\mathbf{R})} = \rho^{(n+1)}(\{n\},\mathbf{R}) + \rho^{(n)}(\{n\})\left[\sum_{i=1}^{n} \delta(\mathbf{R}_i - \mathbf{R}) - \rho^{(1)}(\mathbf{R})\right]. \tag{2.B.11}$$

The notation becomes simpler if one puts:

$$\hat{\rho}(\mathbf{R}) = \rho^{(1)}(\mathbf{R}); \qquad \hat{\rho}^{(2)}(\mathbf{R}_1,\mathbf{R}_2) = \rho^{(2)}(\mathbf{R}_1,\mathbf{R}_2) + \rho^{(1)}(\mathbf{R}_1)\,\delta(\mathbf{R}_{12})$$

$$\hat{\rho}^{(3)}(\mathbf{R}_1,\mathbf{R}_2,\mathbf{R}_3) = \rho^{(3)}(\mathbf{R}_1,\mathbf{R}_2,\mathbf{R}_3) + \sum_{i>j\neq k} \rho^{(2)}(\mathbf{R}_i,\mathbf{R}_j)\,\delta(\mathbf{R}_{jk}) + \rho^{(1)}(\mathbf{R}_1)\,\delta(\mathbf{R}_{12})\,\delta(\mathbf{R}_{23}).$$

In terms of the $\hat{\rho}^{(q)}$'s (2.B.11) assumes the form

$$\frac{\delta \hat{\rho}_q(\{q\})}{\delta \gamma(\mathbf{R})} = \hat{\rho}^{(q+1)}(\{q\},\mathbf{R}) - \hat{\rho}^{(q)}(\{q\})\rho^{(1)}(\mathbf{R}). \tag{2.B.12}$$

If we define the corresponding Ursell distributions $\hat{\mathscr{F}}_q$ to be

$$\hat{\mathscr{F}}_1(\mathbf{R}_1) = \hat{\rho}^{(1)}(\mathbf{R}_1)$$

$$\hat{\mathscr{F}}_2(\mathbf{R}_1,\mathbf{R}_2) = \hat{\rho}^{(2)}(\mathbf{R}_1,\mathbf{R}_2) - \hat{\rho}^{(1)}(\mathbf{R}_1)\hat{\rho}^{(1)}(\mathbf{R}_2), \cdots$$

the sequence finally reduces to

$$\frac{\delta \hat{\mathscr{F}}_q(\{q\})}{\delta \gamma(\mathbf{R})} = \hat{\mathscr{F}}_{q+1}(\{q\},\mathbf{R}). \tag{2.B.13}$$

The matrix inverse of (2.B.10) will play an important role in the succeeding. Writing it in the form

$$[\rho^{(1)}(\mathbf{R}_1)\rho^{(1)}(\mathbf{R}_2)]^{1/2} \frac{\delta \gamma(\mathbf{R}_2)}{\delta \rho^{(1)}(\mathbf{R}_1)} = \delta(\mathbf{R}_{12}) - T(\mathbf{R}_1,\mathbf{R}_2), \tag{2.B.14}$$

we find from the defining interrelation

$$\int \left[\frac{\delta \rho^{(1)}(\mathbf{R}_2)}{\delta \gamma(\mathbf{R})}\right]\left[\frac{\delta \gamma(\mathbf{R})}{\delta \rho^{(1)}(\mathbf{R}_1)}\right] d\mathbf{R} = \delta(\mathbf{R}_{12}) \tag{2.B.15}$$

that T satisfies the equation

$$G(\mathbf{R}_1,\mathbf{R}_2) = T(\mathbf{R}_1,\mathbf{R}_2) + \int G(\mathbf{R}_1,\mathbf{R})T(\mathbf{R}_2,\mathbf{R})\, d\mathbf{R}, \tag{2.B.16}$$

where

$$\begin{aligned} G(\mathbf{R}_1,\mathbf{R}_2) &= [\rho^{(1)}(\mathbf{R}_1)\rho^{(1)}(\mathbf{R}_2)]^{-\frac{1}{2}}\mathscr{F}_2(\mathbf{R}_1,\mathbf{R}_2) \\ &= [\rho^{(1)}(\mathbf{R}_1)\rho^{(1)}(\mathbf{R}_2)]^{\frac{1}{2}}[g^{(2)}(\mathbf{R}_1,\mathbf{R}_2) - 1] \\ \mathscr{F}_2(\mathbf{R}_1,\mathbf{R}_2) &= \rho^{(2)}(\mathbf{R}_1,\mathbf{R}_2) - \rho^{(1)}(\mathbf{R}_1)\rho^{(1)}(\mathbf{R}_2). \end{aligned} \tag{2.B.17}$$

The existence of the inverse (2.B.14) is a direct consequence of the use of a grand ensemble, for in a petit ensemble, $\rho^{(1)}(\mathbf{R})$ cannot be varied arbitrarily. It is clear from (2.B.16) that T is a correlation function. In fact, as defined, it is the generalization to non-uniform systems of the usual direct correlation function introduced by Ornstein and Zernike. Equations (2.B.14) and (2.B.16) may also be written in the form

$$T(\mathbf{R}_1,\mathbf{R}_2) = \left(\frac{\rho^{(1)}(\mathbf{R}_1)}{\rho^{(1)}(\mathbf{R}_2)}\right)^{\frac{1}{2}} \frac{\delta \ln [\rho^{(1)}(\mathbf{R}_1)e^{-\gamma(\mathbf{R}_1)}]}{\delta \ln \rho^{(1)}(\mathbf{R}_2)} \tag{2.B.18}$$

$$(\mathbf{1} - \mathbf{T}) = (\mathbf{1} + \mathbf{G})^{-1}, \tag{2.B.19}$$

the last being a matrix equation with **1** the unit matrix. The quantities **G** and **T** are always symmetric in their arguments; thus, **G** and **T** are Hermitian.

The effect of a finite density change $\Delta\rho(\mathbf{R})$ on a quantity f specified initially for $\rho_0(\mathbf{R})$ may be determined by a functional Taylor expansion about $f[\rho_0]$. For this purpose, it is convenient to visualize the density change as due to a parameter ξ which varies from 0 to 1,

$$\rho(\mathbf{R},\xi) = \begin{cases} \rho_0(\mathbf{R}); & \xi = 0 \\ \rho(\mathbf{R}); & \xi = 1, \end{cases} \tag{2.B.20}$$

since an ordinary MacLaurin expansion, including remainder term, may then be used:

$$f[\rho] = \sum_{j=0}^{s-1} (j!)^{-1} \left(\frac{\partial^j f(\xi)}{\partial \xi^j}\right)_{\xi=0} + \int_0^1 \frac{\partial^s f(\xi)}{\partial \xi^s} \frac{(1-\xi)^{s-1}}{(s-1)!}\, d\xi. \tag{2.B.21}$$

Now, employing the chain rule,

$$\frac{\partial}{\partial \xi} = \int \frac{\partial \rho(\mathbf{R},\xi)}{\partial \xi} \cdot \frac{\delta}{\delta \rho(\mathbf{R},\xi)}\, d\mathbf{R}, \tag{2.B.22}$$

we have the desired functional expansion

$$f[\rho] = f[\rho_0] + \int \left(\frac{\partial \rho(\mathbf{R}_1,\xi)}{\partial \xi}\right)_{\xi=0} \frac{\delta f[\rho_0]}{\delta \rho_0(\mathbf{R}_1)}\, d\mathbf{R}_1$$
$$+ \frac{1}{2}\left[\int \left(\frac{\partial \rho(\mathbf{R}_1,\xi)}{\partial \xi}\frac{\partial \rho(\mathbf{R}_2,\xi)}{\partial \xi}\right)_{\xi=0} \frac{\delta^2 f[\rho_0]}{\delta \rho_0(\mathbf{R}_1)\,\delta \rho_0(\mathbf{R}_2)}\, d\mathbf{R}_1\, d\mathbf{R}_2\right.$$
$$\left.+ \int \left(\frac{\partial^2 \rho(\mathbf{R}_1,\xi)}{\partial \xi^2}\right)_{\xi=0} \frac{\delta^2 f[\rho_0]}{\delta \rho_0(\mathbf{R}_1)^2}\, d\mathbf{R}_1\right] + \cdots$$
$$+ \int_0^1 \frac{(1-\xi)^{s-1}}{(s-1)!}\left[\int \prod_{i=1}^{s} \frac{\partial \rho(\mathbf{R}_i,\xi)}{\partial \xi} \cdot \frac{\delta^s f[\rho,\xi]}{\prod_{i=1}^{s} \delta \rho(\mathbf{R}_i,\xi)} \prod_{i=1}^{s} d\mathbf{R}_i\, d\xi\right]. \quad (2.B.23)$$

In the special case in which we choose

$$\begin{aligned}\rho(\mathbf{R},\xi) &= (1-\xi)\rho_0(\mathbf{R}) + \xi\rho(\mathbf{R}) \\ &= \rho_0(\mathbf{R}) + \xi\,\Delta\rho(\mathbf{R}),\end{aligned} \quad (2.B.24)$$

equation (2.B.23) reduces to

$$f[\rho] = \sum_{j=0}^{s-1} \frac{1}{j!}\int \prod_{k=1}^{j} \Delta\rho(\mathbf{R}_k) \frac{\delta^j f[\rho_0]}{\prod_{k=1}^{j} \delta\rho_0(\mathbf{R}_k)} \prod_{k=1}^{j} d\mathbf{R}_k$$
$$+ \int_0^1 \frac{(1-\xi)^{s-1}}{(s-1)!} \int \prod_{k=1}^{s} \Delta\rho(\mathbf{R}_k) \frac{\delta^s f[\rho(\xi)]}{\prod_{k=1}^{s} \delta\rho(\mathbf{R}_k,\xi)} \prod_{k=1}^{s} d\mathbf{R}_k\, d\xi. \quad (2.B.25)$$

It is to be noted that the variational derivatives which have direct significance are with respect to $\gamma(\mathbf{R})$, not $\rho(\mathbf{R})$. We must then transform appropriately:

$$\frac{\delta f[\rho]}{\delta \rho(\mathbf{R})} = \int \frac{\delta f[\rho]}{\delta \gamma(\mathbf{R}')} \frac{\delta \gamma(\mathbf{R}')}{\delta \rho(\mathbf{R})}\, d\mathbf{R}'$$
$$\frac{\delta^2 f[\rho]}{\delta \rho(\mathbf{R}_1)\,\delta \rho(\mathbf{R}_2)} = \int \frac{\delta^2 f[\rho]}{\delta \gamma(\mathbf{R}_1')\,\delta \gamma(\mathbf{R}_2')} \frac{\delta \gamma(\mathbf{R}_1')}{\delta \rho(\mathbf{R}_1)} \frac{\delta \gamma(\mathbf{R}_1')}{\delta \rho(\mathbf{R}_2)}\, d\mathbf{R}_1'\, d\mathbf{R}_2'$$
$$+ \int \frac{\delta^2 f[\rho]}{\delta \gamma(\mathbf{R}')^2} \frac{\delta^2 \gamma(\mathbf{R}')}{\delta \rho(\mathbf{R}_1)\,\delta \rho(\mathbf{R}_2)}\, d\mathbf{R}_1'. \quad (2.B.26)$$

The successive derivatives of γ are obtained from the general matrix relation

$$D(A^{-1})_{ij} = -\sum_{k,l} (A^{-1})_{ik} D(A_{kl})(A^{-1})_{lj} \quad (2.B.27)$$

for an arbitrary first-order differential operator D. Thus,

$$\frac{\delta^2\gamma(\mathbf{R}')}{\delta\rho(\mathbf{R}_1)\,\delta\rho(\mathbf{R}_2)} = \int \frac{\delta\gamma(\mathbf{R}'')}{\delta\rho(\mathbf{R}_2)} \frac{\delta}{\delta\gamma(\mathbf{R}'')} \left(\frac{\delta\rho}{\delta\gamma}\right)^{-1} d\mathbf{R}'' \tag{2.B.28}$$

becomes

$$\frac{\delta^2\gamma(\mathbf{R}')}{\delta\rho(\mathbf{R}_1)\,\delta\rho(\mathbf{R}_2)} = -\int \frac{\delta\gamma(\mathbf{R}'')}{\delta\rho(\mathbf{R}_2)} \frac{\delta\gamma(\mathbf{R}')}{\delta\rho(\mathbf{R}_1')} \frac{\delta^2\rho(\mathbf{R}_1')}{\delta\gamma(\mathbf{R}'')\,\delta\gamma(\mathbf{R}''')} \times \frac{\delta\gamma(\mathbf{R}''')}{\delta\rho(\mathbf{R}_1)}\, d\mathbf{R}'''\, d\mathbf{R}''\, d\mathbf{R}_1', \tag{2.B.29}$$

and higher derivatives are similarly found.

We now make use of our general formalism to investigate the asymptotic form of $\rho^{(2)}$ in a uniform fluid. This will be done by considering the response of the fluid to an external potential $\phi(\mathbf{R})$ induced by keeping a fluid particle fixed at $\mathbf{R} = \mathbf{O}$, i.e., $\phi(\mathbf{R}) = u(\mathbf{R})$, the intermolecular potential. Then $\rho(\mathbf{R})$ becomes the density of particles at R when it is known that there is a particle at the origin:

$$\rho(\mathbf{R}) = \frac{\rho^{(2)}(\mathbf{R})}{\rho} = \rho + G(\mathbf{R}), \tag{2.B.30}$$

where, as usual, ρ and $\rho^{(2)}(\mathbf{R})$ are the singlet and pair densities, and $G(\mathbf{R})$, the normalized radial correlation function in the *uniform* fluid, is $\rho(g^{(2)} - 1)$.

An implicit equation for the density $G(\mathbf{R})$ can now be obtained by applying (2.B.23) to $\gamma(\mathbf{R})$, which is known to within the constant chemical potential μ. If the uniform comparison system is that at density ρ, then μ is unaltered by the potential, and we have

$$\begin{aligned}\gamma(\mathbf{R}_1) - \beta\mu - \nu &= -\beta u(\mathbf{R}_1) \\ &= \int \left[\frac{1}{\rho}\,\delta(\mathbf{R}_1 - \mathbf{x}) - X(\mathbf{R}_1 - \mathbf{x})\right] G(\mathbf{x})\, d\mathbf{x} \\ &\quad - \frac{1}{2}\int \hat{\mathscr{F}}_3(\mathbf{x}_1,\mathbf{x}_2,\mathbf{x}_3) \times \\ &\quad \prod_{i=1}^{3} \left[\frac{1}{\rho}\,\delta(\mathbf{R}_i - \mathbf{x}_i) - X(\mathbf{R}_i - \mathbf{x}_i)\right] \\ &\quad \times G(\mathbf{R}_1)G(\mathbf{R}_2)\, d\mathbf{R}_2\, d\mathbf{R}_3\, d\mathbf{x}_1\, d\mathbf{x}_2\, d\mathbf{x}_3 + \cdots .\end{aligned} \tag{2.B.31a}$$

The function $X(\mathbf{R}_1,\mathbf{R}_2)$ is related to $T(\mathbf{R}_1,\mathbf{R}_2)$ by

$$X(\mathbf{R}_1,\mathbf{R}_2) = (\rho^{(1)}(\mathbf{R}_1)\rho^{(1)}(\mathbf{R}_2))^{-1/2}\, T(\mathbf{R}_1,\mathbf{R}_2). \tag{2.B.31b}$$

A superior expansion for many purposes, using a generally smaller expansion parameter, is obtained by taking the uniform comparison system for evaluation of $\gamma(\mathbf{R})$ as that at the local density $\rho^{(1)}(\mathbf{R})$. Then

$$\Delta\rho^{(1)}(\mathbf{x}) = \rho^{(1)}(\mathbf{x}) - \rho^{(1)}(\mathbf{R}) = G(\mathbf{x}) - G(\mathbf{R}), \qquad (2.B.32)$$

so that

$$\begin{aligned}\nu(\mathbf{R}_1) - \nu &= \beta\mu - \beta u(\mathbf{R}_1)\\ &= \beta\mu_0(\rho + G(\mathbf{R}_1)) + \int\left[\frac{\delta(\mathbf{R}_1 - x)}{\rho^{(1)}(\mathbf{R}_1)} - X_0(\mathbf{R}_1 - \mathbf{x})\right]\\ &\quad\times [G(\mathbf{x}) - G(\mathbf{R}_1)]\, d\mathbf{x} - \frac{1}{2}\int \hat{\mathscr{F}}_{30}(\mathbf{x}_1,\mathbf{x}_2,\mathbf{x}_3)\\ &\quad\times \prod_{i=1}^{3}\left[\frac{\delta(\mathbf{R}_i - \mathbf{x}_i)}{\rho^{(1)}(\mathbf{R}_1)} - X_0(\mathbf{R}_i - \mathbf{x}_i)\right]\\ &\quad\times [G(\mathbf{R}_2) - G(\mathbf{R}_1)][G(\mathbf{R}_3) - G(\mathbf{R}_1)]\, d\mathbf{R}_2 \cdots d\mathbf{x}_3, \qquad (2.B.33)\end{aligned}$$

where subscript zero indicates that the quantity is to be taken in a uniform system of density $\rho^{(1)}(\mathbf{R}) = \rho + G(\mathbf{R})$.

To the extent that X_0 and $\hat{\mathscr{F}}_{30}$ of (2.B.33) are of short range, $G(\mathbf{x}) - G(\mathbf{R})$ may be expanded in a Taylor series about $\mathbf{R}$ within the integrals, and we find

$$\begin{aligned}\beta\mu = \beta u(\mathbf{R}) + \beta\mu_0(\rho + G) - \frac{1}{6}\frac{\Lambda_0^{\,2}\beta}{(\rho + G)^2\kappa_0}\nabla^2 G\\ - \frac{1}{6}\frac{l_0^{\,2}}{(\rho + G)^4}\left(\frac{\beta}{\kappa_0}\right)^2(\nabla G)^2 + \cdots, \qquad (2.B.34a)\end{aligned}$$

where X can be expressed in the form:

$$X(\mathbf{R}_1,\mathbf{R}_2) = \frac{\delta\gamma(\mathbf{R}_2)}{\delta\rho^{(1)}(\mathbf{R}_1)} - \frac{\delta(\mathbf{R}_{12})}{\rho^{(1)}(\mathbf{R}_1)}, \qquad (2.B.34b)$$

$$\begin{aligned}\Lambda_0^{\,2} &= \int x^2 X_0(\mathbf{x})\, d\mathbf{x}\left[\int\left(\frac{1}{\rho}\,\delta(\mathbf{x}) - X_0(\mathbf{x})\right) d\mathbf{x}\right]^{-1}\\ &= \frac{\rho^2\kappa_0}{\beta}\int x^2 X_0(\mathbf{x})\, d\mathbf{x}\\ &= \int x^2 G_0(\mathbf{x})\, d\mathbf{x}\left[\int(\delta(\mathbf{x}) + G_0(\mathbf{x}))\, d\mathbf{x}\right]^{-1}, \qquad (2.B.34c)\end{aligned}$$

$$l_0^{\,2} = \frac{1}{\rho^{(1)}(\mathbf{R}_1)}\int \hat{\mathscr{F}}_{30}(\{3\})\left[\frac{\delta(\mathbf{x}_1)}{\rho^{(1)}(\mathbf{R}_1)} - X_0(\mathbf{x}_1)\right]\mathbf{x}_2\cdot\mathbf{x}_3\, d\mathbf{x}_1\, d\mathbf{x}_2\, d\mathbf{x}_3. \qquad (2.B.34d)$$

Here $\kappa_0 = \rho^{-1}(\partial p/\partial \rho)^{-1}$ is the isothermal compressibility, entering through the relation

$$\int \left[\frac{\delta(\mathbf{x})}{\rho^{(1)}(\mathbf{R})} - X_0(\mathbf{x}) \right] d\mathbf{x} = \frac{\beta}{\rho^2 \kappa_0}. \tag{2.B.35}$$

The earliest work on the asymptotic behavior of $G(\mathbf{R})$, where $G(\mathbf{R})$ is small compared to ρ, was done by Ornstein and Zernike (O.Z.), and is essentially equivalent to: (*a*) keeping only terms linear in G, and (*b*) cutting off the series in (2.B.34) after the ∇^2 term. This yields

$$\frac{\partial \mu_0}{\partial \rho} G_\infty(\mathbf{R}) - \frac{1}{6} \frac{\Lambda_0^2}{\rho^2 \kappa_0} \nabla^2 G_\infty(\mathbf{R}) = - u(\mathbf{R}), \tag{2.B.36}$$

where G_∞ is the asymptotic value of G. Since $u(\mathbf{R})$ is the intermolecular potential, it will generally have a short range, i.e., it will vanish in the region in which G assumes its asymptotic form, and the right-hand side of (2.B.36) can be set equal to zero. This leads at once to the usual O.Z. equation (noting $\rho(\partial \mu/\partial \rho) = \partial p/\partial \rho$)

$$\nabla^2 G_\infty = \frac{6}{\Lambda_0^2} G_\infty. \tag{2.B.37}$$

It is easy to obtain an explicit expression for the coefficient of $\nabla^2 G_\infty$, i.e., $\Lambda_0^2/6$, in terms of G. The solution of (2.B.37) in three dimensions is

$$G_\infty = \frac{A}{R} e^{-(\sqrt{6}/\Lambda_0)R}. \tag{2.B.38}$$

The reader should note that this analysis leads only to the envelope of the decaying correlation function. To obtain the oscillations in $g^{(2)}(R)$ for large R, it is necessary to retain terms in (2.B.36) that are omitted in the analysis leading to (2.B.38).

APPENDIX 2.C

Further Comments on the Rigid Sphere Fluid

As shown in Section 2.8, the theory of the rigid sphere fluid has played an important role in the development of the general theory of liquids. For this reason, we consider in this appendix the virial equation of state for the rigid sphere fluid.

The virial coefficients for the hard sphere fluid, up through E, are displayed in Table 2.7.1. Ree and Hoover, using a very clever modification of the Mayer expansion procedure, have recently evaluated F (B_6 in their notation). Since the calculations are both long and involved, the interested reader is referred to the original literature. Herein we merely quote the result

$$F = 0.0386b^5. \tag{2.C.1}$$

Now, if the virial series converges to the true pressure in the density range of the first-order fluid–solid phase transition, some of the higher virial coefficients must necessarily be negative in order to describe a flat or looped isotherm in the usual pV diagram. It is interesting, therefore, to determine the density range in which the five or six term virial series is an adequate approximation to the complete series. In Figure 2.C.1 is plotted the molecular dynamics data of Alder and Wainwright together with the five and six term virial equations of state. Also plotted is the Padé approximant

$$\frac{p}{\rho kT} - 1 = b\rho\,\frac{(1 + 0.063507b\rho + 0.017329b^2\rho^2)}{(1 - 0.561493b\rho + 0.081313b^2\rho^2)}. \tag{2.C.2}$$

It should be noted that both virial expansions predict pressures in the fluid phase which are lower than that computed by Alder and Wainwright. It is therefore to be expected that the next few virial coefficients are positive. Indeed, Ree and Hoover point out that the virial coefficients, B_n, can be fitted to the expression

$$\frac{B_{n+3}}{b^{n+2}} = (0.28515)^n[0.062500 \cos(0.17606n) + 2.2603 \sin(0.17606n)]. \tag{2.C.3}$$

From (2.C.3) it follows that B_{20} has the first negative sign, and the B_n change sign roughly every 16 terms. The values of $(p/\rho kT)$ from the Padé approximant agree very well with the molecular dynamics data. Indeed, the agreement with the pressure in the fluid branch is very good even at phase transition densities (see Appendix Table 2.C.1). However, the Padé approximant does not show any indication of a transition in the pV diagram.

If the Padé approximant is used to estimate B_7 and B_8, the following values are obtained:

$$B_7 = G = 0.0127b^6$$

$$B_8 = H = 0.0040b^7, \tag{2.C.4}$$

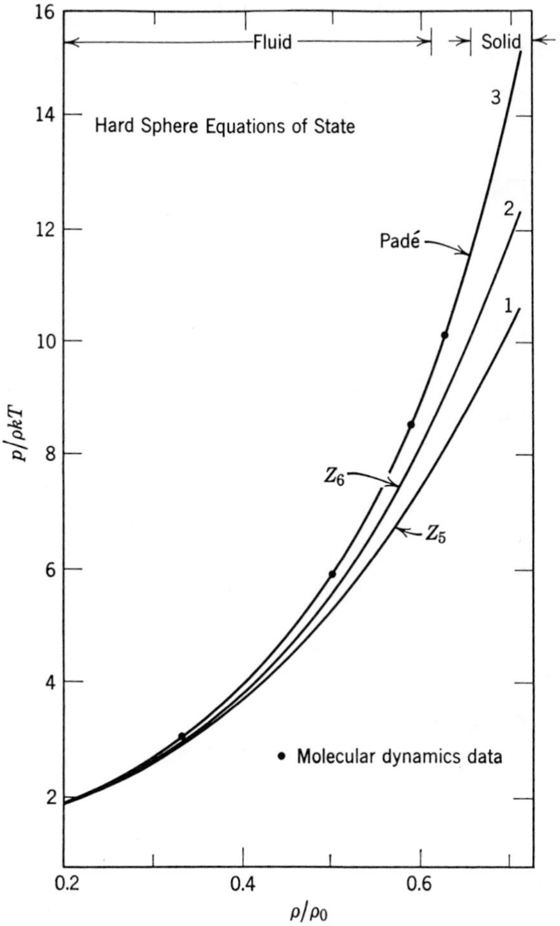

Fig. 2.C.1. Equation of state of the rigid sphere fluid represented as a Padé approximant to the virial series.

whereas, if Z_6 is subtracted from the molecular dynamics curve and the remainder represented by the single term $B_7\rho^6$, it is found that

$$B_7 = 0.03b^6. \tag{2.C.4'}$$

This discrepancy represents the uncertainty in B_7 as determined by these two approximate techniques.

APPENDIX TABLE 2.C.1

Values of $(p/\rho kT)$ From the Five- and Six-Term Virial Series, Padé Approximant, and Molecular Dynamics Calculations (Fluid Branch)

ρ_0/ρ	Z_5	Z_6	Padé	Mol. dyn.
1.60	8.11	8.95	10.11	10.17[a]
1.70	7.17	7.79	8.55	8.59
2.00	5.31	5.59	5.83	5.89
3.00	2.98	3.01	3.03	3.05
10.00	1.36	1.36	1.36	1.36

[a] At this density the MD calculations show both solid and fluid phases, the transition occurring at $(\rho_0/\rho) \sim 1.63$.

REFERENCES

1. Mayer, J. E., and M. G. Mayer, *Statistical Mechanics*, Wiley, New York, 1940.
2. Hill, T. L., *Statistical Mechanics*, McGraw-Hill, 1956.
3. van Leeuwen, J. M., J. Groenweld, and J. de Boer, *Physica*, **25** 792 (1959).
4. Green, M. S., Hughes Aircraft Report, September, 1959.

4*a*. Frisch, H. L., and J. Lebowitz, *The Equilibrium Theory of Classical Fluids*, Benjamin, New York, 1965.

5. Meeron, E. *J. Math. Phys.*, **1**, 192 (1960).
6. Morita, T., and K. Hiroike, *Prog. Theor. Phys.* (*Kyoto*), **23**, 1003 (1960).
7. Rushbrooke, G. S., *Physica* **26**, 259 (1960).
8. Verlet, L., *Nuovo Cimento*, **18**, 77 (1960).
9. Yvon, J., *Actualitiés Scientifiques et Industriel*, Herman et Cie, Paris, 1935.
10. Born, M., and H. S. Green, *Proc. Roy. Soc.* (*London*), **A188**, 10 (1946), *A General Kinetic Theory of Liquids*, Cambridge, University Press, New York, 1949; H. S. Green, *Molecular Theory of Fluids*, North-Holland, Amsterdam, 1952.
11. Kirkwood, J. G., *J. Chem. Phys.*, **3**, 300 (1935); J. G. Kirkwood and E. Monroe, *ibid.*, **9**, 514 (1941); J. G. Kirkwood and E. M. Boggs, *ibid.*, **10**, 394 (1942).
12. Cole, G. H. A., *Adv. Phys.*, **8**, 225 (1959).
13. Fisher, I. Z., *Soviet Phys. Usp.* (*English Transl.*) **5**, 239 (1962); *Usp. Fiz. Nauk*, **76**, 499 (1962).
14. Mayer, J. E., *J. Chem. Phys.*, **10**, 629 (1942).
15. Cramér, H., *Mathematical Methods of Statistics*, Princeton University Press, Princeton, N.J., 1945.
16. Mayer, J. E., *J. Chem. Phys.*, **5**, 67 (1937).
17. Kahn, B., and G. E. Uhlenbeck, *Physica*, **5**, 399 (1938).
18. de Boer, J., *Contribution to the Study of Compressed Gases*, Thesis, University of Amsterdam, 1940.

19. Uhlenbeck, G. E., and G. W. Ford, *Studies in Statistical Mechanics*, Vol. 1, North-Holland, Amsterdam, 1962, p. 123.
20. Ursell, H. D., *Proc. Cambridge Phil. Soc.*, **23,** 685 (1927).
21. Kubo, R., *J. Phys. Soc. Japan*, **17,** 1100 (1962).
22. Green, M. S., *J. Math. Phys.*, **1,** 391 (1960).
23. Lebowitz, J. L., and J. K. Percus, *Phys. Rev.*, **122,** 1675 (1961).
24. Taylor, A., *Functional Analysis*, Wiley, New York, 1958.
24*a*. Volterra, V., *Theory of Functionals*, Dover, New York (1959).
25. Mayer, J. E., and E. W. Montroll, *J. Chem. Phys.*, **9,** 2 (1941).
26. Lowry, B. A., H. T. Davis, and S. A. Rice, *Phys. Fluids*, **7,** 402 (1964).
27. Smith, E. B., and B. J. Alder, *J. Chem. Phys.*, **30,** 1190 (1959).
28. Zwanzig, R. W., *J. Chem. Phys.*, **22,** 1420 (1954).
29. Zwanzig, R. W., *J. Chem. Phys.*, **23,** 1915 (1955).
30. Percus, J. K., and G. J. Yevick, *Phys. Rev.*, **110,** 1 (1958).
31. Stell, G., *Physica*, **29,** 517 (1963).
32. Yvon, J., *Nuovo Cimento*, **9,** 144 (1958).
33. Percus, J. K., *Phys. Rev. Letters*, **8,** 462 (1962).
34. Fisher, I. Z., *Statistical Theory of Liquids*, University of Chicago Press, Chicago, Illinois (1964).
35. Rice, S. A., and J. Lekner, *Bull. Am. Phys. Soc.*, [11], **9,** 661 (1964).
36. Alder, B. J., *Phys. Rev. Letters*, **12,** 317 (1964).
37. Rahman, A., *Phys. Rev. Letters*, **12,** 575 (1964).
38. Rowlinson, J. S., *Mol. Phys.*, **6,** 517 (1963).
38*a*. Weissberg, H. L., and S. Prager, *Phys. Fluids*, **5,** 1390 (1962).
39. Baker, G. A., and J. K. Gammel, *J. Math. Anal. Appl.*, **2,** 21 (1961).
40. Ree, F. H., and W. G. Hoover, *J. Chem. Phys.*, **36,** 3141 (1962).
41. Salpeter, E. E., *Ann. Phys.*, **5,** 183 (1958).
42. Powell, M. J. D., *Mol. Phys.*, **7,** 591 (1964).
43. Hart, R. W., R. Wallis, and L. Pode, *J. Chem. Phys.*, **19,** 139 (1951).
44. Nijboer, B. R. A., and L. van Hove, *Phys. Rev.*, **85,** 777 (1952).
45. Broyles, A. A., *J. Chem. Phys.*, **33,** 456 (1960); **34,** 359 (1961); **34,** 1068 (1961); A. A. Broyles, S. V. Chung, and H. L. Sahlin, *J. Chem. Phys.* **37,** 2462 (1962).
46. Kirkwood, J. G., E. K. Maun, and B. J. Alder, *J. Chem. Phys.*, **18,** 1040 (1950).
47. Kirkwood, J. G., V. A. Lewinson, and B. J. Alder, *J. Chem. Phys.*, **19,** 139 (1951).
48. Thiele, E., *J. Chem. Phys.*, **39,** 474 (1963); M. S. Wertheim, *Phys. Rev. Letters*, **8,** 321 (1963); M. S. Wertheim, *J. Math. Phys.*, **5,** 643 (1964).
49. Verlet, L., and D. Levesque, *Physica*, **28,** 1124 (1962).
50. Reiss, H., H. L. Frisch, and J. L. Lebowitz, *J. Chem. Phys.*, **31,** 369 (1959).
51. Rosenbluth, M. N., and A. W. Rosenbluth, *J. Chem. Phys.*, **22,** 881 (1954), T. Wainwright and B. J. Alder, *Nuovo Cimento Suppl.*, **9,** 116 (1958); B. J. Alder and T. Wainwright, *J. Chem. Phys.*, **27,** 1209 (1957); **31,** 459 (1959); W. W. Wood and J. D. Jacobson, *J. Chem. Phys.*, **27,** 1207 (1957); W. W. Wood and R. F. Parker, *J. Chem. Phys.*, **27,** 720 (1957).
52. Klein, M., and M. S. Green, *J. Chem. Phys.*, **39,** 1367 (1963).
53. This analysis was made by M. Klein, *An Evaluation of the HNC Approximation for the Pair Correlation Function of a Fluid*, Ph.D. Thesis, University of Maryland 1962.

54. Michels, A., H. Wijker, and H. K. Wijker, *Physica*, **15,** 627 (1949); A. Michels, J. M. Levelt, and W. de Graaff, *ibid.*, **24,** 659 (1958); A. Michels, J. M. Levelt, and G. J. Wolkers, *ibid.*, **24,** 769 (1958); A. Michels, W. de Graaff, and T. A. Ten Seldam, *ibid.*, **26,** 393 (1960); A. Michels, J. C. Abels, C. A. Ten Seldam, and W. de Graaff, *ibid.*, **26,** 381 (1960).
55. Johnson, M. D., and N. H. March, *Phys. Letters*, **3,** 313 (1963).
56. Kestner, N., and O. Sinanoglu, *J. Chem. Phys.*, **38,** 1730 (1963).
57. Dobbs, E. R., and G. O. Jones, *Rept. Progr. Phys.*, **20,** 516 (1957).
58. Frisch, H. L., in *Advances in Chemical Physics*, Vol. 6, I. Prigogine, ed., Interscience, New York, 1964, pp. 229–289.

CHAPTER 3

Time-Dependent Systems

3.1. INTRODUCTION

Consider a system which at time t is in a non-equilibrium state defined by a set of macroscopic (or microscopic) constraints. If some of these constraints are removed, it is generally observed that internal processes are initiated which tend to establish a state of equilibrium with respect to the remaining constraints. The various processes may vary from point to point in the system and, at least in systems with which we shall be concerned, are found to depend in a simple way on the deviation from equilibrium at that particular point and time. They are called irreversible processes and the most important ones involve the transport of mass, momentum and energy. The meaning of irreversibility is well understood in thermodynamic terms, but because the equations of motion of molecules are time reversible, no easy interpretation is available at the microscopic level. Indeed, in order to formulate a statistical molecular theory of irreversibility we must first face a difficulty of *principle*. This situation is to be compared with the theory of equilibrium systems briefly surveyed in the previous chapter. The equilibrium theory is complete, in principle, but is beset with numerous mathematical difficulties.

In this chapter we examine the concept of irreversibility and study in what sense the time-reversible equations of motion may be used to describe time-irreversible flows. In subsequent chapters we shall develop a formalism within which the departures from equilibrium may be examined and computed. The complete resolution of all these problems is not accomplished, but impressive advances have been made.

The chapter falls naturally into two parts. The first three sections deal with reversibility and the problem of reconciling the macroscopic and microscopic levels of description. The last section deals with the recurrence of initial states and the approach to equilibrium, in the thermodynamic sense.

3.2. THE LIOUVILLE EQUATION

3.2.A. *Derivation of the Liouville Equation* (1,2)

The starting point for our discussion of the behavior of a system of N molecules contained in a volume, V, is the set of Hamiltonian equations

$$\frac{dq_i}{dt} = \frac{\partial H}{\partial p_i}, \qquad \frac{dp_i}{dt} = -\frac{\partial H}{\partial q_i}, \qquad (1 \leqslant i \leqslant s) \tag{3.2.1}$$

with q_i the coordinate conjugate to the momentum p_i. If the N molecule system has s degrees of freedom, there are $2s$ members of the set of equations (3.2.1). The function $H(\{p_i\},\{q_i\})$ is an integral of the system (3.2.1). Indeed, we have

$$\frac{dH}{dt} = \sum_{i=1}^{s}\left[\frac{\partial H}{\partial q_i}\frac{dq_i}{dt} + \frac{\partial H}{\partial p_i}\frac{dp_i}{dt}\right] = \sum_{i=1}^{s}\left[\frac{\partial H}{\partial q_i}\frac{\partial H}{\partial p_i} - \frac{\partial H}{\partial p_i}\frac{\partial H}{\partial q_i}\right] = 0, \tag{3.2.2}$$

where we have assumed that the Hamiltonian function, H, is not an explicit function of the time. It is important to note that the system (3.2.1) contains only equations of the first order; therefore, the Hamiltonian variables, $\{p_i\}$, $\{q_i\}$, given for some time, $t = t_0$, determine their values for any other time, t, succeeding or preceding t_0. Since the state of the system at any given time determines uniquely its state at any other time, the motion of the point defined by $(\{p_i\}, \{q_i\})$ in the $2s$-dimensional phase space of the system (Γ space) is also uniquely determined by the initial state. Clearly, through each point of the phase space there passes one and only one trajectory, and the kinematic law of motion along this trajectory is uniquely determined.

We now proceed to prove the following theorem due to Liouville: Let M be any measurable set of points of the phase space of the given mechanical system. In the natural motion of this space, the set M_0 goes over into another set, M_t, during an interval of time, t, such that the measure of the set M_t for any t coincides with the measure of the set M_0. Thus, the measure of measurable point sets is an invariant of the natural motion of the space Γ.

Before proving Liouville's theorem, we digress and expand somewhat on the terminology used above. Because a phase point at time t_0 uniquely determines the position of the phase point at time t, it is seen that every point of the phase space goes over to a new position in one to one correspondence with the old position; i.e., all space is transformed into itself. In addition, if t_0 is kept as a fixed reference point and t is varied arbitrarily, the set of all possible changes of state of the system is represented as a continuous sequence of transformations of the system phase space onto itself. The sequence of transformations can also be regarded as a continuous motion of the space in itself, which is denoted the natural motion of the phase space. Now the displacement of any point of the phase space in its natural motion during a time interval, Δt, depends only on the initial position of the point and the length of Δt, and not on the choice of the initial time. Therefore, the natural motion of the phase space is stationary and the velocities of the phase points in this natural motion depend uniquely on the positions of the points, but do not change with the time. As a result of the special form of the Hamiltonian function, not every continuous transformation of the phase space into itself can appear as its natural motion. A natural motion is characterized by some special properties, of which the Liouville theorem describes one.

Finally, let us note that there are cases when the complete phase space contains a subspace such that an arbitrary point of the subspace remains in it during all the natural motion of the complete phase space. Such a subspace participates in the natural motion by transforming into itself, and will be denoted an invariant subspace.

In the phase space description we are using, momentum and position coordinates are put on an equal footing. For convenience we define

$$\begin{aligned} x_i &= q_i \\ x_{s+i} &= p_i \\ X_i &= \frac{\partial H}{\partial p_i} \qquad (1 \leqslant i \leqslant s) \\ X_{s+i} &= -\frac{\partial H}{\partial q_i}. \end{aligned} \tag{3.2.3}$$

From equations (3.2.1) or (3.2.3) using the notation of equation (3.2.3) we observe that

$$\sum_{i=1}^{2s} \frac{\partial X_i}{\partial x_i} = \sum_{i=1}^{s} \left[\frac{\partial^2 H}{\partial p_i\, \partial q_i} - \frac{\partial^2 H}{\partial q_i\, \partial p_i} \right] = 0. \tag{3.2.4}$$

Let $x_i^{(0)}$ $(1 \leqslant i \leqslant 2s)$ be the value of x_i at $t = t_0$. Then the solution of the equations of motion may be symbolically represented in the form

$$x_i = q_i(t; x_1^{(0)}, \cdots, x_{2s}^{(0)}), \quad (1 \leqslant i \leqslant 2s). \tag{3.2.5}$$

Let V_t be the measure of the set M_t defined by

$$V_t = \int_{M_t} \prod_{i=1}^{2s} dx_i. \tag{3.2.6}$$

We now consider a change of variables such that

$$x_i = h_i(t; y_1, \cdots, y_{2s}) \tag{3.2.7}$$

so that

$$V_t = \int_{M} J(t; y_1, \cdots, y_{2s}) \prod_{i=1}^{2s} dy_i, \tag{3.2.8}$$

where J is the Jacobian of the transformation from the set $\{x_i\}$ to the set $\{y_i\}$:

$$J(t; y_1, \cdots, y_{2s}) = \frac{\partial(x_1, \cdots, x_{2s})}{\partial(y_1, \cdots, y_{2s})}. \tag{3.2.9}$$

Now consider the derivative

$$\begin{aligned} \frac{dV_t}{dt} &= \int_{M_t} \frac{\partial J}{\partial t} \prod_{i=1}^{2s} dy_i \\ &= \int_{M_t} \left(\sum_{j=1}^{2s} J_j \right) \prod_{i=1}^{2s} dy_i \end{aligned} \tag{3.2.10}$$

with

$$J_i = \frac{\partial\left(x_1, \cdots, x_{i-1}, \dfrac{\partial x_i}{\partial t}, x_{i+1}, \cdots, x_{2s} \right)}{\partial(y_1, \cdots, y_{2s})}. \tag{3.2.11}$$

But

$$\frac{\partial x_i}{\partial t} = \frac{dx_i}{dt} = X_i(\{x_i\}), \tag{3.2.12}$$

and

$$\frac{\partial X_i}{\partial y_k} = \sum_{r=1}^{2s} \frac{\partial X_i}{\partial x_r} \frac{\partial x_r}{\partial y_k}; \qquad (1 \leqslant i \leqslant 2s; 1 \leqslant k \leqslant 2s), \tag{3.2.13}$$

hence,

$$J_i = \sum_{r=1}^{2s} \frac{\partial X_i}{\partial x_r} \frac{\partial(x_1, \cdots, x_{i-1}, x_r, x_{i+1}, \cdots, x_{2s})}{\partial(y_1, \cdots, y_{2s})}. \tag{3.2.14}$$

The subsidiary Jacobians in the summation in equation (3.2.14) are

$$\frac{\partial(x_1, \cdots, x_{i-1}, x_r, x_{i+1}, \cdots, x_{2s})}{\partial(y_1, \cdots, y_{2s})} = \begin{cases} J & \text{if } r = i; \\ 0 & \text{if } r \neq i; \end{cases} \tag{3.2.15}$$

so that

$$J_i = J \frac{\partial X_i}{\partial x_i}$$

$$\frac{\partial J}{\partial t} = J \sum_{i=1}^{2s} \frac{\partial X_i}{\partial x_i} = 0, \tag{3.2.16}$$

and, therefore,

$$\frac{dV_t}{dt} = 0$$

using equations (3.2.10) and (3.2.4). This proves the invariance of the measure in the natural motion of the phase space.* The reader should note that the time-independence of the Hamiltonian is not required for this theorem.

If we interpret the measure V_t as the volume occupied by a set of points in phase space, then Liouville's theorem states that the volume remains constant under all transformations consistent with the Hamiltonian equations of motion. There is an interesting extension of this argument. If we allow a volume element surrounding a phase point to represent the uncertainty by which we know or describe the phase point, then for Hamiltonian systems the uncertainty in position of the moving phase point at any time t is exactly the same ($V =$ constant) as the uncertainty in the description of the phase point at the initial time,

* If the natural motion of the phase is continuous the word "measure" appearing in our proof of Liouville's theorem may everywhere be replaced by "volume." We have used the word measure to remind the reader that a proof at a higher level of rigor may be carried through in which the Riemann integral appearing in equation (3.2.6), and which defines the measure of a set, is replaced by the Lebesgue integral. This more general proof is valid for systems for which the natural motion of the phase space is not continuous. An example of such a system, in which we shall later be interested, is one in which the constituent molecules possess hard cores; when a hard core collision between two molecules takes place their momenta change discontinuously.

t_0. Within the framework of our present definition, this uncertainty can change with time only in the case of a nonconservative system.

There is a very large discrepancy between the amount of information contained in a thermodynamic description of a system, and that contained in a specification of its representative phase point. It was first pointed out by Gibbs (3) that our knowledge of the macroscopic state of a system is entirely inadequate to specify the positions and momenta of the constituent molecules. In other words, any thermodynamic state may be represented by a (very large) number of representative phase points distributed throughout the accessible region of the phase space. Gibbs introduced the notion of an ensemble to represent this situation. It is imagined that the system under observation is replaced by a (very large) number $\mathcal{N}$ of replica systems in identical physical conditions: that is, if the original system is energetically isolated, then the ensemble of $\mathcal{N}$ replica systems are energetically isolated; if the original system is in contact with a heat bath at temperature T, then so are the constituent systems of the ensemble. (Note that in this description the number of molecules, N, is fixed for each replica, in order that the representative phase points should appear in a space of the same dimensionality.) The representative phase points of the replica systems are distributed throughout the accessible region of the phase space in such a way that the thermodynamic state of the original system is given by the average over the whole ensemble. This requirement coincides with the equilibrium ensemble described in the previous chapter. Now, consider the number of phase points $C^{(N)}$ in a (small) region of the phase space $\Delta\Gamma_N$ $(= \prod_{i=1}^{N} d\mathbf{R}_i\, d\mathbf{p}_i$ for an N-molecule system). According to Hamilton's equations, $C^{(N)}$ does not change during the natural motion of the system,

$$\frac{dC^{(N)}}{dt} = 0, \tag{3.2.17}$$

because the uniqueness of the phase trajectories implies that no phase point originally inside $\Delta\Gamma_N$ can cross the boundary.

According to the intuitive definition of probability, the fraction $\Delta F^{(N)}$ $(= C^{(N)}/\mathcal{N})$ of phase points within $\Delta\Gamma_N$ is the probability that a member of the ensemble, selected at random, will be found to have its representative phase point within $\Delta\Gamma_N$. We therefore define the probability density $f^{(N)}$ for the N-molecule system as

$$f^{(N)}\,\Delta\Gamma_N = \Delta F^{(N)},$$

and obtain

$$\frac{df^{(N)}}{dt} = 0, \tag{3.2.18}$$

in the limit $\Delta\Gamma_N \to 0$, if $\Delta\Gamma_N$ is a region following the natural motion of the phase space. Equation (3.2.18) is often referred to as Liouville's equation. Since $f^{(N)}$ in general depends on time both explicitly and also implicitly through the phase, equation (3.2.18) may be expanded into

$$\frac{df^{(N)}}{dt} = \frac{\partial f^{(N)}}{\partial t} + [H, f^{(N)}] = 0, \tag{3.2.19}$$

where $[H, f^{(N)}]$ is the Poisson bracket of H and $f^{(N)}$. Equation (3.2.19) corresponds to the equation of continuity for an incompressible fluid. For, writing $\mathbf{v} = (\cdots, X_i, \cdots)$ as the $6N$-dimensional velocity of the phase fluid, we immediately obtain from equation (3.2.4)

$$\operatorname{div} \mathbf{v} = \sum_{i=1}^{2s} \frac{\partial X_i}{\partial x_i} = 0,$$

which proves the statement.*

It is pertinent to digress momentarily and examine in further detail the notion of an ensemble and the methods to be used in constructing an ensemble. It has already been noted that a number of completely specified mechanical systems may be formed corresponding to the small number of available macroscopic constraints. In the Gibbs ensembles, a macroscopic property of the system is to be compared with the ensemble average of the appropriate dynamical quantity,

$$\langle Q \rangle = \int Q(\Gamma_N) f^{(N)}(\Gamma_N; t)\, d\Gamma_N,$$

where $f^{(N)}$ is an ensemble distribution function formed with the assumption of equal *a priori* probability of all mechanical states.† One justification for the introduction of ensembles is that a physical system

* None of these statements depends on any assumed form of the distribution of replica phase points.

† "All mechanical states" means those (mechanical) states compatible with the known macroscopic properties of the system represented by the ensemble. The equal weight given to each state is the *least specific* weight consistent with the known restraints. It is shown in Section 3.3.A to be closely connected with the maximization of the entropy (of the description) of the system.

of interest is never completely isolated, that it does not traverse a single trajectory determined by $6N - 2s$ constants of the motion, nor is it confined to one quantum state defined by a complete set of quantum numbers. In this argument it is assumed that the real system is in weak interaction with its surroundings (which may include measuring instruments), but that the interactions are so weak that they need not be explicitly included in the Hamiltonian of the system. The interactions are, however, essential for inducing transitions of the system to all possible phase space trajectories (or quantum states). It is assumed, therefore, that the only constants of motion descriptive of a real system are the additive constants: energy, linear momentum, and angular momentum. Furthermore, the assumption of equal *a priori* probability of mechanical states, which is necessary for the construction and use of ensembles, probably cannot be demonstrated to be valid from the laws of mechanics alone. This assumption is a statistical hypothesis whose validity can be judged by the final agreement between observations and theoretical predictions.

In the construction of ensembles of replicas, it is necessary to use both the stipulated macroscopic constraints and the equal *a priori* distribution among the available microscopic dynamical states. For example, in the microcanonical ensemble of classical statistical mechanics, the phase points arising from all replicas are restricted to a shell bounded by the hypersurfaces of constant energy, E, and $E + \delta E$: equal volumes of the shell are assigned equal *a priori* probability. When a weak interaction between replica systems is allowed, the replica phase points are no longer restricted to lie in the energy shell. The restriction that the total energy of all replicas be fixed, but with energy interchange between replicas included, allows the phase point representing any one replica to move through all of phase space. Consequently, while the microcanonical ensemble describes the distribution of phase points in the energy shell, the canonical distribution describes the distribution in all phase space. Of course, the canonical ensemble in equilibrium assigns a distribution of the energy of one replica of the form $\exp(-\beta E)$.

3.2.B. *Properties of the Liouville Equation*

We now examine the consequences of Liouville's equation through an analysis of the properties of the equation (3.2.19) for the phase space probability density, or distribution function, $f^{(N)}$. For simplicity the discussion is confined to a system of N monatomic molecules all of mass m, with no internal degrees of freedom, and confined in a volume V. In the cases with which we shall be concerned, it is convenient to choose, as the Hamiltonian coordinates, the positions $\{N\} = (\mathbf{R}_1, \cdots, \mathbf{R}_N)$ of the N molecules. The conjugate momenta $\mathbf{p}_i$ $(1 \leqslant i \leqslant N)$ are then the $\dot{\mathbf{R}}_i$ multiplied by the mass m, and equation (3.2.19) may be written in the form

$$\frac{\partial f^{(N)}}{\partial t} + \sum_{i=1}^{N} \left[\frac{\mathbf{p}_i}{m} \cdot \nabla_i + (\mathbf{X}_i + \mathbf{F}_i) \cdot \nabla_{p_i}\right] f^{(N)} = 0, \qquad (3.\ .20)$$

where $\mathbf{F}_i$ is the intermolecular force on molecule i due to the other $N - 1$ molecules of the system, and $\mathbf{X}_i$ is an external force acting on molecule i ($\mathbf{X}_i$ must be conservative, i.e., derived from a potential included in the Hamiltonian).

The use of the terms "irreversible process" or "transport phenomena" implies that a unique direction to time can be specified or, equivalently, that entropy increases as time changes. Contingent upon this requirement for the description of such processes it is seen that the Liouville equation (3.2.20) should indicate a preferred direction of time. But this is easily shown to be a false supposition. If the entropy of the system $S^{(N)}$ is defined in the customary way as

$$S^{(N)} = -kH^{(N)} = -k\int f^{(N)} \ln f^{(N)}\, d\Gamma_N, \qquad (3.2.21)$$

then the time rate of change of entropy is

$$\frac{dS^{(N)}}{dt} = -k\int \frac{\partial f^{(N)}}{\partial t} (\ln f^{(N)} + 1)\, d\Gamma_N. \qquad (3.2.22)$$

Now, from equation (3.2.19) or (3.2.20),

$$\begin{aligned}\int \frac{\partial f^{(N)}}{\partial t} \ln f^{(N)}\, d\Gamma_N &= -\int [H, f^{(N)}] \ln f^{(N)}\, d\Gamma_N \\ &= \int f^{(N)} [H, \ln f^{(N)}]\, d\Gamma_N \\ &= \int [H, f^{(N)}]\, d\Gamma_N \\ &= -\int \frac{\partial f^{(N)}}{\partial t}\, d\Gamma_N. \end{aligned} \qquad (3.2.23)$$

A partial integration is necessary to reach the final member of equation (3.2.23), and it is assumed that the surface term (which does not appear) vanishes because $f^{(N)}$ vanishes at the boundaries of the accessible region of phase space. It follows immediately from equations (3.2.22) and (3.2.23), that

$$\frac{dS^{(N)}}{dt} = 0; \tag{3.2.24}$$

that is, the N-molecule entropy (defined on the assumption that the N-molecule distribution function is known) is a constant of the motion.

Alternatively, we may define a linear differential operator $\mathscr{L}$ by

$$\mathscr{L} f^{(N)} = -[H, f^{(N)}], \tag{3.2.25}$$

so that the distribution function characterizing the ensemble at time t, $f^{(N)}(t)$, *expressed in terms of the phase at time zero*, is given by

$$f^{(N)}(t) = e^{t\mathscr{L}} f^{(N)}(0), \tag{3.2.26}$$

where $\exp(t\mathscr{L})$ is defined by its series expansion. Then if $f^{(N)}(t)$ represents the ensemble at time t, which was characterized by $f^{(N)}(0)$ at time zero, there is also an identical ensemble (mirror ensemble) $f^{(N)}_{\text{mirror}}$ at time $-t$, given by

$$\begin{aligned} f^{(N)}_{\text{mirror}} &= e^{t\mathscr{L}} f^{(N)}(0) \\ &= e^{(-t)(-\mathscr{L})} f^{(N)}(0), \end{aligned} \tag{3.2.27}$$

which is derived from the original ensemble by a reversal of the momenta in $\mathscr{L}$. If we consider the case that $[\partial f^{(N)}/\partial t]_{t=0} = 0$, then the most general form $f^{(N)}(0)$ can have is some function of the Hamiltonian, and this form is invariant for a reversal of the momenta, since the Hamiltonian is an even function of these. We now have the situation that the ensemble at time $-t$ giving rise to $f^{(N)}(0)$ is identical with the ensemble that arises at time t, so that if $S^{(N)}(+t) > S^{(N)}(0)$ then $S^{(N)}(-t) > S^{(N)}(0)$, and the entropy cannot have varied monotonically. Or, put another way, if it is possible to prove that $[dS^{(N)}/dt] > 0$ for $t \geqslant 0$, then it is also true that $[dS^{(N)}/dt] < 0$ for $t \leqslant 0$.

This situation can be summarized by the observation that, if we reverse the direction of time and of the molecular momenta in equation (3.2.20), the equation is unchanged. Thus, the mechanical equations of motion lead to a strictly reversible description of the system. We are, therefore, faced with a seemingly paradoxical situation in that classical mechanics leads to a time reversible description of macroscopic systems, while we know from experience that (most) systems exhibit irreversible behavior. We shall see in the next section that this paradox is intimately connected with our earlier remark, made in connection with equation (3.2.24), that the entropy is constant if the system is completely specified.

3.3. A PARTIAL RESOLUTION OF THE REVERSIBILITY PARADOX

3.3.A. *Coarse Graining and Incomplete Descriptions* (3,4)

The resolution of the paradox that a system described by reversible equations shows irreversible behavior, has been known for fifty years, but has not yet been rigorously demonstrated.* It was first described by Gibbs and formulated mathematically by the Ehrenfests. The idea is essentially simple and is known as phase mixing. Although Liouville's theorem states that the measure of a set of phase points is preserved during the natural motion, it says nothing about the shape of the region occupied by these points. Thus, if we observe the motion of a set of points initially in a cell of parallelopipedal shape, and volume

$$W = \Delta\Gamma_N = \prod_{i=1}^{N} \Delta\Gamma_1(i),$$

(where $\Delta\Gamma_1(i)$ is a phase cell in the 6-dimensional space of molecule i), we will find that after some time there are some of this set of points in many such cells. Conversely, the points found in a particular cell at some instant were, at some earlier time, distributed over many cells. Thus, the phase points initially in one cell continuously mix with those from other cells. Gibbs proposed that every non-stationary, fine grained density distribution will be mixed by the (stationary) streaming in such a way that the coarse grained density will become stationary and uniform in some sense. This conjecture may be illustrated by Gibbs' own example. Suppose a drop of ink is placed in a container of water. The system so formed is non-uniform from a microscopic viewpoint,

* For an interesting discussion see B. Leaf and W. C. Schieve, *Physica*, **30**, 1389 (1964).

since the ink particles are colloidal and may be seen in a microscope as (colored) particles suspended in clear water. The system is also non-uniform from a macroscopic (coarse grained) point of view. Now, if the liquid is stirred it is well known that it will eventually appear to have a uniform color. On a microscopic scale, the system is still non-uniform, however, and ink particles may still be seen to be suspended in clear water.

Gibbs' proposal can be given a more mathematical form in the following way. Suppose, for example, that the energy of a system is known to have some value $\langle E\rangle$; then representation of this system by an ensemble requires

$$\int E f^{(N)}\, d\Gamma_N = \langle E\rangle. \tag{3.3.1}$$

We can easily show that $H^{(N)}$ is a minimum if

$$f^{(N)} = f_1^{(N)} = \exp \beta(A - E). \tag{3.3.2}$$

At equilibrium $\beta = (kT)^{-1}$ and A is the Helmholtz free energy, determined as a normalization constant. Suppose we define another distribution function $f_2^{(N)}$ by

$$f_2^{(N)} = f_1^{(N)} e^{\Delta}. \tag{3.3.3}$$

Then, from equation (3.2.21), we obtain

$$\begin{aligned} H_2^{(N)} - H_1^{(N)} &= -\int \{[\beta(A - E)] \exp [\beta(A - E)] - [\beta(A - E) + \Delta] \\ &\qquad \times \exp [\beta(A - E) + \Delta]\}\, d\Gamma_N \\ &= \int \exp [\beta(A - E)][\Delta e^{\Delta} + 1 - e^{\Delta}]\, d\Gamma_N \geqslant 0, \end{aligned} \tag{3.3.4}$$

where we have used the conditions

$$\left.\begin{aligned} \int E f_1^{(N)}\, d\Gamma_N &= \int E f_2^{(N)}\, d\Gamma_N = \langle E\rangle \\ \int f_1^{(N)}\, d\Gamma_N &= \int f_2^{(N)}\, d\Gamma_N = 1 \end{aligned}\right\}. \tag{3.3.5}$$

The final line of equation (3.3.4) follows because

$$\Delta e^{\Delta} + 1 - e^{\Delta} \geqslant 0$$

for any Δ, equality holding only if $\Delta = 0$. Equation (3.3.4) shows that the entropy is a maximum ($H^{(N)}$ a minimum) if $f^{(N)}$ has the canonical form in the energy. Thus, maximum entropy corresponds to a uniform density on surfaces of constant energy, if the average energy is specified. Conversely, and more generally, knowledge of the values of certain macroscopic variables characteristic of a system allows us to construct an ensemble, giving the maximum entropy, about which we can say no more than that it is uniform in certain regions of the phase space. Suppose, for a particular system, the phase space is divided into cells $\Delta\Gamma_N$, of volume W [the volume of the mth cell will be denoted by $W(m)$], corresponding to these regions of uniform density. If the system is already in a stationary state, then our description of the ensemble will not change in time. However, if it is not in a stationary state, then Gibbs' mixing will occur in the ensemble. If we define a new H-function, $\eta^{(N)}$, for the coarse grained description (Greek letters replacing Roman for all coarse grained quantities) as

$$\eta^{(N)} = \sum_m \varphi^{(N)}(m) \ln \varphi^{(N)}(m)W(m) = \int\cdots\int f^{(N)} \ln \varphi^{(N)}(m)\, d\Gamma_N, \tag{3.3.6}$$

where

$$\varphi^{(N)}(m) = W(m)^{-1}\int\cdots\int_{m\text{th cell}} f^{(N)}\, d\Gamma_N \tag{3.3.7}$$

is a constant over a cell, then we can show that

$$\eta_i^{(N)} \geqslant \eta_f^{(N)}, \tag{3.3.8}$$

the subscripts i and f referring to the initial and final states, respectively. Since the phase cells are defined to coincide with regions in which $f^{(N)}$ is initially uniform, we have

$$\varphi_i^{(N)}(m) = f_i^{(N)} \tag{3.3.9}$$

and

$$\eta_i^{(N)} = \int\cdots\int f_i^{(N)} \ln f_i^{(N)}\, d\Gamma_{Ni}. \tag{3.3.10}$$

Now, Liouville's theorem states that $f^{(N)}$ is constant along a streamline, so that

$$f_i^{(N)} = f_f^{(N)},$$

and the Jacobian of the transformation $\Gamma_{Ni} \to \Gamma_{Nf}$ is unity, so that

$$\eta_i^{(N)} = \int\cdots\int f_f^{(N)} \ln f_f^{(N)}\, d\Gamma_{Nf}. \tag{3.3.11}$$

Also, since $f^{(N)}$ and $\varphi^{(N)}$ are normalized, we have

$$\left.\begin{aligned} &\int\cdots\int f^{(N)}\,d\Gamma_N = 1 \\ &\sum_m \varphi^{(N)}(m)W(m) = \int\cdots\int \varphi^{(N)}(m)\,d\Gamma_N = 1 \end{aligned}\right\}, \tag{3.3.12}$$

so that

$$\begin{aligned} \eta_i^{(N)} - \eta_f^{(N)} \\ &= \int\cdots\int [f_f^{(N)} \ln f_f^{(N)} - f_f^{(N)} \ln \varphi_f^{(N)}(m) - f_f^{(N)} + \varphi_f^{(N)}(m)]\,d\Gamma_N \\ &\geqslant 0, \end{aligned} \tag{3.3.13}$$

because, for any positive x, y,

$$F(x,y) = x \ln x - x \ln y - x + y \geqslant 0, \tag{3.3.14}$$

equality holding only when $x = y$. Equation (3.3.13) shows that the entropy of a non-stationary initial state is less than the entropy of a stationary final state, but does *not* show that the system represented by the ensemble actually approaches a stationary state. Indeed, we cannot show this, but we can make it plausible and, at the same time, gain some insight into the mechanism of coarse graining. The rate of change of $\eta^{(N)}$ is, from equation (3.3.6),

$$\frac{d\eta^{(N)}}{dt} = \sum_m \frac{\partial \varphi^{(N)}(m)}{\partial t} \ln \varphi^{(N)}(m), \tag{3.3.15}$$

where we have invoked the time-invariance of normalization. Now, from equation (3.3.7) and the Liouville equation (3.2.20),

$$\begin{aligned} \frac{\partial \varphi^{(N)}(m)}{\partial t} &= W(m)^{-1} \underset{m\text{th cell}}{\int\cdots\int} \frac{\partial f^{(N)}}{\partial t}\,d\Gamma_N \\ &= -W(m)^{-1} \underset{m\text{th cell}}{\int\cdots\int} [H, f^{(N)}]\,d\Gamma_N \\ &= -W(m)^{-1} \underset{\sigma_N(m)}{\int\cdots\int} f^{(N)} \mathbf{v} \cdot d\boldsymbol{\sigma}_N, \end{aligned} \tag{3.3.16}$$

where $\sigma_N(m)$ is the surface of the mth cell, and $\mathbf{v}$ is the velocity of the phase fluid. Supposing for simplicity that $W(m)$ is independent of m, we find

$$\frac{d\eta^{(N)}}{dt} = -W^{-1}\sum_{m}\int\cdots\int_{\sigma_N(m)} f^{(N)}\mathbf{v}\cdot d\boldsymbol{\sigma}_N \ln \varphi^{(N)}(m). \quad (3.3.17)$$

The sum in equation (3.3.17) is now seen to comprise contributions from all interfaces of contiguous cells. Since $f^{(N)}$ and $\mathbf{v}$ are pointwise continuous across cell boundaries, a non-vanishing contribution to the sum occurs only because $\varphi^{(N)}(m)$ changes discontinuously at a boundary. If two cells m, m' have a mutual interface $[\sigma_N(m),\sigma_N(m')]$, then the contribution for that interface is

$$\int\cdots\int_{[\sigma_N(m),\sigma_N(m')]} f^{(N)}\mathbf{v}\cdot d\boldsymbol{\sigma}_N \ln [\varphi^{(N)}(m)/\varphi^{(N)}(m')], \quad (3.3.18)$$

where the positive direction of flow is $m \rightarrow m'$. We can immediately make reasonable qualitative statements about $(d\eta^{(N)}/dt)$ on the basis of equation (3.3.18). For, if the phase cells are so small that the set of streamlines crossing an interface are in (almost) the same direction, then the relation of $\mathbf{v}$ to $f^{(N)}$ in each cell is through the Liouville equation, and depends not on $f^{(N)}$ but on $(\partial f^{(N)}/\partial t)$, and we can say only that the entropy is not less than the fine grained value. On the other hand, if the interfaces are large compared to the cross section of "bundles" of streamlines crossing in almost the same direction, then the overall picture of the interfaces is one in which the flow across them is random in direction (and also in magnitude, since $f^{(N)}$ will vary considerably over such a region). The flow may then be likened to a pure diffusion process, and we can say with reasonable certainty that the net flow across an interface will be from a region of large $\varphi^{(N)}$ to a region of smaller $\varphi^{(N)}$. The contribution from each interface given by equation (3.3.18) will then be positive, so that

$$\frac{d\eta^{(N)}}{dt} \leqslant 0, \quad (3.3.19)$$

equality holding only when the ensemble is uniform in the coarse grained sense.

This intuitive picture of the motion of phase points in a coarse grained phase space is worth studying in more detail since it suggests the all-important result (3.3.19) (5). Consider a random process to which is available a set of n states $\{k\} = (1, 2, \ldots, k, \cdots, n)$. Suppose that at time t_0 the probability w_k^0 that the process is in state k is given for all k. In order to predict the probability w_j that the process will be in state j at time t we can introduce a set of transition probabilities A_{jk},* so that

$$w_j = \sum_{k=1}^{n} A_{jk} w_k^0. \tag{3.3.20}$$

Of course, the w_k^0, w_k, A_{jk} all satisfy the restrictions

$$0 \leqslant p_k \leqslant 1; \qquad 1 \leqslant k \leqslant n$$
$$\sum_{k=1}^{n} p_k = 1, \tag{3.3.21}$$

where p_k is each of the quantities in turn, and A_{jk} is summed over either subscript. Equation (3.3.20) *defines* a direction of time, and it is easy to show that the equation for w_k^0 in terms of w_j, when both are considered merely as algebraic quantities, does not have a probabilistic interpretation. Since both the sets $\{w_k^0\}$ and $\{w_j\}$ are nontrivial, A_{jk} has an inverse, and

$$w_k^0 = \sum_{j=1}^{n} A_{kj}^{-1} w_j. \tag{3.3.22}$$

Upon substituting for w_j from equation (3.3.20), we obtain, as a consistency condition,

$$\sum_{j=1}^{n} A_{kj}^{-1} A_{ji} = \delta_{ki}. \tag{3.3.23}$$

For $k \neq i$ it is clear that not all the A_{kj}^{-1} can be positive, since from equation (3.3.21) all the A_{ji} are. Thus, equation (3.3.22) is not an equation relating w_k^0 to w_j by a set of transition probabilities.†

* Random processes are discussed in detail in Chapter 4. Equation (3.3.20) is quite unrestricted in validity as it stands, and the A_{jk} will in general be functions, not only of t, but of the sequence of states through which the system may be known to have passed.

† The appropriate set of transition probabilities B_{ij} can easily be calculated. However, they require a knowledge of both initial and final sets of probabilities $\{w_k^0\}$ and $\{w_j\}$. Consider the probability that a sample of the process passes through the states k, j at times zero and t, respectively. This can be expressed as the probability of being in state k at time t_0 multiplied by the probability of a transition from k to j during the period $t - t_0$; thus,

$$\text{prob. (the sequence } k, j) = w_k^0 A_{kj}.$$

Alternatively, it can be expressed as the probability of being in state j at time t multiplied by the probability B_{kj} that, given the final state j, it had undergone a

Since equations (3.3.20–21) define a direction of time, so also do they define an increasing entropy function. Since, from equation (3.3.14)

$$w_k^0(\ln w_k^0 - \ln w_j) + w_j - w_k^0 \geqslant 0 \tag{3.3.24}$$

for any positive w_k^0 and w_j, we have

$$\begin{aligned}\sum_j w_j^0 \ln w_j^0 - \sum_j w_j \ln w_j &= \sum_j w_j^0 \ln w_j^0 - \sum_{j,k} A_{jk} w_k^0 \ln w_j \\ &\geqslant \sum_j w_j^0 \ln w_j^0 - \sum_{j,k} A_{jk}[w_k^0 \ln w_k^0 - (w_k^0 - w_j)] \\ &\geqslant 0, \end{aligned} \tag{3.3.25}$$

by virtue of equation (3.3.21). It is interesting to note that if one attempts to calculate the sign of the difference ($\sum_j w_j \ln w_j - \sum w_j^0 \ln w_j^0$), then the condition that not all the A_{jk}^{-1} can be greater than zero prevents the use of equation (3.3.24). If this condition A_{jk}^{-1} is not taken into account, one is led *erroneously* to the equilibrium condition,

$$\sum_j w_j \ln w_j = \sum_j w_j^0 \ln w_j^0.$$

Equation (3.3.25) defines an entropy function which increases with time. The result depends only on the form of the probability relation (3.3.20), and not at all on the physical interpretation of the probability set.

It is now convenient to establish a differential equation describing the evolution in time of the set $\{w_k\}$. With the definitions

$$A_{ik} = a_{ik}(t - t_0) = a_{ik}\,\Delta t; \qquad \Delta t > 0$$
$$\Delta w_j^0 = w_j - w_j^0; \tag{3.3.26}$$

---

transition from k; thus

$$\text{prob. (the sequence } k,j) = B_{kj} w_j.$$

Consequently,

$$B_{kj} = \frac{w_k^0}{w_j} A_{kj}.$$

Substituting this in equation (3.2.22) we find, of course,

$$\begin{aligned} w_k^0 &= \sum_{j=1}^{n} B_{kj} w_j \\ &= \sum_{j=1}^{n} w_k^0 A_{kj} \\ &= w_k^0. \end{aligned}$$

we readily find

$$w_j - w_j^0 = \sum_k [A_{jk}w_k^0 - A_{kj}w_j^0]$$

$$\frac{\Delta w_j^0}{\Delta t} = \sum_k [a_{jk}w_k^0 - a_{kj}w_j^0], \tag{3.3.27}$$

where a_{jk} is the transition probability per unit time from states j to k. Equation (3.3.27) makes the simple balance statement that w_j is increased by the transition from all states k to the state j, and is decreased by all transitions from the state j to other states k. We have not so far placed any restrictions on the type of process $\{w_k\}$ represents. The balance equation (3.3.27) is also quite general. If, however, the a_{jk} depend only upon j and k (apart from time) then* the process is Markovian. Equation (3.3.27) then contains all the information about the process, as do equations (3.3.20–21) alternatively, and is called the Master equation. $\{w_k\}$ is called the Master function.

It is important to note that although the ansatz (3.3.20) leads to a unique direction for the time in the sense that equation (3.3.22) has no probabilistic interpretation, it is equally possible to define a process with the opposite direction of time. Thus, if we are given the "initial" set of probabilities $\{w_k^0\}$ as before, and also a set of transition probabilities C_{jk} that a state k at time t_0 arose from a state j at time $\tau(= -t;\ t > 0)$ then the set of probabilities $\{w_j\}$ at time τ is given by

$$w_j = \sum_k C_{jk}w_k^0. \tag{3.3.28}$$

If we write

$$\tau_0 = t_0 \tag{3.3.29}$$
$$\tau = \tau_0 + \Delta\tau = t_0 - \Delta t,$$

then by putting

$$C_{jk} = C_{jk}\,\Delta\tau, \tag{3.3.30}$$

we obtain the time inversion of equation (3.3.27):

$$-\frac{\Delta w_j^0}{\Delta t} = \frac{\Delta w_j^0}{\Delta\tau} = \sum_k (C_{jk}w_k^0 - C_{kj}w_j^0), \tag{3.3.31}$$

which is completely incompatible with it. Using the conditions

$$\left.\begin{aligned} \sum_k C_{jk} = \sum_j C_{jk} = 1 \\ 0 \leqslant C_{jk} \leqslant 1 \end{aligned}\right\}, \tag{3.3.32}$$

* See Section 4.2.

it can also be shown that entropy increases with τ:

$$S(\tau) \geqslant S(\tau_0). \tag{3.3.33}$$

The reader should note that the C_{jk} are not related to the B_{jk} defined in the footnote on page 178. Rather, they are related to, though not necessarily the same as, the A_{jk} of equation (3.3.20). The direction of time giving an entropy increase is a direct consequence of the role of the initial ansatz as a boundary condition. Thus, if the set of probabilities is given in the past [cf. equation (3.3.20)], entropy increases towards the *future*, while if it is given in the future [cf. Eq. (3.3.28)], entropy increases towards the past. It is, therefore, the boundary condition that determines the direction of time. The introduction of irreversibility just discussed in no way justifies our selected ansatz or connects it with the fundamental mechanical description of the system. It is, of course, just this connection which is of greatest interest. We consider now the interdependence of the concepts of coarse graining, and initial probability ansatzs.

In the description given earlier of the motion of a point in phase space, insufficient attention was paid to certain characteristics of that motion. Both the position of a phase point and its direction of motion change very rapidly, so that on a coarse grained time scale or on a mesh of coarse grained phase cells the motion *appears* discontinuous. On this coarse grained scale the trajectories appear ragged rather than continuous and the flow in Γ space appears turbulent. The reader should compare this observation with the assumptions usually used in the theory of Brownian motion (to be discussed in the next chapter). Obviously, a Brownian particle has at all times a finite velocity and acceleration, but on the temporal and spatial observation scale the velocity changes so rapidly that the particle *appears* to make a succession of uncorrelated instantaneous jumps. Indeed, Doob (6) has shown that if the Langevin equation is used as the equation of motion of a Brownian particle, the measure of the path described by the particle in a finite time between two points of finite separation is infinite. Similarly, two phase points (representing two replicas) which start out close together will, after a time interval of the order of the duration of a macroscopic observation, represent two entirely different microscopic states. A small uncertainty in the initial specification magnifies so rapidly that soon all knowledge of the details of the microscopic state are lost. Thus, in spite of the microscopic determination of the equations of motion, it might be anticipated that the process described can be treated on a macroscopic scale as if the motion of the phase point had a stochastic character.

To follow up this idea we require a coarse graining of the accessible Γ space (the number of molecules is not important) (7). If $G(\Gamma)$ is some dynamical function defined in the space, then any uncertainty in macroscopic observations leads to a range Δg for $G(\Gamma)$. The scale of all values g accessible to $G(\Gamma)$, may then be subdivided into intervals of size Δg. Each such interval corresponds to a slice of Γ space determined by $g_\nu < G(\Gamma) < g_{\nu+1}$. Clearly, a macroscopic observation of G merely leads to a determination of which slice of Γ space contains the phase point for the relevant microscopic state of the system. If there are a number n of macroscopic observables, $G^{(r)}(\Gamma)$, observation of all such quantities requires the phase point to lie in that region of Γ space common to all the separate particular subdivisions of the Γ space:

$$g_\nu^{(r)} < G^{(r)}(\Gamma) < g_{\nu+1}^{(r)} \qquad (1 \leqslant r \leqslant n). \tag{3.3.34}$$

We take these regions to define our phase cells: each has volume

$$W(j) = \int_{\{g_j^{(r)} \leqslant G(\Gamma) \leqslant g_{j+1}^{(r)}\}} \cdots \int d\Gamma, \tag{3.3.35}$$

with the integration extended over the region determined by the intersection of the n slices of phase space. Although a complete determination of all $G^{(r)}$ fixes the phase cell in which the representative point must lie, there is a (very large) number C [cf. Equation (3.2.17)] of microscopic states compatible with each macroscopic state defined in this way. We have already seen that the introduction of phase cells of finite size permits the definition of an entropy function which increases with time provided we use a coarse grained density function. Now consider the motion of a phase point which is at t_0 in some selected phase cell. From each such point inside a particular phase cell there originates a trajectory. However, corresponding to the large number of phase points within the cell, the trajectories emanate from the phase cell in almost all possible directions. Moreover, because of the finite extension of the phase cells, the representative points jump back and forth in a superficially random fashion, and because of the intercession of interactions on a scale much finer than the phase cell subdivision of the Γ space, a phase point in a particular cell at t_0 may be found in any of the nearby cells for $t > t_0$. The macroscopic definition of the system at t_0 does not provide enough information to even predict the flow between phase cells. Therefore, on the coarse grained scale, the flow in phase space resembles a diffusion process.

Suppose we accept the above description and examine the consequences of an application of diffusion theory to the motion in Γ space. If at t_0 the representative point for a system is in cell j', then it has the probability $K(j \mid j'; s)$ of being in the cell j a time interval s later. From the definition of a conditional probability, $K(j \mid j'; s)$ must satisfy the conditions

$$\begin{aligned} K(j \mid j'; 0) &= \delta_{jj'} \\ K(j \mid j'; s) &\geqslant 0; \qquad s \geqslant 0 \\ \sum_j K(j \mid j'; s) &= 1. \end{aligned} \tag{3.3.36}$$

The transition probability, $K(j \mid j'; s)$, also represents the fraction of the phase points originally inside phase cell j' which have passed into phase cell j in the time interval s when the starting distribution of phase points arose from an ensemble which had at time t_0 constant density inside cell j' and zero density everywhere else in phase space.

It is characteristic of diffusion processes that the transition probability $K(j \mid j'; s)$ is independent of any choice of path from j' to j. Clearly, this leads to the conservation condition

$$K(j \mid j'; s) = \sum_{j''} K(j \mid j''; s - \tau) K(j'' \mid j'; \tau), \tag{3.3.37}$$

when account is taken of all possible intermediate cells, j''.* Because of our original interpretation of $K(j \mid j'; s)$, equation (3.3.37) states that if the phase points that arrive in cell j'' at time $s - \tau$ are redistributed with constant density in j'' and then the process allowed to continue, the final distribution is unaffected by the intermediate redistributions. Furthermore, in the limit of small time intervals, equation (3.3.37) is equivalent to the Master equation (3.3.27). For small Δt,

$$K(j \mid j'; \Delta t) = \delta_{jj'} \left[1 - \Delta t \sum_{j''} a_{j''j'} \right] + a_{jj'} \Delta t, \tag{3.3.38}$$

where $a_{jj'}$ is the transition probability per unit time from cell j' to cell j and Δt must be chosen to be macroscopically small (the macroscopic

* Equation (3.3.37) will be recognized in Chapter 4 as the Chapman-Kolmogorov or Markov (integral) equation (see, for instance, W. Feller, *An Introduction to Probability Theory and its Applications*, Wiley, New York, 1950).

state of the system does not change much) but microscopically long (the microscopic variables undergo large changes). The substitution of equation (3.3.38) into (3.3.37) leads to

$$\frac{\partial K(j \mid j'; t)}{\partial t} = \sum_{j''} [a_{jj''} K(j'' \mid j'; t) - a_{j''j} K(j \mid j'; t)]. \quad (3.3.39)$$

Let $w_j(t)$ be the probability that at time t the representative point of the system is in cell j. The relationship between $w_j(t)$ and $K(j \mid j'; t)$ is

$$w_j(t) = \sum_{j} K(j \mid j'; t) w_{j'}^{0}. \quad (3.3.40)$$

If both the left-hand side and right-hand side of equation (3.3.39) are multiplied by $w_{j'}^{0}$ on the right and the resultant summed over all j', then by using equation (3.3.40) one is led to the Master equation

$$\frac{\partial w_j(t)}{\partial t} = \sum_{j''} (a_{jj''} w_{j''} - a_{j''j} w_j), \quad (3.3.41)$$

which is seen to be the same as equation (3.3.27) (in the limit as $\Delta t \to 0$ in equation (3.3.27)). Inversely, we note that $K(j \mid j'; t)$ is that solution of the Master Equation corresponding to the initial condition $K(j \mid j'; 0) = \delta_{jj'}$.

It should now be clear to the reader that the probability ansatz defined by equation (3.3.20) and the use of a diffusion in coarse grained phase cells are equivalent in the sense that they both lead to the Master equation, a directionality for the flow of time and an increasing entropy function. In particular, equation (3.3.37) plays the role of an assumption concerning the random nature of the diffusive process (see footnote, page 183). Similar randomness assumptions play a fundamental role in the theory of the nonequilibrium behavior of gases and liquids.

The assumptions used in obtaining equation (3.3.41) are worth some further examination. First we note that the initial phase cell density distribution need not be uniform, since even subregions of a given phase cell are characterized by trajectories leaving in (almost) all possible directions, provided only that the subregion is not too small. The details of the initial density distribution are irrelevant provided only that the initial distribution is not freakish. One could, in principle, trace back those phase points in j which came from j' in time t, and then construct a density distribution in a subregion of j' such that only these special points are allowed in the subregion. Then the phase points which leave the specially constructed subregion are always found in j

at time t and the diffusion description is not valid. Now the construction of such a freak initial phase density depends upon detailed knowledge of the mechanical behavior of very large numbers of molecules. Indeed, it would be necessary to know all the trajectories of individual phase points. These trajectories are complex and the phase points which wind up in j are initially spread all over j' so that a complex disentanglement is necessary. Insofar as our macroscopic description of the system results in phase cells of finite volume, this information is never available and the freak ensemble cannot be purposely constructed. Nevertheless, from the point of view of mechanics the freak distributions are possible, and we must therefore explicitly exclude them in our current discussion. Condition (3.3.37), therefore, must be understood to mean that if one starts at t_0 from a density distribution constant in phase cell j' and zero everywhere else, then at $t > t_0$ each phase cell j will contain some representative points. It is assumed that the distribution of representative points does not correspond to a freak density such as constructed before. In addition, the distribution of representative points arriving in j'' from j' is assumed to be uncorrelated with the distribution of those representative points in j'' which will pass into any given other phase cell at some still later time. It is this assumption of lack of correlation which so greatly simplifies the description of the motion of representative points in Γ space.

The possibility of satisfying the requirements on the distribution of representative points in a phase cell depends on the nature of the description of the macroscopic system. Clearly, the phase cells cannot be too small or the randomness assumptions will be incorrect: this implies that the number of macroscopic variables cannot be too large. On the other hand, if the phase cells are too large, corresponding to very few macroscopic observations, the representative points will often remain within one cell or move rarely from cell to cell and the diffusion approximation cannot be used. Basically, this means that phase trajectory memory is important and the representative points will not be randomly distributed in the over-large phase cells. Under these conditions the randomness assumption is also invalid.

In terms of the preceding analysis the critical problem becomes one of abstracting from a many body Hamiltonian function a proper set of macroscopic variables. That is, a set sufficiently large that the future behavior of all members of the set is predictable from a knowledge of the initial values to within the same accuracy as the latter are defined.

For a spatially non-uniform one-component system the set would include the energy, momentum, and number of molecules in a set of (spatially defined) cells distributed throughout the volume of the system. More precisely, the members of a proper set depend upon the relaxation spectrum of the system—for slowly varying phenomena those macroscopic variables which themselves vary rapidly need not be considered if the spectrum breaks up into groups separated by sufficiently large frequency gaps. In general, the more rapid the time variation, the more variables have to be taken into account, and the smaller the phase cells are.

We have seen that the Master equation is associated with an increasing entropy function. Two other properties are of great interest. If the ensemble is composed of isolated systems then the phase space motion of each system is characterized by certain conserved quantities (constants of the motion) such as energy. In this circumstance the transitions between cells corresponding to different values of the constants are suppressed ($a_{jj'} = 0$) and the Master equation (actually a set of equations with one for each phase cell) breaks up into groups for each set of values of the constants. When equilibrium is reached the w_j are time independent, and within any one group of equations we have

$$\sum_{j''} (a_{jj''}w_{j''} - a_{j''j}w_j) = 0. \tag{3.3.42}$$

Equation (3.3.42) is satisfied if

$$\frac{w_j}{w_{j''}} = \frac{a_{jj''}}{a_{j''j}} \tag{3.3.43}$$

for all j, j''. Now we have shown [c.f. equation (3.3.4) *et seq.*] that the entropy is a maximum when the phase density is constant over the surface defined by the constants of motion. Hence, for each group of equations w_j is constant and

$$a_{jj''} = a_{j''j}. \tag{3.3.44}$$

Equations (3.3.43–44) are particular cases of the *principle of detailed balance*. This principle states that when the coarse grained phase density is constant in time, the number of transitions out of a state (per unit time) is balanced by the number of transitions into that state. If we are dealing with a canonical ensemble, then the systems are not isolated, and transitions from one energy shell to another may occur.

Equation (3.3.43) then leads to the relation

$$\frac{a_{jj''}}{a_{j''j}} = \exp\left[-\beta(E_j - E_{j''})\right], \qquad (3.3.45)$$

where E_j is the energy of every system represented by phase points in cell j. We have shown that it is possible to formulate a theory that describes an irreversible approach to equilibrium in the past without contradicting either the basic dynamical theory or the particular theory of irreversible processes under discussion. The important observation is that such an inverted theory is not obtained by simply reversing the sign of the time in the final formalism of a particular theory. Rather, it is necessary to start with the direction of time reversed before the ansatz is introduced. Of course, the prediction of the state of the system in the past cannot be compared with observation and does not have any physical meaning. It is, therefore, necessary to use appropriate boundary conditions to define properly the direction of time.

3.3.B. *Reduced Distribution Functions*

The usual interpretation of Gibbs' theorem (3.3.13) is that coarse graining eliminates the possibility that entropy can decrease, even with the momenta reversed. (Note that no explicit use of the fact that "final" is later in a temporal sense than "initial" was made.) This statement does not go far enough; we have given reasons for expecting that the entropy should increase asymptotically towards some maximum value characteristic of an ensemble uniform in a coarse grained sense. It may be that the coarse graining procedure performs this feat by excluding all distribution functions of physical interest, as may be the case in the manufacture of spin echoes and negative temperatures in a decoupled system of nuclear spins.

Consider, for example, a spin echo experiment (8): spins are aligned and thereby given a large excess *negative* entropy. They are then caused to precess by a transverse magnetic field. The result is that the magnetic moment precesses and also decreases in magnitude since the individual spins do not all precess at exactly the same rate. The excess negative entropy, therefore, decreases towards zero. At time t, the spins are aligned as in a mirror ensemble and we now find that the magnetic moment increases and at time $2t$ attains (almost) its original magnitude. The negative excess entropy is therefore (almost) recovered. The fact that coarse graining evidently does not provide a valid description in this instance is explained when we remark that we are, in effect, observing the individual spins. In other words, each particle (spin) moves almost independently of the others in its own subphase space in a way determined by the external magnetic field, and the macroscopic description of the system contains (almost) all the information that a fine grained description has. Of course, coarse graining does occur to some extent in all experiments, because no system is truly isolated, and fluctuations in environment induce transitions from some initial state to a large number of possible final states, however precisely the initial state is specified. In the case of the spin echo experiment the coarse graining is small because of the very weak interactions between the individual spins, the low temperatures, and the very short time scale (compared to the spin–spin and spin–lattice relaxation times) of the momentum reversal. Under these conditions correlation with the initial state is not lost. In more conventional studies of dissipative phenomena, the strength of the interaction and the time scale of the experiment prevent the observation of such fine grained effects; that is, the correlations spread rapidly to larger and larger groups of molecules and become weakened so that smaller and smaller perturbations destroy them.

An important feature of the foregoing discussion is that coarse graining represents an incomplete, or reduced description of the state of a system. We conclude from this that the irreversible character of a particular process is a function of the level of description involved in specifying that process. Thus macroscopic processes, such as the flow of heat, require only a very coarse description and are clearly irreversible, while processes taking place nearer the microscopic level, such as the diffusion of colloid particles, require a much more detailed description, and show both reversible and irreversible features (see Section 3.4). From this point of view we may ask the question: "Is coarse graining the N-molecule distribution function necessary in order to describe the approach to equilibrium?" The answer is no. Grad (9) has shown that the entropies defined in terms of lower order distribution functions are larger than that defined by the N-molecule distribution function. The lower order distribution functions are analogous to coarse grained N-molecule distribution functions in that they provide incomplete descriptions of the system. In recognition of this we henceforth refer to them as reduced distribution functions.

We follow Grad's argument in detail. From the general definition of the reduced n-molecule distribution function

$$f^{(n)} = \int \cdots \int f^{(N)}\, d\Gamma_{N-n} \tag{3.3.46}$$

we define one- and two-molecule H functions by

$$\begin{aligned} H^{(1)}(1) &= \int f^{(1)}(1) \ln f^{(1)}(1)\, d\Gamma_1(1), \\ H^{(1)}(2) &= \int f^{(1)}(2) \ln f^{(1)}(2)\, d\Gamma_1(2), \\ H^{(2)}(1,2) &= \int f^{(2)} \ln f^{(2)}\, d\Gamma_1(1)\, d\Gamma_1(2). \end{aligned} \tag{3.3.47}$$

The normalization conditions are

$$\begin{aligned} &\int f^{(2)}\, d\Gamma_1(1)\, d\Gamma_1(2) = \int f^{(1)}(1)\, d\Gamma_1(1) = \int f^{(1)}(2)\, d\Gamma_1(2) = 1 \\ &\int f^{(2)}\, d\Gamma_1(1) = f^{(1)}(2) \\ &\int f^{(2)}\, d\Gamma_1(2) = f^{(1)}(1). \end{aligned} \tag{3.3.48}$$

Then by simple subtraction

$$\begin{aligned} H^{(1)}(1) + H^{(1)}(2) - H^{(2)}(1,2) = &-\int f^{(2)} \ln f^{(2)}\, d\Gamma_1(1)\, d\Gamma_1(2) \\ &+ \int f^{(1)}(1) \ln f^{(1)}(1)\, d\Gamma_1(1) \\ &+ \int f^{(1)}(2) \ln f^{(1)}(2)\, d\Gamma_1(2). \end{aligned} \tag{3.3.49}$$

In the absence of interactions between the particles,

$$f^{(2)}(1,2) = f^{(1)}(1) f^{(1)}(2) \tag{3.3.50}$$

and thereby

$$H^{(2)}(1,2) = H^{(1)}(1) + H^{(1)}(2). \tag{3.3.51}$$

When there are interactions between the particles the pair distribution function is not the simple product of two singlet distribution functions. By introduction of a correlation function h_{12}, defined by the relation

$$h_{12} = f^{(2)}(1,2) - f^{(1)}(1) f^{(1)}(2), \tag{3.3.52}$$

it is easily seen that $h_{12} \to 0$ as the interaction becomes vanishingly small. Also,

$$\int h_{12}\, d\Gamma_1(1)\, d\Gamma_1(2) = \int f^{(2)}\, d\Gamma_1(1)\, d\Gamma_1(2) - \int f^{(1)}(1)\, d\Gamma_1(1) \int f^{(1)}(2)\, d\Gamma_1(2) = 0. \quad (3.3.53)$$

Now, the mean value theorem states that if a function $f(x + h)$ is expanded in a Taylor series in powers of h about $f(x)$ then the remainder R_n after n terms, defined by

$$f(x + h) = \sum_{r=0}^{n} \frac{h^r}{r!} f^{(r)}(x) + R_n(\theta), \quad (3.3.54)$$

is given by

$$R_n(\theta) = \frac{h^{n+1}}{(n + 1)!} f^{(n+1)}(x + \theta h), \quad (3.3.55)$$

where θ is a number in the range $0 \leqslant \theta \leqslant 1$. Treating h_{12} as an expansion parameter, we therefore obtain

$$\begin{aligned} \ln [f^{(2)}(1,2)] &= \ln [f^{(1)}(1)f^{(1)}(2) + h_{12}] \\ &= \ln [f^{(1)}(1)f^{(1)}(2)] + \frac{h_{12}}{f^{(1)}(1)f^{(1)}(2) + \theta h_{12}} \end{aligned} \quad (3.3.56)$$

by truncation at $n = 0$. After direct substitution of equation (3.3.56) into (3.3.49) and some algebraic rearrangement it is found that

$$\begin{aligned} H^{(1)}(1) + H^{(1)}(2) - H^{(2)}(1,2) &= \\ -\int h_{12}\left[1 + \frac{(1 - \theta)h_{12}}{f^{(1)}(1)f^{(1)}(2) + \theta h_{12}}\right] d\Gamma_1(1)\, d\Gamma_1(2) &= \\ -\int \frac{(1 - \theta)h_{12}^{\,2}}{f^{(1)}(1)f^{(1)}(2) + \theta h_{12}}\, d\Gamma_1(1)\, d\Gamma_1(2), \end{aligned} \quad (3.3.57)$$

where the last form in equation (3.3.57) follows from the use of relation (3.3.53). It is easily seen that the integrand of equation (3.3.57) is always positive since both numerator and denominator are positive when $h_{12} > 0$ and when

$$h_{12} < 0,\ f^{(1)}(1)f^{(1)}(2) + \theta h_{12} \geqslant f^{(1)}(1)f^{(1)}(2) + h_{12} \geqslant 0,$$

since $h_{12} = f^{(2)} - f^{(1)}(1)f^{(1)}(2)$ and $0 \leqslant \theta \leqslant 1$. We have thereby established the interesting relationship

$$H^{(2)} \geqslant H^{(1)}(1) + H^{(1)}(2) \tag{3.3.58}$$

and, consequently, the entropy is greater when defined in terms of reduced distribution functions.

Finally, we remark that if a reduced distribution function is known to satisfy a closed equation (kinetic equation) which describes the temporal approach of the function to the equilibrium distribution, then it is automatic that the entropy defined for that order of distribution function asymptotically approaches the appropriate value.

3.3.C. *Mayer's Theorem* (10)

The considerations of the preceding sections may be codified and organized with the aid of an important theorem due to Mayer.

Consider the distinction between mechanical reversibility and thermodynamic reversibility. For the purpose of our argument we deliberately define mechanical reversibility in a restrictive manner so as to simplify several aspects of the problem. Consider a system of particles subject to some external forces. Let the forces be varied slowly so that after a suitable elapsed time the external constraints are identical with those acting initially on the system. The set of external forces has put the system through a cyclic variation. If, at the end of this variation, the position and momentum of each particle is identical with the initial position and momentum, then we shall say that such a system is mechanically reversible.

Suppose the system is composed of a tenuous gas enclosed in a cylinder with frictionless piston. Let the piston be cycled slowly until the initial volume is again attained. If this process is sufficiently slow the thermodynamic state of the gas is the same at the end of the cycle as at the start and the process is thermodynamically reversible. But it is evident that the positions and momenta of the individual molecules of the gas are very likely completely different before and after the cycle, hence only certain aspects of the distribution of positions and momenta are reversible. This system, is therefore, thermodynamically reversible but not mechanically reversible in the sense of our definition.

The distinction we have just drawn forms the basis of many of the preceding arguments. This is perhaps most easily seen in quantum mechanical terms. In a system in which the number of particles is small and the spacing of energy levels sufficiently large, mechanical reversibility is attainable. In a system in which the number of particles is very large, it is ordinarily true that the spacing of the energy levels is so small that, for all practical purposes, no matter how slowly we actually perform a cyclic variation of the state of the system the final state is mechanically different from the initial state, even though the final and initial states may be thermodynamically identical. Thus the expansion of a gas on the time scale of hours permits an uncertainty in energy of the order of 10^{-30} ergs, a quantity enormously larger than the separation of translational levels in an ideal gas ($10^{-10^{23}}$ ergs or less).*

With the preceding arguments we are led to conclude that for any macroscopic process the best one can hope to achieve is thermodynamic reversibility, but never mechanical reversibility within the scope of our definition. The fact that the fundamental equations of mechanics are time reversible is of secondary importance with relation to macroscopic dissipation. In particular, the solution of the Liouville equation or its quantum mechanical counterpart must show that for any process in a macroscopic system proceeding at a finite rate, irreversibility is present. That is, Liouville's equation already involves the necessary elements of irreversible behavior and additional hypotheses such as coarse graining or random phasing are not necessary. The actual use of coarse graining or random phasing may then be interpreted as mathematical devices suitable for the selection of certain spectral ranges responsive to specific experiments, and it may be necessary to discuss different phenomena by means of different coarse graining intervals, or by quite different techniques. In making this statement we are assuming the dissipative process can be described by a low order distribution function.

* This estimate is easily made for an ideal gas by recognizing that

$$\Delta E = \frac{dE}{d\Omega} = kTe^{-S/k}$$

since

$$\frac{d\Omega}{dE} = \frac{de^{S/k}}{dE} = (kT)^{-1}\, e^{S/k}$$

with Ω the number of states with energy less than or equal to E. Since $kT \sim 10^{-14}$ergs at room temperature and $e^{-S/k} \sim e^{-N}$, we obtain the result, $\Delta E \sim 10^{-10^{23}}$ergs.

To quantify the preceding arguments we must recognize that the known properties of the system require a given set of distribution functions $f^{(n)}$, for small numbers of molecules, $n < n_0$. Now an ensemble of classical systems is mechanically defined in all details by giving the probability density in Γ space. In an ensemble of open systems, $f^{(N)}$ must be given for all $N \geqslant 0$. Consistent with the observation that only a few low-order distribution functions determine the state of the system for all macroscopic purposes, we note that $f^{(N)}$ is uncertain except that its contraction must give the proper $f^{(1)}, f^{(2)}, f^{(3)}, \cdots$ that is, there is an infinite set of functions $f^{(N)}$ consistent with the available macroscopic information. Consider functions $f_N^{(N)}(V,\lambda,\Gamma_N)$, defined for an open system and which may depend upon a parameter λ. The probability that exactly N molecules are in V is

$$P_N(V,\lambda) = \frac{1}{N!}\int f_N^{(N)}(V,\lambda,\Gamma_N)\, d\Gamma_N. \tag{3.3.59}$$

Compare this with equation (2.4.14) where

$$\sum_{N\geqslant 0} \frac{1}{N!}\int f_N^{(N)}(V,\lambda,\Gamma_N)\, d\Gamma_N = 1. \tag{3.3.60}$$

The reduced probability densities $f^{(n)}(V,\lambda,\Gamma_n)$ are likewise defined by

$$f^{(n)}(V,\lambda,\Gamma_n) = \sum_{N\geqslant 0} \frac{1}{N!}\int f_{N+n}^{(N+n)}(V,\lambda,\Gamma_{N+n})\, d\Gamma_N.$$

$$(f^{(0)} = 1) \tag{3.3.61}$$

This definition is completely equivalent to equation (2.4.15) relating $\rho^{(n)}$ to $\rho_N^{(n)}$. Now if we differentiate equation (3.3.61) with respect to λ, we find

$$\frac{\partial f^{(n)}}{\partial \lambda} = \sum_{N\geqslant 0} \frac{1}{N!}\int \frac{\partial f_{N+n}^{(N+n)}}{\partial \lambda}\, d\Gamma_N \tag{3.3.62}$$

$$\frac{\partial^2 f^{(n)}}{\partial \lambda^2} = \sum_{N\geqslant 0} \frac{1}{N!}\int \frac{\partial^2 f_{N+n}^{(N+n)}}{\partial \lambda^2}\, d\Gamma_N, \tag{3.3.63}$$

provided V does not depend on λ, and necessarily $(\partial f^{(0)}/\partial\lambda) = (\partial^2 f^{(0)}/\partial\lambda^2) = 0$. Consider a set of correlation functions defined in terms of $f_N^{(\nu)}$ for $0 \leqslant \nu \leqslant n$ by

$$\phi_n = \sum_{\nu=0}^{n} \sum_{\{\nu\}_n} (-)^{n-\nu} \ln f_N^{(\nu)}(V,\lambda,\Gamma(\{\nu\}_n)) \tag{3.3.64}$$

where, for a given set of ν molecules, the sum runs over all $(n!/\nu!\,(n-\nu)!)$ different subsets $\{\nu\}_n$ of numbered molecules of the numbered set n. By inversion,

$$\ln f_N^{(N)} = \sum_{n=0}^{N} \sum_{\{n\}_N} \phi_n(V,\lambda,\Gamma(\{n\}_N)). \tag{3.3.65}$$

Equations (3.3.64–65) are, in fact, the same as equations (42) and (41) of Appendix 2.A (because the right-hand side of equation (3.3.64) can be seen to contain *only potential terms*) if λ is the activity.

At equilibrium, the entropy is defined by

$$S = -k \sum_{N\geqslant 0} \frac{1}{N!} \int f_N^{(N)} \ln f_N^{(N)}\, d\Gamma_N, \tag{3.3.66}$$

and Mayer uses this as a general definition for *any* ensemble. Differentiation with respect to λ gives

$$\begin{aligned}\frac{\partial S}{\partial \lambda} &= -k \sum_{N\geqslant 0} \frac{1}{N!} \int \frac{\partial f_N^{(N)}}{\partial \lambda} (\ln f_N^{(N)} + 1)\, d\Gamma_N \\ &= -k \sum_{N\geqslant 0} \frac{1}{N!} \int \frac{\partial f_N^{(N)}}{\partial \lambda} \ln f_N^{(N)}\, d\Gamma_N,\end{aligned} \tag{3.3.67}$$

$$\begin{aligned}\frac{\partial^2 S}{\partial \lambda^2} &= -k \sum_{N\geqslant 0} \frac{1}{N!} \int \left\{ \frac{\partial^2 f_N^{(N)}}{\partial \lambda^2} (\ln f_N^{(N)} + 1) + \frac{1}{f_N^{(N)}} \left(\frac{\partial f_N^{(N)}}{\partial \lambda} \right)^2 \right\} d\Gamma_N \\ &= -k\sigma - k \sum_{N\geqslant 0} \frac{1}{N!} \int \frac{\partial^2 f_N^{(N)}}{\partial \lambda^2} \ln f_N^{(N)}\, d\Gamma_N,\end{aligned} \tag{3.3.68}$$

$$\sigma = \sum_{N\geqslant 0} \frac{1}{N!} \int f_N^{(N)} \left(\frac{\partial \ln f_N^{(N)}}{\partial \lambda} \right)^2 d\Gamma_N. \tag{3.3.69}$$

Since $f_N^{(N)}$ is by definition always positive, the quantity $\sigma \geqslant 0$.

Now we may express the derivatives of S in terms of the correlation functions defined before. By substitution of the summation expansions of each of the derivatives it is found that

$$\frac{\partial S}{\partial \lambda} = -k \sum_{n\geqslant 1} \frac{1}{n!} \int \phi_n \frac{\partial f^{(n)}}{\partial \lambda}\, d\Gamma_n \tag{3.3.70}$$

$$\frac{\partial^2 S}{\partial \lambda^2} = -k\sigma - k \sum_{n\geqslant 1} \frac{1}{n!} \int \phi_n \frac{\partial^2 f^{(n)}}{\partial \lambda^2}\, d\Gamma_n. \tag{3.3.71}$$

Now define

$$\phi_n(V,\lambda = 0, \Gamma_n) = \phi_n{}^0, \tag{3.3.72}$$

and let

$$\phi_n{}^0 \equiv 0; \qquad n \geqslant n_0. \tag{3.3.73}$$

Assume arbitrary functions $\phi_n(V,\lambda,\Gamma_n)$ for $n \geqslant n_0$ consistent with the condition (3.3.73) that they be identically zero when $\lambda = 0$. The functions $\phi_n(V,\lambda,\Gamma_n)$ for $n \geqslant n_0$ may then be chosen such that

$$\frac{\partial f^{(n)}}{\partial \lambda} = \frac{\partial^2 f^{(n)}}{\partial \lambda^2} \equiv 0; \qquad n < n_0, \tag{3.3.74}$$

where this may be done using the general equation relations given in Appendix 2.A, equation (31).

With the use of equations (3.3.73–74), the sums displayed in equations (3.3.70–71) are both zero at $\lambda = 0$, since $\phi_n = 0$, $n \geqslant n_0$, and the derivatives are zero for $n < n_0$. Thus, the entropy is an extremum at $\lambda = 0$. By virtue of the sign of the second derivative, this extremum is a maximum. Thus it has been proved that the function $f_N^{(N)}$ that has maximum entropy consistent with a fixed set of n_0 reduced distribution functions, $f^{(1)}, f^{(2)}, \cdots, f^{(n_0-1)}$ is that function for which $\phi_n \equiv 0$ if $n \geqslant n_0$.

In physical terms it has been shown that the entropy is maximized by the "smoothest" probability density consistent with given restraints. The function $f_N^{(N)}$ for $\lambda \neq 0$ contains correlation functions $\phi_n(n \geqslant n_0)$ involving more than n_0 molecules. At $\lambda = 0$ these correlations are removed, but their averaged effect is retained by solving the integral equations of Appendix 2.A for the $\phi_n(n < n_0)$ keeping the $f^{(n)}$ unchanged for all λ. Thus, the entropy is maximized subject to the given restraints, and the resulting functions $f^{(n)}(n \geqslant n_0)$ are the smoothest functions (i.e., least specific with regard to correlations of n_0 or more molecules).

In the usual transport problem, the system at time $t = 0$ is described by thermodynamic variables (which generally vary from point to point throughout the system). The phase space probability density $f^{(N)}$ describing the totality of systems prepared in this way is that appropriate to thermodynamic equilibrium. Equation (3.3.66) then gives the correct entropy, which is less than the entropy at equilibrium. If the potentials are pairwise additive, then at $t = 0$ $f_N^{(N)}$ is given in terms of $\phi_n(n \leqslant 2)$, only, where $\phi_2 = -\beta u(i,j)$. For an ensemble of hypothetically isolated systems, the subsequent evolution is obtained by solving the Liouville equation, and the $\phi_n(n > 2)$ are found to grow with time. Physically, correlations due to any particular pair of molecules will spread spatially as sound waves, involving, after a time t, a number of molecules given by

$$n \simeq \left(\frac{4\pi}{3}\right)\rho(ct)^3, \tag{3.3.75}$$

that is, the number contained in a sphere whose radius is the linear extent of the propagation of a sound wave at velocity c. In an ordinary laboratory system all the molecules in the system will thus become correlated in times of the order of milliseconds. In actuality, of course, no system is truly isolated. Extremely small (time-dependent) fluctuations at the walls suffice to destroy the high-order correlations, and hence to secure irreversibility. However, if the systems behave as thermodynamically isolated systems, then, *by definition*, the mechanical properties will be those predicted for isolated systems: the functions $f^{(n)}(V,t,\Gamma_n)$ for $n \leqslant n_0$ will be those computed from the correlation functions $\phi_n(V,t,\Gamma_n)$ of the ensemble of strictly isolated systems. The actual correlation functions for large n will be destroyed by the fluctuations, but those for small n will be altered by this "smoothing" so as to retain the $f^{(n)}$ of the isolated ensemble. The course of the negative entropy as a function of time can, therefore, be described as a flow into the high-order correlations functions, followed by a destruction there due to the otherwise trivial time-dependent fluctuations introduced at the walls.

The Mayer formulation in no way deals with the mechanical aspects of irreversibility. In this theorem the irreversibility of $f^{(N)}$ enters at the "walls" through the use of the Grand Ensemble to describe the behavior of the system, while the irreversibility of $f^{(n)}$, where n is small, enters through the flow of correlation towards larger n. This view of the mechanism of the appearance of irreversibility has been investigated in great detail by Bergmann, Lebowitz, and others.

3.4. RECURRENCE OF INITIAL STATES

The most direct criterion of irreversibility is whether a system, initially in a given state, returns to that state, and, if so, how soon. The definition of *state* has both microscopic (mechanical) and macroscopic (thermodynamic) connotations, and in this section we pursue the topic from both points of view.

3.4.A. *Poincaré's Theorem* (11,12)

The paradox which we discussed in the last section was given a formal basis by Poincaré in 1896. He proved the theorem: "In a system of material particles under the influence of forces which depend only on the spatial coordinates, a given initial state (i.e., a representative point in phase space) must, in general, recur, not exactly, but to any desired degree of accuracy, infinitely often, provided that the system always remains in the same finite part of the phase space." It may be proved in the following simple intuitive way: The motion of a phase point is restricted to a finite region of phase space if it represents an isolated system (microcanonical ensemble), or a system immersed in a finite heat bath (canonical ensemble). From Liouville's theorem we know that if V_0 is the measure of some set of phase points at $t = 0$, then V_t at time t satisfies $V_0 = V_t$. Indeed, the Liouville equation defines a one parameter family of transformations, T_t, such that

$$V_t = T_t V_0$$

$$T_{t+s} = T_t T_s.$$

Consider a series of equally spaced time intervals* and the corresponding transformations $T_1, T_2, \cdots$. Clearly, $T_1 = T, T_2 = T^2, T_3 = T^3, \cdots$ for this case. Now consider a point ω of the set V_0. By successive application of the transformations defined above, this point traces a trajectory in phase space. Poincaré's theorem asserts that some $T^k(\omega)$ is again in the set V_0.

We proceed by supposing the theorem to be incorrect; that some points never return to V_0. Let the set B (a subset of V_0) consist of the points which never return to B. Consider the sets $T(B)$, $T^2(B), \cdots$. They can be made non-overlapping. For, if $T(B)$ and $T^n(B)$ were to overlap, some point, P, would belong to both of them. We will suppose that the overlap occurs between the sets $T^m(B)$ and $T^n(B)$ $(m > n)$, and that the point Q in $T^n(B)$ transforms into the point P, which lies in both. Let the source points of Q and P in B be denoted Q_0 and P_0. We may always remove the overlap by excluding either P_0 or Q_0 from B. If we do this for every pair of points Q', P' in $T^r(B)$ such that $Q' \rightarrow P'$ after

* Although the case of continuous time is also easily treated, for simplicity we confine attention to the discrete case.

s transformations, then we can render the countably infinite sequence of sets $B, T(B), T^2(B) \cdots$ non-overlapping. Now, if none of the (remaining) points in B ever returns to V_0 then we have the situation that the finite region of phase space is covered by an infinite number of non-overlapping sets. Since the transformation T preserves the measure of the set, this can only be true if this measure is zero. Conversely, if B, or part of B, returns to V_0 any number of times, then the measure of B is not necessarily zero. We conclude that a phase point will return and pass arbitrarily close to its original position for *almost all* initial states.

3.4.B. *Estimates of Poincaré Recurrence Times* (12)

The statement of Poincaré's theorem in the previous section may be reworded to the effect that the natural motion of a system whose state is confined to a finite region of Γ space has a quasi-periodic character. The sequence of states that a system traverses between two repetitions of a given state (defined with arbitrary precision) is called a Poincaré cycle, and the time between two consecutive repetitions is called a (Poincaré) recurrence time. Clearly, the length of a recurrence time depends upon how precisely the recurrence condition is specified. A simple but crude estimate can be obtained in the following way. Consider a dilute gas in which each molecule undergoes about 10^{10} collisions per second. If the number density is 10^{18} molecules per cubic centimeter, the number of collisions per second in a sample of one cubic centimeter volume is $b = 10^{28}$. If we assume each collision induces a transition between two states of the system, then, since the original state need not recur until the system has passed through all other states, the average recurrence time, Θ, is given by

$$\Theta \simeq \frac{\Omega}{b}, \tag{3.4.1}$$

where Ω is the total number of states. Ω is easily estimated from the largest term approximation to the entropy: $\Omega \simeq \exp(S/k) \simeq 10^{10^{18}}$. Thus,

$$\begin{aligned} \Theta &\sim 10^{10^{18}} \div 10^{28} \\ &\sim 10^{10^{18}} \text{ sec.} \end{aligned} \tag{3.4.2}$$

This is to be compared with the "age" of the universe (inverse of

Hubble's constant) which is of order 10^{17} sec. We see immediately that the recurrence time is greater than this by about 10^{18} *orders of magnitude.*

Boltzmann made a much more detailed calculation than this by estimating the volume of phase space available to the system, and dividing it into small cells representing the accuracy of specification of a recurrence. In the system discussed in the previous paragraph the average separation of neighboring molecules is 10^{-6} cm. Boltzmann supposes that the initial state is one in which all the molecules are moving with velocities of 500 m./sec., and that the initial state is reproduced if the same molecules are in the same positions to within 10^{-7} cm. (10% of the separation) with the same velocities to within 1 m./sec. Since the gas is dilute, the potential energy is very small, and recurrence of the initial state can be discussed by considering the recurrence of velocity and configurational distributions separately. The volume of the velocity space may be calculated in the following way: the molecular subspaces are considered in succession and integrations are carried out over each subspace subject to the condition that the total (kinetic) energy is fixed. Thus, the first molecule may have a speed v_1 anywhere in the range from zero to $a = 500 \times 10^9$ m./sec.,* the second anywhere in the range from zero to $(a^2 - v_1^2)^{1/2}$, and so on. Since the length of a side of a cell in the velocity space is 1 m./sec., a may be treated as a dimensionless number, and the calculated volume of the velocity space will be given as the number of cells Ω_v. We have, from the preceding,

$$\Omega_v = (4\pi)^{n-1}\int_0^a dv_1 v_1^2 \int_0^{(a^2-v_1^2)^{1/2}} dv_2 v_2^2 \cdots \int_0^{(a^2-v_1^2\cdots-v_{n-2}^2)^{1/2}} dv_{n-1}v_{n-1}^2$$

$$= (\pi^{(3n-3)/2}/2\cdot 3\cdot 4\cdots[3(n-1)/2])a^{3(n-1)} \qquad (n \text{ odd})$$

$$= (2(2\pi)^{(3n-4)/2}/3\cdot 5\cdot 7\cdots[3(n-1)])a^{3(n-1)} \qquad (n \text{ even}), \quad (3.4.3)$$

where

$$a = 5\cdot 10^{11}$$
$$n = 10^{18}.$$

The number of possible ways of arranging n-labeled points in m cells is $(m!/(m-n)!)$ so that the number of configurational cells, Ω_R, is

$$\Omega_R = \frac{m!}{(m-n)!}, \qquad (3.4.4)$$

* This value of a exceeds the velocity of light, but we ignore all relativistic effects.

where

$$m = 10^{21}.$$

If the system passes through all possible states before returning to its initial state, the recurrence time is

$$\Theta = \frac{\Omega_v \Omega_R}{b}. \tag{3.4.5}$$

Θ is easily estimated for the very large numbers in the example. One finds

$$\Omega_v \simeq 10^{9(n-1)}; \qquad \Omega_R \simeq m^n$$

so that

$$\Theta \simeq 10^{10^{19}} \text{ sec.,} \tag{3.4.6}$$

which, while enormously different from equation (3.4.2), nevertheless bears a similar relation to the age of the universe.

The numbers involved in the two examples just discussed are so far beyond one's ability to imagine that we conclude this section with the study of a much simpler but physically uninteresting system. We consider a system of N harmonically bound particles (14). The position in phase space is uniquely determined by the phase φ of each oscillator $(0 \leqslant \varphi \leqslant 2\pi)$; normal mode analysis shows that there are $(N - 3)$ oscillators of non-zero frequency ω_i $(1 \leqslant i \leqslant N - 3)$. If observations of the system are taken intermittently at times, $0, \tau, 2\tau, \cdots$, then the average recurrence time, Θ, is given by equations (3.4.35, 37), Section 3.4.C:

$$\Theta = \tau \frac{1 - w(A)}{w(A)(1 - K(A \mid A))}, \tag{3.4.7}$$

where $w(A)$ is the probability that the representative point is found in a region A of the phase space, and $K(A \mid A)$ the probability that it is found in A if it was known to be in A a time τ earlier. If A is the angular interval $\{\Delta\varphi_1, \cdots, \Delta\varphi_{N-3}\}$, then

$$w(A) = \prod_{i=1}^{N-3} \frac{\Delta\varphi_i}{2\pi}. \tag{3.4.8}$$

$w(A)(1 - K(A \mid A))$ is the probability that a point $\{\varphi_1, \cdots, \varphi_{N-3}\}$ is initially in A, and lies outside A after an interval τ. This is seen immediately upon the realization that $w(A)K(A \mid A)$ is the probability that a point lies in A initially, and is still in A an interval τ later.

Similarly, $w(A)$ is the probability that a point lies in A initially and is *anywhere* after an interval τ. If τ is small* this is the same as the probability that a point lies in A initially, and that *either* $\varphi_1 + \omega_1\tau$ lies outside $\Delta\varphi_1$, *or* $\varphi_2 + \omega_2\tau$ lies outside $\Delta\varphi_2$, *or* $\cdots$. Thus,

$$w(A)(1 - K(A \mid A)) = w(A)\tau \sum_{i=1}^{N-3} \frac{\omega_i}{\Delta\varphi_i}, \tag{3.4.9}$$

and equation (3.4.7) becomes, in the limit of small τ,

$$\Theta = \left(1 - \prod_{i=1}^{N-3} \frac{\Delta\varphi_i}{2\pi}\right)\left(\prod_{i=1}^{N-3} \frac{2\pi}{\Delta\varphi_i}\right)\left(\sum_{i=1}^{N-3} \frac{\omega_i}{\Delta\varphi_i}\right)^{-1}. \tag{3.4.10}$$

This formula was first obtained by Hemmer et al. (14), but the derivation given is due to Kac (15). If $N = 15$, $\omega_{\text{max.}} = 10$ sec.$^{-1}$, and $(\Delta\varphi/2\pi) = 0.03$, we find easily that

$$\Theta \simeq 10^{17} \text{ sec.} = 10^{10} \text{ yr.} \tag{3.4.11}$$

These estimates of the mean recurrence time strongly suggest that an initial state is extremely unlikely to recur, and hence we might infer that many processes appear irreversible to us simply because we do not observe them for long enough periods. However, this is not an immediate deduction because the distribution of possible recurrence times has not been calculated. This is a very difficult problem which has not been solved in general, but Kac has shown for some special models that, if θ is the recurrence time ($\langle\theta\rangle = \Theta$),

$$\begin{aligned}\langle(\Delta\theta)^2\rangle^{1/2} &= \langle(\theta - \Theta)^2\rangle^{1/2} \\ &\simeq \Theta.\end{aligned} \tag{3.4.12}$$

Thus, however long the average recurrence time, such systems clearly do not exhibit irreversibility in the usual sense.

3.4.C. *Practical Irreversibility* (12)

The thermodynamic meaning of irreversibility is different from that used in the previous section because we observe a system only in a very gross or imprecise way. Thus, the thermodynamic state of a system corresponds to a large number of possible states, or points, in

* If τ is long enough that $\omega_i\tau$ is not small compared to $\Delta\varphi_i$, then we must consider the possibility that two or more of the $\varphi_i + \omega_i\tau$ lie outside $\Delta\varphi_i$.

phase space, as mentioned in Section 3.2.A. During a Poincaré cycle, the trajectory of the point in phase space will pass more or less close to every point in the space, depending on how precisely we define the recurrence, so that a given thermodynamic state will in general recur many times, depending on what fraction of the phase space is occupied by the points corresponding to that state. In general, then, even large fluctuations from a thermodynamic norm will recur, and it is with the frequency of these events that a discussion of irreversibility is concerned.

The problem of fluctuations and their recurrence was analyzed by Smoluchowski (16) in terms of what he called the probability after-effect: given the state n of a system (generally a vector in hyperspace) at some instant, what can we say about the possible values of n at a time τ later? Obviously, when τ is much shorter than the period of the fluctuations of n we will expect to find the state almost unchanged, while for very large τ we will expect the final state to be independent of the initial state. For intermediate times we must take into account the speed of the fluctuations explicitly. An example considered by Smoluchowski was the number of colloid particles in a small volume defined within a much larger volume. This number was observed at successive instants at intervals of time τ. In a typical sequence of counts the average number was $\sim$2.0, and as many as 5 particles were found frequently. Such sequences, containing frequent large fluctuations from the mean, show none of the expected behavior of an irreversible process, and yet we shall see that they are compatible with the macroscopic irreversible law of diffusion.

Consider a system of colloid particles in diffusion equilibrium. If the concentration is not too high, the probability that a particle will enter or leave the volume is not influenced by the number in the volume or near it outside. The probability distribution for the number n will then be a Poisson distribution

$$w(n) = \frac{e^{-\nu}\nu^n}{n!}, \tag{3.4.13}$$

with

$$\langle n \rangle = \nu$$

and

$$\langle n^2 \rangle = \nu^2 + \nu. \tag{3.4.14}$$

This distribution can be regarded as the limit of a Bernoulli (binomial) distribution as the total number of particles N in the whole system, and its volume V tend to infinity while N/V remains constant: The probability that any particular particle is to be found in the observed volume v is (v/V) if all points in V are equiprobable. Thus, the probability that any n are found in V is

$$w^{(N)}(n) = \binom{N}{n}\left(\frac{v}{V}\right)^n\left(1 - \frac{v}{V}\right)^{N-n}. \qquad (3.4.15)$$

We now let $N,\ V \to \infty$ while $(N/V) = \rho$, the average density. Then equation (3.4.15) becomes

$$w^{(N)}(n) = \operatorname*{Lim}_{N\to\infty} \binom{N}{n}\left(\frac{\nu}{N}\right)^n\left(1 - \frac{\nu}{N}\right)^{N-n},$$

where $\nu = \rho v$. Noting that

$$\binom{N}{n} \to N^n; \qquad \left(1 - \frac{\nu}{N}\right)^{N-n} \to e^{-\nu}$$

or large N, we see that

$$\operatorname*{Lim}_{N\to\infty} w^{(N)}(n) = w(n). \qquad (3.4.16)$$

To discuss the speed of fluctuations we must calculate the transition probability $K(n \mid m)$ that m particles will be observed within v a time τ after n were found.* We can define a probability after-effect factor p that a particle initially in v will have left it during τ. In the present example, individual particles are assumed to obey the macroscopic law of diffusion, which is in effect assuming that in some sense irreversibility is already present in the motion of the particles. The probability that a particle, initially at $\mathbf{r}_1$, will have diffused to $\mathbf{r}_2$ in a time τ is

$$(2\pi\ D\tau)^{-3/2} \exp\left(-\frac{(\mathbf{r}_1 - \mathbf{r}_2)^2}{4D\tau}\right),$$

* In this analysis, the sequence of observations (3.4.30) is regarded as a Markov chain; that is, a Markov process discrete in time, and with a discrete set of states. This is rigorously correct if the probability after effect p can be calculated from a knowledge of only the initial position of a particle (inside or outside v). A more detailed analysis of the physics of the particular process shows that the initial velocity of the particle also affects p, so that it is the sequence of combined occupation numbers *and* velocities which is a Markov process. It is only in the case that v is sufficiently large compared to the diffusion length d [equation (4.4.85)] that the volume of the shell of thickness d at the surface of v is small compared to v, and also that τ is sufficiently large that the probability of a particle diffusing out of v from the interior during τ is not small, is the sequence (3.4.30) a good approximation to a Markov chain.

where D is the diffusion coefficient. p is found by integrating this probability over values of $\mathbf{r}_1$ inside v, and values of $\mathbf{r}_2$ outside v. This definition of p again requires both the assumptions made in deriving $w(n)$.

Now, let $A_i^{(n)}$ denote the probability that if n particles are initially observed some i will have left v after a time τ. $A_i^{(n)}$ is the Bernoulli distribution

$$A_i^{(n)} = \binom{n}{i} p^i(1 - p)^{n-i}. \tag{3.4.17}$$

Also, let E_j denote the probability that j particles will enter v during τ. By assumption, E_j cannot depend on n, and since the *a priori* probabilities of entry and exit must be the same, we have

$$\begin{aligned} E_j &= \langle A_j^{(n)} \rangle \\ &= \sum_{n=j}^{\infty} A_j^{(n)} w(n) \\ &= \frac{(\nu p)^j e^{-\nu p}}{j!}, \end{aligned} \tag{3.4.18}$$

i.e., a Poisson distribution with mean νp. Consequently, $K(n \mid n + k)$ is given by

$$K(n \mid n + k) = \sum_{i=0}^{n} A_i^{(n)} E_{i+k}, \tag{3.4.19}$$

and also

$$K(n \mid n - k) = \sum_{i=k}^{n} A_i^{(n)} E_{i-k}. \tag{3.4.20}$$

In equation (3.4.20) i cannot be less than k because E_j is not defined for $j < 0$. Since we can write

$$A_i^{(n)} = w_1^{(n)}(n - i)$$

as another Bernoulli distribution, and also write

$$E_j = w_2(j),$$

we see that the transition probability is in general given by

$$K(n| \ m) = \sum_{x+y=m} w_1^{(n)}(x) w_2(y), \tag{3.4.21}$$

where the summation is over all values of x (and y) consistent with $x + y = m$. This form of distribution is called the sum or convolution of the two component distributions $w_1^{(n)}$ and w_2. It is easy to show that the mean and mean-square deviation of m for given n are the sums of the corresponding moments of $w_1^{(n)}$ and w_2.

This follows because

$$\sum_m K(n \mid m), \qquad \sum_m mK(n \mid m), \qquad \text{and} \qquad \sum_m (m - \langle m \rangle_1)^2 K(n \mid m)$$

allow x and y to take all their values independently, so that, for instance,

$$\begin{aligned} \sum_m K(n \mid m) &= \sum_m \sum_{x+y=m} w_1^{(n)}(x) w_2(y) \\ &= \left(\sum_x w_1^{(n)}(x)\right)\left(\sum_y w_2(y)\right) \\ &= 1 \end{aligned} \tag{3.4.22}$$

because $w_1^{(n)}$ and w_2 are normalized separately. Thus, we find

$$\langle m \rangle_1 = \sum_m mK(n \mid m) = \langle x \rangle + \langle y \rangle, \tag{3.4.23}$$

$$\langle (\Delta m)^2 \rangle_1 = \langle (\Delta x)^2 \rangle + \langle (\Delta y)^2 \rangle, \tag{3.4.24}$$

where the subscript 1 on $\langle \cdots \rangle_1$ denotes the average conditional on the given value of n. From equations (3.4.14, 18, 23, 24) we now obtain

$$\begin{aligned} \langle x \rangle &= n(1 - p); \qquad & \langle (\Delta x)^2 \rangle &= np(1 - p), \\ \langle y \rangle &= \nu p; & \langle (\Delta y)^2 \rangle &= \nu p, \end{aligned} \tag{3.4.25}$$

so that

$$\langle (m - n) \rangle_1 = \langle m \rangle_1 - n = (\nu - n)p, \tag{3.4.26}$$

and

$$\langle (m - n)^2 \rangle_1 = [(\nu - n)^2 - n]p^2 + (\nu + n)p. \tag{3.4.27}$$

Equation (3.4.26) is important in that it shows that the average tendency is to move towards the mean. This is one of the observed characteristics of irreversible processes, and may be called the regression law.

Upon averaging these results over all values of n, we find

$$\langle \langle (m - n) \rangle_1 \rangle = 0 \qquad \text{since} \qquad \langle n \rangle = \nu \tag{3.4.28}$$

and

$$\langle \langle (m - n)^2 \rangle_1 \rangle = 2\nu p. \tag{3.4.29}$$

Equation (3.4.28) is, of course, to be expected; it simply states the fact that the mean values of two consecutive observations should be the same. This result follows, of course, from the initial assumption that the diffusion is in equilibrium, so that n is a stationary random process (see Chapter 4).

Both equations (3.4.28) and (3.4.29) provide a means of testing the theory of the probability after-effect. Elegant and thorough experiments were performed by Svedberg and by Westgren (17,18), which test Smoluchowski's theory. We shall discuss briefly the results of Westgren's experiments, which were obtained with an experimental arrangement designed specifically with the theory in mind. Westgren set up his experiment in such a way that a volume of fluid of linear dimensions of a few microns, and containing colloidal gold particles of radius approximately 50,000 A., was viewed in an ultramicroscope. The illumination was steady and the number of particles in view was counted at successive instants measured by the ticking of a metronome. Westgren performed experiments with different concentrations of particles, different sizes of volume v, and different time intervals. Each experiment consisted of about 1500 observations. Below we give a sample of 114 consecutive observations for which the time interval $\tau = 0.81$ sec.:

$$\begin{array}{l}023132001121323112351214234323111010214323242235341325323360 2\\ 235413244234230321111221001232100001121232343120210 11. \end{array} \tag{3.4.30}$$

The average value of n for this sample is $\nu = 2.018$. The theoretical number of occurrences of different values of n for a Poisson distribution of this average are displayed in Table 3.1. The agreement is seen to be good. The experimental arrangements under which the sample

TABLE 3.1

Experimental Verification of the Poisson Distribution

n	Obs.	Calc.
0	15	15
1	29	31
2	30	31
3	25	21
4	10	10
5	4	4
6	1	1

(3.4.30) was obtained correspond to a value of the probability after-effect factor p of 0.613. From equation (3.4.29) and the sample, the observed value is 0.582. From the theory of errors we would expect a fractional variation in possible values of $\mathcal{O}((114)^{-\frac{1}{2}}) \sim 9\%$, and the observed value is well within this limit. We may also estimate p from equation (3.4.26) for each value of n. The results are less accurate since only parts of the sample are used each time; we do not give them here, but remark that, although it is possible that negative values of p could be obtained for unusual sequences, this does not, in fact, occur. We may interpret this as a measure of the strength of the regression law (3.4.26).

Despite the fact that regression is very much in evidence, theory shows, and observation confirms, that time symmetry is maintained. Let $H(n, n + k)$ denote the probability that the pair $(n, n + k)$ is observed consecutively. Then it can be shown that

$$\begin{aligned} H(n, n + k) &= w(n)K(n \mid n + k) \\ &= w(n + k)K(n + k \mid n) \\ &= H(n + k, n), \end{aligned} \tag{3.4.31}$$

which is achieved by a rearrangement of factors between the full expressions for $w(n)$ and $K(n \mid n + k)$. This result can be extended to show that the probability of observing the pair (n,m) at instants separated by $s\tau$ is also symmetrical. Thus, we conclude that the sequence of observations is statistically unaltered by time reversal, and this is borne out by the sample fairly well, considering its small size, as shown in Table 3.2. Nevertheless, it is still true that if $n > \nu$ the probability of the pair (n,m) is larger for $m < n$ than for $m > n$.

We have seen how a state different from the average tends to regress towards the average, and now come to the question of how soon this state may recur. (Note that an error has been pointed out in the discussion of this point in Chandrasekhar's article (12), by Bartlett (19), unless the number of possible states is restricted to two.)

Let T_n be the average lifetime of a state n, and let Θ_n be the average recurrence time of that state; then T_n and Θ_n are related in a simple way. If, in any long time T, the system spends intervals $t_1, t_2 \cdots t_N$ (N very large) in the state n, then

$$w(n) = \lim_{N\to\infty} \frac{1}{T} \sum_{i=1}^{N} t_i \tag{3.4.32}$$

TABLE 3.2

Number of Occurrences of Pairs (n,m) for Interval τ, in the Sample (3.4.30) (Top Rows); Calculated Value from equation (3.4.31) (Bottom Rows)

$n \backslash m$	0	1	2	3	4	5
0	4	5	4	1	—	—
	4	*5*	*3*	*1*	—	—
1	5	9	8	3	2	—
	5	*10*	*8*	*4*	*2*	—
2	2	8	3	14	2	1
	3	*8*	*9*	*6*	*3*	*1*
3	1	4	11	1	4	3
	1	*4*	*6*	*5*	*3*	*1*
4	—	2	4	3	1	—
	—	*2*	*3*	*3*	*2*	*1*
5	—	1	—	2	1	—
	—	—	*1*	*1*	*1*	—

and

$$T_n = \operatorname*{Lim}_{N\to\infty} \frac{1}{N}\sum_{i=1}^{N} t_i \simeq \frac{T}{N}\, w(n) \qquad \text{for large} \qquad T,N. \tag{3.4.33}$$

The time spent not in state n is

$$T - \sum_{i=1}^{N} t_i$$

and, therefore,

$$\frac{1}{T}\left(T - \sum_{i=1}^{N} t_i\right) = 1 - w(n). \tag{3.4.34}$$

The average recurrence time of state n is, therefore, from equation (3.4.34),

$$\Theta_n = \frac{1}{N}\left(T - \sum_{i=1}^{N} t_i\right)$$

since the state n has recurred N times. Hence,

$$\Theta_n = \frac{1 - w(n)}{w(n)}\, T_n. \tag{3.4.35}$$

We now calculate T_n following Smoluchowski's work. Since $K(n \mid n)$ is the probability that the state n will be observed on two successive occasions, the probability that the state n will be observed on $(k - 1)$ successive occasions and not on the kth is

$$\phi_n(k\tau) = K^{k-1}(n \mid n)(1 - K(n \mid n)). \tag{3.4.36}$$

We can define the average lifetime in a natural way, as

$$\begin{aligned} T_n &= \sum_{k=1}^{\infty} k\tau\phi_n(k\tau) \\ &= \tau\left(\sum_{k=1}^{\infty} kK^{k-1}(n \mid n)\right)(1 - K(n \mid n)) \\ &= \frac{\tau}{1 - K(n \mid n)}, \end{aligned} \tag{3.4.37}$$

where we have used the result

$$\frac{d}{dK}(1 - K)^{-1} = (1 - K)^{-2} = \sum_{k=1}^{\infty} kK^{k-1}. \tag{3.4.38}$$

The observed average lifetimes and recurrence times for the sample (3.4.30) are displayed in Table 3.3; agreement between theory and experiment is again satisfactory.

If it were possible we should also calculate other moments of the distribution of recurrence times, but the solution to this problem is not known. It is simple, however, to write down the expression for the probability distribution of recurrence times. A state n is said to recur, with recurrence time $\theta_n(k)$ if a sequence of values of the variable $(n, i_1, i_2, \cdots, i_{k-1}, n)$ occurs such that $i_j \neq n$ for any j $(1 \leqslant j \leqslant k - 1)$. This includes sequences, all of which are either above or below n, and also sequences which jump from above to below, or vice versa. The probability of any single sequence is clearly

$$K(n \mid i_1)K(i_1 \mid i_2) \cdots K(i_{k-1} \mid n),$$

and the probability that the recurrence time θ_n is $k\tau$ is

$$\text{prob.}\,(\theta_n = k\tau) = \sum_{\substack{\text{all } i_j \neq n \\ (1 \leqslant j \leqslant k-1)}} K(n \mid i_1)K(i_1 \quad i_2) \cdots K(i_{k-1} \mid n), \qquad k > 1. \tag{3.4.39}$$

Unfortunately, only the first moment (i.e., Θ_n) of equation (3.4.39) is known.

TABLE 3.3

Average Lifetime T_n and Recurrence Time Θ_n of the State n for the Sample (3.4.30); Observed Values (Top Rows) Calculated Values (Bottom Rows)

n	T_n	Θ_n
0	1.5	11.67
	1.41	*9.20*
1	1.45	5.20
	1.49	*4.06*
2	1.125	3.92
	1.42	*3.83*
3	1.08	4.91
	1.31	*5.88*
4	1.33	10
	1.21	*11.97*
5	1	14.67
	1.13	*25.98*

So far we have only discussed the case of intermittent observations. In order to study the relation between the recurrence of mechanical and thermodynamic states we now extend the theory to the case of continuous observations. We must require that the numbers involved are so large that we may ignore the discrete nature of the process, and treat it as continuous. We consider this extension as the limit $\tau \to 0$. Then we must expect $p(\tau) \to 0$ and $K(n \mid n) \to 1$. From the formula for $K(n \mid n)$ we, therefore, select the leading term ($i = 0$):

$$K(n \mid n) = e^{-\nu p}(1 - p)^n + O(p^2)$$
$$= 1 - (n + \nu)p. \tag{3.4.40}$$

Hence, the mean lifetime becomes

$$T_n = \frac{\tau}{(n + \nu)p}, \tag{3.4.41}$$

and in order that this should tend to a finite limit we must have $p(\tau) \to p_0\tau$ for small τ. This is easily seen to be the case if one considers

TABLE 3.4

Recurrence Times for a 1% Deviation in the Density of Oxygen in a Sphere of Radius a at 300°K (ν/v) = 3.10[19] cm.[-3])

a (cm.)	1	$5 \cdot 10^{-5}$	$3 \cdot 10^{-5}$	$2.5 \cdot 10^{-5}$	10^{-5}
Θ (sec.)	$10^{10^{14}}$	10^{68}	10^{6}	1	10^{-11}

the example of the number of gas molecules in a given volume. As $\tau \to 0$ we may ignore the effects of collisions and treat the relevant part of the trajectories of the molecules as linear. Then the number leaving the volume element in a time τ is equal to the number striking the surface in that time and is obviously proportional to τ. It is a simple calculation in kinetic theory.

In the limit of large numbers the Poisson distribution tends to a Gaussian distribution near its peak*:

$$w(n) = (2\pi\nu)^{-\frac{1}{2}} \exp\left(-\frac{(n-\nu)^2}{2\nu}\right); \qquad |n - \nu| \ll \nu. \quad (3.4.42)$$

Equation (3.4.35) then becomes, with equation (3.4.41),

$$\Theta \simeq \frac{v}{\sigma}\left(\frac{m}{kT}\right)^{\frac{1}{2}} \nu^{-\frac{1}{2}} \exp\left(\frac{(n-\nu)^2}{2\nu}\right), \quad (3.4.43)$$

where v and σ are the volume and surface area of the volume considered, m the mass of a gas molecule, and T the absolute temperature. Values of Θ calculated for a 1% deviation in the density of oxygen in a sphere of radius a at 300°K are displayed in Table 3.4. It is at once clear that

* This is easily seen by writing

$$\begin{aligned} \ln w(n) &= n \ln \nu - \nu - \ln n! \\ &= n \ln \nu - \nu - (n + \tfrac{1}{2}) \ln n + n - \tfrac{1}{2} \ln 2\pi + O(n^{-1}), \end{aligned}$$

where we have used Stirling's formula for log $n!$. If

$$\delta = n - \nu$$

and we restrict n so that $(\delta/\nu) \ll 1$ then

$$\begin{aligned} \ln w(n) &= -(\nu + \delta + \tfrac{1}{2}) \ln\left(1 + \frac{\delta}{\nu}\right) + \delta - \tfrac{1}{2} \ln 2\pi\nu + O(n^{-1}) \\ &\simeq -\delta^2/2\nu - \tfrac{1}{2} \ln 2\pi\nu, \end{aligned}$$

whence

$$w(n) = (2\pi\nu)^{-\frac{1}{2}} \exp\left(-\frac{(n-\nu)^2}{2\nu}\right); \qquad |n - \nu| \ll \nu.$$

for volumes just at the limit of unaided visual perception even quite small fluctuations have large recurrence times, so that diffusion is to all intents and purposes an irreversible process. On the other hand, for volumes just at the limit of microscopic vision, large fluctuations occur rapidly, and there is no question of irreversibility in the usual sense. Nevertheless, we have seen from a study of such fluctuations that the results are, on average, in accordance with the macroscopic theory of diffusion.

In this section we have been concerned with, in effect, the singlet number density. In the terms of reference of Section 3.3.B, this is the lowest order reduced distribution function. However small the number of particles considered, it has been possible to discern both the time symmetry (of the sequence of occupation numbers) and the regression towards the mean. If the initial state is sufficiently far from the mean then its recurrence time is extremely long. Alternatively, the recurrence time of a fixed fractional deviation from the mean becomes extremely long as the mean itself increases. The case of the number of gas molecules within a spherical volume discussed above is a striking example of this. It is clear then, that on the gross level of ordinary observation, which might be called the hydrodynamic level in the sense that the numbers of particles considered are always large enough that local thermodynamic variables may be defined, a significant fluctuation has so long a recurrence time that *for practical purposes* it decays irreversibly to equilibrium. Given an ensemble of replica systems, in each of which a prescribed volume element initially contains, say, an excess (over the average number) of particles, a distribution function for the number of particles instantaneously in the volume can be defined. This distribution function satisfies the singular initial delta-function condition and approaches its equilibrium form in a time of the order of that taken by a typical fluctuation to decay. The distribution function remains in its equilibrium form, and does not revert to its initial form if the system is undisturbed. The probability of a fluctuation of the size of the initial value, as calculated from the equilibrium distribution function, is then directly related to its recurrence time. We say then that the distribution function has approached equilibrium irreversibly.*

* This does not mean that the system is not reversible in the sense that reversal of all velocities at any time t after the initial ensemble is set up at 0 leads again to the initial state at $2t$. See Section 7.2.

REFERENCES

1. Goldstein, H., *Classical Mechanics*, Addison-Wesley, Reading, Mass., 1952.
2. Khinchin, A. I., *Mathematical Foundations of Statistical Mechanics*, Dover, New York, 1949.
3. Gibbs, J. W., *Elementary Principles of Statistical Mechanics*, Vol. II of Collected Works, Yale University Press, New Haven, Conn., 1948.
4. Ehrenfest, P., and T. Ehrenfest, *The Conceptual Foundations of the Statistical Approach in Mechanics*, Cornell University Press, New York, 1959.
5. The following example is also discussed by T. Y. Wu and R. L. Rosenberg, *Helv. Phys. Acta*, **34,** 661 (1961).
6. Doob, J. L., *Ann. Math.*, **43,** 351 (1492); see also, *Selected Papers on Noise and Stochastic Processes*, N. Wax, ed., Dover, New York, 1954.
7. Von Kampen, N. G., *Fundamental Problems in Statistical Mechanics*, E. D. G. Cohen, ed., North-Holland Publishing Company, 1962.
8. Hahn, E. L., *Phys. Rev.*, **80,** 580 (1950).
9. Grad, H., *Handbuch der Physik*, Vol. XII, Springer-Verlag, Berlin, 1958, p. 205.
10. Mayer, J. E., *J. Chem. Phys.*, **33,** 1484 (1960); **34,** 261 (1961).
11. Poincaré, H., *Les Methodes Nouvelles de la Mécanique Céleste*, Dover, New York, 1957.
12. Chandrasekhar, S., *Rev. Mod. Phys.*, **15,** 1 (1943); see also ref. 6.
13. Kac, M., "Some Stochastic Problems in Physics and Mathematics," *Colloquium Lectures in Pure and Applied Science*, Vol. 2, 1956, Field Research Laboratory, Socony-Mobil Oil Company, Dallas, Texas.
14. Hemmer, P. C., L. C. Maximon, and H. Wergeland, *Phys. Rev.*, **111,** 689 (1958).
15. Kac, M., *Phys. Rev.*, **115,** 1 (1959).
16. Smoluchowski, M. v., *Physik. Z.*, **17,** 557, 585 (1916).
17. Svedberg, T., *Z. Physik. Chem.*, **77,** 147 (1911).
18. Westgren, A., *Arkiv Matematik, Astronomi och Fysik*, **11,** Nos. 8, 14 (1916); **13,** No. 14 (1918).
19. Bartlett, M. S., *Nature*, **165,** 727 (1950).

CHAPTER 4

Markov Processes and Brownian Motion

4.1. INTRODUCTION

In Chapter 3 it was shown that despite the time reversibility of the Liouville equation (3.2.19) irreversible behavior may be exhibited by the class of systems in which we are interested (namely, those capable of supporting transport processes) because the time scale of observation is minute compared to that of the recurrence of macroscopic fluctuations. It is possible, *in principle*, to have a theory of transport processes based upon a solution of the Liouville equation. Indeed, the formal theories developed on this basis are reviewed in Chapter 7. The fact that it is far outside the realm of possibility (and entirely unnecessary) to deal explicitly with the order of 10^{23} degrees of freedom means that a theory must be developed in terms of a reduced description in order to lead to numerical results. The fluid systems discussed in this book are those in which the molecules can be regarded as particles with no internal degrees of freedom interacting with pairwise additive potentials, so that all thermodynamic and transport properties can be calculated from a knowledge of the two molecule distribution function.

The equations of motion of the twelve degrees of freedom of a two molecule subsystem can be written down immediately from equation (3.2.1), but clearly they involve the remaining $6(N-2)$ degrees of freedom of the system explicitly. The method of the theory presented in Chapter 5 is to introduce a probability ansatz, or statistical hypothesis, to represent the effect of the $6(N-2)$ degrees of freedom which we do not need to know and cannot handle explicitly. Thus, we obtain equations of motion containing terms about which we can only make statistical statements, or, equivalently, equations for the distribution functions containing terms which represent the statistical effect of the rest of the system. The phase of the two molecule subsystem is thereby represented as a certain type of random process. In this chapter, we discuss the development of the statistical mechanical theory from the point of view of the (relevant) theory of random processes.

4.2. GENERAL RANDOM PROCESSES (1,2)

4.2.A. *Classification of Random Processes*

A random process, $y(t)$, defines a variable y which does not depend in a completely definite way on the independent argument, t. The process may be classified in two ways, according to what we may call its representation and its order.

The representation of the process is the set of states available to the process for each value of the independent variable (argument). Thus, the process is said to be discrete if the set of states can be put into one to one correspondence with the positive integers, and continuous if it cannot. The independent variable may also assume discrete, or continuous values. For instance, the diffusion of colloid particles studied in Section 3.3.C is a discrete process defined on discrete time. On the other hand, the density fluctuations, actually a discrete process defined on continuous time, were treated as a continuous process defined on continuous time. The phase of a Brownian particle (a six-component process) and a two molecule subsystem are true continuous processes defined on continuous time. We shall confine our attention to this case, presently.

The order of a random process is a measure of its complexity. In general, the random process is completely specified by a set of probability distributions: $P_1(y_1t_1)\,dy_1$ is the probability that y is found in the range $(y_1, y_1 + dy_1)$ at time t_1, where $y_n = y(t_n)$, $P_2(y_1t_1;y_2t_2)\,dy_1\,dy_2$ is the joint probability that y is found in the range $(y_1, y_1 + dy_1)$ at t_1 and in the range $(y_2, y_2 + dy_2)$ at t_2, $P_3(y_1t_1;y_2t_2;y_3t_3)\,dy_1\,dy_2\,dy_3$ is the joint probability that y is found in the range $(y_1, y_1 + dy_1)$ at t_1, in $(y_2, y_2 + dy_2)$ at t_2, and in $(y_3, y_3 + dy_3)$ at t_3, and so on.

These probability distributions must satisfy the following conditions:

(*a*) $P_n \geqslant 0$,

(*b*) $P_n(y_1t_1; \cdots y_nt_n)$ is a symmetric function* of the set of variables $y_1, \cdots, y_n$, and

$$\text{(c)}\quad P_k(y_1t_1; \cdots ; y_kt_k) = \int \cdots \int P_n(y_1t_1; \cdots ; y_nt_n)\,dy_{k+1} \cdots dy_n, \tag{4.2.1}$$

* If we fix y_j for all $j \neq i$ then $P_n(y_1t_1; \cdots y_it_i; \cdots y_nt_n)\,dy_i$ is the probability that y is found in the range $(y_i, y_i + dy_i)$ *given* the values of $(y_1, \cdots, y_{i-1}, y_{i+1}, \cdots, y_n)$. This must be true for all i.

since each function P_n must imply all the reduced functions $P_k(k < n)$. The set of functions $P_1 \cdots P_n$ constitutes a hierarchy which, in general, describes the random process in successively greater detail.

The set of probability distributions provides a convenient scheme for classifying the random process.

(*a*) The process may be called a pure random, or completely random, process if

$$P_2(y_1t_1;y_2t_2) = P_1(y_1t_1)P_1(y_2t_2), \tag{4.2.2}$$

because the successive values of y are not correlated: all the information about the process is contained in P_1. When t is discrete it is easy to give examples of such processes. For instance, if the number of colloid particles (cf. Sec. 3.3.C) is observed at intervals of τ so long that $p \to 1$ then we have from equation (3.3.17),

$$\begin{aligned} A_i^{(n)} &= 0 \qquad i \neq n \\ &= 1 \qquad i = n \end{aligned} \tag{4.2.3}$$

so that, from equation (3.3.19)

$$\begin{aligned} \lim_{p\to 1} K(n \mid n + k) &= E_{n+k}(p = 1) \\ &= w(n + k). \end{aligned} \tag{4.2.4}$$

Consequently,

$$\begin{aligned} \lim_{p\to 1} H(n,m) &= \lim_{p\to 1} w(n)K(n \mid m) \\ &= w(n)w(m). \end{aligned} \tag{4.2.5}$$

If t is continuous one would expect that the values of y for times separated by a small interval become correlated as the interval becomes smaller. An exception to this occurs in the idealized study of Brownian motion, where it appears that the fluctuating force [see Eq. (4.5.28)] is a pathological function, discontinuous for every instant of time.

(*b*) The next most complicated process, and the one with which we shall be mainly concerned, is that in which all the information is contained in P_2. It is called a Markov process. It is convenient to introduce the conditional probability $K_1(y_1t_1 \mid y_2t_2)\, dy_2$ that y is found in the range $(y_2, y_2 + dy_2)$ at t_2, if y had the value y_1 at t_1. Accordingly, one has

$$P_2(y_1t_1;y_2t_2) = P_1(y_1t_1)K_1(y_1t_1 \mid y_2t_2). \tag{4.2.6}$$

K_1 must obviously fulfill the relations

$$K_1(y_1t_1 \mid y_2t_2) \geqslant 0,$$
$$\int K_1(y_1t_1 \mid y_2t_2)\, dy_2 = 1, \tag{4.2.7}$$

and, of course,

$$\int P_1(y_1t_1)K_1(y_1t_1 \mid y_2t_2)\, dy_1 = P_1(y_2t_2). \tag{4.2.8}$$

If periodicities, such as signals in the presence of noise, are excluded from consideration, then one also has

$$\operatorname*{Lim}_{|t_1-t_2|\to\infty} K_1(y_1t_1 \mid y_2t_2) = P_1(y_2t_2).$$

Since the Markov process is completely specified by P_2, the conditional probability that y lies in the range $(y_n, y_n + dy_n)$ at t_n given that y had the values $y_1, y_2, \cdots, y_{n-1}$ at times $t_1, t_2, \cdots, t_{n-1}$, depends only on y_{n-1}:

$$K_{n-1}(y_1t_1; y_2t_2; \cdots; y_{n-1}t_{n-1} \mid y_nt_n) = K_1(y_{n-1}t_{n-1} \mid y_nt_n). \tag{4.2.9}$$

Equation (4.2.9) states that, given the state of a Markov process at some time $t_{n-1}(<t_n)$, the future of the process (i.e., the value at t_n) is independent of all states the process has occupied at prior times. Equation (4.2.9) is often used as the definition of the Markov process since it is equivalent to the earlier statement that the process is of second order.

(*c*) Higher order processes; the next most complicated process is completely specified by P_3, and so on. Very few examples of such non-Markovian processes are studied in physics. *If a process is non-Markovian, then it can often be considered to be the projection of a higher-dimensional Markov process.* We shall find that this observation gives an important insight into the development of the statistical mechanical theory.

A final subsidiary classification of great importance is that of *stationarity*: such a characterization is applicable when the statistical character of the process is invariant to a change of the origin of the time or to a translation in time. Thus,

$$P_1(y_1t_1) = P_1(y_1)$$
$$P_2(y_1t_1; y_2t_2) = P_2(y_1, y_2; t_2 - t_1), \quad \text{etc.} \tag{4.2.10}$$

4.2.B. *Moments and Correlation Functions* (1)

An alternative description equivalent to specifying a random process by means of its distribution is to specify the set of all moments. For instance, the moments of a Markov process are

$$\langle y_1 \rangle = \iint y_1 P_2(y_1 t_1; y_2 t_2)\, dy_1\, dy_2$$

$$\langle y_2 \rangle = \iint y_2 P_2(y_1 t_1; y_2 t_2)\, dy_1\, dy_2. \tag{4.2.11}$$

If the process is stationary then, by equation (4.2.10),

$$\langle y_1 \rangle = \langle y_2 \rangle.$$

The second moments are

$$\mu_{jk}^{(2)} = \iint (y_1 - \langle y_1 \rangle)^j (y_2 - \langle y_2 \rangle)^k P_2(y_1 t_1; y_2 t_2)\, dy_1\, dy_2, \qquad (j + k = 2). \tag{4.2.12}$$

There are three second moments. The moments $\mu_{20}^{(2)}$ and $\mu_{02}^{(2)}$ are the mean-square deviations, and are equal if the process is stationary. The moment $\mu_{11}^{(2)}$ is related to the autocorrelation function of y, $\psi(t_1,t_2)$, by

$$\psi(t_1,t_2) = \frac{\mu_{11}^{(2)}}{(\mu_{20}^{(2)} \mu_{02}^{(2)})^{1/2}}. \tag{4.2.13}$$

If the process is stationary, equation (4.2.13) simplifies to

$$\psi(t_2 - t_1) = \frac{\mu_{11}^{(2)}}{\mu_{20}^{(2)}} = \frac{\mu_{11}^{(2)}}{\mu_{02}^{(2)}}. \tag{4.2.14}$$

Higher moments are defined in an analogous way; so are also the moments of higher order processes.

Consider now the characteristic function $\mathscr{P}(\omega_1,\omega_2)$ of $P_2(y_1 t_1; y_2 t_2)$. This is defined by

$$\mathscr{P}(\omega_1,\omega_2) = \iint \exp\,[i(\omega_1 y_1 + \omega_2 y_2)] P_2(y_1 t_1; y_2 t_2)\, dy_1\, dy_2. \tag{4.2.15}$$

The reader will recognize this as the moment-generating function of Section 2.3.C with imaginary ξ. It is also the Fourier transform of P_2, and hence if $\mathscr{P}(\omega_1,\omega_2)$ is known, P_2 can be calculated from the inversion

$$P_2(y_1t_1;y_2t_2) = \frac{1}{(2\pi)^2}\iint_{-\infty}^{\infty} \exp\,[-i(\omega_1 y_1 + \omega_2 y_2)]\mathscr{P}(\omega_1,\omega_2)\, d\omega_1\, d\omega_2. \tag{4.2.16}$$

Now, equation (4.2.15) may be rewritten as

$$\mathscr{P}(\omega_1,\omega_2) = e^{i(\omega_1\langle y_1\rangle+\omega_2\langle y_2\rangle)} \times \iint e^{i(\omega_1[y_1-\langle y_1\rangle]+\omega_2[y_2-\langle y_2\rangle])} P_2(y_1t_1;y_2t_2)\, dy_1\, dy_2$$

$$= e^{i(\omega_1\langle y_1\rangle+\omega_2\langle y_2\rangle)} \sum_j \sum_k \frac{(i\omega_1)^j}{j!}\frac{(i\omega_2)^k}{k!}\mu_{jk}^{(j+k)}. \tag{4.2.17}$$

Thus, the characteristic function may be found if the moments are known.

The first and second moments are frequently of most interest in a physical context, the first giving the average value of the variable, and the second the magnitude of the fluctuations. For instance, the first moment of the momentum distribution function of the molecules at some point in a fluid yields the fluid flow velocity, while the second yields a measure of the temperature. The example cited refers to a three-dimensional variable, or vector, and the moments will have the form of a vector (first moment), a matrix (second moment), and, in general, an n-dimensional array (nth moment).

Finally, we point out that according to the tenets of information theory, if some but not all of the moments are known, then the best estimate of the unknown moments can be obtained from the distribution which gives the known moments correctly and also maximizes the "information-entropy" I, which is given by

$$I = -\int P \ln P\, dy. \tag{4.2.18}$$

4.3. MARKOV PROCESSES

In what follows we focus attention on the treatment of physical processes of interest as Markov processes. It will emerge that it would be advantageous to consider non-Markovian processes, but no such theory has yet been developed to a sufficient level to permit either numerical calculations of transport coefficients, or a detailed theoretical assessment of the Markovian approximation.

4.3.A. *The Markov Integral Equation* (2)

A special case of equation (4.2.1) for which $n = 3$, is

$$P_2(y_1t_1;y_3t_3) = \int P_3(y_1t_1;y_2t_2;y_3t_3)\,dy_2. \tag{4.3.1}$$

If y is a Markov process, then by definition we have

$$\begin{aligned} P_3(y_1t_1;y_2t_2;y_3t_3) &= P_1(y_1t_1)K_1(y_1t_1 \mid y_2t_2)K_2(y_1t_1;\, y_2t_2 \mid y_3t_3) \\ &= P_1(y_1t_1)K_1(y_1t_1 \mid y_2t_2)K_1(y_2t_2 \mid y_3t_3), \end{aligned} \tag{4.3.2}$$

and substitution of this in equation (4.3.1), followed by cancellation of $P_1(y_1t_1)$ from both sides, yields

$$K_1(y_1t_1 \mid y_3t_3) = \int K_1(y_1t_1 \mid y_2t_2)K_1(y_2t_2 \mid y_3t_3)\,dy_2. \tag{4.3.3}$$

Equation (4.3.3) is Markov's integral equation, sometimes referred to as the Chapman-Kolmogorov equation. In our subsequent study of Brownian motion and molecular motion in liquids we shall be concerned, in the distribution function approach, with stationary processes. The notation of equation (4.3.3) may then be simplified to

$$K_1(y_1 \mid y;\, t) = \int K_1(y_1 \mid y_0;\, t_0)K_1(y_0 \mid y;\, t - t_0)\,dy_0. \tag{4.3.4}$$

Equation (4.3.4) [and equation (4.3.3)] expresses the fact that the probability that the variable is in the state y at time t is the sum of the probabilities that it was in state y_0 at some time $t_0(<t)$ and underwent a transition from y_0 to y in the interval $(t - t_0)$. Such a statement is, of course, true of any random process. The Markovian nature of the process is expressed in the assumed form of K_1.

4.3.B. *Gaussian Markov Processes: Two Theorems* (2)

Let $\mathbf{y} = (y_1, \cdots, y_s)$ be an s-dimensional Gaussian random process. At the moment we are not concerned whether the y_i are the values of y at successive time points in a Markov process, whether they are the simultaneous values of s variables, or a combination. In general, the y_i are correlated, so that the distribution function $P(\mathbf{y})$ has the form (Gaussian process)

$$P(\mathbf{y}) = C \exp(-\tfrac{1}{2}\tilde{\mathbf{y}} \cdot \mathbf{A} \cdot \mathbf{y}), \tag{4.3.5}$$

where $\tilde{\mathbf{y}}$ is the transpose of $\mathbf{y}$. C is a normalization constant determined by the condition

$$\int P(\mathbf{y})\, d\mathbf{y} = 1. \tag{4.3.6}$$

We now introduce a transformation matrix $\mathbf{B}$ such that

$$\mathbf{y} = \mathbf{B} \cdot \boldsymbol{\xi}, \tag{4.3.7}$$

which diagonalizes $\mathbf{A}$:

$$\tilde{\mathbf{y}} \cdot \mathbf{A} \cdot \mathbf{y} = \tilde{\boldsymbol{\xi}} \cdot \boldsymbol{\lambda} \cdot \boldsymbol{\xi}, \tag{4.3.8}$$

where

$$\boldsymbol{\lambda} = \tilde{\mathbf{B}} \cdot \mathbf{A} \cdot \mathbf{B} \tag{4.3.9}$$

is a diagonal matrix with elements λ_i. From equation (4.3.7) we see that $P(\mathbf{y})$ in equation (4.3.5) may now be written as

$$P(\mathbf{y}) = Q(\boldsymbol{\xi}) = C \exp\left(-\frac{1}{2}\sum_i \lambda_i \xi_i^2\right). \tag{4.3.10}$$

Since cross products $\xi_i \xi_j$ do not appear in the exponent, the integration of the normalization condition (4.3.6) can be carried out independently for each ξ_i. The Jacobian of the transformation $\mathbf{y} \rightarrow \boldsymbol{\xi}$ is

$$\begin{aligned} J(\mathbf{y},\boldsymbol{\xi}) &= \frac{\partial(y_1, \cdots, y_s)}{\partial(\xi_1, \cdots, \xi_s)} \\ &= |B|, \end{aligned} \tag{4.3.11}$$

where $|B|$ is the determinant of $\mathbf{B}$, so that the left-hand side of equation (4.3.6) becomes

$$\begin{aligned} \int P(\mathbf{y})\, d\mathbf{y} &= C\,|B| \int \exp\left(-\frac{1}{2}\sum_i \lambda_i \xi_i^2\right) d\boldsymbol{\xi} \\ &= C\,|B| \left(\prod_{i=1}^{s} \lambda_i^{-1/2}\right)(2\pi)^{s/2}. \end{aligned} \tag{4.3.12}$$

Now, from the properties of determinants,

$$|\tilde{B}| = |B|$$

and

$$|\lambda| = \prod_{i=1}^{s} \lambda_i$$
$$= |B|^2 \, |A|, \qquad (4.3.13)$$

so that equation (4.3.6) is satisfied if

$$C(2\pi)^{s/2} \, |B| = |\lambda|^{1/2}$$

and

$$C = (2\pi)^{-s/2} \, |A|^{1/2}. \qquad (4.3.14)$$

The physical significance of the matrix **A** can be seen by calculating the correlation matrix $\langle \mathbf{y}\tilde{\mathbf{y}} \rangle$, where

$$\langle \mathbf{y}\tilde{\mathbf{y}} \rangle = \begin{pmatrix} \langle y_1^2 \rangle & \langle y_1 y_2 \rangle & \cdots \\ \langle y_2 y_1 \rangle & \langle y_2^2 \rangle & \cdots \\ \langle y_3 y_1 \rangle & \cdots & \end{pmatrix}, \qquad (4.3.15)$$

and

$$\langle \varphi \rangle = \int \varphi P(\mathbf{y}) \, d\mathbf{y}. \qquad (4.3.16)$$

From the definition (4.3.7) of $\boldsymbol{\xi}$, we have

$$\langle \mathbf{y}\tilde{\mathbf{y}} \rangle = \langle \mathbf{B} \cdot \boldsymbol{\xi}\tilde{\boldsymbol{\xi}} \cdot \tilde{\mathbf{B}} \rangle$$
$$= \mathbf{B} \cdot \langle \boldsymbol{\xi}\tilde{\boldsymbol{\xi}} \rangle \cdot \tilde{\mathbf{B}}. \qquad (4.3.17)$$

The distribution function $Q(\boldsymbol{\xi})$ [equation (4.3.10)] is diagonal in $\boldsymbol{\xi}$ so that $\langle \boldsymbol{\xi}\tilde{\boldsymbol{\xi}} \rangle$ is a diagonal matrix with elements $\langle \xi_i \xi_j \rangle = \lambda_i^{-1} \, \delta_{ij}$. It follows from the multiplicative properties of diagonal matrices that

$$\langle \boldsymbol{\xi}\tilde{\boldsymbol{\xi}} \rangle = \boldsymbol{\lambda}^{-1}, \qquad (4.3.18)$$

so that from equations (4.3.9,17,18) we find

$$\langle \mathbf{y}\tilde{\mathbf{y}} \rangle = \mathbf{A}^{-1} = \mathbf{D} = \|d_{ij}\|. \qquad (4.3.19)$$

The distribution function P may now be written in the form

$$P(\mathbf{y}) = ((2\pi)^s \, |D|)^{-1/2} \exp\left(- \frac{1}{2\,|D|} \sum_{i,j} d^{ij} y_i y_j \right), \qquad (4.3.20)$$

where d^{ij} is the cofactor of d_{ij} in the matrix **D**.

Suppose now that P is the second order distribution function for a stationary Markov process. The vector $\mathbf{y}$ is divided into two n-dimensional vectors $\mathbf{y}(t_1)$, $\mathbf{y}(t_2)$. Denoting the components of $\mathbf{y}(t_1)$ as $(z_1, \cdots, z_n)$ and of $\mathbf{y}(t_2)$ as $(z_{n+1}, \cdots, z_{2n})$, we have

$$P_2(\mathbf{y}(t_1);\mathbf{y}(t_2)) = ((2\pi)^{2n} \, |D^{(2)}|)^{-\frac{1}{2}} \exp\left(-\frac{1}{2}\sum_{i,j=1}^{2n} a_{ij}^{(2)} z_i z_j\right), \quad (4.3.21)$$

where $\mathbf{A}^{(2)} = \mathbf{D}^{(2)-1}$ as before. From equation (4.3.19), $\mathbf{D}^{(2)}$ may be written in the form of an array of $(n \times n)$ submatrices $\mathbf{R}(0)$, $\mathbf{R}(t_1 - t_2)$, $\mathbf{R}(t_2 - t_1)$ as

$$\mathbf{D}^{(2)}(t_2 - t_1) = \begin{pmatrix} \mathbf{R}(0) & \mathbf{R}(t_2 - t_1) \\ \mathbf{R}(t_1 - t_2) & \mathbf{R}(0) \end{pmatrix}, \quad (4.3.22)$$

where $\mathbf{R}(0)$ is the variance (or mean square deviation) matrix of $\mathbf{y}$ and $\mathbf{R}(t)$ is its autocorrelation matrix for an interval of time t. From the stationary property of the process we may deduce that

$$\begin{aligned} \langle y_i(t_1) y_j(t_1 + t_2 - t_1)\rangle &= \langle y_i(2t_1 - t_2) y_j(t_1)\rangle \\ &= \langle y_i(t_1) y_j(t_1 - [t_2 - t_1])\rangle, \end{aligned} \quad (4.3.23)$$

by translation of the origin of time through $t_2 - t_1$, so that

$$\mathbf{R}(t_2 - t_1) = \tilde{\mathbf{R}}(t_1 - t_2). \quad (4.3.24)$$

The use of (4.3.24) in (4.3.22) shows that $\mathbf{D}^{(2)}$ is symmetric:

$$\mathbf{D}^{(2)}(t_2 - t_1) = \mathbf{D}^{(2)}(t_1 - t_2). \quad (4.3.25)$$

If P_3 is the third order distribution function for the process at the instants t_1, t_2, t_3, then

$$\begin{aligned} P_3(\mathbf{y}(t_1);\mathbf{y}(t_2);\mathbf{y}(t_3)) &= ((2\pi)^{3n} \, |D^{(2)}|)^{-\frac{1}{2}} \\ &\quad \times \exp\left(-\frac{1}{2}\sum_{i,j=1}^{3n} a_{ij}^{(3)} z_i z_j\right), \end{aligned} \quad (4.3.26)$$

where we have extended the notation of equation (4.3.21) in an obvious way. According to the definition (4.2.6) of $K_1(\mathbf{y}(t_1) \mid \mathbf{y}(t_2))$, the quotient

$$\frac{P_3(\mathbf{y}(t_1),\mathbf{y}(t_2),\mathbf{y}(t_3))}{P_2(\mathbf{y}(t_1),\mathbf{y}(t_2))} = K_1(\mathbf{y}(t_2) \mid \mathbf{y}(t_3)) \quad (4.3.27)$$

should be independent of $\mathbf{y}(t_1)$, i.e., no terms containing $z_i (1 \leqslant i \leqslant n)$ should appear in the exponent of the left-hand side of equation (4.3.27).

The exponent is

$$-\frac{1}{2}\sum_{i,j=1}^{3n} a_{ij}^{(3)} z_i z_j + \frac{1}{2}\sum_{i,j=1}^{2n} a_{ij}^{(2)} z_i z_j$$
$$= -\frac{1}{2}\left[\sum_{i,j=1}^{2n} (a_{ij}^{(3)} - a_{ij}^{(2)}) z_i z_j + 2\sum_{i=2n+1}^{3n}\sum_{j=1}^{3n} a_{ij}^{(3)} z_i z_j + \sum_{i,j=2n+1}^{3n} a_{ij}^{(3)} z_i z_j\right], \quad (4.3.28)$$

where we have used the fact that $\mathbf{A}^{(3)}$ is symmetric. The condition leads to

$$a_{ij}^{(3)} = 0 \quad \text{when} \quad j = 1, \cdots, n \quad \text{and} \quad i = 2n+1, \cdots, 3n, \quad (4.3.29)$$

and

$$a_{ij}^{(3)} = a_{ij}^{(2)} \quad \text{when} \quad i = 1, \cdots, n \quad \text{and} \quad j = 1, \cdots, 2n. \quad (4.3.30)$$

It is convenient to divide $\mathbf{A}^{(3)}$ into $(n \times n)$ submatrices $\mathbf{X}_{ij}^{(3)}$; since $\mathbf{A}^{(3)} = \mathbf{D}^{(3)-1}$, we have

$$\begin{pmatrix} \mathbf{R}(0) & \mathbf{R}(t_2 - t_1) & \mathbf{R}(t_3 - t_1) \\ \mathbf{R}(t_1 - t_2) & \mathbf{R}(0) & \mathbf{R}(t_3 - t_2) \\ \mathbf{R}(t_1 - t_3) & \mathbf{R}(t_2 - t_3) & \mathbf{R}(0) \end{pmatrix} \begin{pmatrix} \mathbf{X}_{11}^{(3)} & \mathbf{X}_{12}^{(3)} & \mathbf{X}_{13}^{(3)} \\ \mathbf{X}_{21}^{(3)} & \mathbf{X}_{22}^{(3)} & \mathbf{X}_{23}^{(3)} \\ \mathbf{X}_{31}^{(3)} & \mathbf{X}_{32}^{(3)} & \mathbf{X}_{33}^{(3)} \end{pmatrix} = \begin{pmatrix} \mathbf{I} & \mathbf{O} & \mathbf{O} \\ \mathbf{O} & \mathbf{I} & \mathbf{O} \\ \mathbf{O} & \mathbf{O} & \mathbf{I} \end{pmatrix}, \quad (4.3.31)$$

where $\mathbf{I}$ and $\mathbf{O}$ are the unit and null matrices of order $(n \times n)$. From equation (4.3.29) we find that

$$\mathbf{X}_{13}^{(3)} = \tilde{\mathbf{X}}_{31}^{(3)} = \mathbf{O}$$

and

$$\mathbf{X}_{11}^{(3)} = \mathbf{X}_{11}^{(2)}; \quad \mathbf{X}_{12}^{(3)} = \tilde{\mathbf{X}}_{21}^{(3)} = \mathbf{X}_{12}^{(2)} = \tilde{\mathbf{X}}_{21}^{(2)}.$$

Now, it is no loss of generality to assume that $\mathbf{R}(0) = \mathbf{I}$, because it is always possible to find a linear transformation of $\mathbf{y}$ which satisfies this condition. Consequently, three of the nine matrix equations implicit in equation (4.3.31) are

$$\begin{aligned}
&\mathbf{X}_{11}^{(2)} + \mathbf{R}(t_2 - t_1) \cdot \mathbf{X}_{21}^{(2)} = \mathbf{I} \\
&\mathbf{R}(t_1 - t_2) \cdot \mathbf{X}_{11}^{(2)} + \mathbf{X}_{21}^{(2)} = \mathbf{O} \\
&\mathbf{R}(t_1 - t_3) \cdot \mathbf{X}_{11}^{(2)} + \mathbf{R}(t_2 - t_3) \cdot \mathbf{X}_{21}^{(2)} = \mathbf{O}.
\end{aligned} \tag{4.3.32}$$

Upon eliminating $\mathbf{X}_{21}^{(2)}$ from the first two of these equations, we obtain

$$\{\mathbf{I} - \mathbf{R}(t_2 - t_1) \cdot \mathbf{R}(t_1 - t_2)\} \cdot \mathbf{X}_{11}^{(2)} = \mathbf{I}. \tag{4.3.33}$$

Equation (4.3.33) may be solved for $\mathbf{X}_{11}^{(2)}$ provided that the matrix in curly brackets is not singular. Now, $\mathbf{R}(t_2 - t_1)$ is certainly not singular for finite $(t_2 - t_1)$, so that equation (4.3.33) may be alternatively written as

$$\{\mathbf{R}^{-1}(t_2 - t_1) - \mathbf{R}(t_1 - t_2)\} \cdot \mathbf{X}_{11}^{(2)} = \mathbf{R}^{-1}(t_2 - t_1). \tag{4.3.34}$$

Hence, neither $\mathbf{X}_{11}^{(2)}$ nor $\{\mathbf{R}^{-1}(t_2 - t_1) - \mathbf{R}(t_1 - t_2)\}$ is singular, and

$$\mathbf{X}_{11}^{(2)} = \{\mathbf{R}^{-1}(t_2 - t_1) - \mathbf{R}(t_1 - t_2)\}^{-1} \cdot \mathbf{R}^{-1}(t_2 - t_1). \tag{4.3.35}$$

In similar manner we find

$$\mathbf{X}_{21}^{(2)} = -\mathbf{R}(t_1 - t_2) \cdot \{\mathbf{R}^{-1}(t_2 - t_1) - \mathbf{R}(t_1 - t_2)\}^{-1} \cdot \mathbf{R}^{-1}(t_2 - t_1). \tag{4.3.36}$$

Upon substituting equations (4.3.35) and (4.3.36) in the last of equation (4.3.32), we obtain

$$\mathbf{R}(t_1 - t_3) = \mathbf{R}(t_2 - t_3) \cdot \mathbf{R}(t_1 - t_2). \tag{4.3.37}$$

The only solution to equation (4.3.37) which is non-singular (since $\mathbf{R}(0) = \mathbf{I}$) is

$$\mathbf{R}(\tau) = \exp(\mathbf{Q}\tau), \tag{4.3.38}$$

where $\mathbf{Q}$ is some (not generally symmetric) matrix, and the exponential function is defined by its series expansion. *Thus, we have proved that the correlation matrix of a Gaussian Markov process has the exponential form.** This theorem was first proved by Doob, but the proof given before is due to Kac (3).

The exponential behavior should be apparent in the density fluctuations discussed in Section 3.3.C, since we have seen that $w(n)$ tends to a

* The converse of the theorem is certainly *not*, in general, true. For, by the specification of a random process in terms of its moments (Sec. 3.2.B), we cannot assert that a Markov process with exponential correlation function is Gaussian.

Gaussian for large ν and n, and the process is Markovian.* We found in Section 3.3 that the mean change of state for a given initial state n was given by

$$\langle(m - n)\rangle_1 = (\nu - n)p, \qquad (3.3.26)$$

so that the mean change is proportional to the initial deviation from the mean. It is easy to show that in the limit of continuous observations, this goes over to the exponential form. We write

$$\begin{aligned} \langle m\rangle_1 &= \sum_{m=0}^{\infty} mK(n \mid m) \\ &= n(1 - p) + \nu p, \end{aligned} \qquad (4.3.39)$$

where $\langle m\rangle_1$ is the expected state a time τ after the state was known to be n. After a time 2τ, the distribution of states is

$$\sum_{r=0}^{\infty} K(n \mid r)K(r \mid m),$$

where the sum is over all intermediate states. The expected state after a time 2τ is, therefore,

$$\begin{aligned} \langle m\rangle_2 &= \sum_{m=0}^{\infty} \sum_{r=0}^{\infty} mK(n \mid r)K(r \mid m) \\ &= \sum_{r=0}^{\infty} \{r(1 - p) + \nu p\}K(n \mid r) \\ &= \nu p(1 + (1 - p)) + n(1 - p)^2. \end{aligned} \qquad (4.3.40)$$

Similarly, we can show that

$$\begin{aligned} \langle m\rangle_s &= \nu p \sum_{r=0}^{s-1} (1 - p)^r + n(1 - p)^s \\ &= \nu[1 - (1 - p)^s] + n(1 - p)^s \\ &= \nu + (n - \nu)(1 - p)^s. \end{aligned} \qquad (4.3.41)$$

In the limit of large numbers and continuous observations $p(\tau)$ approaches the form

$$\lim_{\tau \to 0} p(\tau) = p_0\tau$$

and, allowing $s \to \infty$, $\tau \to 0$ such that $s\tau = t$ is constant, we find

$$\langle m\rangle_{s\tau} = \nu + (n - \nu) \exp(-p_0 t), \qquad (4.3.42)$$

* The probability of entry into and of exit from the observed volume, for any particle, is assumed independent of the local density.

so that, if $\Delta m(t) = m(t) - \nu$, we have

$$\langle \Delta m(t) \rangle_1 = \Delta m(0) \exp(-p_0 t). \tag{4.3.43}$$

4.3.C. *Processes Undergoing Very Small, or Large, Changes*

Continuous Markov processes occurring in physical systems often fall into one of two limiting cases. They may be subject to frequent small changes or to large discontinuous* changes.

In the small change case a differential equation for the distribution function is obtained in the following way. We suppose that the changes in the variable occur at intervals of the order of τ_c, while the distribution function changes in times of the order of τ_r. If the changes of the variables are very small compared to typical values of the variable, and if the changes are very rapid, then we may reasonably expect these two time scales to be widely separated; in other words, we may expect that a time τ exists which satisfies the inequalities†

$$\tau_c \ll \tau \ll \tau_r. \tag{4.3.44}$$

With these restrictions in mind, we may write the Markov Integral Equation (4.3.4) for a stationary process as

$$K_1(y_1 \mid y; t) = \int K_1(y_1 \mid y_0; t - \tau) K_1(y_0 \mid y; \tau)\, dy_0, \tag{4.3.45}$$

or in a slightly more convenient form,

$$K_1(y_1 \mid y; t + \tau) = \int K_1(y_1 \mid y_0; t) K_1(y_0 \mid y; \tau)\, dy_0. \tag{4.3.46}$$

Equation (4.3.46) is to be interpreted as an equation relating the form of the desired function at two slightly separated time instants, both at finite time, with the limiting form of the function for short times. On this basis $K_1(y_0 \mid y; \tau)$ is distinguished from the solution $K_1(y_1 \mid y_0; t)$ of the equation. The success of the procedure lies in the fact that it is often possible to propose a simple (statistical) model of the randomizing

* The reader will recall that a continuous *process* is one in which the variable may take on any value in a continuous range. Nothing is implied about the continuity or otherwise of the *variable* by this classification.

† τ_c is introduced here for physical reasons; there is no *mathematical* reason why we should not allow $\tau \to 0$ [cf. Eqs. (4.3.52) and (4.3.58)].

mechanism underlying the otherwise deterministic behavior of the variable we are studying.* The assumption of small changes in the variable during τ may be exploited by writing $y - y_0 = \Delta y$ and changing the variable of integration in equation (4.3.46) to Δy. The negative sign arising in the relation between the differentials

$$dy_0 = -d\Delta y$$

is absorbed in an inversion of the limits, and we obtain

$$K_1(y_1 \mid y; t + \tau) = \int K_1(y_1 \mid y - \Delta y; t)\Psi(y - \Delta y \mid \Delta y; \tau)\, d\Delta y. \tag{4.3.47}$$

In equation (4.3.47) we have introduced the notation

$$\Psi(y - \Delta y \mid \Delta y; \tau) = K_1(y - \Delta y \mid y; \tau) \tag{4.3.48}$$

as the probability that y will undergo a transition Δy in an interval τ starting from $y - \Delta y$. This notational change allows us to emphasize the qualitative distinction which we have already discussed between $K_1(y_1 \mid y_0; t)$ and $K_1(y_0 \mid y; \tau)$. $K_1(y_1 \mid y; t + \tau)$ is now expanded in a Taylor series in powers of τ about $K_1(y_1 \mid y; t)$; by virtue of the right-hand inequality (4.3.44) the expansion may be truncated after the second term. We also expand $K_1(y_1 \mid y - \Delta y; t)\Psi(y - \Delta y \mid \Delta y; \tau)$ in powers of Δy about $K_1(y_1 \mid y; t)\Psi(y \mid \Delta y; \tau) = K_1\Psi$, and obtain

$$\begin{aligned} K_1 + \tau \frac{\partial K_1}{\partial t} + \cdots & \\ = \int \Big[K_1\Psi - \Delta y \frac{\partial}{\partial y}(K_1\Psi) &+ \tfrac{1}{2}(\Delta y)^2 \frac{\partial^2}{\partial y^2}(K_1\Psi) + \cdots \Big]\, d\Delta y \\ = K_1 - \frac{\partial}{\partial y}(K_1\langle\Delta y\rangle_1) &+ \frac{1}{2}\frac{\partial^2}{\partial y^2}(K_1\langle(\Delta y)^2\rangle_1) + \cdots, \end{aligned} \tag{4.3.49}$$

* We have in mind such mechanisms as the fluctuating molecular force on a Brownian particle (see Sec. 4.4) which causes the particle to describe a random walk rather than the simple macroscopic motion described by Stokes' Law. In this case the variable studied is the position of the particle.

where we have used*

$$\int \Psi(y \mid \Delta y; \tau)\, d\Delta y = 1, \tag{4.3.50}$$

and $\langle\cdots\rangle_1$ is the average of the enclosed variable conditional upon the given initial value of y:

$$\langle(\Delta y)^n\rangle_1 = \int (\Delta y)^n \Psi(y \mid \Delta y; \tau)\, d\Delta y. \tag{4.3.51}$$

In order that equation (4.3.49) be of use, τ cannot appear explicitly. The time τ will not appear in the equation when the first n moments are proportional to τ, while all other moments are proportional to τ^2 or some higher power of τ; the constant of proportionality in the preceding is of order τ_r^{-1}, so that high-order moments are at least of

* The transition probability, Ψ, is introduced in an intuitive manner which, while it leads to the correct final equations, hides the awkward point that the integration is essentially over the *first* variable (y_0) in the argument of $K_1(y_0 \mid y; \tau)$. An alternative method which is superior mathematically, but which offers no appeal to physical insight is the following:
The integral equation (4.3.46) is multiplied by an arbitrary function $R(y)$ which vanishes at $\mp\infty$ sufficiently rapidly, and the resultant equation is integrated over y. We then have

$$\int R(y) \frac{\partial}{\partial t} K_1(y_1 \mid y; t)\, dy = \lim_{\substack{\tau\to 0\\(\tau \gg \tau_c)}} \left[\int R(y)\left(\frac{K_1(y_1 \mid y; t+t) - K_1(y_1 \mid y; t)}{\tau}\right) dy\right]$$

$$= \lim_{\substack{\tau\to 0\\(\tau \gg \tau_c)}} \frac{1}{\tau}\left[\iint R(y) K_1(y_1 \mid y_0; t) K_1(y_0 \mid y; \tau)\, dy_0\, dy - \int R(y) K_1(y_1 \mid y; t)\, dy\right].$$

We now expand $R(y)$ in a Taylor series about $R(y_0)$, and reverse the order of integration in the first term, obtaining

$$\int R(y) \frac{\partial K_1}{\partial t}\, dy = \int K_1(y_1 \mid y_0; t)[a^{(1)}(y_0)R'(y_0) + \tfrac{1}{2}a^{(2)}(y_0)R''(y_0) + \cdots]\, dy_0.$$

The derivatives of R on the right-hand side are removed by partial integration (the surface terms vanish, by assumption) and we obtain

$$\int R(y)\left[\frac{\partial K_1}{\partial t} + \frac{\partial}{\partial y}(K_1 a^{(1)}) - \frac{1}{2}\frac{\partial^2}{\partial y^2}(K_1 a^{(2)}) + \cdots\right] dy = 0.$$

Since R is arbitrary, equation (4.3.53) follows immediately.

order $(\tau/\tau_r) \ll 1$ in relation to the first n terms. Writing,

$$\operatorname*{Lim}_{\substack{\tau\to 0\\(\tau\gg\tau_c)}} \frac{\langle \Delta y\rangle_1}{\tau} = a^{(1)}(y)$$

$$\operatorname*{Lim}_{\substack{\tau\to 0\\(\tau\gg\tau_c)}} \frac{\langle (\Delta y)^2\rangle_1}{\tau} = a^{(2)}(y), \text{ etc.,} \tag{4.3.52}$$

equation (4.3.49) becomes

$$\frac{\partial K_1}{\partial t} = -\frac{\partial}{\partial y}(a^{(1)}K_1) + \frac{1}{2}\frac{\partial^2}{\partial y^2}(a^{(2)}K_1) + \cdots. \tag{4.3.53}$$

If y has more than one component,

$$\frac{\partial K_1}{\partial t} = -\nabla_y \cdot (\mathbf{a}^{(1)}K_1) + \tfrac{1}{2}\nabla_y\nabla_y : (\mathbf{a}^{(2)}K_1) + \cdots, \tag{4.3.54}$$

where ∇_y is the differential (gradient) operator in $\mathbf{y}$ space, and $\mathbf{a}^{(1)}$, $\mathbf{a}^{(2)}$ are the (vector) first and (tensor) second moments of Ψ, respectively.

Equations (4.3.53–54) are known as the Fokker-Planck equations; their solutions are the transition probabilities K_1, but they may also be written in terms of the absolute probability $P_1(\mathbf{y};t)$, by using the relation

$$P_1(\mathbf{y};t) = \int P_1(\mathbf{y}_1;t_1)K_1(\mathbf{y}_1 \mid \mathbf{y}; t - t_1)\, d\mathbf{y}_1, \tag{4.3.55}$$

for then

$$\frac{\partial P_1}{\partial t} = -\nabla_y \cdot (\mathbf{a}^{(1)}P_1) + \tfrac{1}{2}\nabla_y\nabla_y : (\mathbf{a}^{(2)}P_1), \tag{4.3.56}$$

with the initial condition $P_1(\mathbf{y};0) = \delta(\mathbf{y} - \mathbf{y}_1)$.

The opposite limiting case, in which large discontinuous changes in the variable occur, can sometimes be included in the Fokker-Planck scheme if the moments behave suitably. This is not usually the case, however. If we assume that a time interval τ_c exists, which is the time between the transitions undergone by the variable, but during which the change in $K_1(y_1 \mid y; t)$ is small, then we can immediately write down a master equation analogous to equation (3.2.27) or equation (3.2.39).

Since $K_1(y \mid y_0; \tau)$ is normalized in y_0:

$$\int K_1(y \mid y_0; \tau)\, dy_0 = 1,$$

and we have, upon expanding $K_1(y_1 \mid y; t + \tau)$ in a Taylor series about $K_1(y_1 \mid y; t)$ to first order in τ,

$$\frac{\partial K_1}{\partial t} = \int [K_1(y_1 \mid y_0; t)\Phi(y_0 \mid y) - K_1(y_1 \mid y; t)\Phi(y \mid y_0)]\, dy_0, \quad (4.3.57)$$

where

$$\Phi(y_0 \mid y) = \lim_{\substack{\tau \to 0 \\ (\tau \gg \tau_c)}} \frac{1}{\tau} K_1(y_0 \mid y; \tau) \quad (4.3.58)$$

is the number of transitions from $y_0 \to y$ in unit time. The normalization of $K_1(y_0 \mid y; \tau)$ now requires

$$\int \Phi(y_0 \mid y)\, dy = \lim_{\tau \to \tau_c} \frac{1}{\tau} = \frac{1}{\tau_c},$$

so that the total transition rate out of y_0 is simply the inverse of the time between transitions τ_c. Multiplication of equation (4.3.57) by $P_1(y_1;t_1)$ and use of equation (4.3.55) leads to

$$\frac{\partial P_1(y;t)}{\partial t} = \int [P_1(y_0;t)\Phi(y_0 \mid y) - P_1(y;t)\Phi(y \mid y_0)]\, dy_0, \quad (4.3.59)$$

which is to be compared to equation (3.2.41).

Equation (4.3.59) is of wide applicability in physics. Of particular interest for our purpose here is its relevance to the kinetic theory of gases. In this case, as we shall see in detail in Chapter 5, $P_1(y;t)$ is the momentum distribution function of gas molecules. The transition rate is proportional to the probability that an arbitrary molecule about to collide with a given molecule has the correct momentum to induce the desired transition. Hence, Φ is proportional to P_1 also, and we see at once how the nonlinear integro-differential Boltzmann equation arises.

In developing equations (4.3.54–55) and (4.3.59) the conjectured characteristics of the two processes imposed conditions upon the transition probability $\Psi(y \mid \Delta y; \tau)$ and transition rate $\Phi(y_0 \mid y)$, respectively. Thus, $\Psi(y \mid \Delta y; \tau)$ is assumed to be sharply peaked about

$\Delta y = 0$, and to be negligibly small for values of Δy comparable with $\langle y \rangle$ (or with $\langle y^2 \rangle^{1/2}$ if $\langle y \rangle = 0$), while $\Phi(y_0 \mid y)$ is not sharply peaked, and will be approximately uniform over a range of $(y - y_0)$ comparable to $\langle y^2 \rangle^{1/2}$. The treatment for the two limiting cases may easily be extended to include processes which exhibit both types of behavior, provided that the underlying mechanisms of the two types of transition occur on the same, or similar, time scales. We write the equation for $(\partial K_1/\partial t)$ as in equation (4.3.57) but *before* the limit of small τ is taken,

$$\tau \frac{\partial K_1}{\partial t} + \cdots = \int_a^b [K_1(y_1 \mid y_0; t) K_1(y_0 \mid y; \tau) - K_1(y_1 \mid y; t) K_1(y \mid y_0; \tau)]\, dy_0, \quad (4.3.60)$$

and suppose that y lies in the continuous interval $a \leqslant y \leqslant b$. To exploit the assumption of the dual nature of the randomizing mechanism, we suppose that $K_1(y_0 \mid y; \tau)$ is sharply peaked in the range

$$y_0 - \epsilon < y < y_0 + \epsilon,$$

where $\epsilon \ll \langle y^2 \rangle^{1/2}$, so that the range of integration may be separated into parts covering the peak (including a negligible contribution from the process of "discontinuous" changes, for small values of the change $(y - y_0)$), and covering the rest of the interval $[a,b]$, from which most of the contributions of large "discontinuous" change arise (see Fig. 4.3.1). Equation (4.3.60) now becomes

$$\begin{aligned} \tau \frac{\partial K_1}{\partial t} + \cdots = \left\{ \int_{y_0+\epsilon}^{b} + \int_a^{y_0-\epsilon} \right\} [K_1(y_1 \mid y_0; t) K_1(y_0 \mid y; \tau) \\ - K_1(y_1 \mid y; t) K_1(y \mid y_0; \tau)]\, dy_0 \\ + \int_{-\epsilon}^{\epsilon} [K_1(y_1 \mid y - \Delta y; t) \Psi(y - \Delta y \mid \Delta y; \tau) \\ - K_1(y_1 \mid y; t) \Psi(y \mid \Delta y; \tau)]\, d\Delta y. \quad (4.3.61) \end{aligned}$$

The first two integrals on the right-hand side of equation (4.3.61) may now be cast into the form of the right-hand side of equation (4.3.57), in terms of a transition rate $\Phi(y_0 \mid y)$ which does not include a (negligible) set of "discontinuous" transitions of small magnitude, lying in the range $|y - y_0| < \epsilon$. The third integral may be cast into the Fokker-Planck form because we have assumed that the probability of transition of magnitude larger than ϵ (of the type we have described as "small and

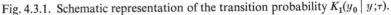

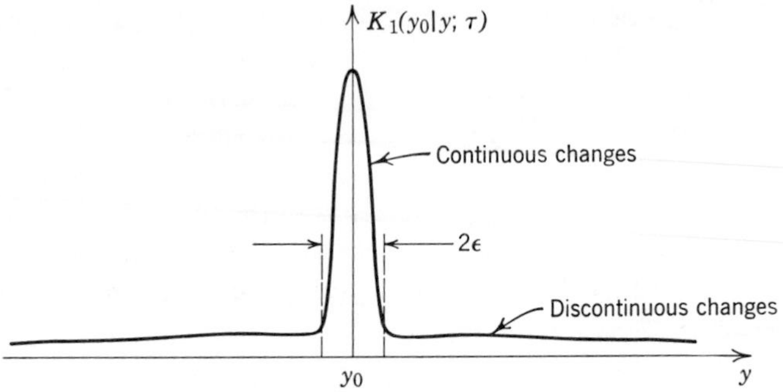

Fig. 4.3.1. Schematic representation of the transition probability $K_1(y_0 \mid y;\tau)$.

frequent") is negligible. Equation (4.3.61) becomes, finally, after multiplication by $P_1(y_1;t_1)$ and integration over y_1,

$$\frac{\partial P_1}{\partial t} = \int [P_1(y_0;t)\Phi(y_0 \mid y) - P_1(y;t)\Phi(y \mid y_0)]\, dy_0 - \frac{\partial}{\partial y}(a^{(1)}P_1) + \frac{1}{2}\frac{\partial^2}{\partial y^2}(a^{(2)}P_1). \quad (4.3.62)$$

We must emphasize that equation (4.3.62) is only applicable to a process in which the two types of transition occur on similar time scales, and in which P_1 changes by only negligible amounts during a transition. The three special processes discussed here exclude a large class of processes of interest; namely, those in which P_1 changes sufficiently fast so that, for instance, $\tau_c(\partial^2 P_1/\partial t^2)$ cannot be neglected in comparison with $(\partial P_1/\partial t)$.

4.4. BROWNIAN MOTION: THE DISTRIBUTION FUNCTION APPROACH (4)

4.4.A. *The One-Dimensional Random Walk*

Brownian motion may be analyzed in two essentially different ways. It can be regarded either as the limit of a discrete random walk in configuration space, or as a more complicated process in phase space.

Both these processes are Markovian, but it will become clear that fundamentally different time scales are involved. While the phase space problem requires the careful analysis of a physical model, and is thereby shown to have certain inherent shortcomings when applied to the motion of the molecules of a liquid, the random walk problem is simple and of general application, and is therefore of little use in the special case of liquids. Nevertheless, it introduces a fundamental definition of the coefficient of diffusion, and we describe it briefly for this reason.

In the previous section we placed considerable emphasis upon the existence, in physical processes, of a lower limit τ_c to the time interval τ for which we can define a Markovian transition probability. For this reason we discuss first the simplest case: a particle undergoes displacements along a straight line in the form of steps of equal length and of equal probability in either direction. After N steps the particle may be at any of the positions

$$\left.\begin{array}{l} -N, -N+2, \cdots, -2, 0, 2, \cdots, N-2, N \\ -N, -N+2, \cdots, -1, +1, \cdots, N-2, N \end{array}\right\}, \qquad (4.4.1)$$

or

according as N is even or odd. If the particle is m steps from its starting point after a total of N steps, then it must have made $(n + m)$ forward steps and n backward steps. Since $(n + m) + n = N$, the number of backward steps, n, is given by

$$n = \tfrac{1}{2}(N - m). \qquad (4.4.2)$$

Further, since the forward and backward steps can occur in any order, the number of ways of reaching m after N steps is

$$\frac{N!}{[\frac{1}{2}(N-m)]!\,[\frac{1}{2}(N+m)]!} = \binom{N}{\frac{1}{2}(N-m)}.$$

The probability of any particular sequence of N steps is simply 2^{-N} (since the probabilities of forward and backward steps are equal), so that the probability $w^{(N)}(m)$ of finding the particle at m after N steps is

$$w^{(N)}(m) = \binom{N}{\frac{1}{2}(N-m)}\left(\frac{1}{2}\right)^N. \qquad (4.4.3)$$

$w^{(N)}(m)$ is a binomial distribution for $\frac{1}{2}(N - m)$, with mean and variance*

$$\begin{aligned} \tfrac{1}{2}\langle N - m\rangle &= \tfrac{1}{2}N, \\ \langle[\tfrac{1}{2}(N - m) - \tfrac{1}{2}N]^2\rangle &= \tfrac{1}{4}N. \end{aligned} \tag{4.4.4}$$

Consequently, the distribution of possible positions m of the particle after N steps is characterized by

$$\begin{aligned} \langle m\rangle &= 0 \\ \langle m^2\rangle &= N. \end{aligned} \tag{4.4.5}$$

The root-mean square displacement is, therefore, $N^{1/2}$.

We are especially interested in the form of $w^{(N)}(m)$ for large N. Using Stirling's theorem, as with the derivation of equation (3.3.42), we easily find

$$w^{(N)}(m) = (2/\pi N)^{1/2} \exp\left(-\frac{m^2}{2N}\right). \tag{4.4.6}$$

* The general Bernoulli distribution with asymmetric probabilities $p, q\,(= 1 - p)$ is

$$w^{(n)}(x) = \binom{n}{x} p^x q^{n-x}; \qquad 0 \leqslant x \leqslant n.$$

Now, $w^{(n)}(x)$ is the coefficient of u^x in $(pu + q)^n$. Consequently,

$$\sum_{x=0}^{n} w^{(n)}(x) = \left[\sum_{x=0}^{n} w^{(n)}(x)u^x\right]_{u=1} = [(pu + q)^n]_{u=1} = 1.$$

The mean value of x is

$$\begin{aligned} \langle x\rangle = \sum_{x=0}^{n} x w^{(n)}(x) &= \left[\sum_{x=0}^{n} x w^{(n)}(x)u^x\right]_{u=1} \\ &= \left[\frac{\partial}{\partial \ln u}\left\{\sum_{x=0}^{n} w^{(n)}(x)u^x\right\}\right]_{u=1} \\ &= \left[\frac{\partial}{\partial \ln u}(pu + q)^n\right]_{u=1} = np. \end{aligned}$$

The variance of x is

$$\delta^2 = \langle x^2\rangle - \langle x\rangle^2$$

and we may show in a similar way that

$$\delta^2 = \left[\frac{\partial^2}{\partial \ln u^2}(pu + q)^n\right]_{u=1} = npq.$$

The Gaussian form of $w^{(N)}(m)$ displayed in equation (4.4.6) is to be expected, since we have already seen [cf. Section 3.3.C] that the Poisson distribution is the limit of a Bernoulli distribution under certain circumstances, and tends also to a Gaussian for large mean values. When N is large, it is convenient to introduce the probability density $P^{(N)}(x)$ such that $P^{(N)}(x)\Delta x$ is the probability that the particle is found at one of the sites lying in the range Δx of x. If the length of an individual step is l, then

$$x = ml. \tag{4.4.7}$$

If N and m are sufficiently large, we may choose Δx large enough to contain many sites, but small compared to x. Then $w^{(N)}(m)$ is approximately constant throughout Δx, and

$$P^{(N)}(x)\,\Delta x = w^{(N)}(m)\,\frac{\Delta x}{2l}\,, \tag{4.4.8}$$

where $(\Delta x/2l)$ is the number of sites in Δx that may be occupied for given N. Substitution of equation (4.4.7) in equation (4.4.8) leads to

$$P^{(N)}(x) = (2\pi N l^2)^{-\frac{1}{2}} \exp\left(-\frac{x^2}{2Nl^2}\right). \tag{4.4.9}$$

A time dependence can be introduced if it is supposed that the particle undergoes n steps in unit time. We then obtain

$$P^{(N)}(x) \to P(x;t) = (4\pi Dt)^{-\frac{1}{2}} \exp\left(-\frac{x^2}{4Dt}\right), \tag{4.4.10}$$

where

$$D = \tfrac{1}{2}nl^2 \tag{4.4.11}$$

is a measure of the rate of spread of P. It appears in the role of diffusion coefficient if instead of only one particle we have a large number, $\mathcal{N}$, present, whereupon P becomes the number density. The quantities n, l appearing in this definition of D are constants for the process, but we can arrive at a more fundamental formula by returning to equation (4.4.9). Comparison of equations (4.4.9) and (4.4.10) yields

$$D = \frac{1}{2}\frac{Nl^2}{t}\,. \tag{4.4.12}$$

If equation (4.4.12) is independent of t over some range then the definition of D becomes independent of the assumption that the process involves steps at regular intervals. The interpretation of equation (4.4.12) may be carried further from the simple random walk model by noting that Nl^2 is the mean-square displacement suffered by the particle in N steps. Hence we may write, in an obvious notation,

$$D = \frac{1}{2}\frac{\langle (x(t) - x(0))^2 \rangle}{t}. \tag{4.4.13}$$

Equation (4.4.13) suggests that we may be able to define a diffusion coefficient independently of a model which is explicit as to the length and frequency of the steps. This possibility is immediately confirmed if we write out equation (4.3.56) at the stage just prior to that of taking the limit of τ; it is

$$\tau \frac{\partial P_1}{\partial t} = -\nabla_R \cdot (\langle \Delta \mathbf{R} \rangle_1 P_1) + \tfrac{1}{2}\nabla_R \nabla_R : (\langle \Delta \mathbf{R}\, \Delta \mathbf{R} \rangle_1 P_1), \tag{4.4.14}$$

where $\mathbf{R}(t)$ is the position vector of the Brownian particle and $\Delta\mathbf{R}$ is the displacement suffered by the particle in the interval τ; $\mathbf{R}(t)$ is the random variable in this case. If the particle is not subject to an external force field then the average displacement vanishes. Moreover, the off-diagonal elements vanish if we make the usual assumption that diffusion is isotropic:

$$\langle \Delta \mathbf{R}\, \Delta \mathbf{R} \rangle_1 = \tfrac{1}{3}\langle (\Delta \mathbf{R})^2 \rangle \mathbf{I}, \tag{4.4.15}$$

where $\mathbf{I}$ is the unit dyad.

We see, therefore, that equation (4.4.14) becomes a differential equation for P_1 if $\langle (\Delta \mathbf{R})^2 \rangle$ is proportional to τ over a range of τ sufficiently large that the quotient

$$D = \frac{1}{6}\frac{\langle (\Delta \mathbf{R})^2 \rangle}{\tau}, \tag{4.4.16}$$

can be said to be sensibly independent of τ. With the form (4.4.16), equation (4.4.14) becomes the diffusion equation

$$\frac{\partial P_1}{\partial t} = D\, \nabla_R{}^2 P_1. \tag{4.4.17}$$

Its solution, with source at $\mathbf{R} = \mathbf{R}_0$, is easily shown to be the three-dimensional equivalent of equation (4.4.10)

$$P_1(\mathbf{R};t) = (4\pi Dt)^{-3/2} \exp\left(-\frac{(\mathbf{R}-\mathbf{R}_0)^2}{4Dt}\right), \tag{4.4.18}$$

$$P_1(\mathbf{R};0) = \delta(\mathbf{R}-\mathbf{R}_0). \tag{4.4.19}$$

We can say no more about the range of τ at this point, because a discussion requires considerations outside the framework of the model.

The reader should note that a coarseness was introduced into the definition of the displacement x in obtaining equation (4.4.9), because x is continuous while the true displacement ml is discrete. A more general analysis, for which there is no space here, considers the more realistic situation in which the steps themselves constitute a continuous (random) process, so that the true displacement is also continuous. Equation (4.4.9) is then the correct distribution subject only to the requirement that N is large enough for the use of Stirling's formula. It might also be supposed that a similar difficulty arises with regard to the definition of the time derivative of P_1. This is indeed the case with the simple random walk model we have discussed because P_1 changes discontinuously every $(1/n)$ of a second. Again, however, a more general model would include the possibility that the steps did not occur at regular intervals and were not instantaneous. Thus, there are no mathematical reasons why a description of the random walk should not involve both continuous space and time. However, as we shall see in the next section, there are physical reasons for a coarseness in both the temporal and spatial definition of P_1, which arise from the fact that a short time must elapse before $\langle(\Delta\mathbf{R})^2\rangle_1$ approaches its asymptotic value $6D\tau$.

4.4.B. *Phase Space Description: The Fokker-Planck Equation* (4)

The passage to a differential equation in the phase space of the particle is very similar in principle to the problem discussed in the last section. However, to evaluate the average moments which appear we must construct a more detailed physical model. We assume that a time interval τ can be chosen which is so long compared to the time scale of molecular fluctuations that any disturbance in the liquid distribution disappears long before a time τ has elapsed, but yet is so short compared to the decay time of the particle's momentum that the momentum increment is very small compared to the initial momentum, i.e., that dynamical motion persists. The random process (**R**,**p**) is then Markovian,* and the integral equation (4.3.47) can be written

$$f(\mathbf{R}, \mathbf{p}; t+\tau) = \int f\left(\mathbf{R} - \frac{1}{m}\mathbf{p}\tau, \mathbf{p} - \Delta\mathbf{p}; t\right)\Psi(\mathbf{p} - \Delta\mathbf{p} \mid \Delta\mathbf{p}; \tau)\, d\Delta\mathbf{p}, \tag{4.4.20}$$

where we have already incorporated the fact that the increments in position have the definite value

$$\Delta\mathbf{R} = \frac{1}{m}\mathbf{p}\tau \tag{4.4.21}$$

to order τ^2. In equation (4.4.18) we have introduced the statistical mechanical notation $f(\mathbf{R},\mathbf{p};t)$ for the distribution function $P_1(y;t)$ of previous sections. The interpretation of $f(\mathbf{R},\mathbf{p};t)\, d\mathbf{R}\, d\mathbf{p}$ either as the probability that a particle is found in the elementary phase cell $d\mathbf{R}\, d\mathbf{p}$ at (**R**,**p**), or as the number of particles with phases in the cell, depends on the normalization of f. In the rest of this chapter we shall maintain the latter interpretation. Thus, if N is the total number of (Brownian) particles in the system considered,

$$\iint_V f(\mathbf{R},\mathbf{p};t)\, d\mathbf{R}\, d\mathbf{p} = N, \tag{4.4.22}$$

where the volume integration is over the volume of the system, V. It must be pointed out, however, that this interpretation is valid only if the Brownian particles remain sufficiently dilute that their mutual interactions are negligible compared to the kinetic energy of a single particle.

We now expand each factor in the integrand of equation (4.4.20) in a Taylor series about $f(\mathbf{R},\mathbf{p};t)\Psi(\mathbf{p} \mid \Delta\mathbf{p}; \tau)$, and obtain [cf. Eq. (4.4.14)]

$$\tau\left\{\frac{\partial f}{\partial t} + \frac{1}{m}\mathbf{p}\cdot\nabla_R f\right\} = -\nabla_p\cdot(\langle\Delta\mathbf{p}\rangle_1 f) + \tfrac{1}{2}\nabla_p\nabla_p : (\langle\Delta\mathbf{p}\,\Delta\mathbf{p}\rangle_1 f). \tag{4.4.23}$$

* If we do not observe the behavior of the particle for times shorter than τ, the "background" of molecular fluctuations shows no dependence upon the instantaneous phase of the particle. At shorter times, or higher time resolution, there will be a coupling between the particle's phase and the molecular fluctuations, so that the possible phases at successive instants depend on this coupling unless they are so far separated that the coupling has relaxed to zero.

Terms which involve τ^2 or higher powers of τ have been omitted from the right-hand side. These include

$$\nabla_R \nabla_p : (\langle \Delta \mathbf{R} \, \Delta \mathbf{p} \rangle_1 f), \quad \nabla_R \nabla_R : (\langle \Delta \mathbf{R} \, \Delta \mathbf{R} \rangle_1 f),$$
$$\nabla_p \nabla_p \nabla_p \vdots (\langle \Delta \mathbf{p} \, \Delta \mathbf{p} \, \Delta \mathbf{p} \rangle_1 f),$$

and so on. The second of these terms appears because τ is (assumed to be) so short that $\langle \Delta \mathbf{R} \, \Delta \mathbf{R} \rangle_1$ has not reached its asymptotic form $6D\tau$ [Eq. (4.4.16)], but has the value for a linear trajectory, namely $\mathbf{pp}(\tau/m)^2$. In the next section we shall describe a method of calculating these moments and show that both the first and second momentum-increment moments are proportional to τ, while higher moments are proportional to τ^2, and so on. Thus, the preceding third term is of $\mathcal{O}(\tau^2)$, as well as the first because for such short τ, $\Delta \mathbf{R}$ and $\Delta \mathbf{p}$ are independent, so that

$$\langle \Delta \mathbf{R} \, \Delta \mathbf{p} \rangle_1 = \langle \Delta \mathbf{R} \rangle_1 \langle \Delta \mathbf{p} \rangle_1 \sim \mathcal{O}(\tau^2).$$

If we denote the limiting values of the momentum increment moments by

$$\operatorname*{Lim}_{\substack{\tau \to 0 \\ (\tau \gg \tau_c)}} \frac{\langle \Delta \mathbf{p} \rangle_1}{\tau} = -\mathbf{a}^{(1)}$$

$$\operatorname*{Lim}_{\substack{\tau \to 0 \\ (\tau \gg \tau_c)}} \frac{\langle \Delta \mathbf{p} \, \Delta \mathbf{p} \rangle_1}{\tau} = \mathbf{a}^{(2)} \tag{4.4.24}$$

as before, then equation (4.4.23) becomes

$$\frac{\partial f}{\partial t} + \frac{1}{m} \mathbf{p} \cdot \nabla_R f = \nabla_p \cdot (\mathbf{a}^{(1)} f) + \tfrac{1}{2} \nabla_p \nabla_p : (\mathbf{a}^{(2)} f). \tag{4.4.25}$$

Now, a physical requirement on the solution of equation (4.4.25) is that when $(\partial f / \partial t) = 0$ one possible form of f (the equilibrium form) is Maxwellian in the momentum. More generally, if the system is subjected to a conservative force field, derived from a potential $W^{(1)}(\mathbf{R})$, the equilibrium solution must have the Maxwell-Boltzmann form

$$f_0 \sim \exp\left(-\beta[p^2/2m + W^{(1)}(\mathbf{R})]\right); \qquad \beta^{-1} = kT. \tag{4.4.26}$$

Owing to the coarseness of the time resolution of equation (4.4.25) it is clear that if $W^{(1)}(\mathbf{R})$ should vary so rapidly in $\mathbf{R}$ that significant changes occur in distances of order $\langle \Delta \mathbf{R} \rangle_1$ the solution will be meaningless; we exclude such potentials from our present consideration.

Substitution of equation (4.4.26) in equation (4.4.25) with $(\partial f/\partial t) = 0$ yields

$$-\frac{\beta}{m}[\mathbf{p}\cdot\nabla_R W^{(1)}]f_0 = \nabla_p\cdot(\mathbf{a}^{(1)}f_0) + \tfrac{1}{2}\nabla_p\nabla_p:(\mathbf{a}^{(2)}f_0). \quad (4.4.27)$$

Now, the possibility that $\mathbf{a}^{(1)}$ and $\mathbf{a}^{(2)}$ depend on both position and momentum is not excluded by their definitions (4.4.24). Performing the differentiation on the right-hand side of equation (4.4.27) we, therefore, obtain

$$-\frac{\beta}{m}\mathbf{p}\cdot\nabla_R W^{(1)} = \nabla_p\cdot\mathbf{a}^{(1)} - \frac{\beta}{m}\mathbf{a}^{(1)}\cdot\mathbf{p} + \frac{1}{2}\left(\frac{\beta}{m}\right)^2\mathbf{p}\cdot\mathbf{a}^{(2)}\cdot\mathbf{p}$$
$$-\frac{\beta}{m}(\nabla_p\cdot\mathbf{a}^{(2)})\cdot\mathbf{p} - \frac{1}{2}\frac{\beta}{m}Tr(\mathbf{a}^{(2)}) + \frac{1}{2}\nabla_p\nabla_p:\mathbf{a}^{(2)}. \quad (4.4.28)$$

Equation (4.4.28) is the most general relation between the moments $\mathbf{a}^{(1)}$, $\mathbf{a}^{(2)}$ for a Markov process in which higher moments are negligible. Simplification can be obtained only by the introduction of a model of the randomizing mechanism. It is consistent with the model of Brownian motion introduced in Section 4.5 in that $\mathbf{a}^{(2)}$ is independent of $\mathbf{p}$. Equation (4.4.28) then simplifies to

$$-\frac{\beta}{m}\mathbf{p}\cdot\nabla_R W^{(1)} = \nabla_p\cdot\mathbf{a}^{(1)} - \frac{\beta}{m}\mathbf{a}^{(1)}\cdot\mathbf{p}$$
$$+\frac{1}{2}\left(\frac{\beta}{m}\right)^2\mathbf{p}\cdot\mathbf{a}^{(2)}\cdot\mathbf{p} - \frac{1}{2}\frac{\beta}{m}Tr(\mathbf{a}^{(2)}). \quad (4.4.29)$$

It is not physically reasonable to suppose that $\mathbf{a}^{(1)}$ is an asymmetric function of the components of $\mathbf{p}$, so that the only terms involving cross products of these components arise from $\mathbf{p}\cdot\mathbf{a}^{(2)}\cdot\mathbf{p}$. Let us assume that $\mathbf{a}^{(2)}$ is diagonal, and indeed, a multiple of the unit tensor:

$$\mathbf{a}^{(2)} = \alpha\mathbf{I}. \quad (4.4.30)$$

It is then evident that $\mathbf{a}^{(1)}$ must be linear in $\mathbf{p}$, and a suitable form is

$$\mathbf{a}^{(1)} = \frac{\zeta}{m}\mathbf{p} + \nabla_R W^{(1)}. \quad (4.4.31)$$

Substitution of equations (4.4.30–31) in equation (4.4.29) leads to

$$0 = 3\frac{\zeta}{m} - \frac{\beta\zeta}{m^2}p^2 + \frac{1}{2}\left(\frac{\beta}{m}\right)^2\alpha p^2 - \frac{3}{2}\frac{\beta}{m}\alpha, \quad (4.4.32)$$

so that

$$\alpha = 2\zeta\beta^{-1}. \tag{4.4.33}$$

Equation (4.4.25) becomes, from equations (4.4.30–33),

$$\frac{\partial f}{\partial t} + \frac{1}{m}\mathbf{p}\cdot\nabla_R f + \mathbf{K}(\mathbf{R})\cdot\nabla_p f = \zeta\left[\nabla_p\cdot\left(\frac{1}{m}\mathbf{p}f\right) + kT\nabla_p{}^2 f\right], \tag{4.4.34}$$

where

$$\mathbf{K}(\mathbf{R}) = -\nabla_R W^{(1)}, \tag{4.4.35}$$

and ζ is known as the friction coefficient.

The moments derived from statistical mechanics in Chapter 5 have also the form of equations (4.4.30–33). It is shown that the friction coefficient so derived depends on the momentum of the particle (or molecule). Equation (4.4.28) is a means by which we can investigate the possible dependence of ζ on $\mathbf{p}$. Using the isotropy (4.4.30) of $\mathbf{a}^{(2)}$, and the solutions (4.4.31,33), we obtain for ζ the differential equation,

$$\nabla_p{}^2\zeta - \frac{\beta}{m}\mathbf{p}\cdot\nabla_p\zeta = 0. \tag{4.4.36}$$

Since ζ is assumed to depend symmetrically on the components of $\mathbf{p}$, equation (4.4.36) reduces to the radial terms only. The resulting equation is related to Hermite's differential equation, and it is easy to show that the only bounded solution is

$$\zeta = \text{constant}. \tag{4.4.37}$$

The solution to equation (4.4.34) can be obtained by first studying the associated homogeneous (i.e., first order) equation

$$\frac{\partial f}{\partial t} + \frac{1}{m}\mathbf{p}\cdot\nabla_R f + \mathbf{K}(\mathbf{R})\cdot\nabla_p f = \frac{\zeta}{m}\nabla_p\cdot(\mathbf{p}f). \tag{4.4.38}$$

The equivalent (characteristic) set of ordinary differential equations is

$$dt = m\frac{dR_i}{p_i} = \frac{dp_i}{K_i - \dfrac{\zeta}{m}p_i} = \frac{m\,df}{3\zeta f}$$

$$(i = 1, 2, 3 \text{ denotes the vector components}). \tag{4.4.39}$$

The general solution of equation (4.4.38) is *any* function of the solutions $u_j(\mathbf{R},\mathbf{p},t) = c_j$ (c_j = constant) of equation (4.4.39). The first six u_j are the "integrals of motion," which may obviously be written in vector form and are obtained by integrating the equations

$$\frac{d\mathbf{R}}{dt} - \frac{1}{m}\mathbf{p} = 0 \tag{4.4.40}$$

$$\frac{d\mathbf{p}}{dt} = \mathbf{K}(\mathbf{R}) - \frac{\zeta}{m}\mathbf{p}, \tag{4.4.41}$$

while the seventh is the integral of

$$\frac{df}{dt} = \frac{3\zeta}{m} f. \tag{4.4.42}$$

Equations (4.4.40, 41) are not integrable in general unless the force takes a simple form. Two examples are the field-free case $\mathbf{K} = 0$ and the harmonic case $\mathbf{K}(\mathbf{R}) = -(\omega_{12}R_1, \omega_2{}^2R_2, \omega_3{}^2R_3)$. We treat only the former here; the extension of the method to the latter is straightforward. In the field-free case the integrals of motion are

$$\mathbf{I}_1 = \mathbf{p}e^{\zeta t/m}; \qquad \mathbf{I}_2 = \mathbf{R} + \mathbf{p}/\zeta, \tag{4.4.43}$$

while that derived from equation (4.4.42) is

$$I_3 = e^{3\zeta t/m}. \tag{4.4.44}$$

Thus, any function of $\mathbf{I}_1$, $\mathbf{I}_2$, I_3 is a solution of the homogeneous equation (4.4.38). In order to solve the inhomogeneous equation (4.4.34) we change to the new variables

$$\boldsymbol{\rho} = \mathbf{p}e^{\zeta t/m}; \qquad \mathbf{P} = \mathbf{R} + \mathbf{p}/\zeta; \qquad t. \tag{4.4.45}$$

Thus,

$$\begin{aligned} \frac{\partial f}{\partial t}(\mathbf{R},\mathbf{p};t) &= \frac{\partial F}{\partial t}(\boldsymbol{\rho},\mathbf{P};t) + \frac{\zeta}{m}\boldsymbol{\rho}\cdot\nabla_\rho F(\boldsymbol{\rho},\mathbf{P};t) \\ \nabla_R f(\mathbf{R},\mathbf{p};t) &= \nabla_P F(\boldsymbol{\rho},\mathbf{P};t) \\ \nabla_p f(\mathbf{R},\mathbf{p};t) &= e^{\zeta t/m}\nabla_\rho F(\boldsymbol{\rho},\mathbf{P};t) + \zeta^{-1}\nabla_P F(\boldsymbol{\rho},\mathbf{P};t) \end{aligned} \tag{4.4.46}$$

and

$$\nabla_p{}^2 f(\mathbf{R},\mathbf{p};t) = e^{2\zeta t/m}\,\nabla_\rho{}^2 F + 2\zeta^{-1}e^{\zeta t/m}\nabla_\rho\cdot\nabla_P F + \zeta^{-2}\,\nabla_P{}^2 F, \tag{4.4.47}$$

where $f(\mathbf{R},\mathbf{p};t) = F(\boldsymbol{\rho},\mathbf{P};t)$. With the substitution

$$f = e^{3\zeta t/m}\chi \tag{4.4.48}$$

it is found that

$$\frac{\partial \chi}{\partial t} = \varphi[e^{2\zeta t/m}\nabla_\rho{}^2\chi + 2\zeta^{-1}e^{\zeta t/m}\nabla_\rho\cdot\nabla_P\chi + \zeta^{-2}\nabla_P{}^2\chi], \tag{4.4.49}$$

where

$$\varphi = \zeta kT. \tag{4.4.50}$$

Consider now the one-dimensional equation corresponding to equation (4.4.49):

$$\frac{\partial \chi}{\partial t} = \phi^2(t)\frac{\partial^2 \chi}{\partial \xi^2} + 2\phi(t)\theta(t)\frac{\partial^2 \chi}{\partial \xi\,\partial \eta} + \theta^2(t)\frac{\partial^2 \chi}{\partial \eta^2}. \tag{4.4.51}$$

The solution of equation (4.4.51), which has a source at $\xi = \eta = 0$ at $t = 0$, is

$$\chi(\xi,\eta;0) = \delta(\xi)\delta(\eta) \tag{4.4.52}$$

$$\chi = \frac{1}{2\pi\,\Delta^{1/2}} \exp\,[-(a\xi^2 + 2h\xi\eta + b\eta^2)/2\Delta], \tag{4.4.53}$$

where

$$a = 2\int_0^t \theta^2(t)\,dt,$$

$$b = 2\int_0^t \phi^2(t)\,dt, \tag{4.4.54}$$

$$h = -2\int_0^t \theta(t)\phi(t)\,dt,$$

and

$$\Delta = ab - h^2.$$

That χ is correctly given by equation (4.4.53) is easily proved by substitution in equation (4.4.51). The behavior for small t can be deduced from the fact that a, b, h are all linear in t as $t \to 0$, while Δ is also; hence, χ is extremely sharply peaked at the origin for small t. Now, we note that the variables in equation (4.4.49) are separable into the pairs (ρ_1,P_1), (ρ_2,P_2), (ρ_3,P_3), and that each $\chi(\rho_i,P_i)$ satisfies an equation of the form (4.4.51). Hence, the solution of equation (4.4.49), which has a source at $\boldsymbol{\rho} = \boldsymbol{\rho}_0$, $\mathbf{P} = \mathbf{P}_0$ at $t = 0$, is

$$\chi = \frac{1}{8\pi^3\,\Delta^{3/2}} \exp\,\{-[a(\boldsymbol{\rho} - \boldsymbol{\rho}_0)^2 + 2h(\boldsymbol{\rho} - \boldsymbol{\rho}_0)\cdot(\mathbf{P} - \mathbf{P}_0) + b(\mathbf{P} - \mathbf{P}_0)^2]/2\Delta\}, \tag{4.4.56}$$

where

$$\phi(t) = \varphi^{1/2} e^{\zeta t/m}; \qquad \theta(t) = \varphi^{1/2}\zeta^{-1}, \tag{4.4.57}$$

so that

$$a = 2kT\zeta^{-1}t$$
$$b = mkT(e^{2\zeta t/m} - 1)$$
$$h = -2mkT\zeta^{-1}(e^{\zeta t/m} - 1)$$
$$\Delta = 2(mkT\zeta^{-1})^2 e^{2\zeta t/m}\left(\frac{\zeta t}{m} - 2 + 4e^{-\zeta t/m} - \left(2 + \frac{\zeta t}{m}\right) e^{-2\zeta t/m}\right). \quad (4.4.58).$$

The full solution to equation (4.4.34) is, from equations (4.4.58,56)

$$f(\mathbf{R},\mathbf{p};t) = \frac{e^{3\zeta t/m}}{8\pi^3\Delta^{3/2}} \exp\{-[a(\boldsymbol{\rho} - \boldsymbol{\rho}_0)^2 + 2h(\boldsymbol{\rho} - \boldsymbol{\rho}_0)\cdot(\mathbf{P} - \mathbf{P}_0) + b(\mathbf{P} - \mathbf{P}_0)^2]/2\Delta\}, \quad (4.4.59)$$

with

$$f(\mathbf{R},\mathbf{p};0) = \delta(\mathbf{R} - \mathbf{R}_0)\delta(\mathbf{p} - \mathbf{p}_0) \quad (4.4.60)$$

and

$$\boldsymbol{\rho} - \boldsymbol{\rho}_0 = \mathbf{p}e^{\zeta t/m} - \mathbf{p}_0$$
$$\mathbf{P} - \mathbf{P}_0 = \mathbf{R} + \mathbf{p}/\zeta - \mathbf{R}_0 - \mathbf{p}_0/\zeta. \quad (4.4.61)$$

The properties of the solution are not immediately accessible in the form (4.4.59), and we therefore introduce the new variables

$$\mathbf{q} = \mathbf{p} - \mathbf{p}_0 e^{-\zeta t/m}$$
$$\mathbf{S} = \mathbf{R} - \mathbf{R}_0 - \zeta^{-1}\mathbf{p}_0(1 - e^{-\zeta t/m}), \quad (4.4.62)$$

so that

$$\boldsymbol{\rho} - \boldsymbol{\rho}_0 = e^{\zeta t/m}\mathbf{q}$$
$$\mathbf{P} - \mathbf{P}_0 = \mathbf{S} + \zeta^{-1}\mathbf{q}. \quad (4.4.63)$$

Equation (4.4.57) becomes

$$f(\mathbf{R},\mathbf{p};t) = \frac{1}{[2\pi(AB)^{1/2}(1 - \psi^2)^{1/2}]^3} \times \exp\left\{-\frac{(q^2/B - [2\psi/(AB)^{1/2}]\mathbf{q}\cdot\mathbf{S} + S^2/A)}{2(1 - \psi^2)}\right\}, \quad (4.4.64)$$

where

$$A = mkT\zeta^{-2}[2\zeta t/m - 3 + 4e^{-\zeta t/m} - e^{-2\zeta t/m}]$$
$$B = mkT[1 - e^{-2\zeta t/m}]$$
$$H = mkT\zeta^{-1}[1 - e^{-\zeta t/m}]^2$$
$$AB - H^2 = e^{-2\zeta t/m}\,\Delta, \quad (4.4.65)$$

and

$$\psi = \frac{H}{(AB)^{1/2}} \tag{4.4.66}$$

is the normalized correlation function of $\mathbf{q}$ and $\mathbf{S}$. Equation (4.4.64) is a special form of the general Gaussian distribution (4.3.22) in which the variable $\mathbf{y}$ is the composite vector

$$\mathbf{y} = (\mathbf{q},\mathbf{S}), \tag{4.4.67}$$

and the only terms appearing in the exponent involve products of the same components of the constituent vectors $\mathbf{q}$, $\mathbf{S}$. The distribution (4.4.64) has the first and second moments

$$\begin{aligned} \langle \mathbf{q} \rangle_1 &= 0 \\ \langle \mathbf{S} \rangle_1 &= 0 \\ \langle q^2 \rangle_1 &= 3B \\ \langle S^2 \rangle_1 &= 3A \\ \langle \mathbf{q} \cdot \mathbf{S} \rangle_1 &= 3H, \end{aligned} \tag{4.4.68}$$

which lead to the results

$$\begin{aligned} &(a) \quad \langle \mathbf{p} \rangle_1 = \mathbf{p}_0 e^{-\zeta t/m} \\ &(b) \quad \langle (\mathbf{R} - \mathbf{R}_0) \rangle_1 = \zeta^{-1} \mathbf{p}_0 (1 - e^{-\zeta t/m}) \\ &(c) \quad \langle p^2 \rangle_1 = {p_0}^2 e^{-2\zeta t/m} + 3mkT(1 - e^{-2\zeta t/m}) \\ &(d) \quad \langle (\mathbf{R} - \mathbf{R}_0)^2 \rangle_1 = \zeta^{-2} {p_0}^2 (1 - e^{-\zeta t/m})^2 \\ &\qquad\qquad + 3mkT\zeta^{-2}[2\zeta t/m - 3 + 4e^{-\zeta t/m} - e^{-2\zeta t/m}] \\ &(e) \quad \langle (\mathbf{p} - \mathbf{p}_0) \cdot (\mathbf{R} - \mathbf{R}_0) \rangle_1 = \zeta^{-1}[3mkT - {p_0}^2][1 - e^{-\zeta t/m}]^2. \end{aligned} \tag{4.4.69}$$

The subscript "1" appears on the average because the moments are calculated for the initial condition (4.4.60); namely,

$$\mathbf{R} = \mathbf{R}_0,\ \mathbf{p} = \mathbf{p}_0;\ t = 0. \tag{4.4.70}$$

It is shown by equations (4.4.69b,d) that the distribution remains spatially located around the (initial) source point $\mathbf{R}_0$, while equations (4.4.69a,c) show that the initial momentum $\mathbf{p}_0$ is forgotten for times $t \gg m\zeta^{-1}$.* Nevertheless, the position and momentum displacements,

* The reader should note that for times $t \ll m\zeta^{-1}$ "dynamical" motion occurs:

$$\langle (\mathbf{R} - \mathbf{R}_0)^2 \rangle_1 = m^{-2} {p_0}^2 t^2.$$

$(\mathbf{R} - \mathbf{R}_0)$ and $(\mathbf{p} - \mathbf{p}_0)$, respectively, are correlated at all times, according to equation (4.4.69*e*). For long times the moments take on the form

$$\begin{aligned}
&(a)\ \langle \mathbf{p} \rangle_1 = 0 \\
&(b)\ \langle (\mathbf{R} - \mathbf{R}_0) \rangle_1 = \zeta^{-1}\mathbf{p}_0 \\
&(c)\ \langle p^2 \rangle_1 = 3mkT \\
&(d)\ \langle (\mathbf{R} - \mathbf{R}_0)^2 \rangle_1 = 6kT\zeta^{-1}t \\
&(e)\ \langle (\mathbf{p} - \mathbf{p}_0) \cdot (\mathbf{R} - \mathbf{R}_0) \rangle_1 = \zeta^{-1}(3mkT - p_0{}^2).
\end{aligned} \tag{4.4.71}$$

These are characteristic of a distribution Maxwellian in the momenta, and of the three-dimensional Gaussian form corresponding to the solution (4.4.10) of the diffusion equation. The transition from equation (4.4.70*d*) to equation (4.4.71*d*) indicates how the mean-square position displacement $\langle (\mathbf{R} - \mathbf{R}_0)^2 \rangle_1 = \langle (\Delta R)^2 \rangle_1$ approaches the asymptotic form (4.4.16) which defines the diffusion coefficient. It is seen, from equation (4.4.71*b*), that the spatial distribution is *not* centered on $\mathbf{R}_0$, but on $(\mathbf{R}_0 + \zeta^{-1}\mathbf{p}_0)$. The displacement of the center is by what we shall later call a "diffusive step"; it corresponds to the distance a macroscopic particle travels to rest when its initial momentum is $\mathbf{p}_0$, and it is subject to a Stokes' law force $-(\zeta/m)\mathbf{p}_0$. If the initial momentum is not fixed at $\mathbf{p}_0$, but also has a Maxwell distribution, then by averaging over $\mathbf{p}_0$ it is found that

$$\begin{aligned}
&(a)\quad \langle \langle \mathbf{p} \rangle_1 \rangle = 0 \\
&(b)\quad \langle \langle (\mathbf{R} - \mathbf{R}_0) \rangle_1 \rangle = 0 \\
&(c)\quad \langle \langle p^2 \rangle_1 \rangle = 3mkT \\
&(d)\quad \langle \langle (\mathbf{R} - \mathbf{R}_0)^2 \rangle_1 \rangle = 6mkT\zeta^{-2}[\zeta t/m - 1 + e^{-\zeta t/m}] \\
&(e)\quad \langle \langle (\mathbf{p} - \mathbf{p}_0) \cdot (\mathbf{R} - \mathbf{R}_0) \rangle_1 \rangle = 0.
\end{aligned} \tag{4.4.72}$$

The momentum dependence is here Maxwellian at all times, and the position dependence is symmetric about $\mathbf{R}_0$. The result (4.4.72*d*) is the important generalization of the asymptotic result (4.4.71*d*), and was given by Einstein and Furth.

We shall see in Section 4.5 that all these results are equally obtainable by using the equation of motion of the particles.

4.4.C. *Diffusion in an External Force Field: The Smoluchowski Equation* (4)

In practice, the apparent behavior of a Brownian particle is determined almost entirely by the range of frequencies to which the eye, or other instrument, can respond. This is because the frequencies actually present in the motion of the particle are not greatly changed from those present in molecular fluctuations; the maximum frequency to which the eye can respond is so many octaves below the high frequencies present that increasing the eye's range by an octave (i.e., doubling the frequency to which it responds) still leaves almost all of the available spectrum unsampled, while greatly changing the apparent behavior. Consequently, the behavior of the particle in momentum space may not be studied directly, but only inferred from a comparison between theoretical predictions and observations of the position displacement as a function of time. We therefore proceed to a discussion of the configuration space projection of the Fokker-Planck equation (4.4.34).

The method we use is related to the discussion of moments (Section 4.2.B); the momentum part of the distribution function is calculated indirectly by forming a set of differential equations for its moments, and these are used to eliminate the momentum part from the equation. We define, therefore, the density $\rho(\mathbf{R};t)$,* flow $\mathbf{j}(\mathbf{R};t)$, the kinetic part of the pressure tensor $\mathsf{P}(\mathbf{R};t)$, the energy-flux tensor $\mathsf{Q}(\mathbf{R};t)$, etc., as

$$\begin{aligned}
\rho &= \int f(\mathbf{R},\mathbf{p};t)\,d\mathbf{p} \\
\mathbf{j} &= \frac{1}{m}\int \mathbf{p}f(\mathbf{R},\mathbf{p};t)\,d\mathbf{p} \\
\mathsf{P} &= \frac{1}{m}\int \mathbf{pp}f(\mathbf{R},\mathbf{p};t)\,d\mathbf{p} \\
\mathsf{Q} &= \frac{1}{m}\int \mathbf{ppp}f(\mathbf{R},\mathbf{p};t)\,d\mathbf{p}.
\end{aligned} \tag{4.4.73†}$$

* The reader is reminded of the alternative interpretations of ρ as either the (configuration-space) probability for a single particle, or as the number density [(cf. the discussion following Eq. (4.4.20)].

† If the fluid in which the Brownian particles are suspended supports a hydrodynamic velocity field $\mathbf{u}(\mathbf{R};t)$, then $\mathbf{p}$ is replaced by $(\mathbf{p} - m\mathbf{u})$ in equations (4.4.31,73), except [cf. (4.2.2) for the definitions of moments] in the case of $\mathbf{j}$.

The equation for the nth momentum moment is obtained by multiplying equation (4.4.34) by the nth rank tensor $\mathbf{pp}\cdots\mathbf{p}$ (n factors) and integrating over momentum space. We obtain

$$(a)\quad \frac{\partial \rho}{\partial t} + \nabla_k j_k = 0$$

$$(b)\quad m\frac{\partial j_k}{\partial t} + \nabla_l P_{lk} - \rho K_k = -\zeta j_k$$

$$(c)\quad m\frac{\partial P_{lk}}{\partial t} + \nabla_n Q_{nlk} - m(K_l j_k + j_l K_k) = 2\zeta(-P_{lk} + kT\rho\delta_{lk}) \quad (4.4.74)$$

$$(d)\quad m\frac{\partial Q_{kln}}{\partial t} + \cdots = \zeta(-3Q_{kln} + 2mkT\{j_k\delta_{ln} + j_l\delta_{kn} + j_n\delta_{kl}\})$$

$$\vdots$$

etc.

Equations (4.4.74) have been written in the notation of Cartesian tensors, and any subscript appearing twice in a term is summed over. Thus, $\nabla_k j_k = \nabla\cdot\mathbf{j}$, etc. We have made the simplifying (but not important) assumption that the pressure tensor is symmetric:

$$P_{ij} = P_{ji}. \quad (4.4.75)$$

In order to obtain equations (4.4.74) it is necessary to perform partial integrations to eliminate the momentum derivatives of f; it is assumed that the resulting surface terms vanish because f approaches zero sufficiently rapidly as $p \to \infty$ [e.g., like $\exp(-p^2/2mkT)$]. Equations (4.4.74) constitute a hierarchy of coupled equations of such complexity that we must adopt some approximation procedure to obtain a solution. In a discussion of transport processes we would only be interested in the fluxes of matter (**j**), of momentum (**P**), and of energy (**Q**), so that we could expect to obtain adequate accuracy by introducing a truncation procedure which expresses $\langle\mathbf{pppp}\rangle$ in terms of **Q**. However, this is not necessary if the friction coefficient is sufficiently large, because we may then order terms in ascending powers of ζ^{-1}, and use an iterative procedure. Thus, we calculate $(\partial j_k/\partial t)$ by differentiating (the right-hand side of) equation (4.4.74*b*) with respect to t, and so on, introducing an extra factor ζ^{-1} each time. In this way we obtain, to order ζ^{-3},

$$\frac{\partial\rho}{\partial t} = \left[\frac{1}{\zeta}\nabla_k(kT\nabla_k\rho - \rho K_k)\right] - \frac{m}{2\zeta^2}\left[kT\nabla^2\frac{\partial\rho}{\partial t} - 2\nabla_k\left(K_k\frac{\partial\rho}{\partial t}\right)\right]$$
$$+ \frac{m}{\zeta^3}\nabla_k\nabla_l[K_l(kT\nabla_k\rho - \rho K_k)]. \tag{4.4.76}$$

The first term (in square brackets) on the right-hand side of equation (4.4.76) is regarded as the first approximation to the differential equation for ρ, and $(\partial\rho/\partial t)$ is eliminated from the second term by substituting this term. The result is

$$\frac{\partial\rho}{\partial t} = \frac{kT}{\zeta}\nabla\cdot\left(\nabla\rho + \frac{\nabla W^{(1)}}{kT}\rho\right) + \frac{m}{\zeta}\left(\frac{kT}{\zeta}\right)^2 F, \tag{4.4.77}$$

where

$$F = -\nabla^4\rho - \frac{1}{kT}[\nabla\rho\cdot\nabla\nabla^2W^{(1)} + \nabla^2\rho\,\nabla^2W^{(1)} + \nabla W^{(1)}\cdot\nabla\nabla^2\rho]$$
$$+ \frac{2}{(kT)^2}[\nabla\rho\cdot\nabla W^{(1)}\nabla^2W^{(1)} + \rho(\nabla^2W^{(1)})^2 + \rho\nabla W^{(1)}\cdot\nabla\nabla^2W^{(1)}] \tag{4.4.78}$$

$$\mathbf{K} = -\nabla W^{(1)}, \tag{4.4.79}$$

and we have reverted to ordinary vector notation. The approximation procedure we have used preserves, as it should, the equilibrium form of the density. It was pointed out in Section 4.4.B that the equilibrium solution of the Fokker-Planck equation should be the Maxwell-Boltzmann distribution; the solution of equations (4.4.77, 78) should be simply the Boltzmann distribution

$$\rho_0 = A\exp(-W^{(1)}/kT). \tag{4.4.80}$$

We can immediately verify this by inspecting equations (4.4.76), since $(\partial\rho/\partial t) = 0$ in equilibrium, and ρ_0 satisfies $(kT\nabla\rho_0 - \rho_0\mathbf{K}) = 0$.

The expansion procedure used to obtain equation (4.4.77–78) is justified, as we already mentioned, if the friction coefficient "is large enough." If the density is not too far from an equilibrium distribution, then the spatial variations of ρ will be similar to those of $W^{(1)}$. Thus, if the scale of length λ associated with significant variations in the external field satisfies the condition

$$\left(m\frac{kT}{\zeta^2}\right)^2\lambda^{-4} \ll 1, \tag{4.4.81}$$

then,

$$\frac{m}{\zeta}\left(\frac{kT}{\zeta}\right)\nabla^4\rho \ll \nabla^2\rho, \tag{4.4.82}$$

and equation (4.4.77) may be replaced by

$$\frac{\partial\rho}{\partial t} = D\,\nabla\cdot\left(\nabla\rho + \frac{\nabla W^{(1)}}{kT}\,\rho\right), \tag{4.4.83}$$

where we have introduced

$$D = \frac{kT}{\zeta} \tag{4.4.84}$$

as the definition of the diffusion coefficient. The length scale d typical of Brownian motion (as opposed to that typical of the external field) is, from equation (4.4.81),

$$d = \left(\frac{mD}{\zeta}\right)^{1/2}. \tag{4.4.85}$$

d was referred to in connection with equation (4.4.71b) as a diffusive step. Equations (4.4.71b,85) have precisely the same form when the magnitude of $\mathbf{p}_0$ is the root mean-square momentum. If the fluid in which the particles are suspended has a velocity field $\mathbf{u}$, then it is easily shown that equation (4.4.83) becomes

$$\frac{\partial\rho}{\partial t} = D\,\nabla\cdot\left(\nabla\rho + \left(\frac{\nabla W^{(1)}}{kT} - \frac{\mathbf{u}}{D}\right)\rho\right). \tag{4.4.86}$$

Finally, we remark that the inequalities (4.4.81–82) imply that the solution of equation (4.4.83) will not describe correctly either the initial evolution of a sharply peaked density function or the evolution of any density function in a sufficiently inhomogeneous force field.

The presence of an external force field gives rise to a drift of the particles. Equation (4.4.83) is multiplied by $\mathbf{R}$ and integrated over a region $\mathscr{V}$ of space throughout which the force $\mathbf{K}(\mathbf{R})$ is approximately constant. We obtain the relation

$$\langle\mathbf{u}\rangle = \frac{\mathbf{K}}{m\zeta} \tag{4.4.87}$$

for the drift velocity of the particle, if the particles are concentrated in the interior of $\mathscr{V}$ so that the surface terms resulting from partial integration vanish. The particle flux density $\mathbf{j}_K$ induced by the force

$\mathbf{K}$ is then

$$\mathbf{j}_K = \rho\langle \mathbf{u} \rangle = \frac{\rho}{m\zeta}\mathbf{K}. \tag{4.4.88}$$

In equilibrium the total flux $\mathbf{j}$ satisfies

$$\frac{\partial \rho}{\partial t} = -\nabla \cdot \mathbf{j} = 0, \tag{4.4.89}$$

and it may be assumed that

$$\mathbf{j} = D\nabla\rho - \mathbf{j}_K = 0. \tag{4.4.90}$$

Hence, in equilibrium the drift flux $\mathbf{j}_K$ is equal and opposite to the flux due to the concentration gradient $-D\nabla\rho$.

4.5. BROWNIAN MOTION: THE EQUATION OF MOTION APPROACH (5,6)

We now describe a model of Brownian motion which is idealized in a sense to be made clear later. When a macroscopic body moves through a continuous fluid it experiences a resistive force which is, by Stokes' law, proportional to its momentum. If the body is also small enough to respond, not necessarily to the impact of individual molecules, but to fluctuations in the total rate of impacts over its surface, then it may be reasonably supposed that the body will show an average behavior in accordance with Stokes' law, on which is superimposed an erratic motion caused by the force fluctuations. Thus, the average increment of momentum in a time τ is

$$\langle \Delta \mathbf{p} \rangle_1 = -\frac{\zeta}{m}\mathbf{p}\tau, \tag{4.5.1}$$

where

$$\zeta = 6\pi\eta a, \tag{4.5.2}$$

and η, a are the coefficient of shear viscosity and radius of the (spherical) particle, respectively. Equation (4.5.1) has the form of the first moment $\mathbf{a}^{(1)}$ in equation (4.4.24). In order to be able to calculate higher moments of $\Delta\mathbf{p}$, equation (4.5.1) is replaced by a stochastic equation, called the Langevin equation:

$$\frac{d\mathbf{p}}{dt} = -\frac{\zeta}{m}\mathbf{p} + \mathbf{X}(t), \tag{4.5.3}$$

in which $\mathbf{X}(t)$ is a fluctuating force with the statistical properties

$$\langle \mathbf{X}(t) \rangle_1 = \langle \mathbf{X}(t) \rangle = 0, \tag{4.5.4}$$

$$\langle \mathbf{X}(t)\mathbf{X}(t+\tau) \rangle = \varphi(\tau)\mathbf{I}. \tag{4.5.5}$$

Thus, the total instantaneous force on the particle,

$$\mathbf{F}(t) = \frac{d\mathbf{p}}{dt},$$

is assumed to be separable into a systematic, or frictional force $-(\zeta/m)\mathbf{p}$, and a fluctuating force $\mathbf{X}(t)$. In equation (4.5.4) the equivalence of the conditional and full ensemble averages of $\mathbf{X}(t)$ represents the supposition that the fluctuating force is independent of the behavior of the particle (see the opening paragraph of Sec. 4.4.B). Its value, zero, guarantees that equation (4.5.1) will be recovered. Equation (4.5.5) states that the components of $\mathbf{X}(t)$ are independent random variables, and that they are stationary. The physical picture of a Brownian particle as massive and responding only slowly compared to the rate at which $\mathbf{X}(t)$ fluctuates leads to the hypothesis, of which we shall make considerable use, that $\varphi(\tau)$ has an indefinitely sharp peak on the time scale of the motion of the Brownian particle.

4.5.A. *The Expression for the Friction Coefficient*

An expression for the friction coefficient in terms of the statistical properties of $\mathbf{X}(t)$ may easily be deduced by integrating the Langevin equation (4.5.3) and requiring that the solution $\mathbf{p}(t)$ have the equipartition property

$$\lim_{t\to\infty} \langle p^2(t) \rangle = 3mkT. \tag{4.5.6}$$

The solution of equation (4.5.3), for the case that $\mathbf{p}(0) = \mathbf{p}_0$, is

$$\mathbf{p}(t) = \mathbf{p}_0 e^{-\zeta t/m} + e^{-\zeta t/m} \int_0^t e^{\zeta s/m} \mathbf{X}(s)\, ds. \tag{4.5.7}$$

Upon squaring equation (4.5.7) and averaging in the ensemble of Brownian particles all of which initially have momentum $\mathbf{p}_0$, we obtain

$$\langle p^2(t) \rangle_1 = p_0{}^2 e^{-2\zeta t/m} + 3e^{-2\zeta t/m} \int_0^t \int_0^t e^{\zeta(s+s')/m} \varphi(s-s')\, ds\, ds'. \tag{4.5.8*}$$

* The factor 3 appears because the scalar product $\langle \mathbf{X}(s) \cdot \mathbf{X}(s') \rangle$ is the trace of the tensor (4.5.5).

In order to evaluate the integral on the right hand side of equation (4.5.8) we introduce the new variables

$$v = s + s'$$
$$w = s - s'. \tag{4.5.9}$$

The region of integration is shown in Figure 4.5.1. Since $\mathbf{X}(t)$ is a stationary process we may assume without loss of generality that $\varphi(\tau)$

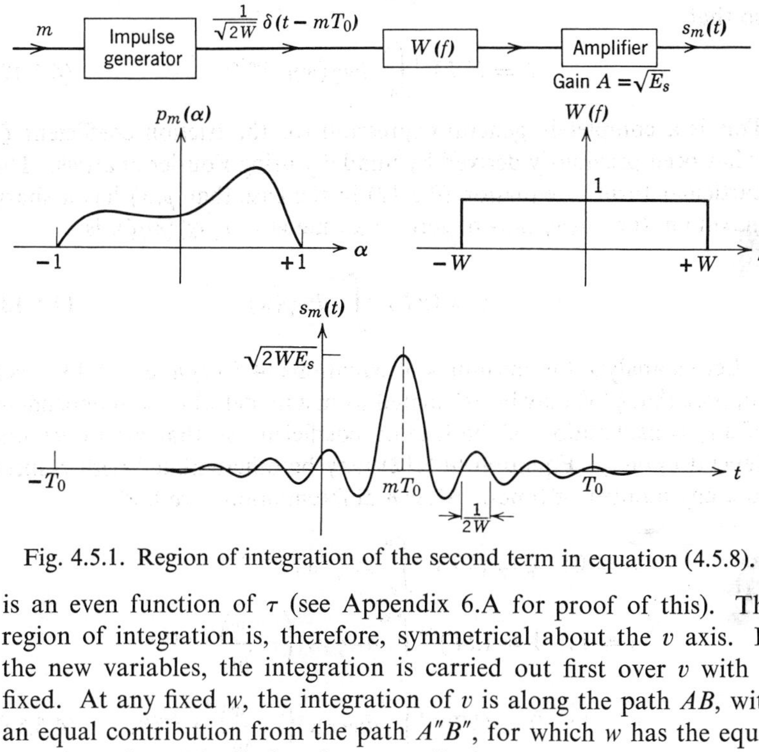

Fig. 4.5.1. Region of integration of the second term in equation (4.5.8).

is an even function of τ (see Appendix 6.A for proof of this). The region of integration is, therefore, symmetrical about the v axis. In the new variables, the integration is carried out first over v with w fixed. At any fixed w, the integration of v is along the path AB, with an equal contribution from the path $A''B''$, for which w has the equal negative value. The limits of v are easily found from equation (4.5.9) to be

$$v_A = v_{A'} = v_{A''} = w$$

and then we have

$$v_B = v_{B'} = v_{B''} = 2t - w, \tag{4.5.10}$$

$$\int_0^t \int_0^t e^{\zeta(s+s')/m} \varphi(s - s')\, ds\, ds' = \tfrac{1}{2} \cdot 2 \int_0^t dw\varphi(w) \int_w^{2t-w} dv e^{\zeta v/m}$$
$$= \frac{m}{\zeta} \int_0^t dw \varphi(w)(e^{\zeta(2t-w)/m} - e^{\zeta w/m}). \tag{4.5.11}$$

In the first line of equation (4.5.11) the factor $\frac{1}{2}$ results from the Jacobian of the transformation, while the factor 2 results from the symmetry of the w integration. Substituting equation (4.5.11) in equation (4.5.8), and taking the limit $t \to \infty$ yields

$$3mkT = \frac{3m}{\zeta}\int_0^\infty dw\varphi(w)e^{-\zeta w/m},$$

so that

$$\zeta = (kT)^{-1}\int_0^\infty dw\varphi(w)e^{-\zeta w/m}. \qquad (4.5.12)$$

This is a completely general expression for the friction coefficient ζ; it has been previously derived by Suddaby using Fourier analysis. The particular form of equation (4.5.12) in the case that $\varphi(w)$ has a sharp maximum (i.e., $\varphi(w)$ falls to zero in a time $w = \tau_1 \ll (m/\zeta)$, is

$$\zeta = (kT)^{-1}\int_0^\infty dw\varphi(w). \qquad (4.5.13)$$

Let us analyze the meanings of equations (4.5.12) and (4.5.13). We suppose that $\varphi(w)$ may be calculated from a model which is independent of any consideration of the friction coefficient, so that $\varphi(w)$ does not depend upon ζ. Equation (4.5.12) may be differentiated with respect to ζ any number of times. After n differentiations, we find

$$n = 0: \quad \zeta = (kT)^{-1}\int_0^\infty dw\varphi(w)\, e^{-\zeta w/m}$$

$$n = 1: \quad 1 = (kT)^{-1}\int_0^\infty dw\varphi(w)\left(-\frac{w}{m}\right)e^{-\zeta w/m}$$

$$n > 1: \quad 0 = (kT)^{-1}\int_0^\infty dw\varphi(w)\left(-\frac{w}{m}\right)^n e^{-\zeta w/m}. \qquad (4.5.14)$$

We now multiply the nth derivative by $(-\zeta)^n/n!$, and add all the resulting terms. The left-hand side vanishes, and we obtain the result

$$0 = \int_0^\infty dw\varphi(w)e^{-\zeta w/m}\sum_{n=0}^{\infty}\left(\frac{\zeta w}{m}\right)^n\frac{1}{n!} = \int_0^\infty dw\varphi(w), \qquad (4.5.15)$$

in contradiction to equation (4.5.13). It therefore follows that *the statistical properties of the fluctuating force cannot be defined* *independently of the friction coefficient.** We suppose, then, that $\varphi(w)$ is some function of the friction coefficient ζ:

$$\varphi(w) = \varphi(\zeta,w). \tag{4.5.16}$$

Performing the differentiations as in equation (4.5.14), we now obtain

$$\begin{aligned}
n = 0:&\quad \zeta = (kT)^{-1}\int_0^\infty dw\varphi^{(0)}(\zeta,w)e^{-\zeta w/m} \\
n = 1:&\quad 1 = (kT)^{-1}\int_0^\infty dw\left[\varphi^{(1)}(\zeta,w) - \frac{w}{m}\varphi^{(0)}(\zeta,w)\right]e^{-\zeta w/m} \\
n > 1:&\quad 0 = (kT)^{-1}\int_0^\infty dw\left[\sum_{j=0}^{n}\binom{n}{j}\left(-\frac{w}{m}\right)^{n-j}\varphi^{(j)}(\zeta,w)\right]e^{-\zeta w/m},
\end{aligned} \tag{4.5.17}$$

where

$$\varphi^{(j)}(\zeta,w) = \left(\frac{\partial}{\partial\zeta}\right)^j\varphi^{(0)}(\zeta,w)$$

and

$$\varphi^{(0)}(\zeta,w) = \varphi(\zeta,w). \tag{4.5.18}$$

We again multiply the nth derivative by $(-\zeta)^n/n!$ and add all the terms. Again the left-hand side vanishes, and it is found that

$$\begin{aligned}
0 &= \sum_{n=0}^{\infty}\sum_{j=0}^{n}\frac{(-\zeta)^n}{n!}\int_0^\infty dw\left[\binom{n}{j}\left(-\frac{w}{m}\right)^{n-j}\varphi^{(j)}(\zeta,w)\right]e^{-\zeta w/m} \\
&= \sum_{j=0}^{\infty}\sum_{n=j}^{\infty}\int_0^\infty dw(-\zeta)^j\left(\frac{w\zeta}{m}\right)^{n-j}\varphi^{(j)}(\zeta,w)\frac{e^{-\zeta w/m}}{j!\,(n-j)!},
\end{aligned}$$

where we have interchanged the order of the summations over n and j. Writing now $n - j = k$, we have

$$\begin{aligned}
0 &= \sum_{j=0}^{\infty}\int_0^\infty dw\,\frac{(-\zeta)^j\varphi^{(j)}(\zeta,w)}{j!}\left[\sum_{k=0}^{\infty}\left(\frac{w\zeta}{m}\right)^k\frac{1}{k!}\right]e^{-\zeta w/m} \\
&= \int_0^\infty dw\varphi(0,w).
\end{aligned} \tag{4.5.19}$$

* This conclusion follows in any case from the assumptions (4.5.4) and (4.5.5) regarding the properties of $\mathbf{X}(t)$: if the force between the Brownian particle and the liquid molecules is a function of their separation only, then $\mathbf{F}(t)$ is independent of $\mathbf{p}$ so that $\mathbf{X}(t)$ cannot be. Thus, $\mathbf{F}(t)$ depends not only on the friction coefficient *but also on the momentum.* Equation (4.5.4) can be regarded as approximately true if the Brownian particle is large enough that the number of molecules which are interacting with it at any instant is sufficiently great that the size of the fluctuations is small compared to the mean value.

Equation (4.5.19) follows because $e^{-\zeta w/m}$ is cancelled by the term in square brackets, and because

$$\sum_{j=0}^{\infty} \frac{(-\zeta)^j \varphi^{(j)}(\zeta,w)}{j!}$$

is the Taylor expansion of $\varphi(0,w)$ in powers of ζ about $\varphi(\zeta,w)$. Equation (4.5.19) involves the correlation function of the fluctuating force when the friction coefficient vanishes. In this limit the fluctuating force is identical with the total force on the particle:

$$\operatorname*{Lim}_{\zeta\to 0} \mathbf{X}(t) = \mathbf{F}(t) = \frac{d\mathbf{p}}{dt}, \tag{4.5.20}$$

so that equation (4.5.19) may be written as

$$\int_0^\infty \langle \mathbf{F}(t) \cdot \mathbf{F}(t+\tau)\rangle \, d\tau = 0. \tag{4.5.21}$$

The reader should note that, although averages of quantities associated with the Brownian particle, as opposed to the fluctuating force, are conditional averages, equation (4.5.21) is developed from equation (4.5.12), which is valid in the limit $t \to \infty$ when the particle has "forgotten" its initial momentum.

Equation (4.5.21) focuses attention upon the total force, which is defined without reference to the existence of a frictional and a fluctuating force, and in the next section we shall investigate the possibility of defining the friction coefficient in terms of $\langle \mathbf{F}(t) \cdot \mathbf{F}(t+\tau)\rangle$.

4.5.B. *The Autocorrelation Function of the Total Force* (6)

The relation between the total force and fluctuating force is, from equation (4.5.3),

$$\mathbf{F}(t) = \mathbf{X}(t) - \frac{\zeta}{m}\mathbf{p}(t). \tag{4.5.22}$$

The autocorrelation function of the total force is, therefore, given by

$$\langle \mathbf{F}(t) \cdot \mathbf{F}(t+\tau)\rangle_1 = 3\varphi(\tau) - \frac{\zeta}{m}\{\langle \mathbf{X}(t) \cdot \mathbf{p}(t+\tau)\rangle_1 + \langle \mathbf{X}(t+\tau) \cdot \mathbf{p}(t)\rangle_1\} + \left(\frac{\zeta}{m}\right)^2 \langle \mathbf{p}(t) \cdot \mathbf{p}(t+\tau)\rangle_1. \tag{4.5.23}$$

We wish to evaluate $\langle \mathbf{F}(t) \cdot \mathbf{F}(t+\tau)\rangle_1$. Since $\mathbf{p}(t)$ is given by equation (4.5.7), we have

$$\langle \mathbf{X}(t+\tau) \cdot \mathbf{p}(t)\rangle_1 = 3e^{-\zeta t/m} \int_0^t e^{\zeta s/m} \varphi(t+\tau-s)\, ds. \qquad (4.5.24)$$

Using the approximation (4.5.13) that $\varphi(\tau)$ is sharply peaked at $\tau = 0$, equation (4.5.24) becomes

$$\langle \mathbf{X}(t+\tau) \cdot \mathbf{p}(t)\rangle_1 = 0, \qquad (4.5.25)$$

because $(t+\tau)$ lies outside the range of integration of s. Thus, the momentum is not correlated with the fluctuating force at a later time. By replacing t by $(t+\tau)$ in equation (4.5.7), multiplying by $\mathbf{X}(t)$, and averaging, we obtain

$$\begin{aligned} \langle \mathbf{X}(t) \cdot \mathbf{p}(t+\tau)\rangle_1 &= 3e^{-\zeta(t+\tau)/m} \int_0^{t+\tau} e^{\zeta s/m} \varphi(t-s)\, ds \\ &= 6\zeta kT e^{-\zeta\tau/m}, \end{aligned} \qquad (4.5.26)$$

since the range of integration passes through $t = s$, and $\varphi(\tau)$ is assumed to be peaked sharply enough that all values different from zero occur in a range of τ so small that $e^{-\zeta\tau/m}$ does not change significantly. It should be noted that, in the special case $\tau = 0$, the ranges of integration in both equations (4.5.24) and (4.5.26) include the point $t - s = 0$ as an end-point, and thus each contributes half of the value (4.5.26). For the momentum autocorrelation function we obtain

$$\begin{aligned} \langle \mathbf{p}(t) \cdot \mathbf{p}(t+\tau)\rangle_1 &= p_0^2 e^{-\zeta(2t+\tau)/m} \\ &\quad + 3e^{-\zeta(2t+\tau)/m} \int_0^t \int_0^{t+\tau} e^{\zeta(s+s')/m} \varphi(s-s')\, ds\, ds'. \end{aligned} \qquad (4.5.27)$$

The second term on the right-hand side of equation (4.5.27) is evaluated by introducing again the variables $v = s + s'$ and $w = s - s'$. We integrate first over w giving φ the explicit form

$$\varphi(\tau) = 2\zeta kT\, \delta(\tau), \qquad (4.5.28)$$

consistent with equation (4.5.13); we obtain

$$\begin{aligned} \langle \mathbf{p}(t) \cdot \mathbf{p}(t+\tau)\rangle_1 &= p_0^2 e^{-\zeta(2t+\tau)/m} + e^{-\zeta(2t+\tau)/m} 3\zeta kT \int_0^{2t} e^{\zeta v/m}\, dv \\ &= e^{-\zeta\tau/m}(3mkT + e^{-2\zeta t/m}[p_0^2 - 3mkT]). \end{aligned} \qquad (4.5.29)$$

The upper limit of the v integral expresses the fact that non-zero values of φ lie close to the v axis, and hence at the extreme value of v we have $s = s' = t$. Substitution of equations (4.5.25), (4.5.26), and (4.5.29) in equation (4.5.23) now gives

$$\langle \mathbf{F}(t) \cdot \mathbf{F}(t + \tau) \rangle_1 = 3\varphi(\tau) - \frac{3\zeta^2 kT}{m} e^{-\zeta\tau/m} + \left(\frac{\zeta}{m}\right)^2 e^{-\zeta(2t+\tau)/m}(p_0{}^2 - 3mkT). \quad (4.5.30)$$

Integration of equation (4.5.30) over τ confirms equation (4.5.21):

$$\int_0^\infty \langle \mathbf{F}(t) \cdot \mathbf{F}(t + \tau) \rangle_1 \, d\tau = \frac{\zeta}{m} e^{-2\zeta t/m}(p_0{}^2 - 3mkT). \quad (4.5.31)$$

If we either proceed to the limit $t \to \infty$, or average over the initial momentum (which is physically equivalent), it is found that

$$\operatorname*{Lim}_{t \to \infty} \int_0^\infty \langle \mathbf{F}(t) \cdot \mathbf{F}(t + \tau) \rangle_1 \, d\tau = \int_0^\infty \langle \mathbf{F}(t) \cdot \mathbf{F}(t + \tau) \rangle \, d\tau = 0. \quad (4.5.32)$$

Equation (4.5.30) suggests a means by which the friction coefficient might be calculated from molecular dynamics. For, if $\varphi(\tau)$ does indeed have the sharply peaked property, so that

$$\varphi(\tau) = 0 \quad \text{for} \quad \tau > \tau_1, \quad (4.5.33)$$

where τ_1 satisfies the requirement already stated, namely,

$$\tau_1 \ll m/\zeta, \quad (4.5.34)$$

then, in the limit $t \to \infty$, the equilibrium value of $\langle \mathbf{F}(t) \cdot \mathbf{F}(t + \tau) \rangle$ is given by

$$\langle \mathbf{F}(t) \cdot \mathbf{F}(t + \tau) \rangle = \operatorname*{Lim}_{t \to \infty} \langle \mathbf{F}(t) \cdot \mathbf{F}(t + \tau) \rangle_1 = 3\varphi(\tau) - \frac{3\zeta^2 kT}{m} e^{-\zeta t/m}. \quad (4.5.35)$$

Now $\langle \mathbf{F}(t) \cdot \mathbf{F}(t + \tau) \rangle$, given by equation (4.5.35), is illustrated in Figure (4.5.2); it has a peak at the origin of height $\sim 3\zeta kT/\tau_1$ and width τ_1, representing $\varphi(\tau)$, and for $\tau > \tau_1$ it is negative. According to equation (4.5.32) the positive area A and the negative area B, are equal in magnitude, but the extent to which $\langle \mathbf{F}(t) \cdot \mathbf{F}(t + \tau) \rangle$ goes negative is very small compared to the height of the peak at the origin. The integral

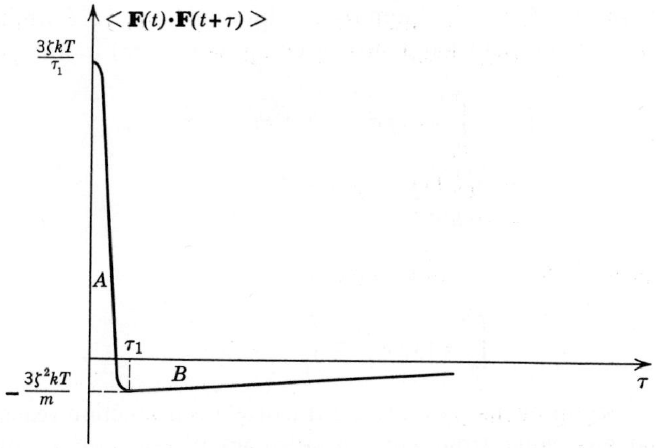

Fig. 4.5.2. Autocorrelation function of the total force as a function of τ.

$I(r)$ of $\langle \mathbf{F}(t) \cdot \mathbf{F}(t+\tau) \rangle$ over a range $0 \leqslant \tau \leqslant r$, where r is arbitrary, is

$$I(r) = 3\int_0^r \varphi(\tau)\, d\tau + 3\zeta kT(e^{-\zeta r/m} - 1), \tag{4.5.36}$$

and the integral $\int_0^r \varphi(\tau)\, d\tau$ is illustrated in Figure (4.5.3). It is seen that if the inequalities (4.5.33) and (4.5.34) are satisfied, then $\int_0^r \varphi(\tau)\, d\tau$

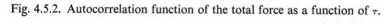

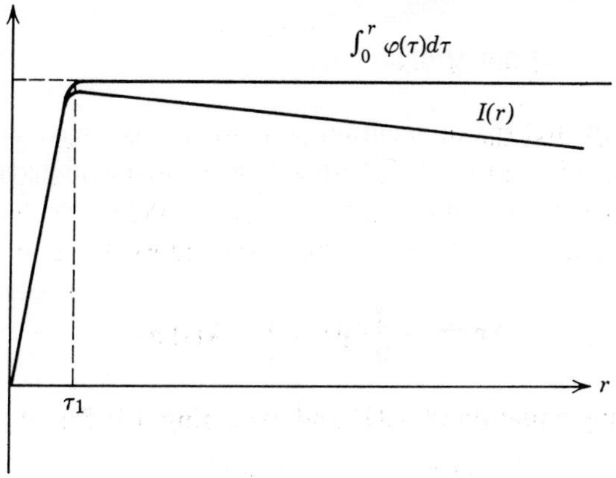

Fig. 4.5.3. Autocorrelation integrals of the fluctuating force $\int_0^r \varphi(\tau)\, d\tau$ and of the total force $I(r)$.

reaches its plateau (i.e., maximum or asymptotic) value $3\zeta kT$ while the second term on the right hand side of equation (4.5.36) is still small:

$$\begin{aligned} I(\tau_1) &= 3\int_0^{\tau_1} \varphi(\tau)\,d\tau + 3\zeta kT(e^{-\zeta\tau_1/m} - 1) \\ &= 3\zeta kT(1 - \zeta\tau_1/m + \cdots) \\ &\simeq 3\zeta kT, \end{aligned} \tag{4.5.36'}$$

because, according to equation (4.5.33)

$$\int_0^{\tau_1} \varphi(\tau)\,d\tau \simeq \int_0^{\infty} \varphi(\tau)\,d\tau.$$

Thus, the integral of the total force autocorrelation function reaches a "quasi-plateau" value, from which it falls back to zero in times of the order of (m/ζ). It follows that if the inequalities (4.5.33) and (4.5.34) are satisfied then the relation

$$\zeta = (3kT)^{-1}\int_0^{r} \langle \mathbf{F}(t)\cdot\mathbf{F}(t+\tau)\rangle\,d\tau; \qquad r > \tau_1 \tag{4.5.36''}$$

is sensibly independent of r for $r \ll m/\zeta$, and is a means by which the friction coefficient can, in principle at least, be calculated directly from molecular dynamics.

4.5.C. *Moments of the Motion*

We consider first the momentum increments. We have already seen that $\langle\Delta\mathbf{p}\rangle_1$ [equation (4.5.1)] conforms to the form postulated in equation (4.4.31). To calculate the second moment of $\Delta\mathbf{p}$, we integrate the Langevin equation (4.5.3) over a short time interval τ, and obtain

$$\Delta\mathbf{p} = -\frac{\zeta}{m}\,\mathbf{p}\tau + \int_t^{t+\tau} \mathbf{X}(s)\,ds. \tag{4.5.37}$$

Upon squaring equation (4.5.37) and averaging it is found that

$$\begin{aligned} \langle\Delta\mathbf{p}\,\Delta\mathbf{p}\rangle_1 &= \left(\frac{\zeta^2}{m}\right)\mathbf{pp}\tau^2 + \int_t^{t+\tau}\int_t^{t+\tau} \varphi(s - s')\,ds\,ds'\,\mathbf{I} \\ &= 2\zeta kT\tau\mathbf{I} + \mathcal{O}(\tau^2). \end{aligned} \tag{4.5.38}$$

Thus, $\langle \Delta\mathbf{p}\Delta\mathbf{p}\rangle_1$ is isotropic because $\langle \mathbf{X}(t)\mathbf{X}(t+\tau)\rangle$ is isotropic; equation (4.5.38) is in agreement with the form of $\mathbf{a}^{(2)}$ proposed in Section 4.4.B, equations (4.4.30) and (4.4.33).

The displacement of the particle, initially at $\mathbf{R}_0$ with momentum $\mathbf{p}_0$, is obtained by integrating equation (4.5.7):

$$\begin{aligned}\mathbf{R}(t) - \mathbf{R}_0 &= \frac{1}{m}\int_0^t \mathbf{p}(s)\,ds \\ &= \frac{1}{m}\,\mathbf{p}_0\int_0^t e^{-\zeta s/m}\,ds + \frac{1}{m}\int_0^t dse^{-\zeta s/m}\int_0^s ds' e^{\zeta s'/m}\mathbf{X}(s') \\ &= \zeta^{-1}\left[\mathbf{p}_0(1 - e^{-\zeta t/m}) + \int_0^t (1 - e^{\zeta(s-t)/m})\mathbf{X}(s)\,ds\right]. \quad (4.5.39)\end{aligned}$$

If equation (4.5.39) is averaged, we immediately obtain equation (4.4.69*b*). The mean-square displacement is

$$\begin{aligned}\langle(\mathbf{R} - \mathbf{R}_0)^2\rangle_1 = \zeta^{-2}\Big[& p_0^{\,2}(1 - e^{-\zeta t/m})^2 \\ & + 3\int_0^t\int_0^t (1 - e^{\zeta(s-t)/m})(1 - e^{\zeta(s'-t)/m})\varphi(s - s')\,ds\,ds'\Big].\end{aligned} \quad (4.5.40)$$

The integral on the right-hand side of equation (4.5.40) is evaluated by inserting the explicit form (4.5.28) for $\varphi(\tau)$; it becomes

$$\begin{aligned}3\int_0^t\int_0^t & (1 - e^{\zeta(s-t)/m})(1 - e^{\zeta(s'-t)})\varphi(s - s')\,ds\,ds' \\ &= 6\zeta kT\int_0^t (1 - e^{\zeta(s-t)/m})^2\,ds \\ &= 3mkT(2\zeta t/m - 3 + 4e^{-\zeta t/m} - e^{-2\zeta t/m}). \quad (4.5.41)\end{aligned}$$

Substitution of equation (4.5.41) in equation (4.5.39) then yields equation (4.4.69*d*). From equation (4.5.7) we can write the momentum displacement $(\mathbf{p} - \mathbf{p}_0)$ as

$$\mathbf{p} - \mathbf{p}_0 = \mathbf{p}_0(e^{-\zeta t/m} - 1) + e^{-\zeta t/m}\int_0^t e^{\zeta s/m}\mathbf{X}(s)\,ds. \quad (4.5.42)$$

The average of equation (4.5.42) yields equation (4.4.69*a*). If we insert equation (4.5.28) in equation (4.5.8), the integration may be carried out immediately, and we obtain equation (4.4.69*c*) Finally, if equation

(4.5.42) is multiplied by equation (4.5.39), and averaged, we obtain

$$\langle(\mathbf{p}-\mathbf{p}_0)\cdot(\mathbf{R}-\mathbf{R}_0)\rangle_1 = \zeta^{-1}\Big[-p_0^2(1-e^{-\zeta t/m})^2 + 3\int_0^t\int_0^t (1-e^{\zeta(s-t)/m})e^{\zeta(s'-t)/m}\varphi(s-s')\,ds'\,ds\Big]$$
$$= \zeta^{-1}(3mkT - p_0^2)(1-e^{-\zeta t/m})^2, \qquad (4.5.43)$$

in agreement with equation (4.4.69*e*).

We have shown, therefore, that the moments of the solution (4.4.59) or (4.4.64) of the Fokker-Planck equation are exactly reproduced by an appropriate analysis of the equation of motion (4.5.3). In solving the equation of motion we have used the sharp-peak approximation throughout. This approximation is already implicit in the derivation of the Fokker-Planck equation in Section 4.4.B, because it was necessary to introduce a lower limit, called there τ_c, to the time interval over which the transition probability was expanded. In equation (4.5.38) we see that the exponential weighting factor, which appears in the general expression (4.5.12) for ζ, is not present; hence, the definition of ζ used must be that appropriate to the sharp-peak approximation (4.5.13). Thus, we confirm the fact that the Fokker-Planck equation does not describe events happening in times shorter than $\tau_1 \ll m/\zeta$.

REFERENCES

1. Bartlett, M. S., *An Introduction to Stochastic Processes*, Cambridge University Press, New York, 1955.
2. Wang, M. C., and G. E. Uhlenbeck, *Rev. Mod. Phys.*, **17**, 323 (1945); see ref. 6, chap. 3.
3. *Ibid.*
4. Chandrasekhar, S., *Rev. Mod. Phys.*, **15**, 1 (1943); see ref. 6, chap. 3.
5. Uhlenbeck, G. E., and L. S. Ornstein, *Phys. Rev.*, **36**, 823 (1930); see ref. 1, chap. 3.
6. Suddaby, A., and P. Gray, *Proc. Phys. Soc.* (*London*), **75**, 109 (1960).

CHAPTER 5

The Kinetic Equations

5.1. INTRODUCTION

A kinetic equation is any equation determining the time evolution and phase dependence of some kind of ensemble probability distribution. This chapter is devoted to the derivation and solution of kinetic equations applicable to the description of transport phenomena in simple dense fluids. The application of the solutions obtained in this chapter to the problems of the calculation of particular transport coefficients is described in Chapter 6.

The calculation of transport coefficients is, in fact, only a small part of the general problem of describing time-dependent phenomena. Namely, it is concerned with that state of a fluid in which all time-dependence resides in the local thermodynamic variables, temperature and density, and in the local hydrodynamic flow velocity. The general problem also involves the description of those short-lived processes whose time dependence is explicit. Such processes are generally non-Markovian of a high order, and the asymptotic approach of the exact kinetic equations describing them to the Markovian equations of the hydrodynamic regime with which we are concerned in this chapter, is discussed in Chapter 7.

As we shall see in Chapter 7, the exact kinetic equations for a dense fluid can be displayed only in the most formal way at the present time. Consequently, their asymptotic Markovian form is unknown, and the forms of the equations derived in this chapter are based on an intuitive analysis of the nature of random processes in a dense fluid. Our analysis builds on the pioneering work of J. G. Kirkwood (1).

5.2. TIME COARSE GRAINING (1)

The method of obtaining equations satisfied by the one- and two-molecule distribution functions $f^{(1)}(\Gamma_1;t)$, $f^{(2)}(\Gamma_2;t)$, respectively, is essentially that of integrating the N-molecule distribution function $f^{(N)}(\Gamma_N;t)$ over the sub-phase space of all the other molecules in the system. Now, $f^{(N)}$ satisfies the Liouville equation, (3.2.20), and is not known explicitly. Therefore, one may only obtain differential equations for $f^{(1)}$ and $f^{(2)}$ by integrating the Liouville equation term by term. The result is a coupled hierarchy of equations: i.e., the equation for $f^{(1)}$ also involves $f^{(2)}$, the equation for $f^{(2)}$ also involves $f^{(3)}$, and so on [see Eq. (5.3.3)]. It is necessary to truncate this hierarchy at some point in order to obtain closed equations for $f^{(1)}$ and $f^{(2)}$.

The problems resulting from the apparent incompatibility of the formal reversibility of the Liouville equation and the everyday experience of the irreversible approach to equilibrium* have been discussed in Chapter 3. In Chapter 7 we shall see how the rigorous theory of Prigogine and co-workers has solved these problems. Unfortunately, the resulting kinetic equations for dense systems cannot be written down explicitly. Nevertheless, an important general result has emerged which forms the basis of the intuitive analysis in this chapter.

Consider first an implication of the Hamiltonian equations of motion (3.2.1). Since there is one equation for each degree of freedom of the system, it follows that the phase of the system at any instant is uniquely determined by the phase at any other instant. In accordance with the definition of a Markov random process given in Section 4.3, it follows that the phase of the system Γ_N may be regarded as a Markov process of a simple kind.† The kinetic equations for the reduced distribution functions $f^{(1)}, f^{(2)}, \cdots$, are concerned with the random variables $\Gamma_1(1), \Gamma_2(1,2), \cdots$, which are of smaller dimensionality. Now, it is well known that the projection of a Markov process of $6N$ dimensions onto a space of smaller dimensionality $(6, 12, \cdots$, dimensions) generally yields a random process of higher order. Thus, $\Gamma_1(1), \Gamma_2(1,2), \cdots$ will be non-Markovian processes of high order. This general feature has been obtained in the analysis of Prigogine and co-workers. They find that the stochastic term‡ has the form of a time-convolution over the history of the variable. The important result is, that when the system has reached a stationary state, the kinetic equations reduce to Markovian form.

* With the possible exception of systems interacting through gravitational forces.

† The transition probability is a δ-function, since the increment of the variable Γ_N has only one possible value for each time instant.

‡ That is, the term appearing in the place of the collision operator in equation (4.3.59), and the Fokker-Planck operator in equation (4.3.56).

At this point it is legitimate to raise the question: What is the connection, if any, between the equations of hydrodynamics in microscopic or macroscopic form and stationary states? The first answer is obvious: It is quite possible to discuss the hydrodynamics of a system in a *non-equilibrium* stationary state in which transport coefficients play a crucial role. This is a rather trivial statement, and the argument may be developed much further. The equations of hydrodynamics deal adequately with processes which are non-stationary on a macroscopic time-scale.* Useful results have been obtained even for such rapidly varying processes as shock waves in dilute gases. All these processes are, in fact, very slow compared to the time scale of molecular fluctuations, on which non-Markovian processes are important. Generally, one would expect that the kinetic equations should be Markovian if the processes described are sufficiently slow that local thermodynamic equilibrium is maintained in the fluid.

The problem of truncating the coupled hierarchy of kinetic equations has, therefore, two distinct features. Since an integration over the sub-phase space of $(N - 1)$ or $(N - 2)$ molecules leaves the equations completely reversible, the truncation procedure must in the first place make the equations irreversible. Secondly, it must provide a means of singling out the Markovian features that the kinetic equations contain in the hydrodynamic regime. The introduction of irreversibility is not difficult; it is merely contingent upon the particular method by which the Markovian feature of the truncation is achieved. At the present time, however, no systematic procedure for obtaining the Markovian feature is known, and the one we adopt is based on that first proposed by Kirkwood(1).

Let us return briefly to the basic definitions of random processes given in Section 4.2. Consider a third-order process, i.e., one completely specified by a P_3. According to the definition of the conditional probability densities K_n, P_3 may be written as

$$P_3(y_1t_1;y_2t_2;y_3t_3) = P_2(y_1t_1;y_2t_2)K_2(y_1t_1;\, y_2t_2 \,|\, y_3t_3). \tag{5.2.1}$$

Consequently, the probability distribution for the variable at four times may be written

$$P_4(y_1t_1;y_2t_2;y_3t_3;y_4t_4) = P_2(y_1t_1;y_2t_2) \times K_2(y_1t_1;\, y_2t_2 \,|\, y_3t_3)K_2(y_2t_2;\, y_3t_3 \,|\, y_4t_4). \tag{5.2.2}$$

* This argument, and indeed all our considerations, are restricted to normal, or Newtonian fluids: see Section 6.2.

If we define a hyperstate of this process as $[y_n t_n; y_{n+1} t_{n+1}]$, then equation (5.2.2) may be written in terms of hyperstates in a manner similar to the Markovian equation (4.2.6):

$$P_2'([y_1t_1;y_2t_2];\,[y_3t_3;y_4t_4]) = P_1'([y_1t_1;y_2t_2]) \times K_1'([y_1t_1;y_2t_2] \mid [y_3t_3;y_4t_4]), \quad (5.2.3)$$

where

$$K_1'([y_1t_1;y_2t_2] \mid [y_3t_3;y_4t_4]) = K_2(y_1t_1;\, y_2t_2 \mid y_3t_3) \times K_2(y_2t_2;\, y_3t_3 \mid y_4t_4). \quad (5.2.4)$$

Equations (5.2.3) and (5.2.4) suggest the possibility that a third-order process may be treated as a second-order process (Markov process) of higher dimensionality by combining states of the original process into hyperstates of the new process. We wish to assert that an nth order process can be treated as an n-dimensional Markov process, the reduction being accomplished in an analogous way. Each hyperstate in the Markov process contains information about the history of the system during the interval t_m to t_{m+n-1}. Much of this information is superfluous for the evaluation of the distribution functions in the hydrodynamic regime, but the information needed is contained within the hyperstate. The method of truncation of the hierarchy of coupled equations for the distribution functions is, therefore, *a means of extracting the relevant information from the hyperstate.* The particular contribution to the theory made by Kirkwood, which we have already mentioned, is the hypothesis that the relevant information for present purposes is contained in the exact distribution function averaged over an interval of time τ. The average value for an interval τ on the fine grained time scale is then associated with a single point on a coarse grained time scale, and the process is known as coarse graining (in time*). The kinetic equations obtained in this way are, in principle, difference equations, but it turns out that the times during which changes become significant on a hydrodynamic scale are so long compared to the coarse graining time that no significant error is introduced by treating the differences as differentials.

The introduction of irreversibility which must accompany the coarse graining is accomplished by the assumption that a time interval τ exists such that the dynamical behavior of the system during one

* It is possible also to coarse grain in space; similar kinetic equations are obtained.

interval is related in a simple *statistical* manner to the dynamical events of the previous interval. As we saw in Section 3.3 the statistical character of the relation is sufficient to render the process irreversible.

The statistical assumption, or *ansatz*, can be analyzed on the basis of our intuitive picture of the dynamics of liquid molecules. Consider first the Fokker-Planck equation. In Section 4.4.B it was shown that this equation describes a stochastic process under conditions such that the transition probability (for the phase Γ of the Brownian particle) is that for a stationary Markov process. In turn, this was shown to be the result of allowing the time resolution of the description of the Brownian particle to be sufficiently coarse that transient behavior associated with the approach to local equilibrium in the molecular motions could not be resolved. Thus, the description of Brownian motion as a Markov process applies only to the discussion of processes taking place on a time scale longer than some τ_c characteristic of the liquid molecules. In the development of the theory τ_c is chosen using physical criteria such that the basic dynamical event (in this case molecular fluctuations) is statistically independent of prior events. Were this not the case, the transition probability connecting two dynamical states of the Brownian particle would not be Markovian.

The problem of Brownian motion is concerned with numerous small momentum transfers, or numerous small particle displacements. At the other extreme of behavior, where momentum transfers may frequently be large and where displacements may be large, is the dilute gas. Transport phenomena in a dilute gas are usually described by a one molecule distribution function, which satisfies a kinetic equation [Boltzmann equation, cf. Eq. (4.3.59)] in which the effects of molecular interaction appear in the form of isolated binary collisions. The rate of change of the distribution function is determined by the slow secular variations of $f^{(1)}$ due to streaming in phase space on which are superimposed the effects of the binary collisions. On the average, a molecule moves a long distance (relative to its size or the range of the intermolecular forces) before undergoing an encounter. Although there is a large volume of phase space wherein there occur small angle deflections resulting from binary collisions, large angle deflections are also frequent. Indeed, large angle deflections are responsible for most of the transport of energy and momentum due to collisions.

There have been numerous attempts to derive the Boltzmann equation from the first principles of statistical mechanics with the aid of some auxiliary non-mechanical assumptions that relate to the irreversibility (2–13). The assumptions required to effect a derivation are basically three in number: the truncation of interactions of higher order than binary collisions, the condition of molecular chaos (i.e., the condition that every pair of colliding molecules is statistically independent prior to the collision), and the slow secular variation of $f^{(1)}$ in space. Of these conditions, only the molecular chaos is responsible for the irreversibility.

The restriction that the singlet distribution function vary slowly in space is very mild. Even under the extreme conditions in a shock front it may be a useful approximation, and under ordinary circumstances it is certainly valid to the same extent that local parameters such as temperature, pressure, etc. can be employed as useful variables. The binary collision approximation is also valid in the limit of low densities, and we therefore focus attention on the question of molecular chaos and the related coarse graining.

At least part of the difficulty in analyzing the chaos property arises from the intuitive nature of this assumption. That is, the usual mental image of the gaseous collision process leads to the expectation that chaos (lack of correlation in both positions and momenta) will be produced even if absent initially, though this may require many collisions to accomplish. However, if such chaos requires a time interval corresponding to many collision times, then it does not lead to the Boltzmann equation which describes transport phenomena in the dilute gas. For, in the Boltzmann equation the binary collisions are taken to be independent* and the relevant time interval is therefore long compared to the duration of a collision but short compared to the mean time between collisions. The problem separates into two overlapping questions: is the initial distribution "chaotic" and is the chaos propagated?

Consider first the question of initial chaos. Grad (8) has claimed that the class of functions $\{f_n^{(2)}\}$ which is obtained by integration of the class $\{f^{(n)}\}$ chosen to be consistent with a given singlet function, $f^{(1)}$, converges to the product $f^{(1)}(1)f^{(1)}(2)$ as $n \to \infty$. The argument centers on the symmetry of the distribution function in the arguments, positions, and momenta, with the net result that the probability density is peaked

* The successive collisions suffered by a particular molecule are the result of its motion through an environment which is assumed to be (statistically) unaffected by the rebounding molecules.

in those regions of phase space for which the factorized product condition is valid. However, it is not clear that this theorem is of any use for the study of dense media, since those portions of phase space where chaos is not exhibited are just the regions most important for the description of the liquid phase. In the case of the dilute gas, where at equilibrium the pair correlation function is unity, the demonstration that the pair distribution approaches a product of singlet distributions is tantamount to the demonstration that chaos exists. Note that so far we have said nothing about the temporal or spatial scale over which chaos is to be expected. To examine this question we assume that at a given time chaos is established. It is clear that whether chaos will or will not be propagated depends in part on the time scale for which the Liouville equation is solved. Even with an initially factorized distribution, it is certainly true that for time intervals that are short compared to the mean time between collisions, a pair of molecules that has just collided will be strongly correlated with one another. It is only by the intercession of further collisions with third and fourth molecules that this correlation can be destroyed. Whereas at equilibrium, $g^{(2)}$ has a correlation range (i.e., a volume element within which it differs from unity) only of order of magnitude of the range of intermolecular forces, out of equilibrium the correlation range may be much larger. This is a result of the persistence of the initial state. Briefly stated, as time increases there will be an increasingly large number of initial configurations that result in collision, and thus in a certain sense the correlations grow in time. In the absence of intervening collisions the correlations for a pair of molecules are essentially constant over a distance equal to the relative velocity multiplied by the time. Now, the derivation of the Boltzmann equation by Kirkwood uses coarse graining to isolate a binary collision and define the extent of the memory of correlation. That is, the fundamental dynamical event is taken to be a binary collision and it is assumed that τ is long compared to the duration of a collision but short compared with the time between collisions. A second coarse graining is later performed upon the integrand of the collision operator. We immediately note that the formal effect of coarse graining is to limit the correlation time to τ, successive intervals of length τ being uncorrelated. If τ is taken as long relative to the duration of an encounter, but short relative to the time between encounters, then coarse graining over an interval τ successfully breaks the correlations between successive collisions. This truncation is accomplished by taking the length of the collision cylinder defining the volume of space relevant to two molecules about to collide as proportional to τ. There remains, however, an indirect correlation due to the coupling through third molecules. Consider the following collision sequences: molecule 1 collides with molecule 2, molecule 2 rebounds and collides with molecule 3, etc., the trajectories being so constructed that molecules 2 and 3 would not have collided at that time, except for the prior collision with molecule 1. It is clear that for this example molecule 1 has influenced the collision between molecules 2 and 3. For geometric reasons, the correlation due to these indirect collision sequences must decrease with increasing distance between molecules 1 and 2. That is, in a homogeneous gas, the probability that no intermediate collisions occur between the indirectly coupled collision of molecules 2 and 3 following the collision of molecules 1 and 2 is of the approximate form $\exp(-R_{12}/\lambda_f)$, where λ_f is the mean free path and R_{12} is the distance between molecules 1 and 2. Therefore, outside a sufficiently large volume element in configuration space, the correlation due to indirect collision paths vanishes. We may now state a more restrictive condition on the time interval used for the second coarse graining. It must be chosen so as to render the correlations due to indirect collisions negligible. Note that a time interval is equivalent to a linear extension of order $\Delta R(\tau)$. Clearly, in the dilute gas $\Delta R(\tau)$ ought to be longer than the range of the intermolecular potential but shorter than a mean free path.

The case of a dense fluid is qualitatively different. The meaning of molecular chaos in a dilute gas is that molecule 2 (which is due to collide with molecule 1) has approached molecule 1 from infinity and its distribution of possible velocities has not been affected by collisions with molecules which have recently collided with molecule 1. In a dense fluid, molecule 1 may undergo a rigid core collision with a second molecule which has for some time past been in the region of the first coordination shell of molecule 1. Thus, molecule 2 should already have an intimate statistical "knowledge" of molecule 1, and may indeed have undergone a rigid core collision with molecule 1 in the immediate past. However, if the quasi-Brownian motion produced in the molecules by the van der Waals part of the forces is sufficiently effective in causing molecule 2 to forget its previous experience, then successive rigid core collisions should satisfy the simple form of molecular chaos used.

But aside from questions of how chaos and time coarse graining are related in very short time intervals, it is pertinent to inquire how much chaos is required for the derivation of the Boltzmann equation, and whether or not chaos propagates when large time intervals are considered.

It has not yet been possible to prove in general that chaos is propagated by the Boltzmann equation although it can be shown to be true for some configurations. These configurations are just those for which the pair of molecules is widely separated and do not collide. The basic idea is that when the molecules are not close to one another, $f^{(2)}$ and $f^{(1)}(1)f^{(1)}(2)$ have similar time dependence. The residual difference, $f^{(2)} - f^{(1)}(1)f^{(1)}(2)$, can then be related to the residual differences between products of singlet distribution functions and the corresponding higher distribution functions, $f^{(n)}$. When the molecules do not collide, simple rectilinear trajectories are traversed and thereby the two molecule residuals are related to the initial values of the n-particle residuals. But if $f^{(n)}$ is initially chaotic, the nth order residuals tend to zero and the time dependence of the two molecule residuals also tends to zero. Thus, the initial chaos is propagated in that set of configurations in which collisions do not occur. Due to the large correlations in the short time immediately following a collision, no general proof of the propagation of chaos has yet been constructed.

To complete this discussion of coarse graining we seek a consistency condition on the passage from the non-Markovian to the Markovian description of the fluid. In a sense, the distribution function may be thought of as a vector in a continuous space whose components represent the occupation probabilities of the various states of the phase space. In the most general case, the probability of finding the set of states $(\mathbf{p}^{(n)},\{n\})$ depends on the past history of the system. There are, however, two limiting cases where the past can be ignored (14):

(a) If the probability for moving to the set of states denoted $(\mathbf{p}^{(n)},\{n\})_t$ at time t from any substate $(\mathbf{p}_i,(i))_{t-\tau}$ at time $t-\tau$ is the same for all the states of $(\mathbf{p}^{(n)},\{n\})_{t-\tau}$, then the probabilities for being in each substate of $(\mathbf{p}^{(n)},\{n\})_{t-\tau}$ do not effect the outcome of the transition $(\mathbf{p}^{(n)},\{n\})_{t-\tau} \rightarrow (\mathbf{p}^{(n)},\{n\})_t$.

(b) If, no matter what the sequence $(\mathbf{p}^{(n)},\{n\})_{t_1}$, $(\mathbf{p}^{(n)},\{n\})_{t_2}, \cdots$ is, we always end up with the same assignment of probabilities for being in each of the states in $(\mathbf{p}^{(n)},\{n\})_t$, then the preceding sequence can have no influence on the transition $(\mathbf{p}^{(n)},\{n\})_{t-\tau} \rightarrow (\mathbf{p}^{(n)},\{n\})_t$.

In what follows we shall introduce an analysis of simple liquids based on the following hypothesis. There exists a time interval τ such that the following dynamical event, defined in τ, defines a Markov process. The dynamical event consists of a strongly repulsive binary encounter followed by a quasi-Brownian motion of the pair of molecules in the fluctuating field of all the neighboring molecules. Because the destruction of correlations by the quasi-Brownian motion is efficient, successive strongly repulsive encounters are statistically independent. The compound dynamical event is, therefore, asserted to be independent of prior events of the same kind.*†

Consider now the relationship between this hypothesis and the consistency conditions imposed by coarse graining. Which of the two limiting cases is applicable in our situation? Consider the description of the strongly repulsive binary encounter portion of the fundamental dynamical event. The transition probability for scattering from the pair of momentum states $\mathbf{p}_1^*$, $\mathbf{p}_2^*$ to $\mathbf{p}_1$, $\mathbf{p}_2$ is a function of the impact parameter, intermolecular potential, etc. Clearly, the scattering to a set of final states $\mathbf{p}_1$, $\mathbf{p}_2$ is not independent of $\mathbf{p}_1^*$, $\mathbf{p}_2^*$ and, therefore, limiting case (a) is inapplicable. If coarse graining is to perform the function required we must establish that condition (b) is applicable.

If, no matter what the sequence $(\mathbf{p}^{(n)},\{n\})_{t_1}$, $(\mathbf{p}^{(n)},\{n\})_{t_2}$, $\cdots$ is, we always end up with the same assignment of probabilities for being in each of the states of $(\mathbf{p}^{(n)},\{n\})_t$, then it is necessary that the relaxation time for return to the states of $(\mathbf{p}^{(n)},\{n\})_t$ be short relative to the time interval on which the fundamental dynamical event is defined. Thus, if it can be shown that the relaxation time for the return to local equilibrium is much shorter than the time between strongly repulsive binary encounters, then the initiation of the dynamical event consisting of a strongly repulsive binary encounter followed by a quasi-Brownian motion always starts from the same distribution function. In this case the probabilities for being in each of the states of $(\mathbf{p}^{(n)},\{n\})_t$ just define the distribution function, and the conditions of case (b) are satisfied. It will be shown in the succeeding sections that the analysis of the liquid

* Recent studies of neutron diffraction from liquid Ar confirm the accuracy of this hypothesis: B. A. Dasamacharya and K. R. Rao, *Phys. Rev.*, **137,** A417 (1965).

† The dynamical events are, of course, the interaction of the molecule, pair of molecules, etc., under consideration, *with their environment*. Clearly, the phase of the molecule, pair, etc., is not independent of the phase during a previous interval; it is the phase of the environment which is (assumed) independent of the phase during a previous interval.

discussed herein does satisfy this condition on the relaxation times. In a sense, this is a necessary consistency condition, not one which can be imposed in advance of the formulation of the theoretical analysis.

5.3. THE RICE-ALLNATT EQUATIONS (15,16)

A theory of irreversible phenomena applicable to the problem of transport in dense fluids has been developed by Rice and Allnatt. In the first instance the analysis was applied to a model monatomic dense fluid in which the intermolecular potential has the form of a rigid core repulsion superimposed on an arbitrary soft potential, as shown in Figure 5.3.1. Subsequent analysis (17) has shown that the extension of the model to include more realistic potentials presents no formal difficulty. Discussion of the extension is, however, delayed until Section 5.5, in order that the essential ideas of the theory may be presented unaccompanied by any marginal arguments.

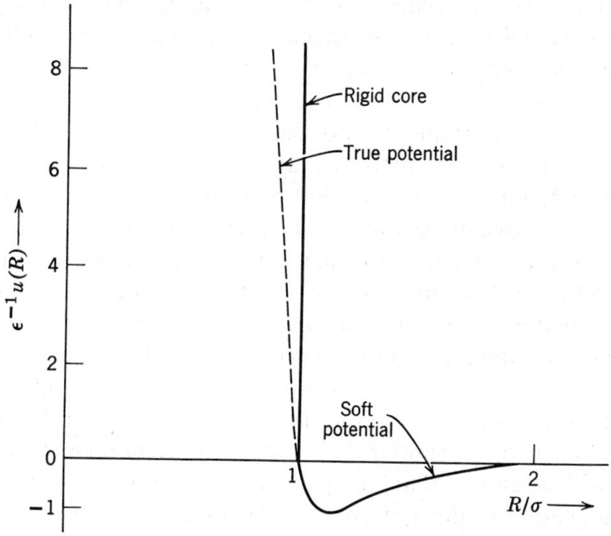

Fig. 5.3.1. Diagramatic representation of the model intermolecular potential. The true potential is drawn from the Lennard-Jones 6-12 formula:

$$u(R) = 4\epsilon\left[\left(\frac{\sigma}{R}\right)^{12} - \left(\frac{\sigma}{R}\right)^{6}\right].$$

What advantage results from separating the intermolecular potential into two parts and treating their effects separately? Let us briefly recapitulate the discussion presented in the previous section. The difference in range and strength of the repulsive core and the soft potential allows the discussion of the molecular motion in terms of two time scales: one corresponds to the large momentum and energy transfers which occur during a strongly repulsive encounter, while the other corresponds to the frequent small momentum and energy transfers which occur during the quasi-Brownian motion of a molecule in the superimposed soft force field of all the molecules in its surroundings. The short range of the strongly repulsive core implies that the first class of encounters are of short duration, so that the probability that a molecule undergoes such encounters with two or more others simultaneously is sufficiently small that it may be neglected. The introduction of the idealized rigid core representation for this class of encounters may thus be regarded as a formal device for restricting consideration to binary encounters (i.e., rigid core encounters between not more than two molecules). It has the additional advantage of considerably simplifying the mathematical details of the solutions of the equations but, we believe, without significantly affecting the numerical results.

Irreversibility is introduced into the analysis by the use of the Kirkwood hypothesis that a time interval τ exists such that the dynamical events occurring in one interval are independent of those in the preceding intervals. The dynamical event is identified as a rigid core encounter followed by erratic or quasi-Brownian motion in the fluctuating soft force field of the neighboring molecules. This identification is contingent upon the effectiveness of the quasi-Brownian motion at causing the environment to forget the momentum with which a molecule was rebounded after the rigid core encounter. This in turn implies that the relaxation time for the equilibration of the momentum due to the soft force alone is much shorter than that due to rigid core encounters alone. It will be shown that this physical statement is supported by detailed calculation of the appropriate relaxation times for the motion considered.

The introduction of irreversibility in the manner described leads to a set of integrodifferential equations describing the evolution of the coarse grained singlet $\bar{f}^{(1)}(1)$, doublet $\bar{f}^{(2)}(1,2)$, etc., distribution functions.

5.3.A. *The Singlet Equation* (15)

The starting point for the analysis is the Liouville equation (3.2.20) which we may write in a slightly different form

$$\left[\frac{\partial}{\partial t}+\sum_{i=1}^{N}\left\{\frac{1}{m}\mathbf{p}_i\cdot\nabla_i+\sum_{j(\neq i)=1}^{N}\mathbf{F}_{ij}\cdot\nabla_{p_i}\right\}\right]f^{(N)}(\Gamma_N;t)=0, \quad (5.3.1)$$

with the pairwise superposition of the intermolecular forces explicitly displayed.* Assuming, as before, that the forces are functions of position only, the equation for the reduced generic n-molecule distribution function $f^{(n)}(\Gamma_n;t)$, defined by

$$f^{(n)}(\Gamma_n;t)=\frac{N!}{(N-n)!}\int\cdots\int f^{(N)}(\Gamma_N;t)\,d\Gamma_{N-n}, \quad (5.3.2)$$

is

$$\left[\frac{\partial}{\partial t}+\sum_{i=1}^{n}\left\{\frac{1}{m}\mathbf{p}_i\cdot\nabla_i+\sum_{j(\neq i)=1}^{n}\mathbf{F}_{ij}\cdot\nabla_{p_i}\right\}\right]f^{(n)}(\Gamma_n(\{n\});t)$$
$$=-\sum_{i=1}^{n}\int\cdots\int\mathbf{F}_{i,n+1}\cdot\nabla_{p_i}f^{(n+1)}(\Gamma_{n+1}(\{n\},n+1);t)\,d\Gamma_1(n+1),$$
$$(1\leqslant n\leqslant N-1). \quad (5.3.3)$$

All the terms in equation (5.3.1) for which $i > n$ vanish because Gauss' theorem can be used to convert the integrals of the gradient operators ∇_i and ∇_{p_i} into surface integrals over the boundaries of configuration and momentum space, at which the integrand is assumed to vanish sufficiently rapidly that the integrals vanish. In equations (5.3.3) the set of molecules whose phases are the arguments of $f^{(n)}$ and $f^{(n+1)}$ has been made explicit for clarity. The left-hand side represents the hydrodynamic or streaming term in the n-molecule sub-phase space. The right-hand side represents the interaction of the n-molecule subset with its environment. The reduction of the description of the environment to the generic distribution of one molecule [labeled $(n+1)$] is, of course, contingent upon the assumption that all the molecules of the system are identical, apart from labels. The set of equations (5.3.3) is the coupled hierarchy previously referred to. As might be expected, the coupling between one member of the hierarchy and a higher one is (physically) through the effect of the environment.

* The phase of a subsystem of n molecules may be written Γ_n, $(\mathbf{p}^{(n)},\{n\})$, or in full as $(\mathbf{p}_1,\cdots,\mathbf{p}_n,\mathbf{R}_1,\cdots,\mathbf{R}_n)$ according to the demands of the context.

Time coarse graining is now introduced by means of the *definition*

$$\bar{f}^{(n)}(\Gamma_n;t) = \frac{1}{\tau}\int_0^\tau f^{(n)}(\Gamma_{n,t};\, t+s)\, ds. \tag{5.3.4}$$

The notation $\Gamma_{n,t}$ denotes the phase Γ_n of the set of molecules $\{n\}$ at the instant t. Thus, the meaning of the coarse graining is that the value of $f^{(n)}$ is averaged at each point in phase space over the interval τ.

The lowest member of the hierarchy, coupling $\bar{f}^{(1)}$ to $\bar{f}^{(2)}$, is obtained by putting $n = 1$ explicitly in equations (5.3.3). It is convenient to write this equation in the form

$$\left[\frac{\partial}{\partial t} + \frac{1}{m}\mathbf{p}_1 \cdot \nabla_1\right] \bar{f}^{(1)} = \Omega_H + \Omega_S, \tag{5.3.5}$$

where

$$\Omega_H = -\frac{1}{\tau}\int_0^\tau \int \mathbf{F}_{12}^{(H)} \cdot \nabla_{p_1} f^{(2)}(\Gamma_{2,t};\, t+s)\, d\Gamma_1(2)\, ds,$$

$$\Omega_S = -\frac{1}{\tau}\int_0^\tau \int \mathbf{F}_{12}^{(S)} \cdot \nabla_{p_1} f^{(2)}(\Gamma_{2,t};\, t+s)\, d\Gamma_1(2)\, ds. \tag{5.3.6}$$

The force on molecule 1 due to molecule 2, $\mathbf{F}_{12}$, has been separated into two components, $\mathbf{F}_{12}^{(H)}$ the strongly repulsive force between the molecules, and $\mathbf{F}_{12}^{(S)}$ the soft force between the molecules.

We are now in a position to consider the evaluation of Ω_H and Ω_S. To facilitate this we introduce the phase space transition probabilities (Green's functions) $K^{(n)}(\Gamma_n \mid \Gamma_n'; s)$. $K^{(n)}$ is the probability density that the phase of the subsystem of n molecules will undergo a transition from Γ_n' to Γ_n in an interval s. $K^{(n)}$ is essentially a specific function. Since the system is stationary (or almost so), $K^{(n)}$ is not a function of the initial time. Corresponding to equation (4.2.8) we have the functional definition of $K^{(n)}$:

$$f^{(n)}(\Gamma_n;\, t+s) = \int K^{(n)}(\Gamma_n \mid \Gamma_n';\, s) f^{(n)}(\Gamma_n';t)\, d\Gamma_n'. \tag{5.3.7}$$

Here $f^{(n)}$ may be either specific or generic, as normalization is conserved. From our earlier remark that the phase of the whole system is a (simple) Markov process, it follows that $K^{(N)}$ also satisfies Liouville's equation:

$$\left[\frac{\partial}{\partial s}+\sum_{i=1}^{N}\left\{\frac{1}{m}\mathbf{p}_i\cdot\nabla_i+\sum_{j(\neq i)=1}^{N}\mathbf{F}_{ij}\cdot\nabla_{p_i}\right\}\right]K^{(N)}=0;$$

$$K^{(N)}(\Gamma_N\mid\Gamma_N';0)=\delta(\Gamma_N-\Gamma_N')$$

$$=\prod_{i=1}^{N}\delta(\mathbf{R}_i-\mathbf{R}_i')\,\delta(\mathbf{p}_i-\mathbf{p}_i'). \quad (5.3.8)$$

Combination of equations (5.3.2) and (5.3.7) for $n = n$ and $n = N$ leads to a relation between the Green's functions for N and molecules:

$$K^{(n)}(\Gamma_n\mid\Gamma_n';s)=\iint K^{(N)}(\Gamma_n,\Gamma_{N-n}\mid\Gamma_n',\Gamma'_{N-n};s)\times$$
$$f^{(N-n/n)}(\Gamma'_{N-n}\mid\Gamma_n';t)\,d\Gamma_{N-n}\,d\Gamma'_{N-n}, \quad (5.3.9)$$

where $f^{(N-n/n)}$ is the specific phase space probability density* for the other $(N - n)$ molecules conditional upon the (given) phase of the subset of n molecules. The function $f^{(2)}(\Gamma_{2,t}; t + s)$ in the expressions for Ω_H and Ω_S is now expressed in terms of $f^{(2)}(\Gamma_2';t)$ and $K^{(2)}(\Gamma_2\mid\Gamma_2';s)$ by means of equation (5.3.7). The assumptions, already discussed, concerning the two types of motion are now employed to deduce an equation for $K^{(2)}$ for each case.

We deal first with the strongly repulsive part of the intermolecular potential. It is easily shown that equation (5.3.8) for $K^{(N)}$ may be contracted in a similar way to that in which equation (5.3.3) was derived. The exact equation for $K^{(2)}$ is thereby found to be

$$\left[\frac{\partial}{\partial s}+\sum_{i=1,2}\left\{\frac{1}{m}\mathbf{p}_i\cdot\nabla_i+\sum_{j(\neq i)=1,2}\mathbf{F}_{ij}\cdot\nabla_{p_i}\right\}\right]K^{(2)}$$
$$=-\sum_{j=3}^{N}\int[\mathbf{F}_{1j}\cdot\nabla_{p_1}+\mathbf{F}_{2j}\cdot\nabla_{p_2}]K^{(N)}(\Gamma_N\mid\Gamma_N';s)$$
$$\times f^{(N-2/2)}(\Gamma'_{N-2}\mid\Gamma_2';t)\,d\Gamma_{N-2}\,d\Gamma_N'. \quad (5.3.10)$$

The formal solution of equation (5.3.10) is

$$K^{(2)}(\Gamma_2\mid\Gamma_2';s)=\prod_{i=1,2}\delta(\mathbf{R}_i-\mathbf{R}_i'-\Delta\mathbf{R}_i(s))\,\delta(\mathbf{p}_i-\mathbf{p}_i'-\Delta\mathbf{p}_i(s)),$$
$$(5.3.11)$$

* The definition of $f^{(N-n/n)}$ follows from an obvious extension of equations (4.2.6) and (4.2.7):

$$f^{(N)}(\Gamma_N;t)=f^{(n)}(\Gamma_n;t)f^{(N-n/n)}(\Gamma_{N-n}\mid\Gamma_n;t).$$

where $\Delta\mathbf{R}_i(s)$ and $\Delta\mathbf{p}_i(s)$ are obtained as solutions of the N-body equations of motion of the system. Neither equation (5.3.10) nor (5.3.11) is, however, of any use for calculation until some assumption about the nature of the intermolecular potential is introduced. We now introduce as a model potential the special case that the repulsive potential is representable as a rigid core. We make no assumption about the soft part of the potential. In particular, the soft part of the potential may contain a repulsive contribution. For example, it is often convenient to take $u^{(S)}$ as the Lennard-Jones potential for $R_{12} > \sigma$, and $u^{(H)}$ as a hard core starting at $u = 0$ $(R_{12} = \sigma)$ (see Figure 5.3.1). Mathematically this means that $u^{(H)}$ may be represented as, say, $(\sigma/R_{12})^n$, and for our model we take the limit as $n \to \infty$. According to the separation of the potential just defined, we note that the force between molecule 1 and molecule 2 satisfies

$$\begin{aligned} \mathbf{F}_{12} &= \mathbf{F}_{12}^{(H)}, \qquad R_{12} = \sigma \\ &= \mathbf{F}_{12}^{(S)}, \qquad R_{12} > \sigma. \end{aligned} \tag{5.3.12}$$

Considering now Ω_H, we see that the first member of equation (5.3.12) applies. Also, we suppose that the soft forces due to the rest of the molecules have negligible effect on the rigid core collision of molecule 1 and molecule 2. There are two reasons for this. First, it is reasonable to suppose that the duration of the rigid core collision is short compared to the times in which the soft forces change appreciably. Second, the combined soft forces due to the environment are weak; this is borne out by a calculation of the average potential at the center of a "cage," which potential is very flat (18). For the present purpose equation (5.3.10) reduces to

$$\left[\frac{\partial}{\partial s} + \frac{1}{m}\mathbf{p}_1 \cdot \nabla_1 + \frac{1}{m}\mathbf{p}_2 \cdot \nabla_2 + \mathbf{F}_{12}^{(H)} \cdot \nabla_{p_1} + \mathbf{F}_{12}^{(H)} \cdot \nabla_{p_2}\right] K_0^{(2)} = 0. \tag{5.3.13}$$

Thus, $K_0^{(2)}$ satisfies a Liouville equation in pair space. Equation (5.3.13) is solved for $\mathbf{F}_{12}^{(H)} \cdot \nabla_{p_1} K_0^{(2)}$ and the resulting expression substituted in that for Ω_H. Since $\mathbf{F}_{21}^{(H)}$ is a function of R_{12} only, the term $\mathbf{F}_{21}^{(H)} \cdot \nabla_{p_2} K_0^{(2)}$ may be converted to a surface integral in $\mathbf{p}_2$ space and vanishes. The expression for Ω_H becomes

$$\Omega_H = \frac{1}{\tau}\int_0^\tau \int \left[\left(\frac{\partial}{\partial s} + \frac{1}{m}\mathbf{p}_1 \cdot \nabla_1 + \frac{1}{m}\mathbf{p}_2 \cdot \nabla_2\right) K_0^{(2)}\right] \times f^{(2)}(\Gamma_2';t)\, d\Gamma_1(2)\, d\Gamma_2'\, ds. \tag{5.3.14}$$

We suppose now that the rigid core collision occurs in the initial subinterval τ_1 of $\tau(\tau_1 \ll \tau)$ so that $K_0^{(2)}(s = 0)$ refers to the phase of the two molecules *before* the collision, while $K_0^{(2)}(s = \tau)$ refers to the phase *after* the collision.* The first term in equation (5.3.14) therefore becomes

$$\Omega_H^{(1)} = \frac{1}{\tau}\int\Bigg[\prod_{i=1,2}\delta(\mathbf{R}_i - \mathbf{R}_i' - \Delta\mathbf{R}_i(\tau))\,\delta(\mathbf{p}_i - \mathbf{p}_i' - \Delta\mathbf{p}_i(\tau)) - \prod_{i=1,2}\delta(\mathbf{R}_i - \mathbf{R}_i')\,\delta(\mathbf{p}_i - \mathbf{p}_i')\Bigg] f^{(2)}(\Gamma_2';t)\,d\Gamma_1(2)\,d\Gamma_2'$$

$$= \frac{1}{\tau}\int [f^{(2)}(\mathbf{R}_1 - \Delta\mathbf{R}_1(\tau), \mathbf{R}_2 - \Delta\mathbf{R}_2(\tau), \mathbf{p}_1 - \Delta\mathbf{p}_1(\tau), \mathbf{p}_2 - \Delta\mathbf{p}_2(\tau); t) - f^{(2)}(\mathbf{R}_1,\mathbf{R}_2,\mathbf{p}_1,\mathbf{p}_2;t)]\,d\mathbf{p}_2\,d\mathbf{R}_2, \quad (5.3.15)$$

after an integration over Γ_2' and writing out $\Gamma_1(2)$ fully. As explained in the preceding footnote, it is consistent with our assumptions to neglect the changes in positions of the molecules during τ, so that $\Delta\mathbf{R}_i(\tau) \simeq 0$. On the other hand, $\Delta\mathbf{p}_1(\tau)$ [$= -\Delta\mathbf{p}_2(\tau)$] is the change of momentum occurring during a rigid core collision, and is nonzero. The $\mathbf{R}_2$ integration is taken over the volume that molecule 2 could be scattered into during τ, for a given relative momentum, $\mathbf{p}_{12}$. This volume is generated by a set of cylindrical filaments parallel to $\mathbf{p}_{12}$ of length $(p_{12}\tau/m)$ and cross-sectional area $b\,db\,d\epsilon$, where b and ϵ are the radial and azimuthal coordinates in a cylindrical polar system of which the z axis passes through the center of molecule 1 parallel to $\mathbf{p}_{12}$. If ϕ is the angle between $\mathbf{p}_{12}$ and the unit vector $\mathbf{k}$ pointing from the center of molecule 1 to that of molecule 2 at the instant of contact ($\mathbf{R}_{12} = \sigma\mathbf{k}$ at contact), then $b = \sigma \sin\phi$ is the off-axis distance of the collision. $\Omega_H^{(1)}$, therefore, becomes

$$\Omega_H^{(1)} = \frac{1}{m}\int_{(\mathbf{k}\cdot\mathbf{p}_{12}>0)} [f^{(2)}(\mathbf{R}_1, \mathbf{R}_1 + \sigma\mathbf{k}, \mathbf{p}_1^*, \mathbf{p}_2^*; t) - f^{(2)}(\mathbf{R}_1, \mathbf{R}_1 + \sigma\mathbf{k}, \mathbf{p}_1, \mathbf{p}_2; t)]p_{12}b\,db\,d\epsilon\,d\mathbf{p}_2, \quad (5.3.16)$$

* During the remainder of the interval τ, while the two molecules are separating after their rigid core collision, small changes in their phases occur. These changes in momentum are negligible (in a statistical sense) because they are associated with the establishment of a plateau value to the soft force autocorrelation integral (see Sections 4.4.B, and 4.5.A, and later in this section). The trajectories of the molecules during τ are thus almost linear. The changes in relative position, $(p_{12}\tau/m)$, are assumed small in comparison with distances in which the pair correlation function changes significantly. This is, indeed, reasonable since the length of a diffusive step is only about one-fourteenth of the nearest neighbor separation in liquid argon, and this requires a time far longer than (the present) τ to establish.

where the asterisk on $\mathbf{p}_i^*$ denotes the value before collision. The restriction $\mathbf{k} \cdot \mathbf{p}_{12} > 0$ on the integration ensures that only the molecules which are indeed receding from one another (after a collision) are included. The second and third terms of equation (5.3.14) are treated together. It is convenient to extend the spatial integration also over the coordinates of molecule 1, and to this end the δ function, $\delta(\mathbf{R}_1 - \mathbf{R}_1{}^0)$, is introduced. The coordinates are then transformed to relative and center of mass coordinates by means of the relations

$$\mathbf{R}_{12} = \mathbf{R}_2 - \mathbf{R}_1{}^0, \qquad \mathbf{p}_{12} = \mathbf{p}_2 - \mathbf{p}_1,$$
$$\mathbf{R} = \tfrac{1}{2}(\mathbf{R}_1{}^0 + \mathbf{R}_2), \qquad \mathbf{P} = \tfrac{1}{2}(\mathbf{p}_1 + \mathbf{p}_2). \tag{5.3.17}$$

After integration over Γ_2' and introduction of equation (5.3.17) these terms become

$$\Omega_H^{(2)} = \frac{1}{m\tau}\int_0^\tau \int \{[\mathbf{p}_1 \cdot \nabla_1 + \mathbf{p}_2 \cdot \nabla_2]K_0^{(2)}\} f^{(2)}(\Gamma_2';t)\, d\Gamma_1(2)\, d\Gamma_2'\, ds$$
$$= \frac{1}{m}\int \{[\mathbf{P} \cdot \nabla + \mathbf{p}_{12} \cdot \nabla_{12}] f^{(2)}(\Gamma_2;t)\}$$
$$\times\, \delta(\mathbf{R}_1 - \mathbf{R} + \tfrac{1}{2}\mathbf{R}_{12})\, d\mathbf{R}\, d\mathbf{R}_{12}\, d\mathbf{p}_2. \tag{5.3.18}$$

The operators ∇ and ∇_{12} in equation (5.3.18) are the gradient operators in the center of mass and relative coordinates, respectively, and the Jacobian for the transformation $(\mathbf{R}_1{}^0,\mathbf{R}_2) \to (\mathbf{R},\mathbf{R}_{12})$ is unity. At this point we could introduce the approximation $f^{(2)} = \bar{f}^{(2)}$. It has little importance in the hydrodynamic regime, but will be discussed in more detail at the end of this section. Of the two terms in equation (5.3.18), the first (center of mass) term is seen to vanish. Integration over $\mathbf{R}_{12}$ first yields an expression of the form

$$\int \mathbf{P} \cdot \nabla f^{(2)}(\mathbf{R} - \mathbf{R}_1, \mathbf{R}, \mathbf{p}_1, \mathbf{p}_2; t)\, d\mathbf{R}\, d\mathbf{p}_2,$$

which becomes a surface integral in $\mathbf{R}$ space and vanishes. The second term is first integrated over $\mathbf{R}$, and then converted to a surface integral in $\mathbf{R}_{12}$ space which vanishes at the external boundaries of the system, but, since the integration is restricted by $R_{12} > \sigma$, there remains a contribution from the surface of the rigid core:

$$\Omega_H^{(2)} = \frac{1}{m}\int\{\mathbf{p}_{12}\cdot\nabla_{12}f^{(2)}(\mathbf{R}_1{}^0,\mathbf{R}_2,\mathbf{p}_1,\mathbf{p}_2;t)\}$$

$$\times\,\delta(\mathbf{R}_1{}^0 - \mathbf{R} + \tfrac{1}{2}\mathbf{R}_{12})\,d\mathbf{R}\,d\mathbf{R}_{12}\,d\mathbf{p}_2$$

$$= \frac{1}{m}\int\mathbf{p}_{12}\cdot\nabla_{12}f^{(2)}(\mathbf{R}_1, \mathbf{R}_1 + \mathbf{R}_{12}, \mathbf{p}_1, \mathbf{p}_2; t)\,d\mathbf{R}_{12}\,d\mathbf{p}_2$$

$$= \frac{\sigma^2}{m}\int f^{(2)}(\mathbf{R}_1, \mathbf{R}_1 + \sigma\mathbf{k}, \mathbf{p}_1, \mathbf{p}_2; t)\mathbf{p}_{12}\cdot\mathbf{k}\,d\mathbf{k}\,d\mathbf{p}_2, \qquad (5.3.19)$$

where $d\mathbf{k}$ is an element of solid angle and $\sigma^2\mathbf{k}\,d\mathbf{k}$ is a vector element of area at the surface of the rigid core. The product $\sigma^2\mathbf{p}_{12}\cdot\mathbf{k}\,d\mathbf{k}$ projects this element onto the equatorial plane in which b and ϵ are defined: thus,

$$\sigma^2\mathbf{p}_{12}\cdot\mathbf{k}\,d\mathbf{k} = p_{12}b\,db\,d\epsilon.$$

Now the surface integration in equation (5.3.19) is over the whole of the rigid core surface. Thus, $\Omega_H^{(2)}$ may be written

$$\Omega_H^{(2)} = \frac{1}{m}\int_{(\mathbf{k}\cdot\mathbf{p}_{12}>0)} f^{(2)}(\mathbf{R}_1, \mathbf{R}_1 + \sigma\mathbf{k}, \mathbf{p}_1, \mathbf{p}_2; t)p_{12}b\,db\,d\epsilon\,d\mathbf{p}_2$$

$$+ \frac{1}{m}\int_{(\mathbf{k}\cdot\mathbf{p}_{12}<0)} f^{(2)}(\mathbf{R}_1, \mathbf{R}_1 + \sigma\mathbf{k}, \mathbf{p}_1, \mathbf{p}_2; t)p_{12}b\,db\,d\epsilon\,d\mathbf{p}_2$$

$$= \frac{1}{m}\int_{(\mathbf{k}\cdot\mathbf{p}_{12}>0)} f^{(2)}(\mathbf{R}_1, \mathbf{R}_1 + \sigma\mathbf{k}, \mathbf{p}_1, \mathbf{p}_2; t)p_{12}b\,db\,d\epsilon\,d\mathbf{p}_2$$

$$- \frac{1}{m}\int_{(\mathbf{k}\cdot\mathbf{p}_{12}>0)} f^{(2)}(\mathbf{R}_1, \mathbf{R}_1 - \sigma\mathbf{k}, \mathbf{p}_1, \mathbf{p}_2; t)p_{12}b\,db\,d\epsilon\,d\mathbf{p}_2, \qquad (5.3.20)$$

where, to obtain the final member, the direction of $\mathbf{k}$ has been reversed. Combining equations (5.3.16) and (5.3.20), we finally obtain for Ω_H

$$\Omega_H = \frac{1}{m}\int_{(\mathbf{k}\cdot\mathbf{p}_{12}>0)} [f^{(2)}(\mathbf{R}_1, \mathbf{R}_1 + \sigma\mathbf{k}, \mathbf{p}_1{}^*, \mathbf{p}_2{}^*; t)$$

$$- f^{(2)}(\mathbf{R}_1, \mathbf{R}_1 - \sigma\mathbf{k}, \mathbf{p}_1, \mathbf{p}_2; t)]p_{12}b\,db\,d\epsilon\,d\mathbf{p}_2. \qquad (5.3.21)$$

A second time average is now introduced which replaces $f^{(2)}$ by $\bar{f}^{(2)}$ in Ω_H. Since $\bar{f}^{(2)}$ is assumed to depend upon time only implicitly through local thermodynamic variables in the hydrodynamic regime, this operation will not affect $\bar{f}^{(1)}$, which already appears on the left-hand side of equation (5.3.5).

In order to truncate the hierarchy, $\bar{f}^{(2)}$ in equation (5.3.21) must be expressed in terms of $\bar{f}^{(1)}$. Quite generally,

$$\bar{f}^{(2)}(\mathbf{R}_1,\mathbf{R}_2,\mathbf{p}_1,\mathbf{p}_2;t)=\bar{f}^{(1)}(\mathbf{R}_1,\mathbf{p}_1;t)\bar{f}^{(1)}(\mathbf{R}_2,\mathbf{p}_2;t)\mathscr{G}^{(2)}(\mathbf{R}_1,\mathbf{R}_2,\mathbf{p}_1,\mathbf{p}_2;t), \quad (5.3.22)$$

where $\mathscr{G}^{(2)}$ is an unknown pair phase correlation function. Since the final equation is valid only in the hydrodynamic regime, the singlet distribution functions in equation (5.3.22) will be distorted Maxwellian distributions centered about the local hydrodynamic flow velocity, and characterized by the local temperatures, at the centers of the molecules.* The distortions are assumed to be a function of the gradients of velocity, temperature and density. It is consistent with the meaning which we attach to coarse graining that the correlation function is independent of the momenta, but may depend upon the local gradients. Thus,

$$\mathscr{G}^{(2)}(\mathbf{R}_1,\mathbf{R}_2,\mathbf{p}_1,\mathbf{p}_2;t) = g^{(2)}(\mathbf{R}_1,\mathbf{R}_2) \quad (5.3.23)$$

is the pair correlation function. $g^{(2)}$ is supposed a function of the local thermodynamic variables at the point of contact, and also, since it is not necessarily the equilibrium function, a function of the vector separation of the molecules:

$$\begin{aligned} g^{(2)}(\mathbf{R}_1, \mathbf{R}_1 + \sigma\mathbf{k}) &= g^{(2)}(\mathbf{R}_1 + \tfrac{1}{2}\sigma\mathbf{k}, \sigma\mathbf{k}) \\ &= g_0^{(2)}(\mathbf{R}_1 + \tfrac{1}{2}\sigma\mathbf{k}, \sigma) + g_1^{(2)}(\mathbf{R}_1 + \tfrac{1}{2}\sigma\mathbf{k}, \sigma\mathbf{k}), \quad (5.3.24) \end{aligned}$$

where $g_0^{(2)}$ is the equilibrium pair correlation function and $g_1^{(2)}$, a distortion. Equations (5.3.22), (5.3.23), and (5.3.24) are now substituted in equation (5.3.21). $\sigma\mathbf{k}$ is a small distance on the hydrodynamic scale and the various functions of $(\mathbf{R}_1 + \sigma\mathbf{k})$ and $(\mathbf{R}_1 + \frac{1}{2}\sigma\mathbf{k})$ are expanded in Taylor series about the value at $\mathbf{R}_1$. Only the first power of σ is retained in each case since this will be seen, in the next section, to introduce terms linear in the gradients, and we are not interested in higher order terms for the description of transport processes in a simple liquid. The introduction of the non-equilibrium pair correlation function in equation

* Other, more complicated, solutions exist than those we consider. In particular, solutions with an explicit dependence on time can be found. Whether these solutions have physical significance is, however, in doubt, because such solutions would purport to describe the transient behavior preceding the establishment of local equilibrium, and the general analysis of Prigogine and co-workers has shown that other terms affecting transients are omitted from the final equation achieved here.

(5.3.24), in which the distortion function is obtained only as the solution of the doublet equation, can be shown finally after tedious manipulations to make no contribution. To avoid a lengthy discussion of this point we can utilize two simple properties of the pair correlation function which emerge from the analysis of Sections 6.3.A and 6.3.B. These are: (*a*) the contributions to $g^{(2)}$ from the velocity gradient are even functions of $\mathbf{k}$, and (*b*) the effect of a temperature gradient is to render the pair correlation function for molecules at $\mathbf{R}_1$ and $\mathbf{R}_2$ the equilibrium pair correlation function for a system whose temperature is that at their center of mass. Thus, in both situations, the distortion $g_1^{(2)}$ is an even function of $\mathbf{k}$. The result of these operations is

$$\begin{aligned}\Omega_H &= \frac{g_0^{(2)}(\mathbf{R}_1,\sigma)}{m}\int_{(\mathbf{k}\cdot\mathbf{p}_{12}>0)}[\bar{f}^{(1)}(\mathbf{R}_1,\mathbf{p}_1^*)\bar{f}^{(1)}(\mathbf{R}_1,\mathbf{p}_2^*)\\ &\qquad - \bar{f}^{(1)}(\mathbf{R}_1,\mathbf{p}_1)\bar{f}^{(1)}(\mathbf{R}_1,\mathbf{p}_2)]p_{12}b\,db\,d\epsilon\,d\mathbf{p}_2\\ &+ \frac{\sigma g_0^{(2)}(\mathbf{R}_1,\sigma)}{m}\int_{(\mathbf{k}\cdot\mathbf{p}_{12}>0)}[\bar{f}^{(1)}(\mathbf{R}_1,\mathbf{p}_1^*)\mathbf{k}\cdot\nabla_1\bar{f}^{(1)}(\mathbf{R}_1,\mathbf{p}_2^*)\\ &\qquad + \bar{f}^{(1)}(\mathbf{R}_1,\mathbf{p}_1)\mathbf{k}\cdot\nabla_1\bar{f}^{(1)}(\mathbf{R}_1,\mathbf{p}_2)]p_{12}b\,db\,d\epsilon\,d\mathbf{p}_2\\ &+ \frac{\sigma}{2m}\nabla_1 g_0^{(2)}(\mathbf{R}_1,\sigma)\cdot\int_{(\mathbf{k}\cdot\mathbf{p}_{12}>0)}\mathbf{k}[\bar{f}^{(1)}(\mathbf{R}_1,\mathbf{p}_1^*)\bar{f}^{(1)}(\mathbf{R}_1,\mathbf{p}_2^*)\\ &\qquad + \bar{f}^{(1)}(\mathbf{R}_1,\mathbf{p}_1)\bar{f}^{(1)}(\mathbf{R}_1,\mathbf{p}_2)]p_{12}\,b\,db\,d\epsilon\,d\mathbf{p}_2\\ &= J_1^{(1)} + J_2^{(1)} + J_3^{(1)},\end{aligned} \tag{5.3.25}$$

where $\nabla_1 g_0^{(2)}(\mathbf{R}_1,\sigma)$ is related to the temperature gradient by

$$\nabla_1 g_0^{(2)}(\mathbf{R}_1,\sigma) = \nabla T\left(\frac{\partial g_0^{(2)}(\mathbf{R}_1,\sigma)}{\partial T}\right)_p, \tag{5.3.26}$$

which is valid in the presence of non-uniform velocity and temperature fields, provided the pressure gradient is small enough.*

Equation (5.3.21) is sufficiently important that we digress to give an alternative and more elegant derivation (due to K. Hiroike). We again start with equation (5.3.14)

$$\Omega_H = \frac{1}{\tau}\int_0^\tau\int\left[\left(\frac{\partial}{\partial s} + \frac{1}{m}\mathbf{p}_1\cdot\nabla_1 + \frac{1}{m}\mathbf{p}_2\cdot\nabla_2\right)K_0^{(2)}\right]f^{(2)}(\Gamma_2'; t)\,d\Gamma_1(2)\,d\Gamma_2'\,ds. \tag{5.3.14}$$

---

* We are not interested in, for instance, the propagation of sound.

For convenience we shall now introduce the free-particle Green's function, $K_{0,\text{free}}^{(2)}$, which is defined by the equation

$$\left[\frac{\partial}{\partial s} + \frac{\mathbf{p}_1}{m}\cdot\nabla_1 + \frac{\mathbf{p}_2}{m}\cdot\nabla_2\right]K_{0,\text{free}}^{(2)} = 0$$

$$\lim_{s\to 0} K_{0,\text{free}}^{(2)} = \prod_{i=1,2} \delta(\mathbf{R}_i - \mathbf{R}_i')\,\delta(\mathbf{p}_i - \mathbf{p}_i'). \tag{5.3.21a}$$

The solution of equation (5.3.21a) is

$$K_{0,\text{free}}^{(2)} = \prod_{i=1,2} \delta\left(\mathbf{R}_i - \frac{s}{m}\mathbf{p}_i - \mathbf{R}_i'\right)\delta(\mathbf{p}_i - \mathbf{p}_i'), \tag{5.3.21b}$$

so that

$$\Omega_H = \frac{1}{\tau}\int\int_0^\tau\left[\left(\frac{\partial}{\partial s} + \frac{\mathbf{p}_1}{m}\cdot\nabla_1 + \frac{\mathbf{p}_2}{m}\cdot\nabla_2\right)(K_0^{(2)} - K_{0,\text{free}}^{(2)})\right] \times f^{(2)}(\Gamma_2'; t)\, d\Gamma_1(2)\, d\Gamma_2'\, ds,$$

which reduces, by partial integration over $\mathbf{R}_2$, to

$$\Omega_H = \frac{1}{\tau}\int_0^\tau ds\left[\frac{\partial}{\partial s} + \frac{\mathbf{p}_1}{m}\cdot\nabla_1\right]\int d\Gamma_1(2)\, d\Gamma_2'[K_0^{(2)} - K_{0,\text{free}}^{(2)}]\, f^{(2)}(\Gamma_2'; t). \tag{5.3.21c}$$

We note that equation (5.3.21c) is equivalent to equation (5.3.14) when the interaction potential is continuous, but not when the interaction potential is discontinuous. Insofar as we confine attention to the case of classical mechanics, it is not necessary to replace equation (5.3.21c) with equation (5.3.14), but in the quantum mechanical case we are led directly to equation (5.3.21c), where $f^{(2)}$ is then the two particle Wigner function and $K_0^{(2)}$ the quantum mechanical Green's function.

The Green's function $K_0^{(2)}$ can be factored into two Green's functions describing, respectively, the center of mass and relative motion of the pair of molecules:

$$K_0^{(2)}(\mathbf{R}_1, \mathbf{R}_2, \mathbf{p}_1, \mathbf{p}_2 \mid \mathbf{R}_1', \mathbf{R}_2', \mathbf{p}_1', \mathbf{p}_2'; s) = K_c(\mathbf{R}_c, \mathbf{p}_c \mid \mathbf{R}_c', \mathbf{p}_c'; s)K(\mathbf{r}, \mathbf{p} \mid \mathbf{r}', \mathbf{p}'; s), \tag{5.3.21d}$$

where

$$\mathbf{R}_c = \tfrac{1}{2}(\mathbf{R}_1 + \mathbf{R}_2), \qquad \mathbf{p}_c = \mathbf{p}_1 + \mathbf{p}_2,$$
$$\mathbf{r} = \mathbf{R}_2 - \mathbf{R}_1, \qquad \mathbf{p} = \tfrac{1}{2}(\mathbf{p}_2 - \mathbf{p}_1). \tag{5.3.21e}$$

The center of mass motion is now described by a Green's function for free motion in the absence of external forces,

$$K_c(\mathbf{R}_c, \mathbf{p}_c \mid \mathbf{R}_c', \mathbf{p}_c'; s) = \delta\left(\mathbf{R}_c - \frac{s}{M}\mathbf{p}_c - \mathbf{R}_c'\right)\delta(\mathbf{p}_c - \mathbf{p}_c'), \tag{5.3.21f}$$

where

$$M = 2m,$$

while the Green's function for the relative motion obeys the equations

$$\left[\frac{\partial}{\partial s} + \frac{1}{\mu}\mathbf{p}\cdot\nabla_r + \mathbf{F}^{(H)}\cdot\nabla_p\right]K = 0$$

$$\lim_{s\to 0} K = \delta(\mathbf{r} - \mathbf{r}')\,\delta(\mathbf{p} - \mathbf{p}'), \tag{5.3.21g}$$

where $\mu = m/2$.

Corresponding to equation (5.3.21d), the free-particle Green's function is written in the form

$$K^{(2)}_{0,\text{free}} = K_c(\mathbf{R}_c, \mathbf{p}_c \mid \mathbf{R}_c', \mathbf{p}_c'; s)K_{\text{free}}(\mathbf{r}, \mathbf{p} \mid \mathbf{r}', \mathbf{p}'; s), \tag{5.3.21h}$$

where

$$K_{\text{free}} = \delta\left((\mathbf{r} - \frac{s}{\mu}\mathbf{p} - \mathbf{r}'\right)\delta(\mathbf{p} - \mathbf{p}'). \tag{5.3.21i}$$

Now, equation (5.3.21c) may be rewritten in the form

$$\Omega_H = \frac{1}{\tau}\int_0^\tau ds\left[\frac{\partial}{\partial s} + \frac{\mathbf{p}_1}{m}\cdot\nabla_1\right]\int d\mathbf{r}\, d\mathbf{p}_2\, d\mathbf{r}'\, d\mathbf{p}'[K(\mathbf{r}, \mathbf{p} \mid \mathbf{r}', \mathbf{p}'; s) - K_{\text{free}}] \times$$

$$f^{(2)}\left(\mathbf{R}_1 - \frac{s}{M}\mathbf{p}_c + \frac{\mathbf{r} - \mathbf{r}'}{2}, \mathbf{R}_1 - \frac{s}{M}\mathbf{p}_c + \frac{\mathbf{r} + \mathbf{r}'}{2}, \frac{\mathbf{p}_c}{2} - \mathbf{p}', \frac{\mathbf{p}_c}{2} + \mathbf{p}'; t\right). \tag{5.3.21j}$$

The Green's function, K, for rigid spheres is

$$K(\mathbf{r}, \mathbf{p} \mid \mathbf{r}', \mathbf{p}'; s) = \theta(r - \sigma)\theta(r' - \sigma)\, \delta(\mathbf{r} - \Delta\mathbf{r} - \mathbf{r}')\, \delta(\mathbf{p} - \Delta\mathbf{p} - \mathbf{p}'), \tag{5.3.21k}$$

where $\theta(x)$ is a discontinuous function defined by

$$\begin{aligned} \theta(x) &= 1 \quad \text{when } x \geqslant 0, \\ \theta(x) &= 0 \quad \text{when } x < 0, \end{aligned} \tag{5.3.21l}$$

and $\mathbf{r} - \Delta\mathbf{r}$ and $\mathbf{p} - \Delta\mathbf{p}$ are the initial relative position and momentum of particles 1 and 2; the relative position and momentum at time s are denoted $\mathbf{r}$ and $\mathbf{p}$, respectively. It should be noted that the changes in relative position and momentum, $\Delta\mathbf{r}$ and $\Delta\mathbf{p}$, are functions of $\mathbf{r}$, $\mathbf{p}$, and s. Equation (5.3.21j) reduces, with the aid of equations (5.3.21i) and (5.3.21k), to

$$\Omega_H = \frac{1}{\tau}\int_0^\tau ds\left[\frac{\partial}{\partial s} + \frac{\mathbf{p}_1}{m}\cdot\nabla_1\right]\int d\mathbf{p}_2\, d\mathbf{r}\Big[\theta(r - \sigma)\theta(|\mathbf{r} - \Delta\mathbf{r}| - \sigma) \times$$

$$f^{(2)}\left(\mathbf{R}_1 - \frac{s}{M}\mathbf{p}_c + \frac{\Delta\mathbf{r}}{2}, \mathbf{R}_1 - \frac{s}{M}\mathbf{p}_c + \mathbf{r} - \frac{\Delta\mathbf{r}}{2}, \frac{\mathbf{p}_c}{2} - \mathbf{p} + \Delta\mathbf{p}, \frac{\mathbf{p}_c}{2} + \mathbf{p} - \Delta\mathbf{p}; t\right)$$

$$- f^{(2)}\left(\mathbf{R}_1 - \frac{s}{M}\mathbf{p}_c + \frac{s}{2\mu}\mathbf{p}, \mathbf{R}_1 - \frac{s}{M}\mathbf{p}_c + \mathbf{r} - \frac{s}{2}\mathbf{p}, \frac{\mathbf{p}_c}{2} - \mathbf{p}, \frac{\mathbf{p}_c}{2} + \mathbf{p}; t\right)\Big] \tag{5.3.21m}$$

$$\Omega_H \equiv \frac{1}{\tau}\int_0^\tau ds\left[\frac{\partial}{\partial s} + \frac{\mathbf{p}_1}{m}\quad {}_1\right]\int d\mathbf{p}_2 I. \tag{5.3.21n}$$

We choose a cylindrical coordinate system (z, b, ϵ) with origin on particle 1 and z axis parallel to the relative momentum $\mathbf{p}$, and assume that $s > 0$. It is then clear that

$$\Delta\mathbf{r} = \frac{s}{\mu}\mathbf{p}, \qquad \Delta\mathbf{p} = 0, \qquad \mathbf{r} > \sigma, \qquad |\mathbf{r} - \Delta\mathbf{r}| > \sigma \tag{5.3.21o}$$

when $b > \sigma$, or when $b < \sigma$ and $z > \sigma\cos\theta + \frac{s}{\mu}p$, or when $b < \sigma$ and $z < -r\cos\theta$, since then no collision occurs. Therefore,

$$I = \int_0^{2\pi} d\epsilon \int_0^{\sigma} b\,db \int_{\sigma\cos\theta}^{\sigma\cos\theta+(s/\mu)p} dz \Big[f^{(2)}\Big(\mathbf{R}_1 - \frac{s}{M}\mathbf{p}_c + \frac{\Delta\mathbf{r}}{2}, \mathbf{R}_1 - \frac{s}{M}\mathbf{p}_c + \mathbf{r} - \frac{\Delta\mathbf{r}}{2}, \frac{\mathbf{p}_c}{2} - \mathbf{p} + \Delta\mathbf{p}, \frac{\mathbf{p}_c}{2} + \mathbf{p} - \Delta\mathbf{p}; t\Big) - f^{(2)}\Big(\mathbf{R}_1 - \frac{s}{M}\mathbf{p}_c + \frac{s}{2\mu}\mathbf{p}_1\mathbf{R}_1 - \frac{s}{M}\mathbf{p}_c + \mathbf{r} - \frac{s}{2\mu}\mathbf{p}, \frac{\mathbf{p}_c}{2} - \mathbf{p}, \frac{\mathbf{p}_c}{2} + \mathbf{p}; t\Big)\Big] - \int_0^{2\pi} d\epsilon \int_0^{\sigma} b\,db \int_{-\sigma\cos\theta}^{\sigma\cos\theta} dz f^{(2)}\Big(\mathbf{R}_1 - \frac{s}{M}\mathbf{p}_c + \frac{s}{2\mu}\mathbf{p}, \mathbf{R}_1 - \frac{s}{M}\mathbf{p}_c + \mathbf{r} - \frac{s}{2\mu}\mathbf{p}, \frac{\mathbf{p}_c}{2} - \mathbf{p}, \frac{\mathbf{p}_c}{2} + \mathbf{p}; t\Big)$$

$$= \int_0^{2\pi} d\epsilon \int_0^{\sigma} b\,db \int_{\sigma\cos\theta}^{\sigma\cos\theta+(s/\mu)p} dz \Big[f^{(2)}\Big(\mathbf{R}_1 - \frac{s}{M}\mathbf{p}_c + \frac{\Delta\mathbf{r}}{2}, \mathbf{R}_1 - \frac{s}{M}\mathbf{p}_c + \mathbf{r} - \frac{\Delta\mathbf{r}}{2}, \frac{\mathbf{p}_c}{2} - \mathbf{p} + \Delta\mathbf{p}, \frac{\mathbf{p}_c}{2} + \mathbf{p} - \Delta\mathbf{p}; t\Big) - f^{(2)}\Big(\mathbf{R}_1 - \frac{s}{m}\mathbf{p}_1, \mathbf{R}_1 + \mathbf{r} - \frac{s}{m}\mathbf{p}_2, \mathbf{p}_1, \mathbf{p}_2; t\Big)\Big] - \int_{r\leqslant\sigma} d\mathbf{r} f^{(2)}\Big(\mathbf{R}_1 - \frac{s}{m}\mathbf{p}_1, \mathbf{R}_1 + \mathbf{r} - \frac{s}{m}\mathbf{p}_2, \mathbf{p}_1, \mathbf{p}_2; t\Big). \tag{5.3.21p}$$

Equation (5.3.21n) is now written in the form

$$\Omega_H = J_1 + J_2 + J_3, \tag{5.3.21q}$$

where

$$J_1 = \frac{1}{\tau}\int_0^{\tau} ds \frac{\partial}{\partial s} \int d\mathbf{p}_2 \int_0^{2\pi} d\epsilon \int_0^{\sigma} b\,db \int_{\sigma\cos\theta}^{\sigma\cos\theta+(s/\mu)p} dz \Big[f^{(2)}\Big(\mathbf{R}_1 - \frac{s}{M}\mathbf{p}_c + \frac{\Delta\mathbf{r}}{2}, \mathbf{R}_1 - \frac{s}{M}\mathbf{p}_c + \mathbf{r} - \frac{\Delta\mathbf{r}}{2}, \frac{\mathbf{p}_c}{2} - \mathbf{p} + \Delta\mathbf{p}, \frac{\mathbf{p}_c}{2} + \mathbf{p} - \Delta\mathbf{p}; t\Big) - f^{(2)}\Big(\mathbf{R}_1 - \frac{s}{m}\mathbf{p}_1, \mathbf{R}_1 + \mathbf{r} - \frac{s}{m}\mathbf{p}_2, \mathbf{p}_1, \mathbf{p}_2; t\Big)\Big] \tag{5.3.21r}$$

$$J_2 = \frac{1}{\tau}\int_0^{\tau} ds \int \frac{\mathbf{p}_1}{m}\cdot\nabla_1 d\mathbf{p}_2 \int_0^{2\pi} d\epsilon \int_0^{\sigma} b\,db \int_{\sigma\cos\theta}^{\sigma\cos\theta+(s/\mu)p} dz \Big[f^{(2)}\Big(\mathbf{R}_1 - \frac{s}{M}\mathbf{p}_c + \frac{\Delta\mathbf{r}}{2}, \mathbf{R}_1 - \frac{s}{M}\mathbf{p}_c + \mathbf{r} - \frac{\Delta\mathbf{r}}{2}, \frac{\mathbf{p}_c}{2} - \mathbf{p} + \Delta\mathbf{p}, \frac{\mathbf{p}_c}{2} + \mathbf{p} - \Delta\mathbf{p}; t\Big) - f^{(2)}\Big(\mathbf{R}_1 - \frac{s}{m}\mathbf{p}_1, \mathbf{R}_1 + \mathbf{r} - \frac{s}{m}\mathbf{p}_2, \mathbf{p}_1, \mathbf{p}_2; t\Big)\Big] \tag{5.3.21s}$$

$$J_3 = -\frac{1}{\tau}\int_0^{\tau} ds \Big[\frac{\partial}{\partial s} + \frac{\mathbf{p}_1}{m}\cdot\nabla_1\Big] \int d\mathbf{p}_2 \int_{r\leqslant\sigma} d\mathbf{r} f^{(2)}\Big(\mathbf{R}_1 - \frac{s}{m}\mathbf{p}_1, \mathbf{R}_1 + \mathbf{r} - \frac{s}{m}\mathbf{p}_2, \mathbf{p}_1, \mathbf{p}_2; t\Big) \tag{5.3.21t}$$

As before, we shall evaluate J_1, J_2, and J_3 in the limit of $\tau \to 0+$. (We here take $\tau_1 = 0+$.) It is easily seen that

$$\lim_{\tau\to 0+} J_2 = 0, \tag{5.3.21u}$$

since the range of integration over z shrinks to zero and the integrand does not contain a term of the form $\delta(z - c)$. Next we find

$$\begin{aligned}\lim_{\tau\to 0+} J_1 &= \int d\mathbf{p}_2 \frac{|\mathbf{p}|}{\mu} \int_0^{2\pi} d\epsilon \int_0^{\sigma} b\, db \Big[f^{(2)}\Big(\mathbf{R}_1, \mathbf{R}_1 + \mathbf{r}, \frac{\mathbf{p}_c}{2} - \mathbf{p} + \Delta\mathbf{p}(0),\\ &\qquad \frac{\mathbf{p}_c}{2} + \mathbf{p} - \Delta\mathbf{p}(0); t\Big) - f^{(2)}(\mathbf{R}_1, \mathbf{R}_1 + \mathbf{r}, \mathbf{p}_1, \mathbf{p}_2; t)\Big]_{z=\cos\theta}\\ &= \int d\mathbf{p}_2 \frac{|\mathbf{p}|}{\mu} \int_0^{2\pi} d\epsilon \int_{\substack{0\\ \mathbf{p}\cdot\mathbf{k}>0}}^{\sigma} b\, db \Big[f^{(2)}\Big(\mathbf{R}_1, \mathbf{R}_1 + \sigma\mathbf{k}, \frac{\mathbf{p}_c}{2} - \mathbf{p} + \Delta\mathbf{p}(0),\\ &\qquad \frac{\mathbf{p}_c}{2} + \mathbf{p} - \Delta\mathbf{p}(0); t\Big) - f^{(2)}(\mathbf{R}_1, \mathbf{R}_1 + \sigma\mathbf{k}, \mathbf{p}_1, \mathbf{p}_2; t)\Big],\end{aligned} \tag{5.3.21v}$$

where $\mathbf{k}$ is a unit vector in the direction of the line of centers of the colliding spheres at contact, and $\Delta\mathbf{p}(0)$ is the relative momentum change because of the collision. Expression (5.3.21t) is now transformed as follows:

$$\begin{aligned}\lim_{\tau\to 0+} J_3 &= -\lim_{\tau\to 0+} \frac{1}{\tau} \int_0^{\tau} ds \int d\mathbf{p}_2 \int_{r\leqslant\sigma} d\mathbf{r} \Big[-\frac{\mathbf{p}_2}{m} + \frac{\mathbf{p}_1}{m}\Big]\\ &\qquad \cdot \nabla_r f^{(2)}\Big(\mathbf{R}_1 - \frac{s}{m}\mathbf{p}_1, \mathbf{R}_1 + \mathbf{r} - \frac{s}{m}\mathbf{p}_2, \mathbf{p}_1, \mathbf{p}_2; t\Big)\\ &= \int d\mathbf{p}_2 \int_{r\leqslant\sigma} d\mathbf{r} \frac{\mathbf{p}}{\mu} \cdot \nabla_r f^{(2)}(\mathbf{R}_1, \mathbf{R}_1 + \mathbf{r}, \mathbf{p}_1, \mathbf{p}_2; t)\\ &= \int d\mathbf{p}_2 \int \sigma^2\, d\mathbf{k} \frac{\mathbf{p}}{\mu} \cdot \mathbf{k} f^{(2)}(\mathbf{R}_1, \mathbf{R}_1 + \sigma\mathbf{k}, \mathbf{p}_1, \mathbf{p}_2; t)\\ &= \int d\mathbf{p}_2 \Big[\int_{\mathbf{k}\cdot\mathbf{p}>0} \sigma^2\, d\mathbf{k} + \int_{\mathbf{k}\cdot\mathbf{p}<0} \sigma^2\, d\mathbf{k}\Big] \frac{\mathbf{p}}{\mu} \cdot \mathbf{k} f^{(2)}(\mathbf{R}_1, \mathbf{R}_1 + \sigma\mathbf{k}, \mathbf{p}_1, \mathbf{p}_2; t)\\ &= \int d\mathbf{p}_2 \int_{\mathbf{k}\cdot\mathbf{p}>0} \sigma^2\, d\mathbf{k} \frac{\mathbf{p}}{\mu} \cdot \mathbf{k} [f^{(2)}(\mathbf{R}_1, \mathbf{R}_1 + \sigma\mathbf{k}, \mathbf{p}_1, \mathbf{p}_2; t)\\ &\qquad - f^{(2)}(\mathbf{R}_1, \mathbf{R}_1 - \sigma\mathbf{k}, \mathbf{p}_1, \mathbf{p}_2; t)]\\ &= \int d\mathbf{p}_2 \frac{|\mathbf{p}|}{\mu} \int_{\substack{0\\ \mathbf{k}\cdot\mathbf{p}>0}}^{2\pi} d\epsilon \int_0^{\sigma} b\, db [f^{(2)}(\mathbf{R}_1, \mathbf{R}_1 + \sigma\mathbf{k}, \mathbf{p}_1, \mathbf{p}_2; t)\\ &\qquad - f^{(2)}(\mathbf{R}_1, \mathbf{R}_1 - \sigma\mathbf{k}, \mathbf{p}_1, \mathbf{p}_2; t)].\end{aligned} \tag{5.3.21w}$$

Collecting together equations (5.3.21u), (5.3.21v), and (5.3.21w), we finally obtain, as before,

$$\lim_{\tau \to 0+} \Omega_H = \int_{\mathbf{k}\cdot\mathbf{p}>0} d\mathbf{p}_2 \frac{|\mathbf{p}|}{\mu} \int_0^{2\pi} d\epsilon \int_0^{\sigma} b\, db[f^{(2)}(\mathbf{R}_1, \mathbf{R}_1 + \sigma\mathbf{k}, \mathbf{p}_1', \mathbf{p}_2'; t) - f^{(2)}(\mathbf{R}_1, \mathbf{R}_1 - \sigma\mathbf{k}, \mathbf{p}_1, \mathbf{p}_2; t)], \quad (5.3.21x)$$

where

$$\mathbf{p}_1' = \mathbf{p}_1 + \Delta\mathbf{p}(0)$$

$$\mathbf{p}_2' = \mathbf{p}_2 - \Delta\mathbf{p}(0).$$

We consider now the evaluation of Ω_S.* The specific two-molecule distribution function is introduced in equation (5.3.6), and with the use of equations (5.3.7) and (5.3.9), Ω_S becomes

$$\Omega_S = \frac{-N(N-1)}{\tau} \int_0^{\tau} \int \cdots \int \mathbf{F}_{12}^{(S)} \cdot \nabla_{p_1} K^{(N)}(\Gamma_N \mid \Gamma_N'; s) \times f^{(N-2/2)}(\Gamma_{N-2}' \mid \Gamma_2'; t) f^{(2)}(\Gamma_2'; t)\, d\Gamma_{N-2}\, d\Gamma_N'\, d\Gamma_1(2)\, ds, \quad (5.3.27)$$

where the prime denotes the initial configuration. The assumption, already stated in the discussion of the evaluation of Ω_H, that the soft forces cause (on average) only a small perturbation to the trajectory of a molecule during τ, can be treated by the weak interaction procedure developed by Ross (19) and Kirkwood (4). The forces $\mathbf{F}_i$ in equation (5.3.8) are now soft forces, and are replaced by $\lambda\mathbf{F}_i^{(S)}$ and a solution in ascending powers of λ is obtained:

$$\left[\frac{\partial}{\partial s} + \sum_{i=1}^{N} \left\{\frac{1}{m} \mathbf{p}_i \cdot \nabla_i + \lambda \mathbf{F}_i^{(S)} \cdot \nabla_{p_1}\right\}\right] K^{(N)} = 0,$$

$$K^{(N)} = \sum_{n=0}^{\infty} \lambda^n K_n^{(N)}. \quad (5.3.28)$$

The introduction of λ labels the forces as perturbations. It serves simply as an ordering parameter for the small quantities, and after forming the solution $K^{(N)}$ from the individual $K_n^{(N)}$ it is set equal to unity.

Equation (5.3.28) is equivalent to the set of equations

$$\left[\frac{\partial}{\partial s} + \sum_{i=1}^{N} \frac{1}{m} \mathbf{p}_i \cdot \nabla_i\right] K_0^{(N)} = 0,$$

$$\left[\frac{\partial}{\partial s} + \sum_{i=1}^{N} \frac{1}{m} \mathbf{p}_i \cdot \nabla_i\right] K_n^{(N)} + \sum_{i=1}^{N} \mathbf{F}_i^{(S)} \cdot \nabla_{p_i} K_{n-1}^{(N)} = 0. \quad (5.3.29)$$

* An alternative to the following derivation, similar to that given by Ross, is described in Appendix 5.A.

If in the Liouville equation there is included an external force $\mathbf{X}_i$ acting on molecule i, the only alteration to the analysis is the replacement everywhere of $\mathbf{F}_i^{(S)}$ by $\mathbf{X}_i + \mathbf{F}_i^{(S)}$.

Now, the first of equations (5.3.29) describes an N-molecule system with no intermolecular (or external) forces. The solution to this free-particle problem is obviously

$$K_0^{(N)} = \prod_{i=1}^{N} \delta(\mathbf{R}_i - \mathbf{R}_i' - \mathbf{p}_i s/m)\, \delta(\mathbf{p}_i - \mathbf{p}_i'). \tag{5.3.30}$$

Further, it may be verified by substitution that the solution of the second of equations (5.3.29) is

$$K_n^{(N)} = -\int_{\tau_1}^{s} \exp\left[(s' - s)\sum_{i=1}^{N} \frac{1}{m}\mathbf{p}_i \cdot \nabla_i\right] \sum_{j=1}^{N} \mathbf{F}_j^{(S)} \cdot \nabla_{p_j} K_{n-1}^{(N)}(s')\, ds'. \tag{5.3.31}$$

Consider the first order term in λ, which is

$$K_1^{(N)} = -\int_{\tau_1}^{s} \exp\left[(s' - s)\sum_{i=1}^{N} \frac{1}{m}\mathbf{p}_i \cdot \nabla_i\right] \sum_{j=1}^{N} \mathbf{F}_j^{(S)} \cdot \nabla_{p_j}\left[\prod_{n=1}^{N} \delta(\mathbf{R}_n - \mathbf{R}_n' - \mathbf{p}_n s'/m)\, \delta(\mathbf{p}_n - \mathbf{p}_n')\right] ds', \tag{5.3.32}$$

after substitution of (5.3.30) into (5.3.31). Now, in general,

$$\exp\left[a\frac{\partial}{\partial x}\right] f(x) = f(x + a)$$

as can be verified by making a Taylor series expansion of $f(x + a)$ and comparing this with the expansion that defines the operator $\exp\left[a\dfrac{\partial}{\partial x}\right]$. Moreover,

$$\exp\left[\alpha y \frac{\partial}{\partial x}\right]\frac{\partial}{\partial y} H(x,y) = \frac{\partial}{\partial y}\left\{\exp\left[\alpha y \frac{\partial}{\partial x}\right] H(x,y)\right\} - \left\{\frac{\partial}{\partial y}\exp\left[\alpha y \frac{\partial}{\partial x}\right]\right\} H(x,y) = \left(\frac{\partial}{\partial y} - \alpha\frac{\partial}{\partial x}\right) H(x + \alpha y,\, y),$$

which may be achieved by considering the transformation $(x,y) \to (x' = x + \alpha y,\, y' = y)$, which is induced by the operator. Thus, the exponential operator in equation (5.3.31) adds $(s' - s)\mathbf{p}_i/m$ to each $\mathbf{R}_i$

appearing in the operand, and $K_1^{(N)}$ assumes the form

$$K_1^{(N)} = -\int_{\tau_1}^{s} \sum_{j=1}^{N} [\mathbf{F}_j^{(S)}(\mathbf{R}^{(N)} + (s' - s)\mathbf{p}^{(N)}/m)] \cdot \left[\nabla_{p_j} + \frac{s - s'}{m} \nabla_j\right] \times \left[\prod_{n=1}^{N} \delta(\mathbf{R}_n - \mathbf{R}_n' - \mathbf{p}_n s/m)\, \delta(\mathbf{p}_n - \mathbf{p}_n')\right] ds'. \quad (5.3.33)$$

Because of the delta function, $\mathbf{R}_n - s\mathbf{p}_n/m$ may be replaced by $\mathbf{R}_n'$ in the force term, and this leads to

$$K_1^{(N)} = -\int_{\tau_1}^{s} \sum_{j=1}^{N} \left[\nabla_{p_j} + \frac{s - s'}{m} \nabla_j\right] \cdot \Delta\mathbf{p}_j^{(1)}(s) \times \left[\prod_{n=1}^{N} \delta\left(\mathbf{R}_n - \mathbf{R}_n' - \frac{\mathbf{p}_n s}{m}\right) \delta(\mathbf{p}_n - \mathbf{p}_n')\right] ds',$$

$$\Delta\mathbf{p}_i^{(1)}(s) = \int_{\tau_1}^{s} \mathbf{F}_i^{(S)}(\mathbf{R}^{(N)'} + \mathbf{p}^{(N)'} s'/m)\, ds'. \quad (5.3.34)$$

If we denote by $\Delta\mathbf{R}_i^{(0)}(s)$ the distance traversed by a free particle i in time s, then $\mathbf{F}_i^{(S)}(\mathbf{R}^{(N)'} + \mathbf{p}^{(N)'} s/m)$ is the force on the particle i traveling along a linear trajectory and $\Delta\mathbf{p}_i^{(1)}(s)$ is the change in momentum due to this force. The terms $\Delta\mathbf{R}_i^{(0)}$ and $\Delta\mathbf{p}_i^{(1)}$ are the first terms, respectively, in the development in powers of λ of $\Delta\mathbf{R}_i$ and $\Delta\mathbf{p}_i$, the change in coordinates and momenta obtained from an exact solution of the equations of motion. That is, if the equations of motion for a particle,

$$\frac{d\mathbf{R}_i}{ds} = \frac{1}{m} \mathbf{p}_i$$

$$\frac{d\mathbf{p}_i}{ds} = \lambda \mathbf{F}_i^{(S)},$$

are solved by the perturbation procedure used to obtain equation (5.3.29), it is found that

$$\Delta\mathbf{R}_i(s) = \Delta\mathbf{R}_i^{(0)} + \lambda\, \Delta\mathbf{R}_i^{(1)} + \cdots$$
$$\Delta\mathbf{p}_i(s) = \lambda\, \Delta\mathbf{p}_i^{(1)} + \lambda^2\, \Delta\mathbf{p}_i^{(2)} + \cdots.$$

The required solution of equation (5.3.28) is the first-order perturbation

$$K^{(N)} = K_0^{(N)} + K_1^{(N)} + \cdots. \quad (5.3.35)$$

Substitution of equation (5.3.35) in equation (5.3.27) now leads to

$$\Omega_S = \Omega_S^{(0)} + \Omega_S^{(1)}, \quad (5.3.36)$$

where $\Omega_S^{(0)}$ is given by

$$\Omega_S^{(0)} = -\frac{N(N-1)}{\tau}\nabla_{p_1}\cdot\left[\int_0^\tau\int \mathbf{F}_{12}^{(S)} f^{(N)}(\Gamma_N;t)\,d\Gamma_{N-1}\,ds\right]$$

$$= -\nabla_{p_1}\cdot[({}^0\langle\mathbf{F}_1^{(S)}\rangle + {}^{(1)}\mathbf{F}_1^{(S)\dagger})f^{(1)}(\Gamma_1;t)], \qquad (5.3.37)$$

and $f^{(1)}$ is now the generic singlet distribution function. The first member of equation (5.3.37) is obtained after an integration over Γ_N'. As with the development of Ω_H the small displacements $\Delta\mathbf{R}_i^{(0)} = \frac{s}{m}\mathbf{p}_i'$ introduced by $K_0^{(N)}$ are assumed to have a negligible effect. The second member of equation (5.3.37) is obtained in the following way. The conditional $(N-1)$ molecule distribution $f^{(N-1/1)}(\Gamma_{N-1} \mid \Gamma_1;t)$ is introduced by

$$f^{(N)}(\Gamma_N;t) = f^{(1)}(\Gamma_1;t)f^{(N-1/1)}(\Gamma_{N-1} \mid \Gamma_1;t), \qquad (5.3.38)$$

and is written as the sum of an equilibrium part and a small correction:

$$f^{(N-1/1)} = {}^0f^{(N-1/1)} + \Delta f^{(N-1/1)}. \qquad (5.3.39)$$

Integration over Γ_{N-2} and $\mathbf{p}_2$ affects only $f^{(N-1/1)}$, and yields

$$\int f^{(N-1/1)}\,d\Gamma_{N-2}\,d\mathbf{p}_2 = \frac{1}{V}[g_0^{(2)}(\mathbf{R}_{12}) + g_1^{(2)}(\mathbf{R}_1,\mathbf{R}_2)], \qquad (5.3.40)$$

where $g_0^{(2)}$ and $g_1^{(2)}$ arise from ${}^0f^{(N-1/1)}$ and $\Delta f^{(N-1/1)}$, respectively. A factor N is absorbed into $f^{(1)}$, converting it to the generic distribution, and we are left with the equilibrium average force ${}^0\langle\mathbf{F}_1^{(S)}\rangle_1$, and the average force due to deviation of the environment from equilibrium ${}^{(1)}\mathbf{F}^{(S)\dagger}$, on molecule 1, which are defined by

$${}^0\langle\mathbf{F}_1^{(S)}\rangle = \rho\int \mathbf{F}_{12}^{(S)}(\mathbf{R}_{12})g_0^{(2)}(\mathbf{R}_{12})\,d\mathbf{R}_{12},$$

$${}^{(1)}\mathbf{F}_1^{(S)\dagger} = \rho\int \mathbf{F}_{12}^{(S)}(\mathbf{R}_{12})g_1^{(2)}(\mathbf{R}_1,\mathbf{R}_2)\,d\mathbf{R}_{12}, \qquad (5.3.41)$$

where $\rho = (N-1)/V$.

$\Omega_S^{(1)}$ is derived from $K_1^{(N)}$. After integration over Γ_N', it may be written in the form

$$\Omega_S^{(1)} = \frac{N(N-1)}{\tau} \nabla_{p_1} \cdot \int_0^\tau \int_{\tau_1}^s \int \mathbf{F}_{12}^{(S)} \sum_{i=1}^N \left[\nabla_{p_i} + \frac{s-s'}{m} \nabla_i \right] \cdot \left[\mathbf{F}_i^{(S)} \left(\mathbf{R}^{(N)} + (s'-s) \frac{\mathbf{p}^{(N)}}{m} \right) \right] \cdot f^{(N)}(\Gamma_{N,0};t)\, d\Gamma_{N-1}\, ds'\, ds \quad (5.3.42)$$

where, again, the spatial displacements introduced by $K_0^{(N)}$ have been neglected. Substitution of equation (5.3.34) in (5.3.42), and integration over the momenta and coordinates of all molecules except 1 and 2, now yields*

$$\Omega_S^{(1)} = \frac{N(N-1)}{\tau} \nabla_{p_1} \cdot \left[\int_0^\tau \int_{\tau_1}^s \mathbf{F}_{12}^{(S)} \left\{ \left\langle \mathbf{F}_1^{(S)} \left(\mathbf{R}^{(N)} + \frac{s'}{m} \mathbf{p}^{(N)} \right) \right\rangle_{1,2} \cdot \nabla_{p_1} + \left\langle \mathbf{F}_2^{(S)} \left(\mathbf{R}^{(N)} + \frac{s'}{m} \mathbf{p}^{(N)} \right) \right\rangle_{1,2} \cdot \nabla_{p_2} \right\} f^{(2)}(\mathbf{R}_1,\mathbf{R}_2,\mathbf{p}_1,\mathbf{p}_2;t)\, d\Gamma_1(2) \right], \quad (5.3.43)$$

where $\langle \cdots \rangle_{1,2}$ is defined by

$$\langle \cdots \rangle_{1,2} = \int \cdots {}^0 f^{(N-2/2)}\, d\Gamma_{N-2}. \quad (5.3.44)$$

The use of the equilibrium conditional distribution function ${}^0 f^{(N-2/2)}$ in equation (5.3.44) is justified since we seek only the first-order deviations from equilibrium, and $\Omega_S^{(1)}$ is already of first order. It is easily seen from the definition of ${}^0 f^{(N-2/2)}$ (obtained from Eq. (5.3.38) upon replacing every "1" by "2") that it is given by

$${}^0 f^{(N-2/2)}(\Gamma_{N-2}/\Gamma_2) = \frac{N(N-1) \exp\left(-\sum_{i=3}^N \frac{p_i^2}{2mkT} - U(\mathbf{R}^{(N)})/kT \right)}{\rho_0^{(2)}(\mathbf{R}_1,\mathbf{R}_2)(2\pi mkT)^{\frac{3N}{2}-3} \int \exp(-U/kT)\, d\mathbf{R}^{(N)}}, \quad (5.3.45)$$

* Strictly, a term arises because of the appearance of $\mathbf{p}_{ij}$ in the argument of $\mathbf{F}_{ij}^{(s)}$. However, this may be shown to be zero by applying the Fourier decomposition of $\mathbf{F}_{ij}^{(S)}\left(\left| \mathbf{R}_{ij} + \frac{s'}{m} \mathbf{p}_{ij} \right| \right)$ in a similar way to that discussed in equation (5.3.52) *et seq.*

where $U(\mathbf{R}^{(N)})$ is the total potential energy of the system, and $\rho_0^{(2)}$ is the equilibrium pair configurational distribution function. From equation (5.3.44) and the definition of $\rho_0^{(2)}$ it is easily seen that

$$\langle \mathbf{F}_1^{(S)} + \mathbf{F}_1^{(H)} \rangle_{1,2} = \frac{kT}{\rho_0^{(2)}} \nabla_1 \rho_0^{(2)} = \frac{kT}{g_0^{(2)}} \nabla_1 g_0^{(2)},$$

$$\langle \mathbf{F}_2^{(S)} + \mathbf{F}_2^{(H)} \rangle_{1,2} = \frac{kT}{\rho_0^{(2)}} \nabla_2 \rho_0^{(2)} = \frac{kT}{g_0^{(2)}} \nabla_2 g_0^{(2)}. \qquad (5.3.46)$$

That is, $\langle \mathbf{F}_1^{(S)} + \mathbf{F}_1^{(H)} \rangle_{1,2}$ is the equilibrium average force on molecule 1 when molecule 2 is fixed at $\mathbf{R}_2$, and vice versa for $\langle \mathbf{F}_2^{(S)} + \mathbf{F}_2^{(H)} \rangle_{1,2}$. We now introduce the approximation

$$\left\langle \mathbf{F}_1^{(S)}\left(\mathbf{R}^{(N)} + \frac{s'}{m}\,\mathbf{p}^{(N)}\right) + \mathbf{F}_1^{(H)}\left(\mathbf{R}^{(N)} + \frac{s'}{m}\,\mathbf{p}^{(N)}\right)\right\rangle_{1,2}$$
$$= \frac{kT}{g_0^{(2)}(R_{12})} \nabla_1 g^{(2)}\left(\left|\mathbf{R}_{12} + \frac{s'}{m}\,\mathbf{p}_{12}\right|\right), \qquad (5.3.47)$$

which implies that coordinates $\mathbf{R}^{(N)}$ may be replaced by $\left(\mathbf{R}^{(N)} + \frac{s'}{m}\,\mathbf{p}^{(N)}\right)$ in the numerator of equation (5.3.45). However, the difference between the variables is of $\mathcal{O}(\lambda)$, and the transformation of variables is therefore completely compatible with our approximation scheme. Upon substitution of equation (5.3.47) in (5.3.43), we find that $\Omega_S^{(1)}$ is given by

$$\Omega_S^{(1)} = -\frac{kT\rho}{\tau} \nabla_{p_1} \cdot \int_0^\tau \int_{\tau_1}^s \int \mathbf{F}_{12}^{(S)}(R_{12}) \nabla_{12} g_0^{(2)}\left(\left|\mathbf{R}_{12} + \frac{s'}{m}\,\mathbf{p}_{12}\right|\right)$$
$$\cdot (\nabla_{p_1} - \nabla_{p_2}) f^{(1)}(\Gamma_1;t) \varphi^{(1)}(\mathbf{p}_2)\, d\mathbf{p}_2\, d\mathbf{R}_{12}\, ds'\, ds, \qquad (5.3.48)$$

where we have replaced $f^{(1)}(\mathbf{R}_2,\mathbf{p}_2;t)$ by

$$f^{(1)}(\mathbf{R}_2,\mathbf{p}_2;t) = \rho\varphi^{(1)}(\mathbf{p}_2), \qquad (5.3.49)$$

and $\varphi^{(1)}(\mathbf{p}_2)$ is the momentum distribution function of molecule 2. When we use equation (5.3.47) to eliminate $\langle \mathbf{F}_1^{(S)} \rangle_{1,2}$ and $\langle \mathbf{F}_2^{(S)} \rangle_{1,2}$ from equation (5.3.43), there are obtained cross terms between the strongly repulsive and the soft forces. Such terms we neglect because it is a fundamental assumption in the Rice–Allnatt theory that the cross effect between strongly repulsive and soft forces can be neglected within the time interval under consideration (cf. pp. 280 and 349).

Evaluation of the force correlation integral appearing in equation (5.3.49) requires some comment. We have already established in Section 4.5.B (see also Section 6.5.C and Appendix 6.A) that for a system pursuing its natural motion, the integral vanishes for $\tau \gg (m/\zeta)$. In the present case, however, the molecules of the system are constrained to move in straight lines so that, in effect, a molecule feels its environment but the environment does not respond to it. In this situation the correlation integral does not vanish as τ increases. We shall assume then that it is permissible to extend the time integration until the integral is no longer sensibly dependent upon its upper limit, and this value will be obtained when we allow $\tau \to \infty$. We therefore calculate the function

$$\mathbf{A} = kT\rho\int_0^\infty \int \mathbf{F}_{12}^{(s)}(R_{12})\nabla_{12}g_0^{(2)}\left(\left|\mathbf{R}_{12} + \frac{s'}{m}\mathbf{p}_{12}\right|\right) d^3R_{12}\, ds, \tag{5.3.50}$$

in which the very small duration, τ_1, of the rigid core encounter has been neglected.

It is clear from the forms of equations (5.3.49) and (5.3.50) that if $\Omega_S^{(1)}$ can be manipulated into the general form of a Fokker–Planck operator, the moments $\mathbf{a}^{(1)}$ and $\mathbf{a}^{(2)}$ will then be momentum dependent. The explicit forms of the moments can be obtained if equation (5.3.50) is analyzed in terms of Fourier transforms, since the linear trajectory restriction then appears in a particularly simple way. Now, the pair potential in Figure 5.3.1. has already been separated in equation (5.3.12) in such a way that values of $R_{12} < \sigma$ are excluded from the domain of R_{12}. It is convenient to define a new potential function, $w(R_{12})$, by

$$\begin{aligned} w(R_{12}) &= 0, \qquad R_{12} < \sigma \\ w(R_{12}) &= u^{(S)}(R_{12}), \qquad R_{12} \geqslant \sigma, \end{aligned} \tag{5.3.51}$$

in order that the Fourier transforms may be defined in the whole domain of R_{12}. The Fourier transform pair, $\tilde{w}(k)$ and $w(R_{12})$, are defined by the relations

$$\begin{aligned} w(R_{12}) &= (2\pi)^{-3}\int d\mathbf{k}\tilde{w}(k)\exp(i\mathbf{k}\cdot\mathbf{R}_{12}), \\ \tilde{w}(k) &= \int d\mathbf{R}_{12}w(R_{12})\exp(-i\mathbf{k}\cdot\mathbf{R}_{12}). \end{aligned} \tag{5.3.52}$$

Note that since $w(R_{12})$ depends only on the magnitude of $\mathbf{R}_{12}$, $\tilde{w}(k)$ depends only on the magnitude of $\mathbf{k}$.

The Fourier transform of $g_0^{(2)}(R_{12})$ does not exist since $g_0^{(2)} \to 1$ as $R_{12} \to \infty$, and its integral is not bounded. However, we can define the structure factor $G(k)$ by

$$g_0^{(2)}(R_{12}) - 1 = (8\pi^3\rho)^{-1} \int d\mathbf{k}[G(k) - 1] \exp(i\mathbf{k} \cdot \mathbf{R}_{12}). \tag{5.3.53}$$

It follows from equation (5.3.53) that

$$g_0^{(2)}\left(\left|\mathbf{R}_{12} + \frac{s'}{m}\mathbf{p}_{12}\right|\right) = 1 + (8\pi^3\rho)^{-1} \int d\mathbf{k}[G(k) - 1] \times \exp\left(i\mathbf{k} \cdot \left[\mathbf{R}_{12} + \frac{s'}{m}\mathbf{p}_{12}\right]\right), \tag{5.3.54}$$

and that

$$\nabla_{12} g_0^{(2)}\left(\left|\mathbf{R}_{12} + \frac{S'}{m}\mathbf{p}_{12}\right|\right) = (8\pi^3\rho)^{-1} \int d\mathbf{k}[G(k) - 1]i\mathbf{k} \times \exp\left(i\mathbf{k} \cdot \left[\mathbf{R}_{12} + \frac{s'}{m}\mathbf{p}_{12}\right]\right). \tag{5.3.55}$$

The time integration of equation (5.3.50) can now be performed explicitly using the definition

$$\int_0^\infty ds e^{i\alpha s} = \pi\delta(\alpha) + i\mathscr{P}\left(\frac{1}{\alpha}\right) = \pi\delta_+(\alpha), \tag{5.3.56}$$

where $\mathscr{P}$ denotes the Cauchy principal value. If equations (5.3.52), (5.3.55), and (5.3.56) are inserted in equation (5.3.50), it is found that $\mathbf{R}_{12}$ appears only in the factor $\exp(i(\mathbf{k} + \mathbf{k}') \cdot \mathbf{R}_{12})$. Integration over $\mathbf{R}_{12}$ then yields a delta-function according to

$$(2\pi)^3\, \delta(\mathbf{k}) = \int d\mathbf{R}_{12} \exp(i\mathbf{k} \cdot \mathbf{R}_{12}). \tag{5.3.57}$$

Thus, we find

$$\begin{aligned}\mathbf{A} &= \int d\mathbf{k}' \int d\mathbf{k}(i\mathbf{k}')(i\mathbf{k})\tilde{w}(k')[G(k) - 1]\, \delta(\mathbf{k} + \mathbf{k}') \times \delta_+\left(\mathbf{k} \cdot \frac{\mathbf{p}_{12}}{m}\right) \\ &= \int d\mathbf{k}(i\mathbf{k})(i\mathbf{k})\tilde{w}(k)[G(k) - 1]\, \delta\left(\mathbf{k} \cdot \frac{\mathbf{p}_{12}}{m}\right).\end{aligned} \tag{5.3.58}$$

The function δ_+ has been replaced by δ in equation (5.3.58), since the integrand has become an even function of $\mathbf{k}$, while the principle value is an odd function. Since $\mathbf{k}$ also appears in a δ-function, integration of $\mathbf{k}$ can now be performed with $\mathbf{p}_{12}$ as polar axis. Upon writing $\mathbf{k}$ in terms of the cartesian components

$$\mathbf{k} = (\mathbf{i} \sin \theta \cos \varphi + \mathbf{j} \sin \theta \sin \varphi + \mathbf{h} \cos \theta)_k,$$

where θ is the colatitude and φ the azimuth, and integrating over φ, equation (5.3.58) becomes

$$\begin{aligned} \mathbf{A} &= -\frac{\pi^2 kT}{(2\pi)^3} \int_0^\infty dk k^4 \tilde{w}(k)[G(k) - 1] \int_{-1}^1 dx\, \delta\left(\frac{kxp_{12}}{m}\right) \\ &\quad \times [(\mathbf{ii} + \mathbf{jj})(1 - x^2) + 2\mathbf{hh}x^2] \\ &= \frac{\pi^2 mkT}{(2\pi)^3 p_{12}} \int_0^\infty dk k^3 \tilde{w}(k)[G(k) - 1][\mathbf{ii} + \mathbf{jj}], \end{aligned} \tag{5.3.59}$$

where the substitution $x = \cos\theta$ has been used. The dyadic $(\mathbf{ii} + \mathbf{jj})$ is expressed in terms of the cartesian axes defined by $\mathbf{p}_{12}$. This dependence can be removed by using the fact that $\mathbf{h} = p_{12}^{-1}\mathbf{p}_{12}$, so that

$$\mathbf{ii} + \mathbf{jj} = \mathbf{I} - p_{12}^{-2}\mathbf{p}_{12}\mathbf{p}_{12}. \tag{5.3.60}$$

Substitution of equations (5.3.59) and (5.3.60) into (5.3.50), and hence into equation (5.3.48), now yields, for $\Omega_S^{(1)}$,

$$\Omega_S^{(1)} = B \int d^3p_2 \nabla_{p_1} \cdot p_{12}^{-1}(\mathbf{I} - p_{12}^{-2}\mathbf{p}_{12}\mathbf{p}_{12}) \cdot (\nabla_{p_1} - \nabla_{p_2}) f^{(1)}(\Gamma_1;t)\varphi^{(1)}(\mathbf{p}_2), \tag{5.3.61}$$

where B is given by

$$B = \frac{\pi^2 mkT}{(2\pi)^3} \int_0^\infty dk k^3 \tilde{w}(k)[G(k) - 1]. \tag{5.3.62}$$

Equation (5.3.61) may be written in a more compact form by using the fact that, for any differentiable function $m(p_{12})$ of p_{12},

$$\nabla_{p_1} m(p_{12}) = -\nabla_{p_2} m(p_{12}).$$

Using this relation for the operator at the extreme left of equation (5.3.61), and performing a partial integration, we can transfer this operator to $\varphi^{(1)}(\mathbf{p}_2)$ at the extreme right. In this way equation (5.3.61) becomes

$$\Omega_S^{(1)} = B \int p_{12}^{-1}(\mathscr{D}_{(1)} - \mathscr{D}_{(2)}) f^{(1)}(\Gamma_1;t)\varphi^{(1)}(\mathbf{p}_2)\, d\mathbf{p}_2, \tag{5.3.63}$$

where

$$\mathscr{D}_{(i)} = \nabla_{p_i}{}^2 - p_{12}{}^{-2}\mathbf{p}_{12}\mathbf{p}_{12}\colon \nabla_{p_i}\nabla_{p_i}. \tag{5.3.64}$$

Equation (5.3.63) is now in the form given by Prigogine.* Evaluation of the integral over $\mathbf{p}_2$ in equation (5.3.63) is discussed in detail by Prigogine and we shall not repeat it here. Nevertheless, some comments are in order. Consider the symmetry of the operator $(\mathscr{D}_{(1)} - \mathscr{D}_{(2)})$ between $\mathbf{p}_1$ and $\mathbf{p}_2$. Clearly, for any function $f(\mathbf{p}_1)$ such that $\mathscr{D}_{(1)}f(\mathbf{p}_1) = 0$, it follows that $\mathscr{D}_{(2)}f(\mathbf{p}_2) = 0$. The circumstances in which $\Omega_S^{(1)}$ vanishes are clear: namely, they are those in which the left-hand side of equation (5.3.5), and Ω_H, both vanish. One of these circumstances obviously is the case that the system is in equilibrium, or in the state of local equilibrium for some particular values of the hydrodynamic flow velocity and temperature. Thus, for $\varphi^{(1)}(\mathbf{p}_2)$ we choose the local equilibrium Maxwellian distribution

$$\varphi^{(1)}(\mathbf{p}_2) = (2\pi mkT)^{-3/2}\exp(-p_2{}^2/2mkT). \tag{5.3.65}$$

With this function the integration over $\mathbf{p}_2$ may be carried out to obtain the moments [cf. Eq. (4.3.56)]

$$\begin{aligned}&(a)\ B^{-1}(2mkT)\mathbf{a}^{(1)} = -8g(W_1)\mathbf{W}_1/W_1,\\ &(b)\ B^{-1}(2mkT)^{1/2}\mathbf{a}^{(2)} = 3[g(W_1) - \tfrac{1}{3}\operatorname{erf}(W_1)]\mathbf{W}_1\mathbf{W}_1/W_1{}^3 + a(W_1)\,\mathbf{I},\end{aligned} \tag{5 3,66}$$

where

$$\begin{aligned}&(a)\ \mathbf{W}_1 = (2mkT)^{-1/2}\mathbf{p}_1,\\ &(b)\ g(W_1) = [\operatorname{erf}(W_1) - 2(W_1/\pi^{1/2})\exp(-W_1{}^2)]/2W_1{}^2,\\ &(c)\ a(W_1) = [2(W_1/\pi^{1/2})\exp(-W_1{}^2) + (2W_1{}^2 - 1)\operatorname{erf}(W_1)]/2W_1{}^3.\end{aligned} \tag{5.3.67}$$

Thus, $\Omega_S^{(1)}$ becomes

$$\Omega_S^{(1)} = \nabla_{p_1}\cdot[-\mathbf{a}^{(1)}f^{(1)}(\Gamma_1;t) + \nabla_{p_1}\cdot\mathbf{a}^{(2)}f^{(1)}(\Gamma_1;t)]. \tag{5.3.68}$$

It is left to the reader to verify that the moments $\mathbf{a}^{(1)}$ and $\mathbf{a}^{(2)}$ given by equation (5.3.66*a*,*b*) satisfy equation (4.4.28).

Finally, $f^{(1)}$ in equation (5.3.68) is replaced by its time coarse grained value $\bar{f}^{(1)}$. As we remarked previously, this substitution should have negligible effect, because we expect that the kinetic equation obtained is valid only in the hydrodynamic regime, in which changes occur very slowly on the time scale defined by τ.

* Reference 13, p. 94, equation (14).

Equation (5.3.68) is essentially a Fokker-Planck operator with momentum dependent friction coefficients. The coefficients are complicated functions of the momentum, and at the present time eigenfunctions of the operator are not known. We propose, therefore, to adopt, as a first approximation, the alternative form of the operator (which still yields the Maxwellian equilibrium momentum distribution) discussed in Section 4.4.B. That is, the operator with constant friction coefficient, which we shall denote by ζ_S. In this case the eigenfunctions are well known (they are the Kihara functions) (20), and the solutions to the kinetic equation may be obtained without difficulty.

The final singlet kinetic equation is, therefore,

$$\mathscr{D}^{(1)}\bar{f}^{(1)} = \sum_{i=1}^{3} J_i^{(1)} + \zeta_S \mathscr{A}^{(1)}\bar{f}^{(1)}, \tag{5.3.69}$$

where $J_1^{(1)}$, $J_2^{(1)}$ and $J_3^{(1)}$ are given by equation (5.3.25),

$$\mathscr{D}^{(1)}\bar{f}^{(1)} = \left(\frac{\partial}{\partial t} + \frac{1}{m}\mathbf{p}_1 \cdot \nabla_1 + \mathbf{F}_1{}^* \cdot \nabla_{p_1}\right)\bar{f}^{(1)}, \tag{5.3.70}$$

$$\mathscr{A}^{(1)}\bar{f}^{(1)} = \nabla_{p_1} \cdot \left(\frac{1}{m}\mathbf{p}_1\bar{f}^{(1)} + kT\nabla_{p_1}\bar{f}^{(1)}\right), \tag{5.3.71}$$

and

$$\mathbf{F}_1{}^* = {}^0\langle \mathbf{F}_1^{(S)} \rangle + {}^{(1)}\mathbf{F}_1^{(S)\dagger}. \tag{5.3.72}$$

If an external force $\mathbf{X}_1$ acts on molecule 1, and the fluid has a hydrodynamic velocity $\mathbf{u}$, then it is easily shown that

$$\mathscr{D}^{(1)}\bar{f}^{(1)} = \left(\frac{\partial}{\partial t} + \frac{1}{m}\mathbf{p}_1 \cdot \nabla_1 + (\mathbf{X}_1 + \mathbf{F}_1{}^*) \cdot \nabla_{p_1}\right)\bar{f}^{(1)}, \tag{5.3.73}$$

and

$$\mathscr{A}^{(1)}\bar{f}^{(1)} = \nabla_{p_1} \cdot \left(\left[\frac{\mathbf{p}_1}{m} - \mathbf{u}\right]\bar{f}^{(1)} + kT\nabla_{p_1}\bar{f}^{(1)}\right). \tag{5.3.74}$$

5.3.B. *The Doublet Equation* (16)

An integro-differential equation for the n-molecule distribution function may be derived following the procedure outlined in the previous section for the singlet case. With the assumption of pairwise additive intermolecular potentials, which we have already used in Chapter 2, it is only necessary to consider the case for $n = 2$, since all the steady-state transport coefficients may be considered known once $\bar{f}^{(1)}$ and $\bar{f}^{(2)}$ are known.

Equation (5.3.3) for $n = 2$ may be written, after time coarse graining,

$$\left[\frac{\partial}{\partial t} + \frac{1}{m}(\mathbf{p}_1 \cdot \nabla_1 + \mathbf{p}_2 \cdot \nabla_2) + \mathbf{F}_{12} \cdot (\nabla_{p_1} - \nabla_{p_2})\right] \bar{f}^{(2)}(\Gamma_2(1,2);t)$$
$$= -\frac{1}{\tau}\int_0^\tau \int \cdots \int (\mathbf{F}_{13} \cdot \nabla_{p_1} + \mathbf{F}_{23} \cdot \nabla_{p_2})$$
$$\times f^{(3)}(\Gamma_3(1,2,3);\, t + s)\, d\Gamma_1(3)\, ds. \quad (5.3.75)$$

As before, the force $\mathbf{F}_{ij}$ between molecules i and j is separated into a strongly repulsive component and a weak component. Thus, the right-hand side of equation (5.3.75) may be expressed in the form

$$-\frac{1}{\tau}\int_0^\tau \int \cdots \int (\mathbf{F}_{13} \cdot \nabla_{p_1} + \mathbf{F}_{23} \cdot \nabla_{p_2}) f^{(3)}(\Gamma_3;\, t + s)\, d\Gamma_1(3)\, ds$$
$$= \Omega_{H2} + \Omega_{S2}, \quad (5.3.76)$$

where

$$\Omega_{H2} = -\frac{1}{\tau}\int_0^\tau \int \cdots \int (\mathbf{F}_{13}^{(H)} \cdot \nabla_{p_1} + \mathbf{F}_{23}^{(H)} \cdot \nabla_{p_2})$$
$$\times f^{(3)}(\Gamma_3;\, t + s)\, d\Gamma_1(3)\, ds \quad (5.3.77)$$

and

$$\Omega_{S2} = -\frac{1}{\tau}\int_0^\tau \int \cdots \int (\mathbf{F}_{13}^{(S)} \cdot \nabla_{p_1} + \mathbf{F}_{23}^{(S)} \cdot \nabla_{p_2})$$
$$\times f^{(3)}(\Gamma_3;\, t + s)\, d\Gamma_1(3)\, ds. \quad (5.3.78)$$

In considering the development of Ω_{H2}, equation (5.3.77), we suppose that if the strongly repulsive part of the pair potential is sufficiently short ranged, the probability that molecules 1 and 2 will simultaneously undergo strongly repulsive encounters with other molecules is negligibly small. The direct interaction force ($\mathbf{F}_{12}$) between molecules 1 and 2 need not be separated, since we shall see shortly that it disappears from the left-hand side of equation (5.3.75) by cancellation with a term on the right. This is an important observation since the probability that, for instance, molecule 2 will be scattered onto molecule 1 by a strongly repulsive collision with molecule 3 is not small. However, for simplicity we ignore the complex situation which would arise by taking account of molecule 3 rebounding from molecule 2 to molecule 1.

In the situation in which the coordinates and momenta of both molecules 1 and 2 are given initially, the strongly repulsive encounter between molecule 3 and either 1 or 2 is not symmetric. This asymmetry manifests itself as a non vanishing mean force on molecules 1 and 2. For instance, when the centers of 1 and 2 are separated by less than 2σ, molecule 3 cannot get between 1 and 2, whereupon the strongly repulsive encounters tend on the average to force them closer together. It is clear that, in the absence of soft force, the forces resulting from asymmetric rigid core encounters are the gradients of the potential of mean hard force $W_H^{(2)}$ (apart from a small contribution due to deviations of $f^{(N-3/3)}$ from equilibrium). As usual, the mean hard force is related to the rigid sphere radial distribution function, $g_{0H}^{(2)}$, by

$$g_{0H}^{(2)} = \exp(-W_H^{(2)}/kT). \tag{5.3.79}$$

We shall suppose that the potentials of mean hard and soft forces are additive, and treat the asymmetry approximately by separating the mean hard forces ${}^{(2)}\mathbf{F}_i^{(H)}$ out of equation (5.3.77), and subsequently regarding the rigid core encounters as symmetric. The quantity ${}^{(2)}\langle\mathbf{F}_i^{(H)}\rangle^0$ is formally defined to be the mean force in a fluid of rigid spheres acting on a sphere at $\mathbf{R}_i$ when another sphere is fixed at $\mathbf{R}_j$ $(i, j = 1, 2)$. Ω_{H2}, therefore, becomes

$$\begin{aligned}\Omega_{H2} &= -\frac{1}{\tau}\int_0^\tau \underset{(\mathrm{sym})}{\int\cdots\int} (\mathbf{F}_{13}^{(H)}\cdot\nabla_{p_1} + \mathbf{F}_{23}^{(H)}\cdot\nabla_{p_2}) f^{(3)}(\Gamma_3; t+s)\, d\Gamma_1(3)\, ds \\ &\quad - \sum_{i=1,2} {}^{(2)}\mathbf{F}_i^{(H)}\cdot\nabla_{p_i}\bar{f}^{(2)}(\Gamma_2;t) \\ &= \Omega_{H2(\mathrm{sym})} - \sum_{i=1,2} {}^{(2)}\mathbf{F}_i^{(H)}\cdot\nabla_{p_i}\bar{f}^{(2)}(\Gamma_2;t),\end{aligned} \tag{5.3.80}$$

where the subscript (sym) denotes the constraint that molecule 3 interacts with either molecules 1 or 2 independently of the presence of the other.

To evaluate $\Omega_{H2(\mathrm{sym})}$ we now introduce the three-molecule Green's function, $K^{(3)}$, in a manner analogous to that used in the singlet case. $K^{(3)}(s)$ satisfies the equation

$$\begin{aligned}\left[\frac{\partial}{\partial s} + \sum_{i=1}^{3}\left(\frac{1}{m}\mathbf{p}_i\cdot\nabla_i + \sum_{j(\neq i)=1}^{3}\mathbf{F}_{ij}\cdot\nabla_{p_i}\right)\right] K^{(3)}(\Gamma_3 \mid \Gamma_3'; s) \\ = -\sum_{i=1}^{3}\sum_{j=4}^{N}\int\cdots\int \mathbf{F}_{ij}\cdot\nabla_{p_i} K^{(N)}(\Gamma_N \mid \Gamma_N'; s) \\ \times f^{(N-3/3)}(\Gamma'_{N-3} \mid \Gamma_3'; t)\, d\Gamma_{N-3}\, d\Gamma'_{N-3}.\end{aligned} \tag{5.3.81}$$

Suppose that during a short time interval $0 \leqslant s \leqslant \tau_1$, molecule 3 undergoes a rigid core encounter with one of the molecules 1 and 2, and that none of 1, 2, or 3 interacts in this way with any other molecule.

As before, we suppose also that the soft forces $\mathbf{F}_{ij}^{(S)}$ $(1 \leqslant i \leqslant 3;$ $4 \leqslant j \leqslant N)$ have negligible effect on the configurations of the three-molecule system during this time, so that the right-hand side of equation (5.3.81) may be replaced by zero. The corresponding formal solution of (5.3.81) is denoted $K_0^{(3)}$,

$$K_0^{(3)} = K_0^{(1)}(\Gamma_1(1) \mid \Gamma_1'(1); s) K_0^{(2)}(\Gamma_2(2,3) \mid \Gamma_2'(2,3); s), \quad (5.3.82)$$

where we have selected molecule 2 as the member of the pair undergoing a rigid core encounter with molecule 3. $K_0^{(1)}$ and $K_0^{(2)}$ are given by

$$K_0^{(1)}(1;s) = \delta(\mathbf{R}_1 - \mathbf{R}_1' - \Delta\mathbf{R}_1(s))\, \delta(\mathbf{p}_1 - \mathbf{p}_1'),$$
$$K_0^{(2)}(2,3;s) = \prod_{i=2,3} \delta(\mathbf{R}_i - \mathbf{R}_i' - \Delta\mathbf{R}_i(s))\, \delta(\mathbf{p}_i - \mathbf{p}_i' - \Delta\mathbf{p}_i(s)). \quad (5.3.83)$$

To evaluate $\Omega_{H2(\mathrm{sym})}$, we replace

$$(\mathbf{F}_{13}^{(H)} \cdot \nabla_{p_1} + \mathbf{F}_{23}^{(H)} \cdot \nabla_{p_2}) K_0^{(3)} (\Gamma_3 \mid \Gamma_3'; s)$$

in the expression

$$\Omega_{H2(\mathrm{sym})} = -\frac{1}{\tau} \int_0^\tau \underset{(\mathrm{sym})}{\int \cdots \int} [\mathbf{F}_{13}^{(H)} \cdot \nabla_{p_1} + \mathbf{F}_{23}^{(H)} \cdot \nabla_{p_2}]$$
$$\times K_0^{(3)}(\Gamma_3 \mid \Gamma_3'; s) f^{(3)}(\Gamma_3'; t)\, d\Gamma_3'\, d\Gamma_1(3)\, ds \quad (5.3.84)$$

by substitution from equation (5.3.81) for $K_0^{(3)}$. The terms $\mathbf{F}_{3j} \cdot \nabla_{p_3} K_0^{(3)}$ vanish upon partial integration over $\mathbf{p}_3$, and we obtain

$$\Omega_{H2(\mathrm{sym})} = \frac{1}{\tau} \int_0^\tau \underset{(\mathrm{sym})}{\int \cdots \int} \left[\frac{\partial}{\partial s} + \frac{1}{m} \sum_{i=1}^{3} \mathbf{p}_i \cdot \nabla_i \right] K_0^{(3)}(\Gamma_3 \mid \Gamma_3'; s)$$
$$\times f^{(3)}(\Gamma_3'; t)\, d\Gamma_3'\, d\Gamma_1(3)\, ds + \mathbf{F}_{12} \cdot (\nabla_{p_1} - \nabla_{p_2}) \bar{f}^{(2)}; \quad (5.3.85)$$

a result which includes the two terms in $\mathbf{F}_{12}$ already mentioned and which cancel with those on the left-hand side of equation (5.3.75).

Using equation (5.3.83), the first term in equation (5.3.85) becomes [cf. equation (5.3.15)]

$$\Omega_{H2(\mathrm{sym})}^{(1)} = \frac{1}{\tau} \underset{(\mathrm{sym})}{\int \cdots \int} [f^{(3)}(\mathbf{R}_1 - \Delta\mathbf{R}_1(\tau), \mathbf{R}_2 - \Delta\mathbf{R}_2(\tau), \mathbf{R}_3 - \Delta\mathbf{R}_3(\tau),$$
$$\mathbf{p}_1, \mathbf{p}_2 - \Delta\mathbf{p}_2(\tau), \mathbf{p}_3 - \Delta\mathbf{p}_3(\tau); t)$$
$$- f^{(3)}(\mathbf{R}_1, \mathbf{R}_2, \mathbf{R}_3, \mathbf{p}_1, \mathbf{p}_2, \mathbf{p}_3; t)]\, d\Gamma_1(3)$$
$$= \frac{1}{m} \underset{(\mathbf{k} \cdot \mathbf{p}_{23} > 0;\ \mathrm{sym})}{\int \cdots \int} [f^{(3)}(\mathbf{R}_1, \mathbf{R}_2, \mathbf{R}_2 + \sigma\mathbf{k}; \mathbf{p}_1, \mathbf{p}_2^*, \mathbf{p}_3^*; t)$$
$$- f^{(3)}(\mathbf{R}_1, \mathbf{R}_2, \mathbf{R}_2 + \sigma\mathbf{k}, \mathbf{p}_1, \mathbf{p}_2, \mathbf{p}_3; t)] p_{23}\, d\mathbf{p}_3 b\, db\, d\epsilon, \quad (5.3.86)$$

where, of course, $\Delta\mathbf{p}_2 = -\Delta\mathbf{p}_3$, and the asterisk denotes the momenta prior to collision. $\mathbf{R}_{23} = \sigma\mathbf{k}$ at rigid core contact, and we have neglected the effect of the small displacements $\Delta\mathbf{R}_i(\tau)$.

The three terms remaining under the integral in equation (5.3.85) are also treated in a manner analogous to that used in the discussion of the singlet equation. After an integration over Γ_3' and s, which replaces $K_0^{(3)}(\Gamma_3 \mid \Gamma_3'; s)f^{(3)}(\Gamma_3';t)$ by $\bar{f}^{(3)}(\Gamma_3;t)$, delta functions $\delta(\mathbf{R}_1 - \mathbf{R}_1^0)\delta(\mathbf{R}_2 - \mathbf{R}_2^0)$ and integration over $\mathbf{R}_1^0$, $\mathbf{R}_2^0$ are inserted. The variables are then transformed to

$$\begin{aligned}\mathbf{R}_{13} &= \mathbf{R}_3 - \mathbf{R}_1,\\ \mathbf{R}_{23} &= \mathbf{R}_3 - \mathbf{R}_2,\\ \mathbf{R} &= \tfrac{1}{3}(\mathbf{R}_1 + \mathbf{R}_2 + \mathbf{R}_3),\end{aligned} \tag{5.3.87}$$

with a similar set for the momenta. It is found that

$$\sum_{i=1}^{3} \mathbf{p}_i \cdot \nabla_i = \mathbf{p}_{13} \cdot \nabla_{13} + \mathbf{p}_{23} \cdot \nabla_{23} + \mathbf{P} \cdot \nabla \tag{5.3.88}$$

and

$$d\mathbf{R}_1\, d\mathbf{R}_2\, d\mathbf{R}_3 = d\mathbf{R}_{13}\, d\mathbf{R}_{23}\, d\mathbf{R}. \tag{5.3.89}$$

As in the previous section, the center of mass term may be shown to vanish by integrating first over $\mathbf{R}_{13}$ and $\mathbf{R}_{23}$, so that $\mathbf{R}$ appears only in the argument of $\bar{f}^{(3)}$, and then using Gauss' theorem for the integration over $\mathbf{R}$. Now, since the asymmetries of the spatial integrations have been removed by the mean force terms, and we are treating the situation in which molecule 3 undergoes a rigid core collision with molecule 2 only, the integration of the term in $\mathbf{p}_{13}$ is not subject to the constraint $R_{13} \geqslant \sigma$, and may be shown to vanish. We are left then with the term in $\mathbf{p}_{23}$, which leads to [cf. equations (5.3.19) and (5.3.20)]

$$\begin{aligned}\Omega_{H2(\mathrm{sym})}^{(2)} &= \frac{\sigma^2}{m} \iint_{(\mathrm{sym})} \bar{f}^{(3)}(\mathbf{R}_1, \mathbf{R}_2, \mathbf{R}_2 + \sigma\mathbf{k}, \mathbf{p}_1, \mathbf{p}_2, \mathbf{p}_3; t)\mathbf{p}_{23} \cdot \mathbf{k}\, d\mathbf{k}\, d\mathbf{p}_3 \\ &\quad + \mathbf{F}_{12} \cdot (\nabla_{p_1} - \nabla_{p_2})\bar{f}^{(2)} \\ &= \frac{1}{m} \iint_{(\mathbf{k}\cdot\mathbf{p}_{23}>0;\ \mathrm{sym})} \bar{f}^{(3)}(\mathbf{R}_1, \mathbf{R}_2, \mathbf{R}_2 + \sigma\mathbf{k}, \mathbf{p}_1, \mathbf{p}_2, \mathbf{p}_3; t) \\ &\qquad\qquad \times p_{23} b\, db\, d\epsilon\, d\mathbf{p}_3 \\ &\quad - \frac{1}{m} \iint_{(\mathbf{k}\cdot\mathbf{p}_{23}>0;\ \mathrm{sym})} \bar{f}^{(3)}(\mathbf{R}_1, \mathbf{R}_2, \mathbf{R}_2 - \sigma\mathbf{k}, \mathbf{p}_1, \mathbf{p}_2, \mathbf{p}_3; t) \\ &\qquad\qquad \times p_{23} b\, db\, d\epsilon\, d\mathbf{p}_3 + \mathbf{F}_{12} \cdot (\nabla_{p_1} - \nabla_{p_2})\bar{f}^{(2)}.\end{aligned} \tag{5.3.90}$$

Upon substituting equations (5.3.76), (5.3.80), (5.3.86) and (5.3.90) in equation (5.3.75), we obtain, for the kinetic equation,

$$\left[\frac{\partial}{\partial t} + \sum_{i=1,2}\left(\frac{1}{m}\mathbf{p}_i \cdot \nabla_i + {}^{(2)}\langle \mathbf{F}_i^{(H)}\rangle^0 \cdot \nabla_{p_i}\right)\right]\bar{f}^{(2)}$$
$$= \frac{1}{m}\int_{(\mathbf{k}\cdot\mathbf{p}_{23}>0;\ \mathrm{sym})}\cdots\int [\bar{f}^{(3)}(\mathbf{R}_1, \mathbf{R}_2, \mathbf{R}_2 + \sigma\mathbf{k}, \mathbf{p}_1, \mathbf{p}_2{}^*, \mathbf{p}_3{}^*; t)$$
$$- \bar{f}^{(3)}(\mathbf{R}_1, \mathbf{R}_2, \mathbf{R}_2 - \sigma\mathbf{k}, \mathbf{p}_1, \mathbf{p}_2, \mathbf{p}_3; t)]\, p_{23} b\, db\, d\epsilon\, d\mathbf{p}_3 + \Omega_{S2}. \tag{5.3.91}$$

The collision integral in equation (5.3.91), which results from the terms $\Omega_{H2(\mathrm{sym})}^{(1)}$ and $\Omega_{H2(\mathrm{sym})}^{(2)}$, may be simplified in a manner similar to that used in the singlet case. We shall again use the assumption (5.3.23) that the correlation functions are independent of the momenta, which is adequate in the hydrodynamic regime. The three-molecule distribution function factorizes into the product of a triplet correlation function, $g^{(3)}$, and a triplet momentum function, $M^{(3)}$ (which includes the density factor ρ^3):

$$\bar{f}^{(3)}(\mathbf{R}_1, \mathbf{R}_2, \mathbf{R}_2 + \sigma\mathbf{k}, \mathbf{p}_1, \mathbf{p}_2, \mathbf{p}_3; t)$$
$$= g^{(3)}(\mathbf{R}_1, \mathbf{R}_2, \mathbf{R}_2 + \sigma\mathbf{k}) M^{(3)}(\mathbf{R}_1, \mathbf{p}_1; \mathbf{R}_2, \mathbf{p}_2; \mathbf{R}_2 + \sigma\mathbf{k}, \mathbf{p}_3; t). \tag{5.3.92}$$

The appearance of the coordinates in the argument of the momentum function is due to the fact that the distribution of any $\mathbf{p}_i$ depends parametrically on the local values of the thermodynamic variables at $\mathbf{R}_i$ $(i = 1,2,3)$. In order to close equation (5.3.91), at least as far as the collision integral is concerned, we introduce the hypothesis of molecular chaos in the form

$$M^{(3)}(1,2,3) = \prod_{i<j=1}^{3} M^{(2)}(i,j) \Big/ \prod_{i=1}^{3} M^{(1)}(i). \tag{5.3.93}$$

From the definition of the momentum factors given, it follows that

$$M^{(1)}(i) = \bar{f}^{(1)}(\Gamma_1(i); t). \tag{5.3.94}$$

It is convenient to suppose that if $M_0^{(2)}(i,j)$ is the local equilibrium, two-molecule Maxwellian function, then

$$M^{(2)}(i,j) = M_0^{(2)}(i,j)(1 + \Phi^{(2)}(i,j) + \cdots), \tag{5.3.95}$$

where $\Phi^{(2)}(i,j)$ is a perturbation term which is linear in the gradients,*

* The validity of this form of $M^{(2)}(i,j)$ for the hydrodynamic regime will be demonstrated in Section 5.4.

and that

$$M_0^{(2)}(i,j) = M_0^{(1)}(i)M_0^{(1)}(j). \tag{5.3.96}$$

It then follows that the expansion of $M^{(3)}$ as a function of $\mathbf{R}_3 = \mathbf{R}_2 + \sigma\mathbf{k}$, about $\mathbf{R}_2$, yields

$$\begin{aligned} &M^{(3)}(\mathbf{R}_1, \mathbf{p}_1; \mathbf{R}_2, \mathbf{p}_2; \mathbf{R}_2 + \sigma\mathbf{k}, \mathbf{p}_3; t) \\ &= M^{(3)}(\mathbf{R}_1,\mathbf{p}_2;\mathbf{R}_2,\mathbf{p}_2;\mathbf{R}_2,\mathbf{p}_3;t) + M^{(1)}(\mathbf{R}_1,\mathbf{p}_1)M^{(1)}(\mathbf{R}_2,\mathbf{p}_2)\sigma\mathbf{k}\cdot\nabla_2 M^{(1)}(\mathbf{R}_2,\mathbf{p}_3) \end{aligned} \tag{5.3.97}$$

to first order in the gradients.

In keeping with the symmetry constraint on the collision integral, it is consistent that $g^{(3)}$ in equation (5.3.92) be given by

$$g^{(3)}(\mathbf{R}_1, \mathbf{R}_2, \mathbf{R}_2 + \sigma\mathbf{k}) = g^{(2)}(\mathbf{R}_1,\mathbf{R}_2)g^{(2)}(\mathbf{R}_2, \mathbf{R}_2 + \sigma\mathbf{k}). \tag{5.3.98}$$

Note that equation (5.3.98) is equivalent to setting $g^{(2)}(\mathbf{R}_1,\mathbf{R}_3) = 1$ for all $\mathbf{R}_3$. $g^{(2)}(\mathbf{R}_2, \mathbf{R}_2 + \sigma\mathbf{k})$ is now expressed in terms of the values of the thermodynamic variables at $\mathbf{R}_2$ by a Taylor expansion in powers of $\frac{1}{2}\sigma\mathbf{k}$ [cf. equation (5.3.24)]:

$$\begin{aligned} g^{(2)}(\mathbf{R}_2, \mathbf{R}_2 + \sigma\mathbf{k}) &= g^{(2)}(\mathbf{R}_2 + \tfrac{1}{2}\sigma\mathbf{k}, \sigma\mathbf{k}) \\ &= g_0^{(2)}(\mathbf{R}_2,\sigma) + \tfrac{1}{2}\sigma\mathbf{k}\cdot\nabla_2 g_0^{(2)}(\mathbf{R}_2,\sigma) + g_1^{(2)}(\mathbf{R}_2,\sigma\mathbf{k}) + \cdots. \end{aligned} \tag{5.3.99}$$

Using equations (5.3.92)–(5.3.99), the collision integral of equation (5.3.91) is finally found to be

$$\begin{aligned} &\Omega^{(1)}_{H2(\mathrm{sym})} + \Omega^{(2)}_{H2(\mathrm{sym})} \\ &= \frac{1}{m} g^{(2)}(\mathbf{R}_1,\mathbf{R}_2)g_0^{(2)}(\mathbf{R}_2,\sigma)\Bigg\{ \int_{(\mathbf{k}\cdot\mathbf{p}_{23}>0;\ \mathrm{sym})} [M^{(3)}(\mathbf{R}_1,\mathbf{p}_1;\mathbf{R}_2,\mathbf{p}_2{}^*;\mathbf{R}_2,\mathbf{p}_3{}^*;t) \\ &\qquad - M^{(3)}(\mathbf{R}_1,\mathbf{p}_1;\mathbf{R}_2,\mathbf{p}_2;\mathbf{R}_2,\mathbf{p}_3;t)]p_{23}b\,db\,d\epsilon\,d\mathbf{p}_3 \\ &\quad + \sigma \int_{(\mathbf{k}\cdot\mathbf{p}_{23}>0;\ \mathrm{sym})} [M^{(1)}(\mathbf{R}_1,\mathbf{p}_1)M^{(1)}(\mathbf{R}_2,\mathbf{p}_2{}^*)\mathbf{k}\cdot\nabla_2 M^{(1)}(\mathbf{R}_2,\mathbf{p}_3{}^*) \\ &\qquad + M^{(1)}(\mathbf{R}_1,\mathbf{p}_1)M^{(1)}(\mathbf{R}_2,\mathbf{p}_2)\mathbf{k}\cdot\nabla_2 M^{(1)}(\mathbf{R}_2,\mathbf{p}_3)]p_{23}b\,db\,d\epsilon\,d\mathbf{p}_3\Bigg\} \\ &\quad + \frac{\sigma}{2m} g^{(2)}(\mathbf{R}_1,\mathbf{R}_2)\,\nabla_2 g_0^{(2)}(\mathbf{R}_2,\sigma) \\ &\quad \cdot \int_{(\mathbf{k}\cdot\mathbf{p}_{23}>0;\ \mathrm{sym})} \mathbf{k}[M^{(1)}(\mathbf{R}_1,\mathbf{p}_1)M^{(1)}(\mathbf{R}_2,\mathbf{p}_2{}^*)M^{(1)}(\mathbf{R}_2,\mathbf{p}_3{}^*) \\ &\quad + M^{(1)}(\mathbf{R}_1,\mathbf{p}_1)M^{(1)}(\mathbf{R}_2,\mathbf{p}_2)M^{(1)}(\mathbf{R}_2,\mathbf{p}_3)]p_{23}b\,db\,d\epsilon\,d\mathbf{p}_3. \end{aligned} \tag{5.3.100}$$

Since molecule 3 may undergo a rigid core encounter with either molecule 2 or molecule 1, the total collision integral is the sum of two sets of terms

$$\Omega_{H2(\mathrm{sym})} = \sum_{i,j=1,2} \Omega^{(i)}_{H2(\mathrm{sym})}(j), \tag{5.3.101}$$

where $\Omega^{(i)}_{H2(\mathrm{sym})}(j)$ is the collision integral term for which molecule 3 interacts with molecule j. Finally, we define three collision terms $J_i^{(2)}$ in analogy with equation (5.3.25) as

$$\Omega_{H2(\mathrm{sym})} = \sum_{i=1}^{3} J_i^{(2)}, \tag{5.3.102}$$

$$(a)\ J_1^{(2)} = J_1^{(2)}(1) + J_1^{(2)}(2)$$

$$= \frac{1}{m} g^{(2)}(\mathbf{R}_1,\mathbf{R}_2) g(\sigma) \Bigg[\int_{(\mathbf{k}\cdot\mathbf{p}_{13}>0;\ \mathrm{sym})} [M^{(3)}(\mathbf{R}_1,\mathbf{p}_1{}^*;\mathbf{R}_2,\mathbf{p}_2;\mathbf{R}_1,\mathbf{p}_3{}^*;t)$$

$$- M^{(3)}(\mathbf{R}_1,\mathbf{p}_1;\mathbf{R}_2,\mathbf{p}_2;\mathbf{R}_1,\mathbf{p}_3;t)] p_{13} b\, db\, d\epsilon\, d\mathbf{p}_3$$

$$+ \int_{(\mathbf{k}\cdot\mathbf{p}_{23}>0;\ \mathrm{sym})} [M^{(3)}(\mathbf{R}_1,\mathbf{p}_1;\mathbf{R}_2,\mathbf{p}_2{}^*;\mathbf{R}_2,\mathbf{p}_3{}^*;t)$$

$$- M^{(3)}(\mathbf{R}_1,\mathbf{p}_1;\mathbf{R}_2,\mathbf{p}_2;\mathbf{R}_2,\mathbf{p}_3;t)] p_{23} b\, db\, d\epsilon\, d\mathbf{p}_3 \Bigg],$$

$$(b)\ J_2^{(2)} = J_2^{(2)}(1) + J_2^{(2)}(2)$$

$$= \frac{\sigma}{m} g^{(2)}(\mathbf{R}_1,\mathbf{R}_2) g(\sigma)$$

$$\times \Bigg[\int_{(\mathbf{k}\cdot\mathbf{p}_{13}>0;\ \mathrm{sym})} [M^{(1)}(\mathbf{R}_1,\mathbf{p}_1{}^*) M^{(1)}(\mathbf{R}_2,\mathbf{p}_2) \mathbf{k}\cdot\nabla_1 M^{(1)}(\mathbf{R}_1,\mathbf{p}_3{}^*)$$

$$+ M^{(1)}(\mathbf{R}_1,\mathbf{p}_1) M^{(1)}(\mathbf{R}_2;\mathbf{p}_2) \mathbf{k}\cdot\nabla_1 M^{(1)}(\mathbf{R}_1,\mathbf{p}_3)] p_{13} b\, db\, d\epsilon\, d\mathbf{p}_3$$

$$+ \int_{(\mathbf{k}\cdot\mathbf{p}_{23}>0;\ \mathrm{sym})} [M^{(1)}(\mathbf{R}_1,\mathbf{p}_1) M^{(1)}(\mathbf{R}_2,\mathbf{p}_2{}^*) \mathbf{k}\cdot\nabla_2 M^{(1)}(\mathbf{R}_2,\mathbf{p}_3{}^*)$$

$$+ M^{(1)}(\mathbf{R}_1,\mathbf{p}_1) M^{(1)}(\mathbf{R}_2,\mathbf{p}_2) \mathbf{k}\cdot\nabla_2 M^{(1)}(\mathbf{R}_2,\mathbf{p}_3)] p_{23} b\, db\, d\epsilon\, d\mathbf{p}_3 \Bigg],$$

$$
\begin{aligned}
(c)\ J_3^{(2)} &= J_3^{(2)}(1) + J_3^{(2)}(2) \\
&= \frac{\sigma}{2m} g^{(2)}(\mathbf{R}_1,\mathbf{R}_2) \\
&\times \Bigg[\int_{(\mathbf{k}\cdot\mathbf{p}_{13}>0;\ \mathrm{sym})} [M^{(1)}(\mathbf{R}_1,\mathbf{p}_1{}^*)M^{(1)}(\mathbf{R}_2,\mathbf{p}_2)M^{(1)}(\mathbf{R}_1,\mathbf{p}_3{}^*) \\
&\qquad + M^{(1)}(\mathbf{R}_1,\mathbf{p}_1)M^{(1)}(\mathbf{R}_2,\mathbf{p}_2)M^{(1)}(\mathbf{R}_1,\mathbf{p}_3)] \\
&\qquad \times \mathbf{k}\cdot\nabla_1 g^{(2)}(\mathbf{R}_1,\sigma)p_{13}b\,db\,d\epsilon\,d\mathbf{p}_3 \\
&+ \int_{(\mathbf{k}\cdot\mathbf{p}_{23}>\sigma;\ \mathrm{sym})} [M^{(1)}(\mathbf{R}_1,\mathbf{p}_1)M^{(1)}(\mathbf{R}_2,\mathbf{p}_2{}^*)M^{(1)}(\mathbf{R}_2,\mathbf{p}_3{}^*) \\
&\qquad + M^{(1)}(\mathbf{R}_1,\mathbf{p}_1)M^{(1)}(\mathbf{R}_2,\mathbf{p}_2)M^{(1)}(\mathbf{R}_2,\mathbf{p}_3)] \\
&\qquad \times \mathbf{k}\cdot\nabla_2 g^{(2)}(\mathbf{R}_2,\sigma)p_{23}b\,db\,d\epsilon\,d\mathbf{p}_3 \Bigg]. \qquad (5.3.103)
\end{aligned}
$$

The contribution of the soft forces, Ω_{S2}, equation (5.3.78), can be treated by the technique used in the previous section. Introducing the specific N-molecule distribution function, $f_{sp}^{(N)}$ and the N-molecule Green's function, $K^{(N)} = K_0^{(N)} + K_1^{(N)}$ [see equations (5.3.30), (5.3.31) and (5.3.34)], we find

$$
\begin{aligned}
\Omega_{S2} &= -\frac{N!}{(N-3)!}\frac{1}{\tau}\int_0^\tau ds \int d\Gamma_{N-2}(\mathbf{F}_{13}^{(S)}\cdot\nabla_{p_1} + \mathbf{F}_{23}^{(S)}\cdot\nabla_{p_2})f_{sp}^{(N)} \\
&\qquad\qquad \times (\Gamma_N; t+s) \\
&= -\frac{N!}{(N-3)!}\frac{1}{\tau}\int_0^\tau ds \iint d\Gamma_{N-2}\,d\Gamma_N{}'(\mathbf{F}_{13}^{(S)}\cdot\nabla_{p_1} + \mathbf{F}_{23}^{(S)}\cdot\nabla_{p_2}) \\
&\qquad\qquad \times (K_0^{(N)} + K_1^{(N)})f_{sp}^{(N)}(\Gamma_N{}';t) \\
&= \Omega_{S2}^{(0)} + \Omega_{S2}^{(1)}, \qquad (5.3.104)
\end{aligned}
$$

where

$$\Omega_{S2}^{(0)} = -\sum_{i=1,2} {}^{(2)}\mathbf{F}_i^{(S)}\cdot\nabla_{p_i}\bar{f}^{(2)}, \qquad (5.3.105)$$

$${}^{(2)}\mathbf{F}_i^{(S)} = \rho\int \mathbf{F}_{i3}^{(S)}\frac{g^{(3)}(\mathbf{R}_1,\mathbf{R}_2,\mathbf{R}_3)}{g^{(2)}(\mathbf{R}_1,\mathbf{R}_2)}\,d\mathbf{R}_3;\ i = 1,2, \qquad (5.3.106)$$

and

$$
\begin{aligned}
\Omega_{S2}^{(1)} &= \frac{N!}{(N-3)!}\frac{1}{\tau}\int_0^\tau ds \int d\Gamma_{N-2}(\mathbf{F}_{13}^{(S)}\cdot\nabla_{p_1} + \mathbf{F}_{23}^{(S)}\cdot\nabla_{p_2}) \\
&\times \int_0^s ds' \sum_{i=1}^{N}\sum_{j(\neq i)=1}^{N} \mathbf{F}_{ij}^{(S)}\left(\left|\mathbf{R}_{ij} + \frac{s'}{m}\mathbf{p}_{ij}\right|\right)\cdot\nabla_{p_i} f_{sp}^{(N)}(\Gamma_N;t). \qquad (5.3.107)
\end{aligned}
$$

Many terms may be eliminated from equation (5.3.107) since all those for which neither i nor j are 1 or 2 vanish. Thus,

$$\Omega_{S2}^{(1)} = \frac{1}{\tau}\int_0^\tau ds \int_0^s ds' \int d\Gamma_1(3)(\mathbf{F}_{13}^{(S)} \cdot \nabla_{p_1} + \mathbf{F}_{23}^{(S)} \cdot \nabla_{p_2})\{\mathbf{F}_{12}^{(S)}(s') \cdot (\nabla_{p_1} - \nabla_{p_2})$$
$$+ (N-2)[\mathbf{F}_{13}^{(S)}(s') \cdot (\nabla_{p_1} - \nabla_{p_3}) + \mathbf{F}_{23}^{(S)}(s') \cdot (\nabla_{p_2} - \nabla_{p_3})]\} f^{(3)}(\Gamma_3;t) \quad (5.3.108)$$

where we have introduced the notation

$$\mathbf{F}_{ij}^{(S)}(s') = \mathbf{F}_{ij}^{(S)}\left(\left| \mathbf{R}_{ij} + \frac{s'}{m}\mathbf{p}_{ij} \right|\right)$$

for brevity.

It is clear from the general appearance of equation (5.3.108) that $\Omega_{S2}^{(1)}$ has the form of a Fokker-Planck operator in $\mathbf{p}_1 - \mathbf{p}_2$ space, in which space there is a cylindrical symmetry due to the appearance of a fixed value of $\mathbf{R}_{12}$ (compare to the spherical symmetry in the singlet case). This, and other features, will be discussed further in Section 5.5. Unfortunately, the complex nature of $\Omega_{S2}^{(1)}$ has so far precluded its reduction to a useful general form. In order to obtain explicit solutions to the doublet equation we shall, therefore, adopt the simplified version of the Fokker-Planck operator which has constant friction coefficients. Moreover, since we cannot discuss the dependence of the friction coefficients upon $\mathbf{R}_{12}$, we shall assume they are equal to the singlet values.

If we denote the hydrodynamic flow velocity and temperature at $\mathbf{R}_i$ by $\mathbf{u}_i$ and T_i, respectively, the final form of the doublet equation is

$$\mathscr{D}^{(2)}\bar{f}^{(2)} = \sum_{i=1}^{3} J_i^{(2)} + \sum_{i=1}^{2} \zeta_S(\mathbf{R}_i)\mathscr{A}_i^{(1)}\bar{f}^{(2)}, \quad (5.3.109)$$

where the $J_i^{(2)}$ are given by equation (5.3.103), and

$$\mathscr{D}^{(2)}\bar{f}^{(2)} = \left[\frac{\partial}{\partial t} + \sum_{i=1,2}\left(\frac{1}{m}\mathbf{p}_i \cdot \nabla_i + \mathbf{F}_i^{(2)} \cdot \nabla_{p_i}\right)\right]\bar{f}^{(2)} \quad (5.3.110)$$

$$\mathscr{A}_i^{(1)}\bar{f}^{(2)} = \nabla_{p_i} \cdot \left[\left(\frac{1}{m}\mathbf{p}_i - \mathbf{u}_i\right) + kT_i\nabla_{p_i}\right]\bar{f}^{(2)} \quad (5.3.111)$$

$$\mathbf{F}_i^{(2)} = {}^{(2)}\mathbf{F}_i^{(H)} + {}^{(2)}\mathbf{F}_i^{(S)} \quad (5.3.112)$$

$${}^{(2)}\mathbf{F}_i^{(R)} = {}^{(2)}\langle\mathbf{F}_i^{(R)}\rangle^0 + {}^{(2)}\mathbf{F}_i^{(R)\dagger}, \qquad \text{where} \qquad R = H \text{ or } S. \quad (5.3.113)$$

${}^{(2)}\langle \mathbf{F}_i^{(H)} \rangle^0$ and ${}^{(2)}\langle \mathbf{F}_i^{(S)} \rangle^0$ are the mean hard and soft forces on a molecule at $\mathbf{R}_i$ when another molecule is fixed at $\mathbf{R}_j$. The forces ${}^{(2)}\mathbf{F}_i^{(H)\dagger}$ and ${}^{(2)}\mathbf{F}_i^{(S)\dagger}$ are perturbations to the mean forces arising from the departure of $f^{(N-3/3)}$ from its equilibrium form; they are responsible for non-linear effects in $\nabla_i \ln T_i$ and $\nabla_i \mathbf{u}_i$, and we shall not need to consider them further. The external force $\mathbf{X}_i$ may be inserted in equation (5.3.107) in the same way as in the singlet equation (5.3.73).

The reader should note that the proposed form of the doublet equation is such that upon integration term by term over the coordinates and momenta of one of the molecules, it reduces to the singlet equation except for terms of $\mathcal{O}(N^{-1})$. The reduction is easily seen in the case of the streaming terms and of the Fokker-Planck operators. In the case of the collision integrals use is made of the result that

$$\begin{aligned} \int \left[\int J_i^{(2)}(j)\, d\mathbf{p}_k \right] d\mathbf{R}_k &= (N-2) J_i^{(1)}(j); \quad j \neq k \\ &= 0; \quad j = k, \end{aligned} \tag{5.3.114}$$

where $i = 1, 2, 3$ and $j, k = 1, 2$. The first member of equation (5.3.114) involves an integration over the phase of the molecule *not* undergoing a rigid core encounter. The second member involves an integration over the phase of the molecule undergoing the rigid core encounter, and may be seen to vanish by an extension of equation (5.4.18) and (5.4.25), in which $\chi = 1$.

5.4. SOLUTION OF THE KINETIC EQUATIONS (21,22)

5.4.A. *Preliminary Remarks*

The derivation of a set of kinetic equations is only the first step in constructing a theory of transport phenomena. There still remains the problem of obtaining a solution (or solutions) to the equations and the subsequent utilization of these solutions to compute transport coefficients. Details of the computation of selected transport coefficients are discussed in Chapter 6; here we examine the construction of a non-equilibrium distribution function which satisfies equation (5.3.73) or equation (5.3.106), and which is displayed in terms of the external constraints defining the non-equilibrium state of the fluid.

The method we shall use to obtain solutions to the kinetic equations was introduced by Hilbert (23) and exploited by Enskog (24) and Chapman (21). The analysis starts with the assumption that the distribution function may be represented in the form

$$\bar{f}^{(1)} = \sum_{l=0}^{\infty} \epsilon^l \bar{f}_l^{(1)}. \tag{5.4.1}$$

This distribution function is to be inserted into the kinetic equation, also modified to include the perturbation parameter, ϵ,

$$\mathscr{D}^{(1)}\bar{f}^{(1)} = \epsilon^{-1}[J_1^{(1)} + \zeta_S \mathscr{A}^{(1)}\bar{f}^{(1)}] + J_2^{(1)} + J_3^{(1)}. \tag{5.4.2}$$

The parameter ϵ, which has been introduced as a formal device to order the terms in the expansion, will later be set equal to unity. Physically, the small quantity in which the expansion is made is the fractional variation of the macroscopic parameters $(T,\rho,\mathbf{u})$ over a characteristic mean relaxation distance (say $\zeta_S^{-1}(kT/m)^{-1/2}$ or $\rho^{-1/3}$). Thus, ϵ may be considered to be related to a mean free path. The way in which ϵ appears in equation (5.4.2) may be understood in the following fashion. The structure of the operators $\mathscr{D}^{(1)}\bar{f}^{(1)}$, $J_2^{(1)}$, and $J_3^{(1)}$ is such that they introduce an extra power or derivative of the macroscopic field gradients, thus making a term $\bar{f}_l^{(1)}$ in equation (5.4.1) of the same order in ϵ as $\bar{f}_{l+1}^{(1)}$ in (5.4.2). The operator $[J_1^{(1)} + \zeta_S \mathscr{A}^{(1)}\bar{f}^{(1)}]$ does not have this effect, and, therefore, must be multiplied by ϵ^{-1} to be combined as in equation (5.4.2). The final result is, as displayed in equation (5.4.2), that at each order in ϵ a function $\bar{f}_l^{(1)}$ is related to $\bar{f}_{l+1}^{(1)}$. Assuming that the equations represent an adequate model of the liquid, it is clear that under all ordinary circumstances $\rho^{-1/3}\nabla \ln T$, etc., are small and the expansion should converge rapidly.

To study the hydrodynamic regime we seek solutions of the kinetic equations that depend on the time only implicity through the time dependence of T, ρ and $\mathbf{u}$, for which we note that

$$\rho(\mathbf{R}_1;t) = \int \bar{f}^{(1)}(1)\, d\mathbf{p}_1$$

$$\mathbf{u}(\mathbf{R}_1;t) = \frac{1}{\rho m} \int \mathbf{p}_1 \bar{f}^{(1)}(1)\, d\mathbf{p}_1$$

$$T(\mathbf{R}_1;t) = \frac{1}{3k\rho m} \int (\mathbf{p}_1 - m\mathbf{u}_1)^2 \bar{f}^{(1)}\, d\mathbf{p}_1. \tag{5.4.3}$$

The method of solution is one of successive approximations. Substituting the series (5.4.1) into the terms in the right-hand side of equation (5.4.2), and equating the coefficients of equal powers of ϵ we obtain the following equations:

$$0 = J_1^{(1)}[\bar{f}_0^{(1)}(1), \bar{f}_0^{(1)}(2)] + \zeta_S \mathscr{A}^{(1)}[\bar{f}_0^{(1)}(1)] \tag{5.4.4}$$

$$\begin{aligned} \mathscr{D}^{(1)}\bar{f}_0^{(1)}(1) = {} & J_1^{(1)}[\bar{f}_0^{(1)}(1), \bar{f}_1^{(1)}(2)] \\ & + J_1^{(1)}[\bar{f}_1^{(1)}(1), \bar{f}_0^{(1)}(2)] + J_2^{(1)}[\bar{f}_0^{(1)}(1), \bar{f}_0^{(1)}(2)] \\ & + J_3^{(1)}[\bar{f}_0^{(1)}(1), \bar{f}_0^{(1)}(2)] + \zeta_S \mathscr{A}^{(1)}[\bar{f}_1^{(1)}(1), \bar{f}_0^{(1)}(1)], \\ & \cdots \end{aligned} \tag{5.4.5}$$

where

$$\bar{f}_l^{(1)}(i) = \bar{f}_l^{(1)}(\mathbf{R}_i, \mathbf{p}_i; t)$$

and

$$\mathscr{A}^{(1)}[\bar{f}_0^{(1)}(1)] = \nabla_{p_1} \cdot [(\mathbf{p}_1/m - \mathbf{u}_1^{(0)})\bar{f}_0^{(1)}(1) + kT_1^{(0)} \nabla_{p_1} \bar{f}_0^{(1)}(1)] \tag{5.4.6}$$

$$\begin{aligned} \mathscr{A}^{(1)}[\bar{f}_1^{(1)}(1), \bar{f}_0^{(1)}(1)] = {} & \nabla_{p_1} \cdot [(\mathbf{p}_1/m - \mathbf{u}_1^{(0)})\bar{f}_1^{(1)}(1) + kT_1^{(0)} \nabla_{p_1} \bar{f}_1^{(1)}(1)] \\ & + \nabla_{p_1} \cdot [- \mathbf{u}_1^{(1)} \bar{f}_0^{(1)}(1) + kT_1^{(1)} \nabla_{p_1} \bar{f}_0^{(1)}(1)]. \end{aligned} \tag{5.4.7}$$

The remaining undefined symbols are all related to the macroscopic variables defined by equation (5.4.3), and are

$$\mathbf{u}_1^{(0)} = \frac{1}{\rho^{(0)} m} \int \mathbf{p}_1 \bar{f}_0^{(1)}(1)\, d\mathbf{p}_1$$

$$\mathbf{u}_1^{(1)} = \frac{1}{\rho^{(0)} m} \int (\mathbf{p}_1 - m\mathbf{u}_1^{(0)}) \bar{f}_1^{(1)}(1)\, d\mathbf{p}_1$$

$$\cdots$$

$$\rho_1^{(0)} = \int \bar{f}_0^{(1)}(1)\, d\mathbf{p}_1$$

$$\rho_1^{(1)} = \int \bar{f}_1^{(1)}(1)\, d\mathbf{p}_1$$

$$\cdots$$

$$kT_1^{(0)} = \frac{1}{3\rho^{(0)} m} \int (\mathbf{p}_1 - m\mathbf{u}_1^{(0)})^2 \bar{f}_0^{(1)}(1)\, d\mathbf{p}_1$$

$$kT_1^{(1)} = \frac{1}{3\rho^{(0)} m} \int (\mathbf{p}_1 - m\mathbf{u}_1^{(0)})^2 \bar{f}_1^{(1)}(1)\, d\mathbf{p}_1 - \frac{\rho_1^{(1)} kT_1^{(0)}}{\rho_1^{(0)}}$$

$$\cdots$$

The equations for $\bar{f}_l^{(1)}(1)$ $(l > 0)$ do not determine the velocities $\mathbf{u}_1^{(l)}$, temperatures $T_1^{(l)}$, and number densites $\rho_1^{(l)}$, uniquely. We therefore define the $\bar{f}_l^{(1)}$ $(l > 0)$ by requiring that $\rho_1^{(l)}$, $\mathbf{u}_1^{(l)}$ and $T_1^{(l)}$ are zero for $l > 0$, and that $\rho_1^{(0)}$, $\mathbf{u}_1^{(0)}$ and $T_1^{(0)}$ are the local equilibrium values.* The following relations, therefore, constitute auxiliary conditions on the solution:

$$\begin{aligned}
\rho_1 &= \int \bar{f}_0^{(1)}(1)\, d\mathbf{p}_1 \\
\mathbf{u}_1 &= \frac{1}{\rho m} \int \mathbf{p}_1 \bar{f}_0^{(1)}(1)\, d\mathbf{p}_1 \\
kT_1 &= \frac{1}{3\rho m} \int (\mathbf{p}_1 - m\mathbf{u}_1)^2 \bar{f}_0^{(1)}(1)\, d\mathbf{p}_1 \\
0 &= \int \bar{f}_1^{(1)}(1)\, d\mathbf{p}_1 \\
0 &= \int (\mathbf{p}_1 - m\mathbf{u}_1) \bar{f}_1^{(1)}(1)\, d\mathbf{p}_1 \\
0 &= \int (\mathbf{p}_1 - m\mathbf{u}_1)^2 \bar{f}_1^{(1)}(1)\, d\mathbf{p}_1.
\end{aligned} \tag{5.4.8}$$

Now, one solution of the singlet kinetic equation is

$$\bar{f}_0^{(1)}(1) = \rho_1^{(0)}(2\pi mkT_1^{(0)})^{-3/2} \exp\left(-\frac{[\mathbf{p}_1 - m\mathbf{u}_1^{(0)}]^2}{2mkT_1^{(0)}}\right), \tag{5.4.9}$$

and with our choice of conditions on $\rho^{(l)}$, $\mathbf{u}^{(l)}$ and $T^{(l)}$ it is readily seen that equation (5.4.9) is the local equilibrium, singlet distribution function.

To proceed further we must evaluate the unexpanded operator terms of equations (5.4.4)–(5.4.7). Using (5.4.9), equation (5.4.7) becomes

$$\begin{aligned}
\mathscr{A}^{(1)}[\bar{f}_1^{(1)}(1), \bar{f}_0^{(1)}(1)] &= \mathscr{A}^{(1)}[\bar{f}_1^{(1)}(1)] \\
&= \nabla_{p_1} \cdot [(\mathbf{p}_1/m - \mathbf{u}_1)\bar{f}_1^{(1)}(1) + kT_1 \nabla_{p_1} \bar{f}_1^{(1)}(1)] \\
&= kT_1 \nabla_{p_1} \cdot [\bar{f}_0^{(1)}(1)\, \nabla_{p_1}(\bar{f}_1^{(1)}(1)/\bar{f}_0^{(1)}(1))].
\end{aligned} \tag{5.4.10}$$

It is convenient to introduce a new perturbation function, $\Phi^{(1)}$, by the definition

$$\begin{aligned}
\bar{f}_1^{(1)}(i) &= \bar{f}_0^{(1)}(i)\Phi^{(1)}(i) \\
\bar{f}^{(1)}(i) &= \bar{f}_0^{(1)}(i)(1 + \Phi^{(1)}(i)).
\end{aligned} \tag{5.4.11}$$

* This procedure breaks down unless the system is sufficiently close to local equilibrium.

In the following equations we shall examine only the first-order corrections to the distribution functions, so that no terms of higher order than those introduced in equation (5.4.11) need be considered. To this order, the description of a liquid system which has been developed is confined to the description of linear dissipative phenomena; i.e., those phenomena in which mass, momentum, and energy transfer are directly proportional to the gradients of the hydrodynamic field variables ρ_1, $\mathbf{u}_1$ and T_1.

The hydrodynamic equations are derived by taking the zeroth, first and second momentum moments of the kinetic equation, according to equations (5.4.3). Consider first the stochastic term (i.e., the whole of the right-hand side) in equation (5.3.69). It is clear that, after partial integration(s), the moments of the Fokker-Planck operator vanish:

$$\langle \chi(1)\mathscr{A}^{(1)}\bar{f}^{(1)}\rangle = \int \chi(\mathbf{p}_1)\mathscr{A}^{(1)}\bar{f}^{(1)}(1)\, d\mathbf{p}_1 = 0, \tag{5.4.12}$$

where χ represents m, $\mathbf{p}_1$, $p_1^{\,2}$, or any linear combination of these functions.

The moments of $J_1^{(1)}$ may be written, in an obvious notation, as

$$\langle \chi(1)J_1^{(1)}[\bar{f}^{(1)}(1),\bar{f}^{(1)}(2)]\rangle = \langle \chi(1)J_1^{(1)}\rangle = \frac{1}{m}\, g_0^{(2)}(\mathbf{R}_1;\sigma)$$
$$\times \iint_{(\mathbf{k}\cdot\mathbf{p}_{12}>0)} \chi(\mathbf{p}_1)[\bar{f}^{(1)}(\mathbf{p}_1{}^*)\bar{f}^{(1)}(\mathbf{p}_2{}^*) - \bar{f}^{(1)}(\mathbf{p}_1)\bar{f}^{(1)}(\mathbf{p}_2)]p_{12}b\, db\, d\epsilon\, d\mathbf{p}_1\, d\mathbf{p}_2. \tag{5.4.13}$$

The process in which the final momenta are $\mathbf{p}_1{}^*$, $\mathbf{p}_2{}^*$, and the initial momenta are $\mathbf{p}_1$, $\mathbf{p}_2$ is known as the *inverse collision*. Equation (5.4.13) may be expressed in terms of the inverse collision in the form

$$\langle \chi(1)J_1^{(1)}\rangle = \frac{1}{m}\, g_0^{(2)}(\mathbf{R}_1;\sigma)$$
$$\times \iint_{(\mathbf{k}^*\cdot\mathbf{p}_{12}{}^*>0)} \chi(\mathbf{p}_1{}^*)[\bar{f}^{(1)}(\mathbf{p}_1)\bar{f}^{(1)}(\mathbf{p}_2) - \bar{f}^{(1)}(\mathbf{p}_1{}^*)\bar{f}^{(1)}(\mathbf{p}_2{}^*)]$$
$$\times\, p_{12}{}^*b^*\, db^*\, d\epsilon^*\, d\mathbf{p}_1{}^*\, d\mathbf{p}_2{}^*. \tag{5.4.14}$$

Now, by Liouville's theorem,

$$d\mathbf{p}_1\, d\mathbf{p}_2 = d\mathbf{p}_1{}^*\, d\mathbf{p}_2{}^*$$

and also, by the collision geometry,

$$p_{12} = p_{12}^*; \qquad \mathbf{k}^* = -\mathbf{k}$$
$$b^* = b; \qquad \epsilon^* = \epsilon$$

so that equation (5.4.14) becomes

$$\langle \chi(1) J_1^{(1)} \rangle = -\langle \chi^*(1) J_1^{(1)} \rangle, \tag{5.4.15}$$

or

$$\langle [\chi(1) - \chi^*(1)] J_1^{(1)} \rangle = 2\langle \chi(1) J_1^{(1)} \rangle. \tag{5.4.16}$$

The integral in equation (5.4.14) is invariant to a change of the subscripts on the momenta, because both $\bar{f}^{(1)}(1)$ and $\bar{f}^{(1)}(2)$ are evaluated in terms of thermodynamic quantities at the same point. It follows that

$$\langle \chi(1) J_1^{(1)} \rangle = \langle \chi(2) J_1^{(1)} \rangle. \tag{5.4.17}$$

Combining equations (5.4.15)–(5.4.17) it is found that

$$\begin{aligned} \langle \chi(1) J_1^{(1)} \rangle &= \tfrac{1}{4}\langle [\chi(1) + \chi(2) - \chi^*(1) - \chi^*(2)] J_1^{(1)} \rangle \\ &= 0, \end{aligned} \tag{5.4.18}$$

since χ is defined to be a linear combination of the summational invariants.

The moments of $J_2^{(1)}$ and $J_3^{(1)}$ may be derived by similar arguments. Thus,

$$\begin{aligned} \langle \chi(1) J_2^{(1)} \rangle = \frac{\sigma}{m}\, g_0^{(2)}(\mathbf{R}_1;\sigma) \\ \times \iint_{(\mathbf{k}\cdot\mathbf{p}_{12}>0)} \chi(\mathbf{p}_1)[\bar{f}^{(1)}(\mathbf{p}_1^*)\mathbf{k}\cdot\nabla_1 \bar{f}^{(1)}(\mathbf{p}_2^*) \\ + \bar{f}^{(1)}(\mathbf{p}_1)\mathbf{k}\cdot\nabla_1 \bar{f}^{(1)}(\mathbf{p}_2)] p_{12} b\, db\, d\epsilon\, d\mathbf{p}_1\, d\mathbf{p}_2. \end{aligned} \tag{5.4.19}$$

Expressing equation (5.4.19) in terms of the inverse collision, and using the collision geometry yields

$$\langle \chi(1) J_2^{(1)} \rangle = -\langle \chi^*(1) J_2^{(1)} \rangle,$$

so that

$$\langle [\chi(1) - \chi^*(1)] J_2^{(1)} \rangle = 2\langle \chi(1) J_2^{(1)} \rangle. \tag{5.4.20}$$

Again, using the inverse collision description we may introduce the transformation

$$\iint_{(\mathbf{k}\cdot\mathbf{p}_{12}>0)} [\chi(1)-\chi^*(1)]\bar{f}^{(1)}(\mathbf{p}_1^*)\mathbf{k}\cdot\nabla_1\bar{f}^{(1)}(\mathbf{p}_2^*)p_{12}b\,db\,d\epsilon\,d\mathbf{p}_1\,d\mathbf{p}_2$$
$$= \iint_{(\mathbf{k}\cdot\mathbf{p}_{12}>0)} [\chi(1)-\chi^*(1)]\bar{f}^{(1)}(\mathbf{p}_1)\mathbf{k}\cdot\nabla_1\bar{f}^{(1)}(\mathbf{p}_2)p_{12}b\,db\,d\epsilon\,d\mathbf{p}_1\,d\mathbf{p}_2. \tag{5.4.21}$$

We now interchange the labels on the molecules on the right-hand side of equation (5.4.21), which is invariant as a whole. Then

$$[\chi(1)-\chi^*(1)] \rightarrow [\chi(2)-\chi^*(2)],$$

but since χ is a summational invariant

$$[\chi(2)-\chi^*(2)] = -[\chi(1)-\chi^*(1)].$$

Utilizing the fact that $\mathbf{k}\rightarrow -\mathbf{k}$ under this transformation, one obtains the relation

$$\iint_{(\mathbf{k}\cdot\mathbf{p}_{12}>0)} [\chi(1)-\chi^*(1)]\bar{f}^{(1)}(\mathbf{p}_1)\mathbf{k}\cdot\nabla_1\bar{f}^{(1)}(\mathbf{p}_2)p_{12}b\,db\,d\epsilon\,d\mathbf{p}_1\,d\mathbf{p}_2$$
$$= \iint_{(\mathbf{k}\cdot\mathbf{p}_{12}>0)} [\chi(1)-\chi^*(1)]\bar{f}^{(1)}(\mathbf{p}_2)\mathbf{k}\cdot\nabla_1\bar{f}^{(1)}(\mathbf{p}_1)p_{12}b\,db\,d\epsilon\,d\mathbf{p}_1\,d\mathbf{p}_2, \tag{5.4.22}$$

and combining equations (5.4.19)–(5.4.22),

$$\langle\chi(1)J_2^{(1)}\rangle = \frac{\sigma}{2m}\,g_0^{(2)}(\mathbf{R}_1;\sigma)\iint_{(\mathbf{k}\cdot\mathbf{p}_{12}>0)} [\chi(1)-\chi^*(1)]$$
$$\mathbf{k}\cdot\nabla_1\bar{f}^{(1)}(\mathbf{p}_1)\bar{f}^{(1)}(\mathbf{p}_2)p_{12}b\,db\,d\epsilon\,d\mathbf{p}_1\,d\mathbf{p}_2. \tag{5.4.23}$$

By the use of similar arguments, the moments of $J_3^{(1)}$ are found to be

$$\langle\chi(1)J_3^{(1)}\rangle = \frac{\sigma}{2m}\,\nabla_1 g_0^{(2)}(\mathbf{R}_1;\sigma)\cdot\iint_{(\mathbf{k}\cdot\mathbf{p}_{12}>0)} \mathbf{k}[\chi(1)-\chi^*(1)]$$
$$\times\,\bar{f}^{(1)}(\mathbf{p}_1)\bar{f}^{(1)}(\mathbf{p}_2)p_{12}b\,db\,d\epsilon\,d\mathbf{p}_1\,d\mathbf{p}_2, \tag{5.4.24}$$

and the combination of equations (5.4.23) and (5.4.24) yields

$$\begin{aligned}\langle \chi(1)(J_2^{(1)} + J_3^{(1)})\rangle &= -\nabla_1 \cdot \Bigg[\frac{\sigma}{2m}\, g_0^{(2)}(\mathbf{R}_1;\sigma) \iint_{(\mathbf{k}\cdot\mathbf{p}_{12}>0)} [\chi^*(1) - \chi(1)] \\ &\qquad \times \bar{f}^{(1)}(\mathbf{p}_1)\bar{f}^{(1)}(\mathbf{p}_2) p_{12} b\, db\, d\epsilon\, d\mathbf{p}_1\, d\mathbf{p}_2\Bigg] \\ &= -\nabla_1 \cdot \boldsymbol{\chi}(\sigma) \end{aligned} \tag{5.4.25}$$

if χ does not depend upon $\mathbf{R}_1$ or t. We shall restrict our attention to such cases. The significance of $\boldsymbol{\chi}(\sigma)$ becomes apparent when we note that on collision of two rigid spheres, the amount $[\chi^*(1) - \chi(1)]$ of the invariant χ is transferred through a distance $\sigma\mathbf{k}$. Thus, $\boldsymbol{\chi}(\sigma)$ is the collisional transfer contribution to the flux of χ. Equation (5.4.25) is the only contribution to the flux of χ from the stochastic term of the kinetic equation, and is equal to*

$$\langle \chi \mathscr{D}^{(1)} \bar{f}^{(1)}\rangle = \frac{\partial}{\partial t}\langle \rho_1 \chi\rangle + \nabla_1 \cdot \left\langle \frac{\rho_1}{m}\, \mathbf{p}_1 \chi \right\rangle - \rho_1 \langle \mathbf{X}_1 \cdot \nabla_{p_1} \chi\rangle. \tag{5.4.26}$$

In equation (5.4.26) the angular brackets $\langle\cdots\rangle$ represent an average (or simply an integration) over $\mathbf{p}_1$. The general equation for the flux of χ is, therefore,

$$\frac{\partial}{\partial t}\langle \rho_1 \chi\rangle + \nabla_1 \cdot \left\langle \frac{\rho_1}{m}\, \mathbf{p}_1 \chi \right\rangle - \rho_1 \langle \mathbf{X}_1 \cdot \nabla_{p_1} \chi\rangle = -\nabla_1 \cdot \boldsymbol{\chi}(\sigma). \tag{5.4.27}$$

Now, when $\chi = m$, $\boldsymbol{\chi}(\sigma) = 0$, and equation (5.4.27) becomes

$$\frac{\partial \rho_m}{\partial t} + \nabla_1 \cdot (\rho_m \mathbf{u}) = 0, \tag{5.4.28}$$

where $\rho_m = m\rho$ is the mass density. With $\chi = \mathbf{p}_1$ we obtain

$$\frac{\partial}{\partial t}(\rho_m \mathbf{u}) + \nabla_1 \cdot \left\langle \frac{\rho}{m}\, \mathbf{p}_1 \mathbf{p}_1 \right\rangle - \rho \mathbf{X}_1 = -\nabla_1 \cdot \boldsymbol{\chi}_{\mathbf{p}}(\sigma). \tag{5.4.29}$$

By means of the identity

$$\langle \mathbf{p}_1 \mathbf{p}_1 \rangle = \langle (\mathbf{p}_1 - m\mathbf{u})(\mathbf{p}_1 - m\mathbf{u})\rangle + m^2 \mathbf{u}\mathbf{u}, \tag{5.4.30}$$

and the definition

$$\mathbf{P}_K = \frac{1}{m^2}\langle \rho_m (\mathbf{p}_1 - m\mathbf{u})(\mathbf{p}_1 - m\mathbf{u})\rangle \tag{5.4.31}$$

* The average internal forces $\mathbf{F}_1{}^*$ on molecule 1 are assumed here to be negligible.

of the kinetic contribution to the pressure tensor, equation (5.4.29) may be rearranged to give the equation of conservation of momentum

$$\rho_m\left(\frac{\partial}{\partial t} + \mathbf{u}\cdot\nabla_1\right)\mathbf{u} = \rho_m\mathbf{f} - \nabla_1\cdot\mathsf{P}. \tag{5.4.32}$$

In equation (5.4.32),

$$\mathbf{f} = \mathbf{X}_1/m \tag{5.4.33}$$

is the external force per unit mass on the fluid, and

$$\mathsf{P} = \mathsf{P}_K + \boldsymbol{\chi}_{\mathbf{p}}(\sigma) \tag{5.4.34}$$

is the total pressure tensor, which includes the contribution $\boldsymbol{\chi}_{\mathbf{p}}(\sigma)$ from collisional transfer. Finally, if $\chi_{p^2} = \dfrac{p^2}{2m}$, and we define

$$\mathbf{q} = \mathbf{q}_K + \boldsymbol{\chi}_{p^2}(\sigma) \tag{5.4.35}$$

as the total thermal conduction current, where

$$\mathbf{q}_K = \frac{\rho}{2m^2}\langle(\mathbf{p} - m\mathbf{u})(\mathbf{p} - m\mathbf{u})^2\rangle, \tag{5.4.36}$$

then, after using the symmetry of P, and the relations

$$\frac{\rho}{2m^2}\langle\mathbf{p}_1(\mathbf{p}_1 - m\mathbf{u})^2\rangle = \mathbf{q}_K + \tfrac{3}{2}\rho kT\mathbf{u}, \tag{5.4.37}$$

$$\frac{\rho}{m}\langle\mathbf{p}_1(\mathbf{p}_1 - \mathbf{u})\rangle = \mathsf{P}_K,$$

it is found that

$$\tfrac{3}{2}\rho k\left(\frac{\partial}{\partial t} + \mathbf{u}\cdot\nabla\right)T = -\nabla_1\cdot\mathbf{q} - \mathsf{P}_K : \boldsymbol{\epsilon}, \tag{5.4.38}$$

where $(3\rho k/2)$ is the specific heat of a rigid sphere fluid, and

$$\boldsymbol{\epsilon} = \tfrac{1}{2}(\nabla_1\mathbf{u} + \widetilde{\nabla_1\mathbf{u}}) \tag{5.4.39}$$

is the symmetrized rate of strain tensor.

In order to evaluate the streaming term (i.e., the left-hand side) in equation (5.4.5) the zeroth order values of the various quantities appearing in the hydrodynamic equations are required. From equations

(5.4.8) and (5.4.25),

$$\begin{aligned} \rho_m &= \rho_m^{(0)} \\ \mathbf{u} &= \mathbf{u}^{(0)} \\ T &= T^{(0)} \\ \mathsf{P}^{(0)} &= p\mathsf{I}; \qquad (\mathsf{P}_K^{(0)} = \rho k T^{(0)}\mathsf{I}) \\ \mathbf{q}^{(0)} &= \mathbf{0}, \end{aligned} \tag{5.4.40}$$

where p is the equilibrium pressure of a fluid of rigid spheres at density ρ, and is calculated explicitly in Chapter 6. In equilibrium, it is found that $\mathbf{q}^{(0)} = \mathbf{0}$ because it is the average of an odd function over an even interval.

Noting that

$$\begin{aligned} \nabla_1 \cdot \mathsf{P} &= \nabla_1 p \\ \mathsf{P}_K : \boldsymbol{\epsilon} &= \rho k T^{(0)} \nabla \cdot \mathbf{u}, \end{aligned} \tag{5.4.41}$$

the zeroth order hydrodynamic equations are found to be

$$\begin{aligned} &\frac{\partial \rho_m}{\partial t} + \nabla_1 \cdot (\rho_m \mathbf{u}) = 0 \\ &\left(\frac{\partial}{\partial t} + \mathbf{u} \cdot \nabla_1\right)\mathbf{u} + \rho_m^{-1} \nabla_1 p = \mathbf{f} \\ &\left(\frac{\partial}{\partial t} + \mathbf{u} \cdot \nabla_1\right)T + \tfrac{2}{3} T \nabla_1 \cdot \mathbf{u} = 0. \end{aligned} \tag{5.4.42}$$

These are the hydrodynamic equations for non-viscous flow, and they possess solutions describing flow patterns that persist for indefinitely long times.

Evaluation of the streaming term in equation (5.4.5), and replacement of the time derivatives from equations (5.4.42) now yields

$$\mathscr{D}^{(1)} \bar{f}_0^{(1)}(1) = \bar{f}_0^{(1)}(1)\left[2\mathsf{b} : \nabla_1 \mathbf{u} - \left(\frac{2kT}{m}\right)^{1/2} (\tfrac{5}{2} + \alpha T - W_1^2)\mathbf{W}_1 \cdot \nabla_1 \ln T\right], \tag{5.4.43}$$

where

$$\begin{aligned} \mathbf{W}_1 &= \left(\frac{m}{2kT}\right)^{1/2} (\mathbf{p}_1/m - \mathbf{u}) \\ \mathsf{b} &= \mathbf{W}_1\mathbf{W}_1 - \tfrac{1}{3} W_1^2 \mathbf{1} \\ \alpha &= -\left(\frac{\partial \ln \rho}{\partial T}\right)_p. \end{aligned}$$

In order that the kinetic equation should describe the overall approach of the system to equilibrium, the dissipative terms involving the perturbation $\Phi^{(1)}$ must be included. Then the terms

$$J_1^{(1)}[\bar{f}_0^{(1)}(1), \bar{f}_1^{(1)}(2)] + J_1^{(1)}[\bar{f}_1^{(1)}(1), \bar{f}_0^{(1)}(2)] + \zeta_S \mathscr{A}^{(1)}[\bar{f}_1^{(1)}(1)]$$

do not vanish as they did in the case where we integrated over $\mathbf{p}_1$. The nature of the iterative solution should now be clear. At each stage of the iteration, the time dependence of the variables defined by the streaming term, together with $J_2^{(1)}$ and $J_3^{(1)}$, define in turn the time dependence of the next higher order correction through the dependence of the distribution function on the macroscopic variables. An examination of equations (5.4.4) and (5.4.5) shows that the expansion in powers of ϵ formally separates the stages of the iteration in just this way. We see, for example, that the first stage, equation (5.4.4), corresponds to the non-dissipative hydrodynamic equations (5.4.42), while the second stage, equation (5.4.5), will introduce corrections arising from the deviation from equilibrium of a locally Maxwellian distribution function, and thereby introduce dissipation.

5.4.B. *An Aside on Relaxation Times* (15)

Before proceeding to a detailed study of the solutions of the kinetic equations derived in the last section, it is pertinent to examine the internal consistency of the kinetic equations in a different manner than that of Section 5.3. The basic physical argument involved in our analysis is that it is possible to distinguish two time scales in an examination of molecular motion in a liquid. One of these time scales describes the motion when the molecules are in the strongly repulsive region of the intermolecular potential, and the other describes the corresponding soft potential region. It is asserted further that the effect of the rapidly fluctuating soft-force field is to render successive rigid core collisions uncorrelated. A necessary consequence of these two statements is that the relaxation times descriptive of motion in the two regions of the force field be widely different and, moreover, that the relaxation time characteristic of the soft-force field be much smaller than the relaxation time characteristic of the strongly repulsive force field. We now examine the consistency of the Rice-Allnatt equations from this point of view.

We consider as the simplest possible case a fluid which is in equilibrium in configuration space *but not* in equilibrium in momentum space. The singlet kinetic equation then becomes

$$\frac{\partial \bar{f}^{(1)}}{\partial t} + \mathbf{F}_1^* \cdot \nabla_{p_1} \bar{f}^{(1)}$$
$$= \frac{g(\sigma)}{m} \int [\bar{f}^{(1)}(\mathbf{p}_1^*;t)\bar{f}^{(1)}(\mathbf{p}_2^*;t) - \bar{f}^{(1)}(\mathbf{p}_1;t)\bar{f}^{(1)}(\mathbf{p}_2;t)]p_{12}b\, db\, d\epsilon\, d\mathbf{p}_2$$
$$+ \zeta_S \nabla_{p_1} \cdot [(\mathbf{p}_1/m - \mathbf{u}) + kT\, \nabla_{p_1}]\bar{f}^{(1)}(\mathbf{p}_1;t). \quad (5.4.44)$$

We now seek a perturbation solution of equation (5.4.44) with explicit time dependence of the form $\exp(-\lambda t)$. In what follows, a variational method will be used to obtain the longest relaxation time. Restricting attention to perturbation functions which are even in the momentum,

$$\bar{f}^{(1)}(\mathbf{p}_1;t) = \bar{f}_0^{(1)}[1 + e^{-\lambda t}\psi(p_1^2)]$$
$$\bar{f}_0^{(1)}(\mathbf{p}_1) = \rho(2\pi mkT)^{-3/2} \exp\left(-\frac{[\mathbf{p}_1 - m\mathbf{u}]^2}{2mkT}\right). \quad (5.4.45)$$

Substituting in the kinetic equation (5.3.69) we find

$$-\lambda e^{-\lambda t}\psi(p_1^2)\bar{f}_0^{(1)}(\mathbf{p}_1) + \mathbf{F}_1^* \cdot \nabla_{p_1}(\bar{f}_0^{(1)}(\mathbf{p}_1)[1 + e^{-\lambda t}\psi(p_1^2)])$$
$$= e^{-\lambda t}\frac{g(\sigma)}{m} \int \bar{f}_0^{(1)}(\mathbf{p}_1)\bar{f}_0^{(1)}(\mathbf{p}_2)[\psi(p_1^{*2}) + \psi(p_2^{*2})$$
$$- \psi(p_1^2) - \psi(p_2^2)]p_{12}b\, db\, d\epsilon\, d\mathbf{p}_2$$
$$+ \zeta_S \nabla_{p_1} \cdot [(\mathbf{p}_1/m - \mathbf{u}^{(0)})\bar{f}_1^{(1)}(\mathbf{p}_1) + kT^{(0)} \nabla_{p_1}\bar{f}_1^{(1)}(\mathbf{p}_1)]$$
$$+ \zeta_S \nabla_{p_1} \cdot [-\mathbf{u}^{(1)}\bar{f}_0^{(1)}(\mathbf{p}_1) + kT^{(1)} \nabla_{p_1}\bar{f}_0^{(1)}(\mathbf{p}_1)], \quad (5.4.46)$$

where $\mathbf{u}^{(0)}$ and $T^{(0)}$, $\mathbf{u}^{(1)}$ and $T^{(1)}$ are defined in equation (5.4.8), and we write $\bar{f}_0^{(1)}(\mathbf{p}_1)e^{-\lambda t}\psi(p_1^2)$ for the perturbation $\bar{f}_1^{(1)}(\mathbf{p}_1)$. As in the previous paragraph we take $\mathbf{u}^{(1)}$, $T^{(1)}$, and $\rho^{(1)}$ as zero, and replace $\mathbf{u}^{(0)}$, $T^{(0)}$, and $\rho^{(0)}$ by their local equilibrium values. On using equation (5.4.10), equation (5.4.46) becomes

$$-\lambda e^{-\lambda t}\psi(p_1^2)\bar{f}_0^{(1)}(\mathbf{p}_1) + \mathbf{F}_1^* \cdot \nabla_{p_1}(\bar{f}_0^{(1)}(\mathbf{p}_1)[1 + e^{-\lambda t}\psi(p_1^2)])$$
$$= e^{-\lambda t}\frac{g(\sigma)}{m} \int \bar{f}_0^{(1)}(\mathbf{p}_1)\bar{f}_0^{(1)}(p_2)[\psi(\mathbf{p}_1^{*2}) + \psi(p_2^{*2})$$
$$- \psi(p_1^2) - \psi(p_2^2)]p_{12}b\, db\, d\epsilon\, d\mathbf{p}_2$$
$$+ e^{-\lambda t}\zeta_S kT\, \nabla_{p_1} \cdot [\bar{f}_0^{(1)}(\mathbf{p}_1)\, \nabla_{p_1}\psi(p_1^2)]. \quad (5.4.47)$$

We now expand the perturbation function ψ in terms of a set of Sonine polynomials whose argument is the square of the reduced velocity $\mathbf{W}_1$

defined in equation (5.4.43) (20–22):

$$\psi(p_1^2) = \sum_i b_i S^{(i)}_{\frac{1}{2}}(W_1^2)$$

$$S^{(i)}_n(x) = \sum_{j=0}^{i} (-)^j \frac{(i+n)!\, x^j}{(n+j)!\,(i-j)!\,j!}. \tag{5.4.48}$$

The polynomials form an orthogonal set, i.e.,

$$\int S^{(i)}_{\frac{1}{2}}(W_1^2) S^{(j)}_{\frac{1}{2}}(W_1^2) \bar{f}_0^{(1)}(\mathbf{p}_1)\, d\mathbf{p}_1 = \rho C\, \delta_{ij}, \tag{5.4.49}$$

where C is a normalization constant. Actually, any set of orthogonal polynomials may be used, and the Sonine polynomials are chosen because the conservation of mass, momentum, and energy in a binary collision may then be conveniently used.

Appeal to the auxiliary conditions (5.4.8) shows that the conditions $\rho^{(1)} = 0$, $T^{(1)} = 0$ are not satisfied unless

$$b_0 = b_1 = 0. \tag{5.4.50}$$

Substitution of equations (5.4.48) and (5.4.50) in equation (5.4.47), and multiplication by

$$\sum_{j=2}^{\infty} b_j S^{(j)}_{\frac{1}{2}}(W_1^2)$$

yields

$$\begin{aligned}
-\lambda \bar{f}_0^{(1)}(\mathbf{p}_1) \sum_{j,k=2}^{\infty}\sum b_k b_j S^{(j)}_{\frac{1}{2}}(W_1^2) S^{(k)}_{\frac{1}{2}}(W_1^2) \\
= \sum_{j,k=2}^{\infty}\sum \frac{g(\sigma)}{m} \int \bar{f}_0^{(1)}(\mathbf{p}_1)\bar{f}_0^{(1)}(\mathbf{p}_2) b_k b_j S^{(j)}_{\frac{1}{2}}(W_1^2) \\
\times [S^{(k)}_{\frac{1}{2}}(W_1^{*2}) + S^{(k)}_{\frac{1}{2}}(W_2^{*2}) - S^{(k)}_{\frac{1}{2}}(W_1^2) - S^{(k)}_{\frac{1}{2}}(W_2^2)] p_{12} b\, db\, d\epsilon\, d\mathbf{p}_2 \\
+ \sum_{j,k=2}^{\infty}\sum \zeta_S kT b_k b_j S^{(j)}_{\frac{1}{2}}(W_1^2)\, \nabla_{p_1} \cdot (\bar{f}_0^{(1)}(\mathbf{p}_1)\, \nabla_{p_1} S^{(k)}_{\frac{1}{2}}(W_1^2)).
\end{aligned} \tag{5.4.51}$$

Equation (5.4.51) is now integrated over $\mathbf{p}_1$. According to the orthogonality relation (5.4.49) the left-hand side terms vanish except for $j = k$. Also, the function $\bar{f}_0^{(1)}(\mathbf{p}_1) S^{(j)}_{\frac{1}{2}}(W_1^2)$ is an eigenfunction of the Fokker-Planck operator [see equation (5.4.122)] with eigenvalue $-\dfrac{2j}{mkT}$. Consequently, the Fokker-Planck term also vanishes unless $j = k$.

Equation (5.4.51) consequently reduces to

$$-\lambda \sum_{j,k=2}^{\infty}\sum b_j b_k (j,j)\,\delta_{jk} = \sum_{j,k=2}^{\infty}\sum g(\sigma) b_j b_k [\![j,k]\!] - \frac{2\zeta_S}{m}\sum_{j,k=2}^{\infty}\sum j b_j b_k (j,j)\,\delta_{jk}, \quad (5.4.52)$$

where the bracket integrals (j,j) and $[\![j,k]\!]$ are defined by

$$[\![j,k]\!] = \frac{1}{m}\iint \bar{f}_0^{(1)}(\mathbf{p}_1)\bar{f}_0^{(1)}(\mathbf{p}_2)S_{\frac{1}{2}}^{(j)}(W_1^2) \times [S_{\frac{1}{2}}^{(k)}(W_1^{*2}) + S_{\frac{1}{2}}^{(k)}(W_2^{*2}) - S_{\frac{1}{2}}^{(k)}(W_1^2) - S_{\frac{1}{2}}^{(k)}(W_2^2)] \times p_{12} b\, db\, d\epsilon\, d\mathbf{p}_1\, d\mathbf{p}_2, \quad (5.4.53)$$

$$(j,k) = \int \bar{f}_0^{(1)}(\mathbf{p}_1)S_{\frac{1}{2}}^{(j)}(W_1^2)S_{\frac{1}{2}}^{(k)}(W_1^2)\, d\mathbf{p}_1 = \frac{2}{\pi^{\frac{1}{2}}}\frac{\Gamma(\frac{3}{2}+j)}{j!}\,\delta_{jk}. \quad (5.4.54)$$

To determine the longest relaxation time, corresponding to the minimum value of λ, we perform variations with respect to the coefficients b_m, using the conditions $(\delta\lambda/\delta b_m) = 0$, $(m = 2, 3, \cdots)$. We thus obtain the set of linear equations

$$\sum_{j=2}^{\infty} b_j\left[g(\sigma)[\![j,k]\!] + \left(\lambda - \frac{2j\zeta_S}{m}\right)(j,j)\,\delta_{jk}\right] = 0, \qquad (k = 2, 3, \cdots). \quad (5.4.55)$$

The values of λ and the coefficients b_m are determined by the normalization conditions and the roots of the secular determinant

$$\left| g(\sigma)[\![j,k]\!] + \left(\lambda - 2j\frac{\zeta_S}{m}\right)(j,j)\,\delta_{jk} \right| = 0. \quad (5.4.56)$$

Now, it may be shown that consideration of the higher order collision integrals $[\![j,k]\!]$ introduces corrections of only a few per cent to the result obtained with the lowest order integral $[\![2,2]\!]$. Consequently, we shall accept as a good approximation the root given by the leading 2,2 term of the determinant:

$$\lambda = 4\frac{\zeta_S}{m} - g(\sigma)\frac{[\![2,2]\!]}{(2,2)}. \quad (5.4.57)$$

We now proceed to evaluate the bracket integral $[\![2,2]\!]$. Using the symmetry arguments outlined in the previous section, equation (5.4.53) can be transformed to

$$[\![j,k]\!] = -\frac{1}{4m}\iint \bar{f}_0^{(1)}(\mathbf{p}_1)\bar{f}_0^{(1)}(\mathbf{p}_2)[S_{\frac{1}{2}}^{(j)}][S_{\frac{1}{2}}^{(k)}]p_{12}b\; db\; d\epsilon\; d\mathbf{p}_1\; d\mathbf{p}_2, \tag{5.4.58}$$

where

$$[S_{\frac{1}{2}}^{(j)}] = S_{\frac{1}{2}}^{(j)}(W_1{}^{*2}) + S_{\frac{1}{2}}^{(j)}(W_2{}^{*2}) - S_{\frac{1}{2}}^{(j)}(W_1^2) - S_{\frac{1}{2}}^{(j)}(W_2{}^2). \tag{5.4.59}$$

After expansion of $S_{\frac{1}{2}}^{(2)}$ by means of equation (5.4.58), and use of the collision invariance of 1 and $W_i{}^2$, equation (5.4.58) becomes

$$[\![2,2]\!] = -(16\pi^3 m)^{-1}\iint \exp(-W_1{}^2 - W_2{}^2)[W^4]^2 p_{12}b \times db\; d\epsilon\; d\mathbf{W}_1\; d\mathbf{W}_2. \tag{5.4.60}$$

Upon introducing the reduced center of mass velocity $\mathbf{W}$ and relative velocity $\mathbf{w}$, defined by

$$\mathbf{W} = \tfrac{1}{2}(\mathbf{W}_1 + \mathbf{W}_2)$$
$$\mathbf{w} = \mathbf{W}_2 - \mathbf{W}_1, \tag{5.4.61}$$

and the collision relations

$$\mathbf{W}_1{}^* = \mathbf{W}_1 + \mathbf{k}(\mathbf{k}\cdot\mathbf{w})$$
$$\mathbf{W}_2{}^* = \mathbf{W}_2 - \mathbf{k}(\mathbf{k}\cdot\mathbf{w}), \tag{5.4.62}$$

it is found that

$$[W^4] = 8\{(\mathbf{w}\cdot\mathbf{k})^2(\mathbf{W}\cdot\mathbf{k})^2 - (\mathbf{W}\cdot\mathbf{w})(\mathbf{W}\cdot\mathbf{k})(\mathbf{w}\cdot\mathbf{k})\}. \tag{5.4.63}$$

Equation (5.4.63) is substituted into equation (5.4.58), and the integration over the angles of $\mathbf{W}$ performed using the vector theorem

$$\int F(W)(\mathbf{W}\cdot\mathbf{a})(\mathbf{W}\cdot\mathbf{b})(\mathbf{W}\cdot\mathbf{c})(\mathbf{W}\cdot\mathbf{d})\; d\mathbf{W}$$
$$= \frac{4\pi}{15}\int_0^\infty F(W)W^6\, dW\{(\mathbf{a}\cdot\mathbf{b})(\mathbf{c}\cdot\mathbf{d}) + (\mathbf{a}\cdot\mathbf{c})(\mathbf{b}\cdot\mathbf{d}) + (\mathbf{a}\cdot\mathbf{d})(\mathbf{b}\cdot\mathbf{c})\}, \tag{5.4.64}$$

which is valid for any constant vectors **a**, **b**, **c**, and **d**. Integration over the magnitude of **W** is performed by means of the relation

$$\int_0^\infty \exp(-\alpha W^2)\, W^m\, dW = \frac{1}{2}\alpha^{-(m+1)/2}\,\Gamma\left(\frac{m+1}{2}\right)$$

$$= \frac{\pi^{1/2}}{2}\cdot\frac{1}{2}\cdot\frac{3}{2}\cdots\frac{(m-1)}{2}\,\alpha^{-(m+1)/2}, \qquad m \text{ even}$$

$$= \frac{1}{2}\left(\frac{m-1}{2}\right)!\,\alpha^{-(m+1)/2}, \qquad m \text{ odd.} \qquad (5.4.65)$$

It is then found that

$$[\![2,2]\!] = -\left(\frac{2kT}{m}\right)^{1/2}\frac{\rho^2}{2^{7/2}\pi^{3/2}}$$

$$\times \iint_{(\mathbf{k}\cdot\mathbf{w}>0)} \exp(-\tfrac{1}{2}w^2)[w^2(\mathbf{w}\cdot\mathbf{k})^2 - (\mathbf{w}\cdot\mathbf{k})^4]wb\,db\,d\epsilon\,d\mathbf{w}. \qquad (5.4.66)$$

It is now convenient to integrate over the collision cylinder using the definition (cf. Section 5.3.A)

$$b = \sigma \sin\phi$$

$$db = \sigma\cos\phi\,d\phi$$

and the limits

$$0 \leqslant \phi \leqslant \pi/2$$

$$0 \leqslant \epsilon \leqslant 2\pi.$$

After integration over **w**, the final form of $[\![2,2]\!]$ is

$$[\![2,2]\!] = -4\left(\frac{\pi kT}{m}\right)^{1/2}\rho^2\sigma^2. \qquad (5.4.67)$$

Substitution of equations (5.4.54) and (5.4.67) in equation (5.4.57) now yields the result

$$\lambda = 4\frac{\zeta_S}{m} + \tfrac{16}{15}\rho g(\sigma)\Omega^{(2,2)},$$

$$\Omega^{(2,2)} = \left(\frac{4\pi kT}{m}\right)^{1/2}\sigma^2, \qquad (5.4.68)$$

where $\Omega^{(2,2)}$ is one of the reduced rigid sphere cross sections

$$\Omega^{(l,s)} = \left(\frac{4\pi kT}{m}\right)^{1/2} \int_0^\infty \gamma^{2s+3}(1 - \cos^l \theta) \exp(-\gamma^2) b \, db \, d\gamma$$
$$= \left(\frac{\pi kT}{m}\right)^{1/2} \sigma^2 \frac{(s+1)!}{2}\left[1 - \frac{1}{2}\frac{1+(-)^l}{1+l}\right], \tag{5.4.69}$$

and $\theta = \pi - 2\phi$ is the angle of deflection in a binary collision.

The final result (5.4.68) is expected from the simple point of view that the stochastic term of the singlet equation, which is the sum of two independent terms, yields the sum of two inverse relaxation times. In the rigid sphere limit we recover the result of Phillips (25), while in the Fokker-Planck limit, the longest relaxation time is found to be $\tau_{\text{F.P.}} = (m/4\zeta_S)$. It is left as an exercise for the reader to show that the longest relaxation for the solution (4.4.64) of the Fokker-Planck equation is $\tau'_{\text{F.P.}} = (m/2\zeta_S)$. The difference in these results is due to the fact that in the latter case the Brownian particle has not been required to be in thermal equilibrium with its surroundings.

We consider now the numerical magnitudes of the relaxation times. For the pure rigid sphere fluid the smallest relaxation time is

$$\tau_{\text{R.S.}} = 15(16\rho g(\sigma)\Omega^{(2,2)})^{-1}, \tag{5.4.70}$$

which has the value of 6×10^{-13} sec. for a fluid with the density of liquid Ar at 84°K. At this temperature and density, $\zeta_S = 5.8 \times 10^{-10}$ gm./sec.$^{-1}$ (taken from experimental measurements of self-diffusion), which leads to a relaxation time $\tau_{\text{R.A.}}$ for the kinetic equation (5.3.69) of

$$\tau_{\text{R.A.}} = 0.34 \times 10^{-13} \text{ sec.}, \tag{5.4.71}$$

which is considerably smaller than the value for a pure rigid sphere fluid. The value of $\tau_{\text{R.A.}}$ is, in fact, very close to the value characteristic of the pure Fokker-Planck fluid. Thus, the two relaxation times are widely separated, and $\tau_{\text{R.A.}}$ or $\tau_{\text{F.P.}}$ is much smaller than $\tau_{\text{R.S.}}$, confirming thereby the physical arguments underlying the derivation of the kinetic equations.

5.4.C. *The Solution of the Singlet Equation* (15)

We now return to the computation of the perturbation to the singlet distribution function. In equation (5.4.43) we represented the streaming terms of the kinetic equation in terms of **W** and the thermodynamic variables T, ρ, $\mathbf{u}$. It is now necessary to reduce the interaction terms to a representation in the same variables, insofar as this is possible. In the lowest order of perturbation theory, such as we are using herein, derivatives of and second order terms in the perturbation function Φ may be neglected. Following the procedure indicated by equation (5.4.5), we calculate the gradient of $\bar{f}_0^{(1)}(2)$, which is defined in equation (5.4.9). We obtain

$$\nabla_1 \bar{f}_0^{(1)}(2) = \left[\left(-\alpha T - \frac{3}{2} + \frac{(\mathbf{p}_2 - m\mathbf{u})^2}{2mkT}\right) \nabla_1 \ln T + \frac{1}{kT}(\nabla_1 \mathbf{u}) \cdot (\mathbf{p}_2 - m\mathbf{u})\right] \bar{f}_0^{(1)}(2), \quad (5.4.72)$$

where the gradient of density is regarded as arising solely from the variations of temperature. According to the discussion preceding equation (5.3.25), we also have

$$\nabla_1 g_0^{(2)}(\mathbf{R}_1, \sigma) = \left(\frac{\partial g(\sigma)}{\partial T}\right)_p \nabla_1 T, \quad (5.4.73)$$

where the abbreviated notation $g(\sigma)$ has been introduced instead of $g_0^{(2)}(\mathbf{R}_1,\sigma)$. From the definition of $J_2^{(1)}$ and $J_3^{(1)}$ [equations (5.3.25) and (5.3.26)] we obtain, with the aid of equations (5.4.72) and (5.4.73),

$$\begin{aligned} J_2^{(1)}[\bar{f}_0^{(1)}(1), \bar{f}_0^{(1)}(2)] &+ J_3^{(1)}[\bar{f}_0^{(1)}(1), \bar{f}_0^{(1)}(2)] \\ = \rho\sigma g(\sigma) \left(\frac{2kT}{m\pi^3}\right)^{1/2} \bar{f}_0^{(1)}(1) &\int_{(\mathbf{k}\cdot\mathbf{w}>0)} e^{-W_2^2} \\ \mathbf{k}\cdot\Bigg\{\left[-2\alpha T - 3 + \left(\frac{\partial \ln g(\sigma)}{\partial \ln T}\right)_p\right] &\nabla_1 \ln T + (W_2^{*2} + W_2^2)\nabla_1 \ln T \\ &+ \left(\frac{2m}{kT}\right)^{1/2} \nabla_1 \mathbf{u} \cdot (\mathbf{W}_2^* + \mathbf{W}_2)\Bigg\} wb\, db\, d\epsilon\, d\mathbf{W}_2, \quad (5.4.74) \end{aligned}$$

where we have introduced the reduced peculiar velocities $\mathbf{W}_i$ defined by equation (5.4.43), and have used the conservation of energy in the form $\bar{f}_0^{(1)}(1)^* \bar{f}_0^{(1)}(2)^* = \bar{f}_0^{(1)}(1)\bar{f}_0^{(1)}(2)$.

The mechanical equations for a rigid core encounter are

$$\begin{aligned} \mathbf{p}_1^* &= \mathbf{p}_1 + \mathbf{kk}\cdot\mathbf{p}_{12}, \\ \mathbf{p}_2^* &= \mathbf{p}_2 - \mathbf{kk}\cdot\mathbf{p}_{12}, \end{aligned} \quad (5.4.75)$$

and lead to the relations cited in equation (5.4.58) when $\mathbf{u}$ is subtracted from both sides, and they are then divided by $(2mkT)^{1/2}$. We therefore have

$$\mathbf{W}_2{}^* + \mathbf{W}_2 = 2\mathbf{W}_2 - \mathbf{kk}\cdot\mathbf{w}$$
$$W_2{}^{*2} + \mathbf{W}_2{}^2 = 2W_2{}^2 - 2(\mathbf{W}_2\cdot\mathbf{k})(\mathbf{k}\cdot\mathbf{w}) + (\mathbf{k}\cdot\mathbf{w})^2, \quad (5.4.76)$$

since $\mathbf{k}\cdot\mathbf{k} \equiv 1$. Upon substituting equation (5.4.76) into equation (5.4.74), integrals over the collision hemisphere (i.e., $\mathbf{k}\cdot\mathbf{w} > 0$) of three different kinds arise. They are

$$I_1 = \int_{(\mathbf{k}\cdot\mathbf{w}>0)} \mathbf{k}\cdot\mathbf{D}wb\,db\,d\epsilon, \quad (5.4.77)$$

$$I_2 = \int_{(\mathbf{k}\cdot\mathbf{w}>0)} \mathbf{k}\cdot\mathsf{E}\cdot\mathbf{kk}\cdot\mathbf{w}wb\,db\,d\epsilon, \quad (5.4.78)$$

$$I_3 = \int_{(\mathbf{k}\cdot\mathbf{w}>0)} \mathbf{k}\cdot\mathbf{D}(\mathbf{k}\cdot\mathbf{w})^2wb\,db\,d\epsilon, \quad (5.4.79)$$

where $\mathbf{D}$ is $\nabla_1 \ln T$ or $\nabla_1\mathbf{u}\cdot\mathbf{W}_2$, and E is $(\nabla_1 \ln T)\mathbf{W}_2$ or $\nabla_1\mathbf{u}$. The integrals $I_i(i = 1,2,3)$ have been defined in such a way that the vector $\mathbf{D}$ and tensor E are independent of the angles of $\mathbf{k}$. Since the angle between $\mathbf{k}$ and $\mathbf{w}$ is restricted to be less than $\pi/2$, we choose the polar axis of $\mathbf{k}$ to be parallel to $\mathbf{w}$, and define the colatitude ϕ, and azimuth ϵ, so that

$$\mathbf{k} = \mathbf{i}\sin\phi\cos\epsilon + \mathbf{j}\sin\phi\sin\epsilon + \mathbf{h}\cos\phi, \quad (5.4.80)$$

where $\mathbf{i}$, $\mathbf{j}$, $\mathbf{h}$ are the unit vectors in a Cartesian system. The radius b of the cylindrical polar coordinates (z,b,ϵ) is related to ϕ by $b = \sigma\sin\phi$, so that

$$b\,db\,d\epsilon = \sigma^2\sin\phi\cos\phi\,d\phi\,d\epsilon. \quad (5.4.81)$$

The limits of integration for the integrals I_i are $0 \leqslant \phi \leqslant \frac{\pi}{2}$, $0 \leqslant \epsilon \leqslant 2\pi$. They are most easily evaluated by first integrating over ϵ, which makes use of the symmetries. Thus,

$$\begin{aligned} I_1 &= \sigma^2 w\int_0^{2\pi} d\epsilon \int_0^{\pi/2} d\phi\sin\phi\cos\phi \\ &\qquad \times (D_1\sin\phi\cos\epsilon + D_2\sin\phi\sin\epsilon + D_3\cos\phi) \\ &= 2\pi\sigma^2 w\int_0^{\pi/2} d\phi\sin\phi\cos^2\phi\, D_3 \\ &= \frac{2\pi\sigma^2}{3}\mathbf{w}\cdot\mathbf{D}, \end{aligned} \quad (5.4.82)$$

where we have used the fact that $wD_3 = w\mathbf{h}\cdot\mathbf{D} = \mathbf{w}\cdot\mathbf{D}$. I_3 is an integral of similar type. Since $\mathbf{k}\cdot\mathbf{w} = w\cos\phi$,

$$
\begin{aligned}
I_3 &= \sigma^2 w^3 \int_0^{2\pi} d\epsilon \int_0^{\pi/2} d\phi \sin\phi\cos^3\phi \\
&\qquad \times (D_1 \sin\phi\cos\epsilon + D_2\sin\phi\sin\epsilon + D_3\cos\phi) \\
&= 2\pi\sigma^2 w^3 \int_0^{\pi/2} d\phi \sin\phi \cos^4\phi \, D_3 \\
&= \frac{2\pi\sigma^2}{5} w^2 \mathbf{w}\cdot\mathbf{D}. \qquad (5.4.83)
\end{aligned}
$$

I_2 is a little more complicated because it involves the doubly contracted product $\mathbf{k}\cdot\mathbf{E}\cdot\mathbf{k}$. Using again the fact that the integrals over ϵ cover a full cycle, we find that the off-diagonal elements of this product vanish. Thus,

$$
\begin{aligned}
I_2 &= \pi\sigma^2 w^2 \int_0^{\pi/2} d\phi \sin\phi \cos^2\phi([E_{11}+E_{22}]\sin^2\phi + 2E_{33}\cos^2\phi) \\
&= \pi\sigma^2 w^2 \int_0^1 dx x^2([E_{11}+E_{22}][1-x^2] + 2E_{33}x^2) \\
&= \frac{\pi\sigma^2 w^2}{15}(2[E_{11}+E_{22}] + 6E_{33}) \\
&= \frac{2\pi\sigma^2 w^2}{15}([E_{11}+E_{22}+E_{33}] + 2E_{33}) \\
&= \frac{2\pi\sigma^2}{15}(2\mathbf{ww} + w^2\mathbf{I}):\mathbf{E}. \qquad (5.4.84)
\end{aligned}
$$

Substitution of equations (5.4.76)–(5.4.84) in equation (5.4.74) now yields

$$
\begin{aligned}
J_2^{(1)} + J_3^{(1)} &= \frac{2\pi\rho\sigma^3 g(\sigma)}{15\pi^{3/2}}\left(\frac{2kT}{m}\right)^{1/2} \bar{f}_0^{(1)}(1)\,\nabla_1 \ln T \\
&\quad \cdot \int e^{-W_2^2}\left\{5\left[\left(\frac{\partial \ln g(\sigma)}{\partial \ln T}\right)_p - 2\alpha T - 3 + 4W_2^2\right]\mathbf{w}\right. \\
&\qquad \left. - 4(2\mathbf{ww} + w^2\mathbf{I})\cdot\mathbf{W}_2 + w^2\mathbf{w}\right\} d\mathbf{W}_2 \\
&\quad + \frac{4\pi\rho\sigma^3 g(\sigma)}{15\pi^{3/2}} \bar{f}_0^{(1)}(1)\,\nabla_1\mathbf{u} : \int e^{-W_2^2}[10\mathbf{w}\mathbf{W}_2 - (2\mathbf{ww} + w^2\mathbf{I})]\, d\mathbf{W}_2. \qquad (5.4.85)
\end{aligned}
$$

The integration over $\mathbf{W}_2$ is easily performed after $\mathbf{w}$ is replaced by $\mathbf{W}_2 - \mathbf{W}_1$ everywhere in equation (5.4.85). If the perturbation function $\Phi^{(1)}$, equation (5.4.11), is written in the form

$$\Phi^{(1)} = -(\mathbf{A}^{(1)} \cdot \nabla_1 \ln T + \mathbf{B}^{(1)}:\nabla_1 \mathbf{u}), \tag{5.4.86}$$

then linear integral equations for $\mathbf{A}^{(1)}$ and $\mathbf{B}^{(1)}$ may be obtained after the substitution of equations (5.4.43) and (5.4.85) in equation (5.4.5) by equating the coefficients of $\nabla_1 \ln T$ and $\nabla_1 \mathbf{u}$. In this way we obtain

$$\frac{1}{m}\int \bar{f}_0^{(1)}(1)\bar{f}_0^{(1)}(2)[\mathbf{A}^{(1)*}(1) + \mathbf{A}^{(1)*}(2) - \mathbf{A}^{(1)}(1) - \mathbf{A}^{(1)}(2)]p_{12}b\, db\, d\epsilon\, d\mathbf{p}_2 + \frac{kT\zeta_S}{g(\sigma)}\nabla_{p_1} \cdot [\bar{f}_0^{(1)}(1)\, \nabla_{p_1}\mathbf{A}^{(1)}(1)] = \mathbf{K}, \tag{5.4.87}$$

$$\frac{1}{m}\int \bar{f}_0^{(1)}(1)\bar{f}_0^{(1)}(2)[\mathbf{B}^{(1)*}(1) + \mathbf{B}^{(1)*}(2) - \mathbf{B}^{(1)}(1) - \mathbf{B}^{(1)}(2)]p_{12}b\, db\, d\epsilon\, d\mathbf{p}_2 + \frac{kT\zeta_S}{g(\sigma)}\nabla_{p_1} \cdot [\bar{f}_0^{(1)}(1)\, \nabla_{p_1}\mathbf{B}^{(1)}(1)] = \mathbf{L}. \tag{5.4.88}$$

It is left to the reader to verify that $\mathbf{K}$ and $\mathbf{L}$ are given by

$$\mathbf{K} = \bar{f}_0^{(1)}(1)\left(\frac{2kT}{m}\right)^{1/2}\left\{\frac{1}{g(\sigma)}(\tfrac{3}{2} + \alpha T - W_1^2)\mathbf{W}_1 + \left(\frac{2\pi\rho\sigma^3}{15}\right)\left[-\tfrac{5}{2} + 10\alpha T - 5\left(\frac{\partial \ln g(\sigma)}{\partial \ln T}\right)_p - 3W_1^2\right]\mathbf{W}_1\right\}, \tag{5.4.89}$$

$$\mathbf{L} = -\bar{f}_0^{(1)}(1)\left\{\frac{2\mathbf{b}}{g(\sigma)} - \left(\frac{4\pi\rho\sigma^3}{3}\right)[\tfrac{1}{3}(\tfrac{3}{2} - W_1^2)\mathbf{1} - \tfrac{2}{5}\,\mathbf{b}]\right\}\cdot \tag{5.4.90}$$

The reader will observe that equations (5.4.87) and (5.4.88) are inhomogeneous integral equations, but they are not Fredholm equations of either the first or the second kind. However, in the limit $\zeta_S \to 0$, these equations do become Fredholm integral equations. Consider a Fredholm equation (23)

$$\lambda \int K(x,y)G(y)\, dy = S(x), \tag{5.4.91}$$

where $K(x,y)$, the kernel of the integral equation, and $S(x)$, are given functions, λ is a constant and $G(y)$ is the unknown function to be determined. If $S(x)$ vanishes, equation (5.4.91) becomes a homogeneous integral equation, and the solutions to this homogeneous equation will be denoted $G_h(y)$. Then, by a theorem due to Fredholm, the inhomogeneous equation (5.4.91) has solutions if, and only if, the solutions of the homogeneous equation are orthogonal to the inhomogeneity, i.e.,

$$\int G_h(y)S(y)\,dy = 0. \tag{5.4.92}$$

In the limit $\zeta_S \to 0$, when the singlet equation reduces to an equation describing a rigid sphere fluid, equations (5.4.87) and (5.4.88) become Fredholm equations subject to the orthogonality condition (5.4.92). For a rigid sphere fluid there are five invariants of the motion: the energy, number density (mass), and the three components of linear momentum. Each of these is a solution of the homogeneous equation obtained by setting the right-hand side of equations (5.4.87) or (5.4.88) equal to zero. Therefore,

$$\lim_{\zeta_S \to 0} \left\{ \begin{aligned} &\int \mathbf{M}\,d\mathbf{p}_1 = 0 \\ &\int \mathbf{M} \cdot \left[\frac{\mathbf{p}_1}{m} - \mathbf{u}\right] d\mathbf{p}_1 = 0 \\ &\int \mathbf{M} \cdot \left[\frac{\mathbf{p}_1}{m} - \mathbf{u}\right]^2 d\mathbf{p}_1 = 0, \end{aligned} \right. \tag{5.4.93}$$
$$\mathbf{M} = \mathbf{K}, \mathbf{L}.$$

Also, in the limit of a rigid sphere fluid,

$$\lim_{\zeta_S \to 0} \left[\frac{\partial \ln g(\sigma)}{\partial \ln T}\right]_\rho = 0 \tag{5.4.94}$$

and

$$\lim_{\zeta_S \to 0} \alpha = \frac{1}{T}. \tag{5.4.95}$$

We leave it as an exercise for the reader to show that the conditions (5.4.93) are indeed satisfied in the limit $\zeta_S \to 0$. Simple symmetry arguments and elementary quadrature suffice to verify (5.4.93) in this limit.

In the case that $\zeta_S \neq 0$ the orthogonality conditions do not apply. This is compatible with the fact that for a fluid with soft forces as well as rigid cores, equations (5.4.94) and (5.4.95) do not apply either.

To complete the perturbation solution along the lines discussed above we must evaluate $\mathbf{A}^{(1)}$ and $\mathbf{B}^{(1)}$, and thereby the perturbation function

$\Phi^{(1)}$. The procedure we shall follow is to expand $\mathbf{A}^{(1)}$ and $\mathbf{B}^{(1)}$ as finite sums of Sonine polynomials in the square of the reduced velocity, $\mathbf{W}_1$. The coefficients in this expansion are then determined by using a procedure introduced by Curtiss and Hirschfelder.

The orthonormalization condition, (5.4.49), can be more explicitly displayed as

$$\int_0^\infty x^n e^{-x} S_n^{(m)}(x) S_n^{(l)}(x)\, dx = \frac{\Gamma(m+n+1)}{m!}\,\delta_{ml}. \tag{5.4.96}$$

The reader will readily recognize the convenient properties of the polynomials after examination of the following special cases of equation (5.4.96):

$$\begin{aligned}\int \bar{f}_0^{(1)}(W^2) S_{1/2}^{(m)}(W^2)\, d\mathbf{W} &= \rho\left(\frac{m}{2kT}\right)^{3/2} \delta_{m0},\\ \int \bar{f}_0^{(1)}(W^2) W^2 S_{3/2}^{(m)}(W^2)\, d\mathbf{W} &= \frac{3\rho}{2}\left(\frac{m}{2kT}\right)^{3/2} \delta_{m0},\\ \int \bar{f}_0^{(1)}(W^2) W^4 S_{5/2}^{(m)}(W^2)\, d\mathbf{W} &= \frac{15\rho}{4}\left(\frac{m}{2kT}\right)^{3/2} \delta_{m0}.\end{aligned} \tag{5.4.97}$$

These conditions, which are obviously closely related to the conservation of mass, momentum, and energy, will be used later to aid in the selection of a suitable orthonormal set of functions in which to expand the perturbation function.

The general problem of obtaining a series solution of a finite number of terms to the integral equations may be discussed in terms of a variational principle (22). The integral equations (5.4.87) and (5.4.88) are of the form

$$\begin{aligned}F(\mathbf{W}_1) = \frac{1}{m}\int &[\mathscr{F}^*(1) + \mathscr{F}^*(2) - \mathscr{F}(1) - \mathscr{F}(2)]\\ &\times \bar{f}_0^{(1)}(1)\bar{f}_0^{(1)}(2) p_{12} b\, db\, d\epsilon\, d\mathbf{W}_2\\ &+ \frac{kT\zeta_S}{g(\sigma)} \nabla_{p_1}\cdot[\bar{f}_0^{(1)}(1)\,\nabla_{p_1}\mathscr{F}(1)].\end{aligned} \tag{5.4.98}$$

Let $\{M_i(j) \equiv M_i(W_j)\}$ be a set of functions which satisfy the equation

$$\int F(\mathbf{W}_1) M_i(1)\, d\mathbf{W}_1 = \{M_i(1), M_i(1) + M_i(2)\}, \tag{5.4.99}$$

where the operator $\langle\!(\cdots,\cdots)\!\rangle$ is defined by

$$\langle\!(M_i(1),M_i(2))\!\rangle = \frac{1}{m}\int M_i(1)(M_i{}^*(2) - M_i(2)) \times \bar{f}_0^{(1)}(1)\bar{f}_0^{(1)}(2)p_{12}\, bdbd\epsilon d\mathbf{W}_1\, d\mathbf{W}_2 + \frac{kT\zeta_S}{g(\sigma)}\int M_i(1)\,\nabla_{p_1}\cdot[\bar{f}_0^{(1)}(1)\,\nabla_{p_1}M_i(1)]\,d\mathbf{W}_1. \quad (5.4.100)$$

By expressing the collision term in equation (5.4.100) in terms of the inverse collision variables, the equation can be put into the form

$$\langle\!(M_i(1),M_i(2))\!\rangle = -\frac{1}{2m}\int (M_i{}^*(1) - M_i(1))(M_i{}^*(2) - M_i(2)) \times \bar{f}_0^{(1)}(1)\bar{f}_0^{(1)}(2)p_{12}\, bdbd\epsilon d\mathbf{W}_1\, d\mathbf{W}_2 + \frac{kT\zeta_S}{2g(\sigma)}\left\{\int M_i(1)\,\nabla_{p_1}\cdot[\bar{f}_0^{(1)}(1)\,\nabla_{p_1}M_i(1)]\,d\mathbf{W}_1 + \int M_i(2)\,\nabla_{p_2}\cdot[\bar{f}_0^{(1)}(2)\,\nabla_{p_2}M_i(2)]\,d\mathbf{W}_2\right\}. \quad (5.4.101)$$

Hence, the operator $\langle\!(\cdots,\cdots)\!\rangle$ is symmetric:

$$\langle\!(M_i(1),M_i(2))\!\rangle = \langle\!(M_i(2),M_i(1))\!\rangle. \quad (5.4.102)$$

Consider now the definition of a new operator

$$\{M_i,M_j\} \equiv \langle\!(M_i(1) + M_i(2),\, M_j(1) + M_j(2))\!\rangle. \quad (5.4.103)$$

It follows that

$$\{M_i,M_i\} \leqslant 0, \quad (5.4.104)$$

since in this case the collision integral is negative definite, and the Fokker-Planck operators are also, as may be shown by partial integration. It can easily be shown that $\{M_i,M_i\}$ vanishes if, and only if, M_i is a linear combination of the summational invariants. The only such sum which satisfies the auxiliary conditions (5.4.8) is identically zero. Hence $\{M_i,M_i\}$ vanishes if, and only if, $M_i(j)$ is identically zero.

We now introduce a set of trial functions $\{m_i(j)\}$ which contain as many adjustable parameters as desired. The functions $\{m_i(j)\}$ are defined to satisfy the equations

$$\int F(\mathbf{W}_1)m_i(1)\,d\mathbf{W}_1 = \big(m_i(1),\, m_i(1) + m_i(2)\big), \qquad (5.4.105)$$

which are also satisfied by the $\{M_i(j)\}$. However, since the $\{M_i(j)\}$, as exact solutions of the integral equations, also satisfy equations (5.4.98), the $\{m_i(j)\}$ may differ from the $\{M_i(j)\}$ by functions which vanish upon integration. Multiplying equation (5.4.98) with $\mathscr{F} \equiv M_i$, by $m_i(1)$, and integrating over $\mathbf{W}_1$ yields the relation

$$\int F(\mathbf{W}_1)m_i(1)\,d\mathbf{W}_1 = \big(m_i(1),\, M_i(1) + M_i(2)\big). \qquad (5.4.106)$$

The right-hand sides of equations (5.4.105) and (5.4.106) are equal, and use of the symmetry properties of the integrals leads to

$$\{m_i,M_i\} = \{m_i,m_i\}. \qquad (5.4.107)$$

From equations (5.4.104) and (5.4.107) it follows that

$$\{M_i - m_i,\, M_i - m_i\} \leqslant 0, \qquad (5.4.108)$$

and

$$\{m_i,m_i\} \geqslant \{M_i,M_i\}. \qquad (5.4.109)$$

Thus, approximations m_i to the exact solutions M_i may be obtained by minimizing $\{m_i,m_i\}$ with respect to the parameters contained in m_i. This is equivalent to

$$2\delta \int F(\mathbf{W}_1)m(1)\,d\mathbf{W}_1 = \delta\{m,m\} = 0. \qquad (5.4.110)$$

Hereafter, the subscripts on m are suppressed.

In order to use the variational principle (5.4.110), we assume that m is a finite sum of known functions $S_k(\mathbf{W}_j)$:

$$m = \sum_{k=1}^{n} a_k S_k, \qquad (5.4.111)$$

the a_k being the adjustable parameters previously referred to. Now define

$$F_k = \int F(\mathbf{W}_1) S_k(\mathbf{W}_1)\, d\mathbf{W}_1 \tag{5.4.112}$$

and

$$\omega = 2 \sum_{k=1}^{n} a_k F_k - \sum_{k,k'=1}^{n} \sum a_k a_{k'} \{S_k, S_{k'}\}. \tag{5.4.113}$$

From the definitions of $(\cdots, \cdots)$ and $\{\cdots, \cdots\}$ it follows that $\omega = 0$. The formal statement of the variational problem is, therefore,

$$\begin{aligned} \delta\{m,m\} &= 0, \\ \delta \int F(\mathbf{W}_1) m(1)\, d\mathbf{W}_1 &= 0, \\ \omega &= 0. \end{aligned} \tag{5.4.114}$$

It is left as an exercise to the reader to show that the solution to equation (5.4.114) is

$$2F_k = \sum_{k'=1}^{n} a_{k'} \{S_k, S_{k'}\}. \tag{5.4.115}$$

The unique solution to the problem of determining the a_k is now obtained by inverting the matrix $\mathscr{S} = \|\{S_k, S_{k'}\}\|$; then

$$a_k = 2 \sum_{k'=1}^{n} \mathscr{S}_{kk'}^{-1} F_{k'}. \tag{5.4.116}$$

We now proceed with the solution of (5.4.89) and (5.4.90). Since $\mathbf{W}_i$ is the only vector on which $\mathbf{K}$ and $\mathbf{L}$ depend it follows that $\mathbf{A}$ is a scalar multiple of $\mathbf{W}$,

$$\mathbf{A}^{(1)}(i) = \mathbf{W}_i A^{(1)}(|\mathbf{W}_i|), \tag{5.4.117}$$

and that $\mathbf{B}$ is the sum of scalar multiples of $\mathbf{WW}$ and $\mathbf{I}$, the only tensors that can be formed from the vector $\mathbf{W}$. It is convenient to write this sum in the form

$$\begin{aligned} \mathbf{B}^{(1)}(i) &= \mathbf{B}^{(1,1)}(i) + \mathbf{B}^{(1,2)}(i), \\ \mathbf{B}^{(1,1)}(i) &= (\mathbf{W}_i \mathbf{W}_i - \tfrac{1}{3} W_i^2 \mathbf{I}) B^{(1,1)}(W_i), \\ \mathbf{B}^{(1,2)}(i) &= B^{(1,2)}(W_i) \mathbf{I}. \end{aligned} \tag{5.4.118}$$

As variational trial functions approximating the functions $A^{(1)}(W_i)$,

$B^{(1,1)}(W_i)$ and $B^{(1,2)}(W_i)$ we take the finite sums

$$A^{(1)}(i) = \sum_{m=0}^{n} a_m S_{3/2}^{(m)}(W_i^2)$$

$$B^{(1,1)}(i) = \sum_{m=0}^{n} b_m^{(1)} S_{5/2}^{(m)}(W_i^2)$$

$$B^{(1,2)}(i) = \sum_{m=0}^{n} b_m^{(2)} S_{1/2}^{(m)}(W_i^2), \tag{5.4.119}$$

where the $S_k^{(m)}$ are the Sonine polynomials defined in equation (5.4.48). The complete functions of the three series expansions are $\mathbf{W}_i S_{3/2}^{(m)}$, $(\mathbf{W}_i\mathbf{W}_i - \frac{1}{3}W_i^2\mathbf{I})S_{5/2}^{(m)}$ and $S_{1/2}^{(m)}\mathbf{I}$, and are associated with the Kihara functions $\psi_l^{(m)}$ given in equation (6.5.11) (20). If $\mathbf{h}$ is the unit vector along the polar axis to which the Legendre polynomials are referred,

$$\mathbf{A}^{(1)} \cdot \mathbf{h} = \sum_{m=0}^{n} a_m \psi_1^{(m)}$$

$$\mathbf{B}^{(1,1)} : \mathbf{hh} = \sum_{m=0}^{n} b_m^{(1)} \psi_2^{(m)}$$

$$\mathbf{B}^{(1,2)} : \mathbf{hh} = \sum_{m=0}^{n} b_m^{(2)} \psi_0^{(m)}. \tag{5.4.120}$$

The Kihara functions are eigenfunctions of the Fokker-Planck operator:

$$\nabla_{p_1} \cdot [\bar{f}_0^{(1)}(1)\, \nabla_{p_1} \psi_n^{(m)}] = -(2m+n)\psi_n^{(m)} \frac{\bar{f}_0^{(1)}(1)}{mkT}, \tag{5.4.121}$$

so that

$$\nabla_{p_1} \cdot [\bar{f}_0^{(1)}(1)\, \nabla_{p_1} \mathbf{A}^{(1)}] = -\sum_{j=0}^{n} (2j+1) a_j \mathbf{W}_1 S_{3/2}^{(j)}(W_1^2) \frac{\bar{f}_0^{(1)}(1)}{mkT},$$

$$\nabla_{p_1} \cdot [\bar{f}_0^{(1)}(1)\, \nabla_{p_1} \mathbf{B}^{(1,1)}] = -\sum_{j=0}^{n} 2(j+1) b_j^{(1)} \times (\mathbf{W}_1\mathbf{W}_1 - \tfrac{1}{3}W_1^2)\mathbf{I} S_{5/2}^{(j)}(W_1^2) \frac{\bar{f}_0^{(1)}(1)}{mkT},$$

$$\nabla_{p_1} \cdot [\bar{f}_0^{(1)}(1)\, \nabla_{p_1} \mathbf{B}^{(1,2)}] = -\sum_{j=0}^{n} 2j b_j^{(2)} \mathbf{I} S_{1/2}^{(j)}(W_1^2) \frac{\bar{f}_0^{(1)}(1)}{mkT}. \tag{5.4.122}$$

In calculating the coefficients a_j, $b_j^{(1)}$, $b_j^{(2)}$, we shall terminate the series in each case at the first non-vanishing term, and accept the resulting perturbation as one which yields a good approximation to the results obtained asymptotically from much longer series. Indeed, it can be shown by direct calculation, though we shall not do so, that the terms neglected contribute at most a few per cent to the transport coefficients (21).

Insertion of equations (5.4.117)–(5.4.119) into the auxiliary conditions for the perturbation function shows that

$$a_0 = 0,$$
$$b_0^{(2)} = 0,$$
$$b_1^{(2)} = 0. \tag{5.4.123}$$

It also follows that, since the coefficient of **I** in equation (5.4.90) is $S_{1/2}^{(1)}$,

$$b_j^{(2)} = 0, \quad j > 2, \tag{5.4.124}$$

however long the initial series is.

In order to determine a_1, equation (5.4.89) is first rewritten in the form

$$\mathbf{K} = \bar{f}_0^{(1)}(1)\left(\frac{2kT}{m}\right)^{1/2}\left\{\left(\frac{1}{g(\sigma)} + \frac{2\pi\rho\sigma^3}{5}\right)S_{3/2}^{(1)}\mathbf{W}_1 + \left[\frac{\alpha T - 1}{g(\sigma)} + \left(\frac{2\pi\rho\sigma^3}{3}\right)(2\alpha T - 1) - \left(\frac{\partial \ln g(\sigma)}{\partial \ln T}\right)_p\right]S_{3/2}^{(0)}\mathbf{W}_1\right\}. \tag{5.4.125}$$

Both sides of equation (5.4.87) are now multiplied by $S_{3/2}^{(1)}\mathbf{W}_1$ and integrated over $\mathbf{W}_1$. Using the orthogonality relation (5.4.96) and the eigenvalue equations (5.4.122), it is found that

$$\int \mathbf{K}\, S_{3/2}^{(1)}(W_1^2)\mathbf{W}_1\, d\mathbf{W}_1 = \frac{5\rho}{8m^2kT}\left(\frac{1}{g(\sigma)} + \frac{2\pi\rho\sigma^3}{5}\right)\mathbf{I} \tag{5.4.126}$$

and

$$\int S_{3/2}^{(1)}(W_1^2)\mathbf{W}_1\,\nabla_{p_1}\cdot(\bar{f}_0^{(1)}(1)\,\nabla_{p_1}S_{3/2}^{(1)}(W_1^2)\mathbf{W}_1)\,d\mathbf{W}_1 = -\frac{15\rho}{2(2mkT)^{5/2}}\,\mathbf{I}. \tag{5.4.127}$$

The collision integral of equation (5.4.87) with $\mathbf{A}^{(1)} = a_1 S_{3/2}^{(1)}\mathbf{W}$ is evaluated after straightforward but lengthy integrations by noting that, from equation (5.4.48),

$$S_{3/2}^{(1)}(W_1^2) = \tfrac{5}{2} - W_1^2, \tag{5.4.128}$$

so that, using equation (5.4.58), we obtain

$$\begin{aligned}[S_{3/2}^{(1)}(W_1^{*2})\mathbf{W}_1^* + S_{3/2}^{(1)}(W_2^{*2})\mathbf{W}_2^* - S_{3/2}^{(1)}(W_1^2)\mathbf{W}_1 - S_{3/2}^{(1)}(W_2^2)\mathbf{W}_2] \\ = 2(\mathbf{w}\cdot\mathbf{k})[\mathbf{w}(\mathbf{W}\cdot\mathbf{k}) - \mathbf{k}\mathbf{w}\mathbf{W}:(2\mathbf{k}\mathbf{k} - \mathbf{I})].\end{aligned} \tag{5.4.129}$$

It should be noted that both terms of equation (5.4.129) contain products of three (reduced) velocities. The constant terms in equation (5.4.128) vanish in equation (5.4.129) because $\mathbf{W}$ is a summational invariant. The integral may be symmetrized using the inverse collision variables, and the invariance* under interchange of labels on the molecules, to

$$\begin{aligned}\int \bar{f}_0^{(1)}(1)\bar{f}_0^{(1)}(2)B(1)[A^*(1) + A^*(2) - A(1) - A(2)]p_{12}b\,db\,d\epsilon\,d\mathbf{p}_1\,d\mathbf{p}_2 \\ = -\frac{1}{4}\int \bar{f}_0^{(1)}(1)\bar{f}_0^{(1)}(2)[B^*(1) + B^*(2) - B(1) - B(2)] \\ \times [A^*(1) + A^*(2) - A(1) - A(2)]p_{12}b\,db\,d\epsilon\,d\mathbf{p}_1\,d\mathbf{p}_2,\end{aligned} \tag{5.4.130}$$

for any functions A, B of the velocities. In this way we obtain

$$\begin{aligned}\int \bar{f}_0^{(1)}(1)\bar{f}_0^{(1)}(2)S_{3/2}^{(1)}(W_1^2)\mathbf{W}_1 \\ \times \left[\sum_{i=1,2}(S_{3/2}^{(1)}(W_i^{*2})\mathbf{W}_i^* - S_{3/2}^{(1)}(W_i^2)\mathbf{W}_i)\right] p_{12}b\,db\,d\epsilon\,d\mathbf{p}_2\,d\mathbf{W}_1 \\ = \frac{\rho^2}{2\pi^3 mkT}\int e^{-2W^2-w^2/2}\{(5 - \tfrac{1}{2}W^2 - \tfrac{1}{2}w^2) \\ \times (\mathbf{w}\mathbf{W}\mathbf{W}\cdot\mathbf{k} - \mathbf{k}\mathbf{W}\mathbf{W}\mathbf{w}:[2\mathbf{k}\mathbf{k} - \mathbf{I}]) + \mathbf{k}\mathbf{w}\mathbf{w}\cdot\mathbf{W}\mathbf{W}\mathbf{w}:(2\mathbf{k}\mathbf{k} - \mathbf{I}) \\ - \mathbf{w}\mathbf{w}\mathbf{w}\cdot\mathbf{W}\mathbf{W}\cdot\mathbf{k}\}(\mathbf{w}\cdot\mathbf{k})wb\,db\,d\epsilon\,d\mathbf{w}\,d\mathbf{W} = I,\end{aligned} \tag{5.4.131}$$

where we have used the fact that the Jacobian of the transformation $(\mathbf{W}_1,\mathbf{W}_2) \rightarrow (\mathbf{w},\mathbf{W})$ is unity. Integrations over $\mathbf{W}$, the collision hemisphere, and finally over $\mathbf{w}$, lead to

$$I = -\frac{2}{3}\frac{\rho^2\sigma^2(2\pi)^{1/2}}{mkT} = -\frac{4m\rho^2}{3(2mkT)^{3/2}}\,\Omega^{(2,2)}. \tag{5.4.132}$$

* The collision integral in equation (5.4.87) is even in $\mathbf{k}$, and hence is invariant under an interchange of the molecules.

Substitution of equations (5.4.126), (5.4.127), and (5.4.132) in equation (5.4.87) now yields

$$a_1 = -\frac{15}{4}\left(\frac{2kT}{m}\right)^{1/2} \frac{\left[\dfrac{1}{\rho g(\sigma)} + \dfrac{2\pi\sigma^3}{5}\right]}{\left[4\Omega^{(2,2)} + \dfrac{45\zeta_S}{4\rho m g(\sigma)}\right]}, \qquad (5.4.133)$$

where $\Omega^{(2,2)}$ is a reduced collision cross section, given by equation (5.4.64).

The tensor $\mathbf{L}$ [equation (5.4.90)] may be separated into parts $\mathbf{L}^{(1)}$ and $\mathbf{L}^{(2)}$ involving $\mathbf{b}$ and $\mathbf{I}$, respectively, corresponding to the separation of $\mathbf{B}^{(1)}$ in equation (5.4.118). Equation (5.4.88) is now solved for $B^{(1,1)}$ (we have already shown that $B^{(1,2)}$ is zero) with the series expansion (5.4.119) consisting of the single term $n = 0$. Equation (5.4.118) is multiplied by $\mathbf{b}_1$ and integrated over $\mathbf{W}_1$. Using the results

$$\int \mathbf{L}^{(1)}:\mathbf{b}_1 \, d\mathbf{W}_1 = -\frac{5\rho}{(2mkT)^{3/2}}\left(\frac{1}{g(\sigma)} + \frac{4\pi\rho\sigma^3}{15}\right), \qquad (5.4.134)$$

$$\int \mathbf{b}_1:\nabla_{p_1}\cdot\left(\bar{f}_0^{(1)}(1)\,\nabla_{p_1}\mathbf{b}_1\right) d\mathbf{W}_1 = -\frac{10\rho}{(2mkT)^{5/2}}, \qquad (5.4.135)$$

$$\sum_{i=1,2}(\mathbf{b}_i^* - \mathbf{b}_i) = -\mathbf{k}\cdot\mathbf{w}[\mathbf{wk} + \mathbf{kw} - 2\mathbf{kk}(\mathbf{k}\cdot\mathbf{w})], \qquad (5.4.136)$$

$$\mathbf{b}_1:\sum_{i=1,2}(\mathbf{b}_i^* - \mathbf{b}_i) = [-2\mathbf{W}\cdot\mathbf{wW}\cdot\mathbf{kw}\cdot\mathbf{k} + 2(\mathbf{W}\cdot\mathbf{k})^2(\mathbf{w}\cdot\mathbf{k})^2 - \tfrac{1}{2}w^2(\mathbf{w}\cdot\mathbf{k})^2 + \tfrac{1}{2}(\mathbf{w}\cdot\mathbf{k})^4] + \text{terms odd in } \mathbf{W}, \qquad (5.4.137)$$

and

$$\int \bar{f}_0^{(1)}(1)\bar{f}_0^{(1)}(2)\mathbf{b}_1:\sum_{i=1,2}(\mathbf{b}_i^* - \mathbf{b}_i)p_{12}b\,db\,d\epsilon\,d\mathbf{p}_2\,d\mathbf{W}_1 = -\frac{4\rho^2\Omega^{(2,2)}}{(2mkT)^{3/2}}, \qquad (5.4.138)$$

we obtain

$$b_0^{(1)} = 5\,\frac{\left[\dfrac{1}{\rho g(\sigma)} + \dfrac{4\pi\sigma^3}{15}\right]}{\left[4\Omega^{(2,2)} + \dfrac{5\zeta_S}{\rho m g(\sigma)}\right]}. \qquad (5.4.139)$$

We are, therefore, led finally to the perturbed singlet distribution function by substituting equations (5.4.119), (5.4.133) and (5.4.139) in equations (5.4.11) and (5.4.86):

$$f^{(1)}(1) = \bar{f}_0^{(1)}(1)\left[1 + \frac{15}{4}\left(\frac{2kT}{m}\right)^{1/2} \frac{\left[\dfrac{1}{\rho g(\sigma)} + \dfrac{2\pi\sigma^3}{5}\right]}{\left[4\Omega^{(2,2)} + \dfrac{45\zeta_S}{4\rho m g(\sigma)}\right]}(\tfrac{5}{2} - W_1^2)\mathbf{W}_1\right.$$

$$\left.\cdot \nabla_1 \ln T - 5\frac{\left[\dfrac{1}{\rho g(\sigma)} + \dfrac{4\pi\sigma^3}{15}\right]}{\left[4\Omega^{(2,2)} + \dfrac{5\zeta_S}{\rho m g(\sigma)}\right]}(\mathbf{W}_1\mathbf{W}_1 - \tfrac{1}{3}W_1^2\mathbf{1}) : \nabla_1\mathbf{u}\right],$$

$$\bar{f}_0^{(1)}(1) = \rho(2\pi mkT)^{-3/2} \exp\left[-\frac{(\mathbf{p}_1 - m\mathbf{u})^2}{2mkT}\right]. \tag{5.4.140}$$

5.4.D. *The Solution of the Doublet Equation* (16)

The procedure for obtaining the solution of the doublet equation (5.3.109) differs in only minor ways from that used for the singlet equation as described in Sections 5.4.A–C. Most of the details will, therefore, be omitted.

The iterative scheme described in Section 5.4.A is extended in an obvious way to

$$f^{(2)} = \sum_{l=0}^{\infty} \epsilon^l \bar{f}_l^{(2)}$$

$$\mathscr{D}^{(2)} \bar{f}^{(2)} = \frac{1}{\epsilon}[J_1^{(2)} + \zeta_S(\mathscr{A}_1^{(1)} + \mathscr{A}_2^{(1)})\bar{f}^{(2)}] + J_2^{(2)} + J_3^{(2)}. \tag{5.4.141}$$

The first two members of the scheme suffice, as before, to introduce the linear perturbations:

$$0 = J_1^{(2)}[\bar{f}_0^{(3)}] + \zeta_S(\mathscr{A}_1^{(1)}[\bar{f}_0^{(2)}] + \mathscr{A}_2^{(1)}[\bar{f}_0^{(2)}]), \tag{5.4.142}$$

$$\mathscr{D}^{(2)} \bar{f}_0^{(2)} = J_1^{(2)}[\bar{f}_0^{(3)}, \bar{f}_1^{(3)}] + J_2^{(2)}[\bar{f}_0^{(3)}] + J_3^{(2)}[\bar{f}_0^{(3)}]$$
$$+ \zeta_S(\mathscr{A}_1^{(1)}[\bar{f}_0^{(2)}, \bar{f}_1^{(2)}] + \mathscr{A}_2^{(1)}[\bar{f}_0^{(2)}, \bar{f}_1^{(2)}]). \tag{5.4.143}$$

. . .

Inspection of equation (5.4.142) indicates that it is satisfied by the local equilibrium function

$$\bar{f}_0^{(2)} = g_0^{(2)}(\mathbf{R}_1,\mathbf{R}_2)\prod_{i=1,2}\frac{\rho_i}{(2\pi mkT_i)^{3/2}}\exp\left[-\frac{(\mathbf{p}_i - m\mathbf{u}_i)^2}{2mkT_i}\right], \qquad (5.4.144)$$

where ρ_i, $\mathbf{u}_i$, T_i are the local number density, fluid velocity, and temperature at $\mathbf{R}_i$. The notation $J_1^{(2)}[\bar{f}_0^{(3)},\bar{f}_1^{(3)}]$ represents a complex of six terms arising from the extended superposition approximation (5.3.93).

Corresponding to equation (5.4.8), there is one set each of auxiliary conditions for molecules 1 and 2:

$$\rho_i = \frac{1}{N}\int \bar{f}_0^{(2)}\,d\mathbf{p}_1\,d\mathbf{p}_2\,d\mathbf{R}_j,$$

$$\mathbf{u}_i = \frac{1}{N\rho_i m}\int \mathbf{p}_i\bar{f}_0^{(2)}\,d\mathbf{p}_1\,d\mathbf{p}_2\,d\mathbf{R}_j,$$

$$kT_i = \frac{1}{3N\rho_i m}\int (\mathbf{p}_i - m\mathbf{u}_i)^2\bar{f}_0^{(2)}\,d\mathbf{p}_1\,d\mathbf{p}_2\,d\mathbf{R}_j,$$

$$0 = \int \bar{f}_l^{(2)}\,d\mathbf{p}_1\,d\mathbf{p}_2\,d\mathbf{R}_j, \quad l > 0,$$

$$0 = \int (\mathbf{p}_i - m\mathbf{u}_i)\bar{f}_l^{(2)}\,d\mathbf{p}_1\,d\mathbf{p}_2\,d\mathbf{R}_j, \quad l > 0,$$

$$0 = \int (\mathbf{p}_i - m\mathbf{u}_i)^2\bar{f}_l^{(2)}\,d\mathbf{p}_1\,d\mathbf{p}_2\,d\mathbf{R}_j, \quad l > 0,$$

$$i,j = 1,2;\ i \neq j. \qquad (5.4.145)$$

The reader should note that, in the doublet case, the integrations are over the momentum of molecule i, and the *phase* of molecule j. One further condition suffices to specify the perturbation functions uniquely. It is

$$\rho^{(2)} = \rho^{(2)(0)} = \int \bar{f}_0^{(2)}\,d\mathbf{p}_1\,d\mathbf{p}_2,$$

$$\rho^{(2)(l)} = 0,\ l > 0. \qquad (5.4.146)$$

The equations of change of ρ_i, $\mathbf{u}_i$, T_i, which are needed to evaluate the streaming term $\mathscr{D}^{(2)}\bar{f}_0^{(2)}$, are again determined by taking moments of the kinetic equation. The results of this procedure are identical with equations (5.4.28), (5.4.32), and (5.4.38). The treatment of the collision integrals may be understood in the following way. If, for example, $J_i^{(2)}(j)$ is the term of type i ($i = 1,2,3$) in which molecule j ($j = 1,2$), undergoes a rigid core encounter with molecule 3, then $\langle \chi(1) J_i^{(2)}(1) \rangle$ is treated in exactly the same way as $\langle \chi(1) J_i^{(1)}(1) \rangle$ because the momentum of molecule 2 is constant throughout the collision represented by the term. On the other hand, $\langle \chi(1) J_i^{(2)}(2) \rangle = 0$ for all i because these terms may be expressed in the form $\langle \chi(1) \chi'(2) J_i^{(2)}(2) \rangle$, where $\chi'(2)(=1)$ is a constant summational invariant for the collision represented. The equation of change for $\rho^{(2)}$ does not occur in Section 5.4.A. This is obtained by integrating the doublet equation over $\mathbf{p}_1$ and $\mathbf{p}_2$. Then, from equation (5.4.146),

$$\frac{\partial}{\partial t} \rho^{(2)} + \nabla_1 \cdot (\mathbf{u}_1 \rho^{(2)}) + \nabla_2 \cdot (\mathbf{u}_2 \rho^{(2)}) = 0. \tag{5.4.147}$$

The collision integrals $J_2^{(2)}$ and $J_3^{(2)}$ may be written down immediately from equations (5.3.103) and (5.3.25). Inspection of these equations immediately shows that they differ only in that $\bar{f}_0^{(2)}$ factors out in the former case, and $\bar{f}_0^{(1)}$ in the latter case. It follows immediately upon combining equations (5.3.110), (5.4.43), and (5.4.147) that

$$\begin{aligned}
&\mathscr{D}^{(2)} \bar{f}_0^{(2)} - J_2^{(2)}[\bar{f}_0^{(3)}] - J_3^{(2)}[\bar{f}_0^{(3)}] \\
&= \bar{f}_0^{(2)} \sum_{i=1,2} \Bigg[\left\{ 2\mathbf{b}_i - \left(\frac{4\pi\rho\sigma^3}{3} g(\sigma) \right) \left(\tfrac{1}{3}(\tfrac{3}{2} - W_i^2)\mathbf{I} - \tfrac{2}{5}\mathbf{b}_i \right) \right\} : \nabla_i \mathbf{u}_i \\
&\quad - \left(\frac{2kT_i}{m} \right)^{1/2} \Bigg\{ (\tfrac{3}{2} + \alpha T - W_i^2) + \left(\frac{2\pi\rho\sigma^3}{15} g(\sigma) \right) \\
&\quad \times \left(-\tfrac{5}{2} + 10\alpha T - 5 \left(\frac{\partial \ln g(\sigma)}{\partial \ln T} \right)_p - 3W_i^2 \right) \Bigg\} \mathbf{W}_i \cdot \nabla_i \ln T_i \\
&\quad - \left(\frac{2}{mkT} \right)^{1/2} {}^{(2)}\mathbf{G}_i^F \cdot \mathbf{W}_i \Bigg],
\end{aligned} \tag{5.4.148}$$

where $\mathbf{b}_i$ is defined in equation (5.4.43), and

$${}^{(2)}\mathbf{G}_i^F = \mathbf{F}_i^{(2)} - \mathbf{F}_i^* - kT_i \nabla_i \ln g^{(2)}(\mathbf{R}_1, \mathbf{R}_2), \tag{5.4.149}$$

is the net mean force on molecule i when another molecule is at $\mathbf{R}_j$.

The doublet equation is solved for a perturbation $\Phi^{(2)}$ defined by

$$M^{(2)}(i,j) = M_0^{(2)}(i,j)(1 + \Phi^{(2)}(i,j)), \tag{5.4.150}$$

where $M^{(2)}(i,j)$ is the momentum distribution function for molecules i and j. It does not contain the pair correlation function $g^{(2)}(\mathbf{R}_1,\mathbf{R}_2)$, but depends on the coordinates $\mathbf{R}_1$ and $\mathbf{R}_j$ through the local values of ρ, $\mathbf{u}$, and T. The functions $M^{(3)}$ appearing in $J_1^{(2)}$ are now expanded using the extended superposition approximation (5.3.93), (5.4.120), and the definition of the singlet perturbation $\Phi^{(1)}$. For example,

$$M^{(3)}(\mathbf{R}_1,\mathbf{p}_1;\mathbf{R}_2,\mathbf{p}_2{}^*;\mathbf{R}_2,\mathbf{p}_3{}^*)$$
$$= \frac{M^{(2)}(1,2^*)M^{(2)}(1,3^*)M^{(2)}(2^*,3^*)}{M^{(1)}(1)M^{(1)}(2^*)M^{(1)}(3^*)}$$
$$= M_0^{(1)}(1)M_0^{(1)}(2^*)M_0^{(1)}(3^*)(1 + \Phi^{(2)}(1,2^*) + \Phi^{(2)}(1,3^*)$$
$$+ \Phi^{(2)}(2^*,3^*) - \Phi^{(1)}(1) - \Phi^{(1)}(2^*) - \Phi^{(1)}(3^*) + \cdots), \quad (5.4.151)$$

where we have used the fact that

$$M_0^{(2)}(i,j) = M_0^{(1)}(i)M_0^{(1)}(j). \quad (5.4.152)$$

Moreover, we now suppose that $\Phi^{(2)}(i,j)$ is the sum of two similar terms depending on $\mathbf{W}_i$ and $\mathbf{W}_j$ separately,

$$\Phi^{(2)}(i,j) = \Phi^{(2)}(i) + \Phi^{(2)}(j), \quad (5.4.153)$$

and that, as in the singlet case

$$\Phi^{(2)}(i) = -\mathbf{A}^{(2)}(i)\cdot\nabla_i \ln T_i - \mathbf{B}^{(2)}(i){:}\nabla_i\mathbf{u}_i - \mathbf{C}^{(2)}(i)\cdot{}^{(2)}\mathbf{G}_i^F. \quad (5.4.154)$$

By substituting equations (5.4.153) and (5.4.154) in the collision integral $J_1^{(2)}$, and equating coefficients of, for instance, $\nabla_1 \ln T_1$ and $\nabla_1\mathbf{u}_1$, we obtain the equations

$$\frac{1}{m}\int \bar{f}_0^{(1)}(1)\bar{f}_0^{(1)}(3)\{2[\mathbf{A}^{(2)}(1^*) + \mathbf{A}^{(2)}(3^*) - \mathbf{A}^{(2)}(1) - \mathbf{A}^{(2)}(3)]$$
$$- [\mathbf{A}^{(1)}(1^*) + \mathbf{A}^{(1)}(3^*) - \mathbf{A}^{(1)}(1) - \mathbf{A}^{(1)}(3)]\}p_{13}\, b\, db\, d\epsilon\, d\mathbf{p}_3$$
$$+ \frac{\zeta_S k T_1}{g(\sigma)}\nabla_{p_1}\cdot[\bar{f}_0^{(1)}(1)\,\nabla_{p_1}\mathbf{A}^{(2)}(1)] = \mathbf{K}, \quad (5.4.155)$$

$$\frac{1}{m}\int \bar{f}_0^{(1)}(1)\bar{f}_0^{(1)}(3)\{2[\mathbf{B}^{(2)}(1^*) + \mathbf{B}^{(2)}(3^*) - \mathbf{B}^{(2)}(1) - \mathbf{B}^{(2)}(3)]$$
$$- [\mathbf{B}^{(1)}(1^*) + \mathbf{B}^{(1)}(3^*) - \mathbf{B}^{(1)}(1) - \mathbf{B}^{(1)}(3)]\}p_{13}\, b\, db\, d\epsilon\, d\mathbf{p}_3$$
$$+ \frac{\zeta_S k T_1}{g(\sigma)}\nabla_{p_1}\cdot(\bar{f}_0^{(1)}(1)\,\nabla_{p_1}\mathbf{B}^{(2)}(1)) = \mathbf{L}, \quad (5.4.156)$$

where **K** and **L** are given by equations (5.4.89) and (5.4.90). $\mathbf{A}^{(2)}$ and $\mathbf{B}^{(2)}$ are now expanded in series of Sonine polynomials in exactly the same way as for the singlet case:

$$\mathbf{A}^{(2)}(i) = \mathbf{W}_i \sum_{m=0}^{n} A_m S_{3/2}^{(m)}(W_i^2),$$

$$\mathbf{B}^{(2)}(i) = \mathbf{B}^{(2,1)}(i) + \mathbf{B}^{(2,2)}(i),$$

$$\mathbf{B}^{(2,1)}(i) = \mathbf{b}_i \sum_{m=0}^{n} B_m^{(1)} S_{5/2}^{(m)}(W_i^2),$$

$$\mathbf{B}^{(2,2)}(i) = \mathbf{I} \sum_{m=0}^{n} B_m^{(2)} S_{1/2}^{(m)}(W_i^2). \tag{5.4.157}$$

The auxiliary conditions (5.4.145) imply, as with the singlet case,

$$A_0 = 0,$$

$$B_0^{(2)} = B_1^{(2)} = 0, \tag{5.4.158}$$

and we also find

$$B_m^{(2)} = 0,\ m > 2. \tag{5.4.159}$$

We now truncate the series expansion of equation (5.4.157) at the first non-vanishing term in each case. Using the integrations given in equations (5.4.126), (5.4.127), and (5.4.132), together with the form of a_1 [Eq. (5.4.133)], we thus obtain

$$A_1 = -\frac{15}{4}\left(\frac{2kT}{m}\right)^{1/2} \frac{\left(\dfrac{1}{\rho g(\sigma)} + \dfrac{2\pi\sigma^3}{5}\right)}{\left(8\Omega^{(2,2)} + \dfrac{45\zeta_S}{4\rho m g(\sigma)}\right)} \left(1 + \frac{4\Omega^{(2,2)}}{4\Omega^{(2,2)} + \dfrac{45\zeta_S}{4\rho m g(\sigma)}}\right). \tag{5.4.160}$$

Similarly, by using the integrations (5.4.134), (5.4.135), (5.4.138), together with the form of $b_0^{(1)}$ [Eq. (5.4.139)], we obtain

$$B_0^{(1)} = 5\, \frac{\left(\dfrac{1}{\rho g(\sigma)} + \dfrac{4\pi\sigma^3}{15}\right)}{\left(8\Omega^{(2,2)} + \dfrac{5\zeta_S}{\rho m g(\sigma)}\right)} \left(1 + \frac{4\Omega^{(2,2)}}{4\Omega^{(2,2)} + \dfrac{5\zeta_S}{\rho m g(\sigma)}}\right). \tag{5.4.161}$$

An equation for $\mathbf{C}^{(2)}(1)$ is obtained by equating the coefficients of ${}^{(2)}\mathbf{G}_1{}^F$:

$$g(\sigma)^{-1}\bar{f}_0^{(1)}(1)\left(\frac{2}{mkT}\right)^{1/2}\mathbf{W}_1$$
$$= \frac{2}{m}\int \bar{f}_0^{(1)}(1)\bar{f}_0^{(1)}(3)[\mathbf{C}^{(2)}(1^*) + \mathbf{C}^{(2)}(3^*) - \mathbf{C}^{(2)}(1) - \mathbf{C}^{(2)}(3)]$$
$$\times\, p_{13}\, b\, db\, d\epsilon\, d\mathbf{p}_3 + \frac{\zeta_S kT}{g(\sigma)}\nabla_{p_1}\cdot[\bar{f}_0^{(1)}(1)\,\nabla_{p_1}\mathbf{C}^{(2)}(1)]. \qquad (5.4.162)$$

We suppose now that

$$\mathbf{C}^{(2)}(1) = \mathbf{W}_1 \sum_{m=0}^{n} C_m S_{3/2}^{(m)}(W_1^2). \qquad (5.4.163)$$

It will become apparent in Section 6.3.B that the terms $\mathbf{C}^{(2)}(i)\cdot{}^{(2)}\mathbf{G}_i{}^F$ contribute only to the soft-force part of the thermal conductivity, and that, in fact, the term $m = 0$ gives the only non-vanishing contribution. Now, the zeroth term of the series expansion (5.4.163) is a summational invariant. It is left to the reader to verify that the determination of C_0 by the variational method [see Eq. (5.4.116)] is unaffected by the length of the series. It is found that

$$C_0 = -\left(\frac{2m}{kT}\right)^{1/2}\frac{1}{\zeta_S}. \qquad (5.4.164)$$

The final form of the solution of the doublet equation (5.3.109) is, therefore,

$$\bar{f}^{(2)}(1,2) = \bar{f}_0^{(2)}(1,2)\Big[1 - \sum_{i=1,2}\{A_1(\tfrac{5}{2} - W_i^2)\mathbf{W}_i\cdot\nabla_i \ln T_i$$
$$+ B_0^{(1)}\mathbf{b}_i{:}\nabla_i\mathbf{u}_i + C_0\mathbf{W}_i\cdot{}^{(2)}\mathbf{G}_i^F\}\Big], \qquad (5.4.165)$$

where $\bar{f}_0^{(2)}$ is the local equilibrium doublet distribution given in equation (5.4.144), and A_1, $B_0^{(1)}$, and C_0 are given by equations (5.4.160), (5.4.161), and (5.4.164), respectively.

It will be recalled that considerable emphasis was laid upon the mutual consistency of the singlet and doublet equations. In fact, if the doublet equation is integrated over the phase of one molecule, the singlet equation (for the other molecule) is retrieved. As regards the solution, equations (5.4.140) and (5.4.165), however, this is not the case. That is

$$\int \bar{f}^{(2)}(1,2)\, d\Gamma_1(2) \neq \bar{f}^{(1)}(1). \qquad (5.4.166)$$

Nevertheless, it is easily seen that in the limits of vanishing soft forces (the rigid sphere fluid), and of vanishing rigid core (the Fokker-Planck limit),

$$\lim_{\zeta_S\to 0} A_1 = a_1; \qquad \lim_{\sigma\to 0} A_1 = a_1$$
$$\lim_{\zeta_S\to 0} B_0^{(1)} = b_0^{(1)}; \qquad \lim_{\sigma\to 0} B_0^{(1)} = b_0^{(1)}. \tag{5.4.167}$$

The term in the net mean force $C_0\mathbf{W}_i \cdot {}^{(2)}\mathbf{G}_i^F$, which apparently increases indefinitely as $\zeta_S \to 0$, does not in fact do so because the force ${}^{(2)}\mathbf{G}_i^F$ can be shown (at least numerically) to decrease more rapidly in a practical case such as the high temperature limit. Thus, we see that the singlet and doublet solutions are consistent in these limits:

$$\left.\begin{array}{c}\lim\limits_{\zeta_S\to 0}\\ \lim\limits_{\sigma\to 0}\end{array}\right\}\int \bar{f}^{(2)}(1,2)\, d\Gamma_1(2) = \bar{f}^{(1)}(1). \tag{5.4.168}$$

We conclude that the reason for the failure (5.4.166) of consistency (except at the limits) is due to the introduction of the extended superposition approximation (5.4.93) in lieu of some unknown exact relation.

5.4.E. *Evolution in Configuration Space: The Smoluchowski Equation* (26,27)

In order to compute the soft-force contribution to the energy and momentum fluxes in a dense fluid, it is necessary to be able to calculate the pair configurational density*

$$\rho^{(2)} = \rho^{(1)}(1)\rho^{(1)}(2)g^{(2)}(\mathbf{R}_1,\mathbf{R}_2).$$

The perturbations with which we are concerned are gradients of temperature and fluid velocity. Since temperature is a thermodynamic function, it is possible to calculate the effect of a temperature gradient by thermodynamic arguments alone [see Eq. (6.3.80) *et seq.*]. We shall, therefore, be concerned only with velocity gradients in the development of a Smoluchowski equation for $\rho^{(2)}$.

* These quantities, defined for the non-equilibrium state, should not be confused with the equilibrium densities and correlation function, to which they revert in the absence of perturbations.

The equation of change for $\rho^{(2)}$ is obtained by the procedure described in Section 4.4.C. We shall assume that the soft friction coefficient is large enough to ensure the convergence of this procedure. There should be no difficulty if the time dependence of the densities and fluxes is sufficiently small on a miscroscopic scale.

Integration of the doublet equation (5.3.109) over the momenta of both molecules yields the equation of continuity in pair configuration space:

$$\frac{\partial}{\partial t}\rho^{(2)} + \nabla_1 \cdot \mathbf{j}_1^{(2)} + \nabla_2 \cdot \mathbf{j}_2^{(2)} = 0, \qquad (5.4.169)$$

where

$$\mathbf{j}_i^{(2)} = \frac{1}{m}\int \mathbf{p}_i \bar{f}^{(2)}(1,2)\, d\mathbf{p}_1\, d\mathbf{p}_2 \qquad (5.4.170)$$

is the pair flux of molecules at $\mathbf{R}_i$ conditional on the presence of a molecule at $\mathbf{R}_j$, and $\rho^{(2)}$ is defined in equation (5.4.146). No contribution is made by the mean forces, as these depend on coordinates only, and the terms in which they occur vanish after partial integration. The stochastic terms vanish also, as was pointed out in the previous section. The first moments of the doublet equation are obtained by multiplying the equation by $\mathbf{p}_i$ and integrating over the momenta. Denoting the integration by $\langle \cdots \rangle$, we obtain

$$m\frac{\partial}{\partial t}\mathbf{j}_i^{(2)} + \frac{1}{m}\nabla_1 \cdot \langle \mathbf{p}_1\mathbf{p}_i \bar{f}^{(2)}\rangle + \frac{1}{m}\nabla_2 \cdot \langle \mathbf{p}_2\mathbf{p}_i \bar{f}^{(2)}\rangle - \mathbf{F}_i^{(2)}\rho^{(2)}$$
$$= -\zeta_S(\mathbf{j}_i^{(2)} - \rho^{(2)}\mathbf{u}_i) + \langle \mathbf{p}_i(J_2^{(2)} + J_3^{(2)})\rangle. \qquad (5.4.171)$$

From the definition of the temperature,

$$3m\rho^{(2)}kT_i = \int (\mathbf{p}_i - m\mathbf{u}_i)^2 \bar{f}^{(2)}(1,2)\, d\mathbf{p}_1\, d\mathbf{p}_2, \qquad (5.4.172)$$

and the fact that

$$\mathbf{j}_i^{(2)} = \rho^2\mathbf{u}_i + \mathcal{O}(\zeta_S^{-1}) \qquad (5.4.173)$$

to first order in ζ_S^{-1}, it follows that with the neglect terms involving products of the flows

$$\langle \mathbf{p}_i\mathbf{p}_i \bar{f}^{(2)}\rangle \cong \rho^{(2)}mkT_i\mathbf{I},$$
$$\langle \mathbf{p}_1\mathbf{p}_2 \bar{f}^{(2)}\rangle \cong \mathbf{0}. \qquad (5.4.174)$$

Again, we find no contribution arises from $J_1^{(2)}$. The contribution from $J_2^{(2)}$ and $J_3^{(2)}$ is, by the arguments of Sections 5.4.A and 5.4.D, given by, for example,

$$\begin{aligned}\langle \mathbf{p}_1[J_2^{(2)} + J_3^{(2)}]\rangle &= \langle \mathbf{p}_1[J_2^{(2)}(1) + J^{(2)}(1)]\rangle \\ &= \frac{\sigma}{2m} g^{(2)}(\mathbf{R}_1,\mathbf{R}_2) \int \cdots \int_{(\mathbf{k}\cdot\mathbf{p}_{12}>0)} M_0^{(1)}(\mathbf{R}_2,\mathbf{p}_2) \\ &\quad \times \mathbf{k}\cdot\nabla_1[(\mathbf{p}_1 - \mathbf{p}_1{}^*)M_0^{(1)}(\mathbf{R}_1,\mathbf{p}_1)M_0^{(1)}(\mathbf{R}_1,\mathbf{p}_3)g_0^{(2)}(\mathbf{R}_1,\sigma)] \\ &\qquad \times p_{13} b\, db\, d\epsilon\, d\mathbf{p}_1\, d\mathbf{p}_2\, d\mathbf{p}_3 \\ &= -\frac{4\pi\rho\sigma^3}{3} g^{(2)}(\mathbf{R}_1,\mathbf{R}_2)\, \nabla_1[\rho^2 kT g(\sigma)]. \end{aligned} \tag{5.4.175}$$

The restriction of the present development to states of uniform temperature also implies uniform density, since any processes in which significant density gradients occur (such as the propagation of sound waves) also involve non-uniform temperatures. The contribution of $\langle \mathbf{p}_1[J_2^{(2)} + J_3^{(2)}]\rangle$ is, therefore, negligible.

A closed equation for $\rho^{(2)}$ may now be obtained within the present scheme by isolating $\mathbf{j}_i^{(2)}$ from the right-hand side of equations (5.4.171) and substituting the expressions in equation (5.4.169). If the processes we wish to describe with the equation do not vary significantly during times of the order of (m/ζ_S) then the term

$$\frac{m}{\zeta_S}\frac{\partial}{\partial t}\mathbf{j}_i^{(2)}$$

may be neglected with the result

$$\frac{\partial \rho^{(2)}}{\partial t} = \sum_{i=1,2}\left\{\frac{kT}{\zeta_S}[\nabla_i\cdot(\nabla_i\rho^{(2)} - \mathbf{F}_i^{(2)}\rho^{(2)}/kT)] - \nabla_i\cdot[\mathbf{u}_i\rho^{(2)}]\right\}. \tag{5.4.176}$$

The solution of equation (5.4.176) in the viscous flow problem will be discussed in Section 6.3.A.

Equation (5.4.176) bears a strong similarity to the Smoluchowski equation (4.4.83), which describes diffusion in an external force field. In the present case, however, the diffusion is a six-dimensional process and the force field $\mathbf{F}_i^{(2)}$ is internal in origin. The $\mathbf{F}_i^{(2)}$ are, in fact, related to the equilibrium radial distribution function by

$$\mathbf{F}_i^{(2)} = kT\nabla_i \ln g_0^{(2)}(R_{12}). \tag{5.4.177}$$

One of the conditions for the consistency of the development of the Smoluchowski equation is that the length of the diffusive step, d, is small compared to distances in which the "external" potential varies significantly. The states of the system for which equation (5.4.176) is used in Section 6.3.A are such that

$$d \cong \zeta_S^{-1}(mkT)^{1/2} < 0.5 \text{ A.}, \tag{5.4.178}$$

while successive maxima of $g_0^{(2)}$ are separated by about 3.5 A., so that the consistency condition is satisfied quite well.

The failure of the main collision term, $J_1^{(2)}$, to contribute to the flux, $\mathbf{j}_i^{(2)}$, is noteworthy, for it is clear that some equation [e.g., Eq. (5.4.176)] must exist which describes the configurational evolution of a rigid sphere fluid. We can immediately trace this feature to the fact that since only binary collisions are considered, the momentum is a summational invariant. It follows that collisional processes in which the momentum is not an invariant in the simple sense appropriate to binary collisions are important in the configurational evolution. One such process, which was specifically excluded from consideration in the development of the doublet equation, is that in which the incoming molecule three collides with molecule one, and either cannons onto molecule two or causes molecule one to rebound onto molecule two. Clearly, these processes would be most important when molecules one and two are close together. However, such collisional processes are extremely difficult to handle mathematically, and it is unlikely that they are important in a liquid in which the soft forces play a prominent role in the approach to equilibrium.

5.5. A COMMENT ON THE THEORY

The separation of the intermolecular potential into a rigid core contribution and a weak contribution, and the subsequent derivation of mutually independent collisional integrals and Fokker-Planck operators in the stochastic terms of the kinetic equations is an essential feature of the theory presented here; it is, at the same time, the one most open to question of the several assumptions introduced.

The separation of the two types of stochastic term assumes, in effect, that two independent mechanisms inducing the approach to equilibrium are in operation. This supposition is not, of course, correct in general, but simple arguments suffice to establish it within the terms of reference of the theory. The problem can be made more precise by the following questions:

(1) To what extent does the soft interaction interfere with the rigid core encounters?

(2) To what extent do the rigid core encounters interfere with the temporal development of the soft force correlations?

The first of these questions can be answered fairly directly. It was assumed, in the development of the kinetic equations, that soft forces played no part in a rigid core encounter. However, the extension of the filamentary volume element to a length $(p_{12}\tau/m)$ includes configurations in which the direct soft force $\mathbf{F}_{12}^{(S)}$ between the two molecules about to undergo the rigid core encounter causes significant deviations from a linear trajectory in all cases except "head-on" collisions. Provided that the time interval, τ, is not sufficiently long that the two molecules are too widely separated initially, the assumption of zero soft force may be replaced by the assumption of zero soft force *due to the environment*. This assumption owes its strength to calculations based upon the cell model, which show that the average potential in the center of a region surrounded by a spherical distribution of molecules is very flat. However, the neighbors of a colliding pair of molecules are distributed, not spherically about them, but with a cylindrical symmetry, so that the assumption is an approximation. This assumption allows us to replace the rigid core by the cross-section for the actual pair potential, taken out to, say, the minimum of the well (a distance of $2^{1/6}\sigma$ for a Lennard-Jones 6–12 potential). Thus, the rigid core assumption is necessary only in a qualitative sense, although its literal interpretation makes calculations much simpler.

The possibility that rigid core encounters may interfere with the soft force correlations is related to the assumption that the rigid core encounter occurs at the beginning of the interval τ. Clearly, it may occur any time during τ. It appears possible (in a practical mathematical sense) to take account of this interference by calculating the evolution of the soft force correlation for a trajectory formed of two non-parallel linear portions joined at their ends. The result of such a calculation should be a single stochastic term combining the features of a collision integral and a Fokker-Planck operator. However, the complexity of the separate Fokker-Planck operator already calculated in equation (5.3.68) was such that, for practical reasons, it was replaced by an operator with a constant friction coefficient. It is no greater an assumption, therefore, to ignore the interference effect of the rigid core encounters.

The replacement of the Fokker-Planck operators [Eqs. (5.3.68) and (5.3.108)] by operators with constant friction coefficients is, unfortunately, necessary for the practical reason that the eigenfunctions of these operators (and, indeed, the exact form of the moments in the doublet case) are not known at the present time. The choice of the simple operator is, of course, determined by the requirement that one solution must be the equilibrium Maxwellian distribution. In the doublet case, it is also necessary that integration over the phase of one of the molecules reduces the operator to the singlet form.

The effect of introducing a simple form of the operator is probably not serious in the singlet case in the sense that the calculated transport coefficient should be little affected. The reason for this is that the value of the friction constant is determined empirically to give the correct first moment of the operator by means of the diffusion coefficient. It follows that the momentum flux should be correct, but the kinetic-energy flux should not. On the other hand, in the doublet case, all dependence of the moments on the separation $\mathbf{R}_{12}$ is neglected in the simple operator. Thus, the non-isotropic character, and separation dependence of the diffusion tensor in the 6-dimensional configuration space of the pair of molecules is replaced by a constant isotropic friction tensor.

APPENDIX 5.A

Alternative Derivation of the Weak-Coupling Fokker-Planck Operator

The operator Ω_S of equation (5.3.6) can be expressed in the form

$$\Omega_S = -\nabla_{p_1} \cdot \left[\frac{N(N-1)}{\tau}\int_0^\tau \int \mathbf{F}_{12}^{(S)} f^{(N)}(\Gamma_{N,t}; t+s)\, d\Gamma_{N-1}\, ds\right], \qquad (5.A.1)$$

by means of equation (5.3.2), and use of the fact that $\mathbf{F}_{12}^{(S)}$ does not depend on $\mathbf{p}_1$. Now, the N-molecule distribution function is a constant of the natural motion of the phase space, so that we can write

$$f^{(N)}(\Gamma_{N\,t};t) = f^{(N)}(\Gamma_{N,t+s};\, t + s)$$
$$= f^{(N)}(\Gamma_{N,t} + \Delta\Gamma_N(s);\, t + s), \qquad (5.A.2)$$

where $\Delta\Gamma_N(s)$ is the change in the phase $\Gamma_{N,t}$ which occurs in a time s. Substitution of equation (5.A.2) in (5.A.1), therefore, leads to

$$\Omega_S = -\nabla_{p_1} \cdot \left[\frac{N(N-1)}{\tau}\int_0^\tau \int \mathbf{F}_{12}^{(S)} f^{(N)}(\Gamma_N - \Delta\Gamma_N(s);\, t)\, d\Gamma_{N-1}\, ds\right], \qquad (5.A.3)$$

where the fact that Γ_N is the phase at time t is now understood.

If we now introduce the hypothesis of local equilibrium, we can, by means of equation (5.3.38), express $f^{(N)}$ in terms of $f^{(N-2/2)}$ and the pair distribution function given by equations (5.3.22) and (5.3.23):

$$f^{(N)}(\Gamma_N - \Delta\Gamma_N;\, t) = g_0^{(2)}(\mathbf{R}_1 - \Delta\mathbf{R}_1,\, \mathbf{R}_2 - \Delta\mathbf{R}_2)$$
$$\times f^{(1)}(\mathbf{R}_1 - \Delta\mathbf{R}_1,\, \mathbf{p}_1 - \Delta\mathbf{p}_1;\, t) f^{(1)}(\mathbf{R}_2 - \Delta\mathbf{R}_2,\, \mathbf{p}_2 - \Delta\mathbf{p}_2;\, t)$$
$$\times f^{(N-2/2)}(\Gamma_{N-2} - \Delta\Gamma_{N-2} \mid \Gamma_2 - \Delta\Gamma_2). \qquad (5.A.4)$$

In order to make use of equation (5.A.4) in determining Ω_S, it is necessary to evaluate the factors $g_0^{(2)} f^{(N-2/2)}$ of equation (5.A.4) in terms of the same factors, *expressed as functions of the phase at time t*, and some small quantities. To this end we introduce the further approximation that $f^{(N-2/2)}$ can be replaced by its value in equilibrium, which is given by equation (5.3.45). Then, using the fact that the Hamiltonian is invariant to the change of variables $\Gamma_N \to \Gamma_N - \Delta\Gamma_N$, we can express their ratio in terms of $\Delta\mathbf{p}_1$, $\Delta\mathbf{p}_2$, and some terms in $\Delta\mathbf{R}_1$, and $\Delta\mathbf{R}_2$, which are negligible if we assume that the displacements occurring during τ are small:

$$\frac{g_0^{(2)}(\mathbf{R}_1 - \Delta\mathbf{R}_1,\, \mathbf{R}_2 - \Delta\mathbf{R}_2)^0 f^{(N-2/2)}(\Gamma_{N-2} - \Delta\Gamma_{N-2} \mid \Gamma_2 - \Delta\Gamma_2)}{g_0^{(2)}(\mathbf{R}_1, \mathbf{R}_2)^0 f^{(N-2/2)}(\Gamma_{N-2} \mid \Gamma_2)}$$
$$= \exp\left[-\{2\mathbf{p}_1 \cdot \Delta\mathbf{p}_1 + 2\mathbf{p}_2 \cdot \Delta\mathbf{p}_2 + (\Delta\mathbf{p}_1)^2 + (\Delta\mathbf{p}_2)^2 + \mathcal{O}(\Delta\mathbf{R}_1)\}/2mkT\right]$$
$$= 1 - \frac{\mathbf{p}_1 \cdot \Delta\mathbf{p}_1}{mkT} - \frac{\mathbf{p}_2 \cdot \Delta\mathbf{p}_2}{mkT} + \cdots. \qquad (5.A.5)$$

The singlet distribution functions in equation (5.A.4) are also expanded in Taylor series in powers of $\Delta\mathbf{p}_1$, $\Delta\mathbf{p}_2$ about the phase at time t. When this and equation (5.A.5) are substituted in equation (5.A.3), we obtain

$$\Omega_S = -\frac{1}{\tau}\int_0^\tau \int \nabla_{p_1} \cdot \mathbf{F}_{12}^{(S)} g_0^{(2)}(R_{12})^0 f^{(N-2/2)}(\Gamma_{N-2} \mid \Gamma_2)$$
$$\times \left[1 - \Delta\mathbf{p}_1 \cdot \left(\frac{\mathbf{p}_1}{mkT} + \nabla_{p_1}\right) - \Delta\mathbf{p}_2 \cdot \left(\frac{\mathbf{p}_2}{mkT} + \nabla_{p_2}\right)\right]$$
$$\times f^{(1)}(\mathbf{R}_1,\mathbf{p}_1;t) f^{(1)}(\mathbf{R}_2,\mathbf{p}_2;t)\, d\Gamma_{N-1}\, ds$$
$$= \Omega_S^{(0)} + \Omega_S^{(1)} + \Omega_S^{(2)}, \tag{5.A.6}$$

where $\Omega_S^{(0)}$ is given by equation (5.3.37),

$$\Omega_S^{(1)} = \frac{1}{\tau}\int_0^\tau \int_0^s \int \nabla_{p_1} \cdot \left\langle \mathbf{F}_{12}^{(S)} g_0^{(2)}(R_{12}) \mathbf{F}_1^{(S)}\left(\mathbf{R}^{(N)} + \frac{s'}{m}\mathbf{p}^{(N)}\right) f^{(1)}(\mathbf{R}_2,\mathbf{p}_2;t)\right\rangle_{1,2}$$
$$\cdot \left(\frac{\mathbf{p}_1}{mkT} + \nabla_{p_1}\right) f^{(1)}(\mathbf{R}_1,\mathbf{p}_1;t)\, ds'\, ds\, d\Gamma_1(2), \tag{5.A.7}$$

and

$$\Omega_S^{(2)} = \frac{1}{\tau}\int_0^\tau \int_0^s \int \nabla_{p_1} \cdot \mathbf{F}_{12}^{(S)} g_0^{(2)}(R_{12}) \left\langle \mathbf{F}_2^{(S)}\left(\mathbf{R}^{(N)} + \frac{s'}{m}\mathbf{p}^{(N)}; t\right)\right\rangle_{1,2}$$
$$\cdot \left(\frac{\mathbf{p}_2}{mkT} + \nabla_{p_2}\right) f^{(1)}(\mathbf{R}_1,\mathbf{p}_1;t) f^{(1)}(\mathbf{R}_2,\mathbf{p}_2;t)\, d\Gamma_1(2)\, ds'\, ds. \tag{5.A.8}$$

The use of the linear trajectory expressions for the $\Delta\mathbf{p}_i$ in these equations, while not required from the formulation of equation (5.A.5), is nevertheless strictly compatible with the expansion scheme used, and the neglect of terms in $(\Delta\mathbf{p})^2$ and $\Delta\mathbf{R}$. When $f^{(1)}(\mathbf{R}_2,\mathbf{p}_2;t)$ is replaced by ρ times the Maxwellian distribution, $\Omega_S^{(2)}$ vanishes, which is the reason that it did not appear in Section 5.3.A. $\Omega_S^{(1)}$ can be written in the form of a Fokker-Planck operator, with a momentum-dependent friction coefficient $\boldsymbol{\zeta}$:

$$\Omega_S^{(1)} = \nabla_{p_1} \cdot \boldsymbol{\zeta} \cdot \left(\frac{\mathbf{p}_1}{m} + kT\nabla_{p_1}\right) f^{(1)}(\mathbf{R}_1,\mathbf{p}_1;t), \tag{5.A.9}$$

where

$$\boldsymbol{\zeta} = \frac{1}{kT\tau}\int_0^\tau \int_0^s \int \left\langle \mathbf{F}_{12}^{(S)} \mathbf{F}_1^{(S)}\left(\mathbf{R}^{(N)} + \frac{s'}{m}\mathbf{p}^{(N)}\right) g_0^{(2)}(R_{12}) f^{(1)}(\mathbf{R}_2,\mathbf{p}_2;t)\right\rangle_{1,2}$$
$$\times\, ds'\, ds\, d\Gamma_1(2) \tag{5.A.10}$$
$$= \frac{1}{kT\tau}\int_0^\tau \int_0^s \int \mathbf{F}_{12}^{(S)} \mathbf{F}_1^{(S)}\left(\mathbf{R}^{(N)} + \frac{s'}{m}\mathbf{p}^{(N)}\right)$$
$$\cdot f^{(N-1/1)}(\Gamma_{N-1} \mid \Gamma_1)\, d\Gamma_{N-1}\, ds'\, ds. \tag{5.A.11}$$

Equation (5.A.11) is in the form found by Ross. If we apply the arguments leading to equation (5.3.47) to equation (5.A.10), it becomes

$$\zeta = -\frac{\rho}{kT\tau}\int_0^\tau\int_0^s\int \mathbf{F}_{12}^{(S)}\,\nabla_{12}g_0^{(2)}\left(\left|\mathbf{R}_{12}+\frac{s'}{m}\mathbf{p}_{12}\right|\right)\varphi^{(1)}(\mathbf{p}_2)\,d\Gamma_1(2)\,ds'\,ds, \tag{5.A.12}$$

and an analysis similar to that used in proceeding from equation (5.3.50) to equation (5.3.68) establishes the result

$$\zeta = \frac{B}{kT}\,\mathbf{a}^{(2)}, \tag{5.A.13}$$

where B is given by equation (5.3.59) and $\mathbf{a}^{(2)}$ by equations (5.3.66) and (5.3.67).

The final form of $\Omega_S^{(1)}$ is, therefore, seen to be

$$\Omega_S^{(1)} = B\,\nabla_{p_1}\cdot\mathbf{a}^{(2)}\cdot\left(\frac{\mathbf{p}_1}{mkT}+\nabla_{p_1}\right)f^{(1)}(\mathbf{R}_1,\mathbf{p}_1;t). \tag{5.A.14}$$

If the reduced velocity, $\mathbf{W} = (2mkT)^{-1/2}\mathbf{p}_1$, is introduced in equation (5.A.14), it is found that

$$\Omega_S^{(1)} = \frac{B}{2mkT}\,\nabla_W\cdot\mathbf{a}^{(2)}\cdot(2\mathbf{W}+\nabla_W)f^{(1)}(\Gamma_1;t). \tag{5.A.15}$$

Taking now equation (5.3.68) and introducing the reduced velocity, we obtain

$$\Omega_S^{(1)} = \frac{B}{2mkT}\,\nabla_W\cdot(\mathbf{a}^{(1)}(2mkT)^{1/2}+\nabla_W\cdot\mathbf{a}^{(2)})f^{(1)}(\Gamma_1;t), \tag{5.A.16}$$

and expansion of $\nabla_W\cdot(\mathbf{a}^{(2)}f^{(1)})$ converts this to

$$\Omega_S^{(1)} = \frac{B}{2mkT}\,\nabla_W\cdot(\mathbf{a}^{(1)}(2mkT)^{1/2} - 2\mathbf{a}^{(2)}\cdot\mathbf{W} + \mathbf{a}^{(2)}\cdot\nabla_W)f^{(1)}(\Gamma_1;t), \tag{5.A.17}$$

where we have used the result

$$\begin{aligned}\nabla_W\cdot\mathbf{a}^{(2)} &= -2(2mkT)^{-1/2}\left[\operatorname{erf}(W) - \frac{2W}{\pi^{1/2}}e^{-W^2}\right]\frac{\mathbf{W}}{W^2}\\ &= -2\mathbf{a}^{(2)}\cdot\mathbf{W}.\end{aligned} \tag{5.A.18}$$

It is easily verified, from equations (5.3.66) and (5.3.67), that

$$(2mkT)^{1/2}\mathbf{a}^{(1)} = 4\mathbf{a}^{(2)} \cdot \mathbf{W}, \tag{5.A.19}$$

so that we have demonstrated the equivalence of the two forms, equations (5.A.14) and (5.A.16), of $\Omega_S^{(1)}$.

APPENDIX 5.B

The Kinetic Equation for a Brownian Particle

It was intimated in Section 4.5 that the friction coefficient relating the average force on a Brownian particle to its momentum could be related to the correlation integral of the fluctuating force. However, no prescription for the calculation of the correlation integral was obtained from the purely stochastic theory. Indeed, the fluctuating force correlation function was found to be a function of the friction coefficient, so that the definition did not contain sufficient information to enable a calculation to be made.

On the other hand, the calculation of the Fokker-Planck operator for a weakly coupled system [Eq. (5.3.68) and Appendix 5.A] yields a non-isotropic, momentum dependent friction tensor, a result disagreeing with the well-established interpretation of experimental observations of the Brownian motion of particles suspended in fluids. The resolution of this contradiction is seen when it is realized that observable Brownian particles are large compared to the molecules of the fluid in which they are suspended. The interaction between the Brownian particle and molecules of the fluid is strong, not weak, and a different technique is required for describing the evolution of the system.

In this appendix we show how the kinetic equation for a *massive* particle can be obtained using the time coarse graining and Green's function methods described in Chapter 5. The calculation here is approximate to the extent that the use of time coarse graining is a hypothesis and the validity of taking the limit of large τ must be assumed. For completely rigorous derivations the reader is referred to the elegant work of Lebowitz and Rubin (28), and of Résibois and Davis (29).

The notation we use here is an extension of the notation of Chapter 5 to a system comprising N identical fluid molecules of mass m and a

Brownian particle of mass M.* The phase of the whole system is $(\Gamma_N,\gamma) \equiv (\{\mathbf{R}_i,\mathbf{p}_i\},\mathbf{R},\mathbf{P})$ and the distribution function of the system is

$$f^{(N,1)} = f^{(N,1)}(\Gamma_N,\gamma;t). \tag{5.B.1}$$

The pair interaction potential of the fluid molecules is again denoted $u_{ij}(R_{ij})$, and the interaction between the Brownian particle and a fluid molecule is denoted $w_i = w(|\mathbf{R} - \mathbf{R}_i|)$.

The distribution function $f^{(N,1)}$ satisfies a Liouville equation for the whole system

$$\left[\frac{\partial}{\partial t} + \frac{\mathbf{P}}{M}\cdot\nabla_R + \mathbf{f}\cdot\nabla_P + \sum_i\left(\frac{\mathbf{p}_i}{m}\cdot\nabla_i + (\mathbf{F}_i - \mathbf{f}_i)\cdot\nabla_{p_i}\right)\right]f^{(N,1)} = 0, \tag{5.B.2}$$

where

$$\mathbf{f} = \sum_{i=1}^{N}\mathbf{f}_i = -\sum_{i=1}^{N}\nabla w_i, \tag{5.B.3}$$

$$\mathbf{F}_i = -\sum_{j(\neq i)=1}^{N}\nabla_i u_{ij}. \tag{5.B.4}$$

Introducing self-adjoint Liouville operators $\mathscr{L}_f$ and $\mathscr{L}_B$, defined by

$$i\mathscr{L}_f = \sum_{i=1}^{N}\left(\frac{\mathbf{p}_i}{m}\cdot\nabla_i + (\mathbf{F}_i - \mathbf{f}_i)\cdot\nabla_{p_i}\right),$$
$$i\mathscr{L}_B = \left(\frac{\mathbf{P}}{M}\cdot\nabla_R + \mathbf{f}\cdot\nabla_p\right), \tag{5.B.5}$$

we convert equation (5.B.2) to

$$\left(\frac{\partial}{\partial t} + i\mathscr{L}_B + i\mathscr{L}_f\right)f^{(N,1)} = 0. \tag{5.B.6}$$

We now coarse grain equation (5.B.2) in the usual fashion, and integrate out the phase of the fluid:

$$\begin{aligned}\bar{f}(\gamma;t) &= \frac{1}{\tau}\int_0^\tau f(\gamma;t+s)\,ds\\ &= \frac{1}{\tau}\int_0^\tau\int f^{(N,1)}(\Gamma_N,\gamma;t+s)\,d\Gamma_N\,ds.\end{aligned} \tag{5.B.7}$$

* The formulation is obviously valid also for a fluid containing many Brownian particles, which are nevertheless sufficiently dilute that their mutual potential energy is negligible.

Using equation (5.B.7), (5.B.2) becomes

$$\left(\frac{\partial}{\partial t} + \frac{\mathbf{P}}{M}\cdot\nabla_R + \mathbf{f}\cdot\nabla_P\right)\bar{f} = -\frac{1}{\tau}\int_0^\tau\int \nabla_P\cdot \mathbf{f}f^{(N,1)}(\Gamma_N,\gamma;t+s)\,d\Gamma_N\,ds$$
$$= \Omega_B. \tag{5.B.8}$$

The phase space transition probability for the whole system,

$$K^{(N,1)}(\Gamma_N,\gamma \mid \Gamma_N{}',\gamma';s),$$

is defined in analogy with equation (5.3.7) by the relation

$$f^{(N,1)}(\Gamma_N,\gamma;t+s) = \int K^{(N,1)}(\Gamma_N,\gamma \mid \Gamma_N{}',\gamma';s)f^{(N,1)}(\Gamma_N{}',\gamma';t)\,d\Gamma_N{}'\,d\gamma'. \tag{5.B.9}$$

Clearly, $K^{(N,1)}(s)$ satisfies equations (5.B.2) and (5.B.6) with the initial condition

$$K^{(N,1)}(0) = \delta(\mathbf{R}-\mathbf{R}')\,\delta(\mathbf{P}-\mathbf{P}')\prod_{i=1}^{N}\delta(\mathbf{R}_i-\mathbf{R}_i')\,\delta(\mathbf{p}_i-\mathbf{p}_i'). \tag{5.B.10}$$

We now seek a perturbation expansion of $K^{(N,1)}(s)$, and to this end introduce the mass ratio $(m/M) \equiv \mu^2$ as a perturbation parameter. Consider the constituent terms of $\mathscr{L}_B$. Since the average momentum of a Brownian particle is of order $(MkT)^{1/2}$, each term in $\mathscr{L}_B$ is of $\mathcal{O}(M^{-1/2})$ in comparison to those of $\mathscr{L}_f$. Thus, we associate $\mathscr{L}_B$ with a factor μ, and expand $K^{(N,1)}$ as

$$K^{(N,1)}(s) = K_0(s) + \mu K_1(s) + \cdots, \tag{5.B.11}$$

with the initial condition

$$K^{(N,1)}(0) = K_0(0),$$
$$K_n(0) = 0 \quad \text{if} \quad n > 0. \tag{5.B.12}$$

Substitution of equation (5.B.11) in (5.B.6) yields, on equating the coefficients of equal powers of μ, the set of equations

$$\left(\frac{\partial}{\partial s} + i\mathscr{L}_f\right)K_0 = 0,$$
$$\left(\frac{\partial}{\partial s} + i\mathscr{L}_f\right)K_n + i\mathscr{L}_B K_{n-1} = 0, \qquad n \geqslant 1. \tag{5.B.13}$$

The solutions of equations (5.B.1.13) are

$$K_0(s) = e^{-is\mathscr{L}_f}K_0(0),$$
$$K_n(s) = -\int_0^s e^{i(s'-s)\mathscr{L}_f}i\mathscr{L}_B K_{n-1}(s')\,ds', \qquad n \geqslant 1. \tag{5.B.14}$$

Substitution of equations (5.B.14), and integration over Γ_N' and γ', now leads to the following form for Ω_B:

$$\Omega_B = \Omega_B^{(0)} + \mu\Omega_B^{(1)} + \cdots, \tag{5.B.15}$$

where

$$\Omega_B^{(0)} = -\frac{1}{\tau}\nabla_P \cdot \int_0^\tau \int \mathbf{f} e^{-is\mathscr{L}_f} f^{(N,1)}(\Gamma_N, \gamma; t)\, d\Gamma_N\, ds, \tag{5.B.16}$$

and

$$\Omega_B^{(1)} = \frac{1}{\tau}\nabla_P \cdot \int_0^\tau \int_0^s \int \mathbf{f} e^{i(s'-s)\mathscr{L}_f} i\mathscr{L}_B e^{-is'\mathscr{L}_f} f^{(N,1)}(\Gamma_N, \gamma; t)\, d\Gamma_N\, ds'\, ds, \tag{5.B.17}$$

and so on.

It is now convenient to introduce the assumption that the fluid is essentially in equilibrium, and that it recovers very quickly, compared to the Brownian particle, from a small perturbation. More precisely, we shall assume that the fluid is in equilibrium in the potential field of the Brownian particle at the beginning of each interval τ, the Brownian particle having moved a very small amount during each such interval. Thus, the distribution function for the whole system can be factorized into $f(\gamma; t)$ and the equilibrium conditional distribution function ${}^0f^{(N/1)}(\Gamma_N \mid \gamma)$ for the fluid, at $s = 0$:

$${}^0f^{(N,1)} = Z_N^{-1} \exp\left(-\frac{1}{kT}\sum_{i=1}^{N}\left[\frac{p_i^2}{2m} + \sum_{j>i} u_{ij} + w_i\right]\right), \tag{5.B.18}$$

where

$$f^{(N,1)}(\Gamma_N, \gamma; t) = {}^0f^{(N/1)}(\Gamma_N \mid \gamma) f(\gamma; t). \tag{5.B.19}$$

It is clear that ${}^0f^{(N/1)}$ commutes with the Hamiltonian of the fluid in the presence of a Brownian particle fixed at **R**. Thus, from the definition of $\mathscr{L}_f$, equation (5.B.5),

$$e^{-is\mathscr{L}_f}\,{}^0f^{(N/1)} = {}^0f^{(N/1)}. \tag{5.B.20}$$

It now follows from equation (5.B.20), that $\Omega_B^{(0)}$ vanishes because the mean force vanishes,

$$\int \mathbf{f}\; {}^0f^{(N/1)}\, d\Gamma_N = 0, \tag{5.B.21}$$

and $\Omega_B^{(1)}$ reduces to

$$\Omega_B^{(1)} = \frac{1}{\tau}\nabla_P \cdot \int_0^\tau \int_0^s \int \mathbf{f} e^{i(s'-s)\mathscr{L}_f}\left(\frac{\mathbf{P}}{M}\cdot\nabla_R + \mathbf{f}\cdot\nabla_P\right) {}^0f^{(N/1)} f(\gamma; t)\, d\Gamma_N\, ds'\, ds. \tag{5.B.22}$$

From equation (5.B.19) we immediately see that

$$\frac{\mathbf{P}}{M}\cdot\nabla_R{}^0f^{(N/1)}f(\gamma;t) = {}^0f^{(N/1)}\left(\frac{\mathbf{P}}{MkT}\cdot\mathbf{f}f(\gamma;t) + \frac{\mathbf{P}}{M}\cdot\nabla_R f(\gamma;t)\right). \quad (5.B.23)$$

When this is substituted in equation (5.B.22), the second term vanishes from equation (5.B.21), while the first term yields

$$\Omega_B^{(1)} = \nabla_P\cdot\boldsymbol{\zeta}\cdot\left(\frac{\mathbf{P}}{M} + kT\nabla_P\right)f, \quad (5.B.24)$$

where

$$\boldsymbol{\zeta} = \frac{1}{kT\tau}\int_0^\tau\int_0^s\int \mathbf{f}e^{i(s'-s)\mathscr{L}_f}\mathbf{f}\,{}^0f^{(N/1)}\,d\Gamma_N\,ds'\,ds. \quad (5.B.25)$$

Now, the operator exp $[i(s'-s)\mathscr{L}_f]$ operates only on the phase of the fluid molecules. Therefore,

$$e^{i(s'-s)\mathscr{L}_f}\mathbf{f} = \mathbf{f}(s'-s) \quad (5.B.26)$$

is the force on the Brownian particle *fixed at* **R**, due to the fluid molecules, at time $(s'-s)$. The friction coefficient $\boldsymbol{\zeta}$ is, therefore, of the form proposed by Kirkwood,

$$\boldsymbol{\zeta} = \frac{1}{kT\tau}\int_0^\tau\int_0^s\langle\mathbf{f}\mathbf{f}(s'-s)\rangle\,ds'\,ds, \quad (5.B.27)$$

where $\langle\cdots\rangle$ indicates the phase average over the fluid equilibrium distribution in the presence of the fixed Brownian particle. Since neither $\mathscr{L}_f$, ${}^0f^{(N/1)}$ nor **f** depends on the momentum of the Brownian particle, $\boldsymbol{\zeta}$ is momentum independent. Moreover, since the fluid is isotropic we shall assume that $\boldsymbol{\zeta}$ is isotropic:

$$\boldsymbol{\zeta} = \zeta\mathbf{I},$$
$$\zeta = \frac{1}{3kT\tau}\int_0^\tau\int_0^s\langle\mathbf{f}\cdot\mathbf{f}(s')\rangle\,ds'\,ds, \quad (5.B.28)$$

where we have introduced a change of time variable, and used the fact that the correlation function is an even function of the time.

As usual, with the use of coarse graining, we assume that the final equation is independent of τ. Thus, we here assume that τ is sufficiently short that f can be replaced by $\bar{f}$ in $\Omega_B^{(1)}$ [obviously, this need only be correct to $\mathcal{O}(\mu)$], but that τ is long enough that ζ is independent of τ. If ζ is indeed independent of τ its asymptotic value is obtained if we allow $\tau \to \infty$. We then find that

$$\zeta = \frac{1}{3kT} \int_0^\infty \langle \mathbf{f} \cdot \mathbf{f}(s) \rangle \, ds, \tag{5.B.29}$$

provided the integral converges. The correctness of equation (5.B.29) is easily established as follows: Suppose

$$\langle \mathbf{f} \cdot \mathbf{f}(s) \rangle = -\ddot{\varphi}(s), \qquad s > 0. \tag{5.B.30}$$

From equation (5.B.28) we find

$$\begin{aligned} \zeta &= \lim_{\tau \to \infty} - \frac{1}{3kT\tau} \int_0^\tau \int_0^s \ddot{\varphi}(s') \, ds' \, ds \\ &= - \frac{1}{3kT} \dot{\varphi}(0+), \end{aligned} \tag{5.B.31}$$

where $\dot{\varphi}(0+)$ is the value of $\dot{\varphi}(s)$ as s approaches zero through positive values. From equation (5.B.29) we find

$$\zeta = - \frac{1}{3kT} \dot{\varphi}(0+) - \frac{1}{3kT} \lim_{\tau \to \infty} \dot{\varphi}(\tau). \tag{5.B.32}$$

This agrees with equation (5.B.31) if $\dot{\varphi}(\tau)$ vanishes as $\tau \to \infty$. This will *not* be the case in the system we have considered, since it is finite. However, either by taking the limit (28)

$$\zeta = \frac{1}{3kT} \lim_{\substack{p \to 0 \\ Re\, p > 0}} \int_0^\infty e^{-ps} \langle \mathbf{f} \cdot \mathbf{f}(s) \rangle \, ds, \tag{5.B.33}$$

or by considering the limit of an infinite system (29), it can be shown that $\dot{\varphi}(\tau) \to 0$ as $\tau \to \infty$.

An interesting point arises in connection with the relation between equations (5.B.31) and (5.B.32) and the discussion of Section 4.5 and the result of Appendix 6.A. In both of these we were concerned with the fact that, if $\mathbf{f}$ were the total force on a Brownian particle free to move, then $\dot{\varphi}(0)$ vanished. However, this result was a consequence of the assumption that $\varphi(s)$ was continuous and differentiable at $s = 0$. In the present case this is not so.

Finally, it must be mentioned that the foregoing approximate treatment fails to give higher order terms $\Omega_B^{(2)}, \Omega_B^{(3)}, \cdots$, in agreement with results obtained elsewhere (28, 29). This is apparently due to the assumption that $f^{(N/1)}$ has the equilibrium form at the beginning of each interval τ; one would expect it to lag slightly behind the Brownian particle, and hence $f^{(N/1)}$ should differ from that form by an undetermined small quantity.

REFERENCES

1. Kirkwood, J. G., *J. Chem. Phys.*, **14,** 180 (1946).
2. Kirkwood, J. G., *J. Chem. Phys.*, **15,** 72 (1947).
3. Ross, J., and J. G. Kirkwood, *J. Chem. Phys.*, **22,** 1094 (1954).
4. Kirkwood, J. G., and J. Ross, in *Proceedings of the International Symposium on Transport Processes in Statistical Mechanics—Brussels, August*, 27–31, 1956, I. Prigogine, ed., Interscience, New York, 1958, p. 1.
5. Koga, T., *J. Chem. Phys.*, **23,** 2275 (1955).
6. Kac, M., *Probability and Related Topics in Physical Science*, Interscience, New York, 1959.
7. Brout, R., *Physica*, **22,** 509 (1956).
8. Grad, H., *Handbuch der Physik*, Vol. XII, Springer-Verlag, Berlin, 1958, p. 205.
9. Bogolubov, N. N., *J. Phys.* (*USSR*), **10,** 265 (1946).
10. Bogolubov, N. N., in *Problems of a Dynamical Theory in Statistical Physics*, Vol. I of Studies in Statistical Mechanics, J. de Boer and G. E. Uhlenbeck, eds., Interscience, New York, 1962, p. 1.
11. Green, M. S., *J. Chem. Phys.*, **25,** 836 (1956).
12. Green, M. S., and R. A. Piccirelli, *Phys. Rev.*, **132,** 1388 (1963).
13. Prigogine, I., *Non-Equilibrium Statistical Mechanics*, Wiley, New York, 1963.
14. Kemeny, J. G., and J. L. Snell, *Finite Markov Chains*, D. Van Nostrand, Princeton, N.J., 1960.
15. Rice, S. A., and A. R. Allnatt, *J. Chem. Phys.*, **34,** 2144 (1961).
16. Allnatt, A. R., and S. A. Rice, *J. Chem. Phys.*, **34,** 2156 (1961).
17. Berne, B., and S. A. Rice, *J. Chem. Phys.*, **40,** 1336 (1964).
18. Fowler, R. H., and E. A. Guggenheim, *Statistical Thermodynamics*, Cambridge University Press, New York, 1939.
19. Ross, J., *J. Chem. Phys.*, **24,** 375 (1956).
20. Kihara, T., *Rev. Mod. Phys.*, **25,** 844 (1953).
21. Chapman, S., and T. G. Cowling, *Mathematical Theory of Non-Uniform Gases*, Cambridge University Press, New York, 1939.
22. Hirschfelder, J. O., C. F. Curtiss, and R. B. Bird, *Molecular Theory of Gases and Liquids*, Wiley, New York, 1954.
23. See for example, R. Courant and D. Hilbert, *Methods of Mathematical Physics*, Vol. 1, Interscience, New York, 1954.
24. Enskog, D., *Arkiv. Mat. Astronomi o Fys.*, **16,** 16 (1922).
25. Phillips, N. J., *Proc. Phys. Soc.* (*London*), **73,** 800 (1959).
26. Kirkwood, J. G., F. P. Buff, and M. S. Green, *J. Chem. Phys.*, **17,** 988 (1949).
27. Zwanzig, R. W., J. G. Kirkwood, K. Stripp, and I. Oppenheim, *J. Chem. Phys.*, **21,** 2050 (1953).
28. Lebowitz, J. L., and R. J. Rubin, *Phys. Rev.*, **131,** 2381 (1963).
29. Résibois, P., and H. T. Davis, *Physica*, **30,** 1077 (1964).

CHAPTER 6

Applications of the Kinetic Theory of Liquids

6.1. INTRODUCTION

Among the objectives of any molecular theory of dissipative phenomena, two stand out as being of immediate importance. First, the theory must introduce in a realistic manner the element of irreversibility which transforms the description of the system in terms of time reversible microscopic equations of motion into a description in terms of time irreversible macroscopic flow equations. Second, the theory must provide accurate predictions of the various transport coefficients in terms of the presumed known properties of the molecules which constitute the system under investigation. In this monograph we have thus far studied the first of these problems. Our analysis has led to the derivation of a set of kinetic equations defining the rate of change of the set of n-body distribution functions in terms of molecular interactions. We now turn to a study of the second problem. The solution of a kinetic equation is a distribution function expressed in terms of the macroscopic parameters defining the non-equilibrium state, i.e., the temperature gradient, velocity gradient, external field, etc. From this distribution function must be calculated the flux of energy, momentum, . . . in terms of the properties of the molecules constituting the system. The accuracy with which the computed transport coefficients agree with experiment will be an important measure of the accuracy of the theory developed.

In this chapter we shall consider only steady state transport phenomena. Indeed, as mentioned in the previous chapter and in the discussion of the general theories in Chapter 7, the Markovian theory does not apply to time-dependent phenomena in which significant changes take place during the short time-scale of the approach to local equilibrium. After a brief review of the necessary phenomenological theory, we shall examine, in turn, the molecular theory of energy, momentum and matter flow, and a few related topics.

The determination of the friction coefficient by calculation of either the force or momentum correlation functions is a far more difficult problem than the derivation and solution of the kinetic equations. Consequently, agreement of calculated values of the friction coefficient with experiment is generally poor. In comparing the calculated values of thermal conduction, shear viscosity, and ion mobility with experiment we shall, therefore, rely mainly on the determination of the friction coefficient by comparison of the Einstein relation with self-diffusion data.

6.2. THE ENERGY AND MOMENTUM FLUXES

6.2.A. *The Phenomenological Theory*

Let G be any extensive property of a fluid, and g the corresponding specific property, defined as G per unit mass. In general, g will vary from point to point in the fluid. Consider a fixed (but arbitrary) volume V in the fluid. We clearly have the conservation condition

$$G = \int_V \rho_m g \, dV, \tag{6.2.1}$$

with ρ_m the mass density. Since V is fixed,

$$\frac{dG}{dt} = \int_V \frac{\partial}{\partial t} (\rho_m g) \, dV. \tag{6.2.2}$$

Now, the time rate of change of G can also be expressed in terms of the current density $\mathbf{j}_G$ representing the flux of G out of the volume V, and the source density ϕ_G, representing the creation or destruction of G in the volume V. In terms of these variables

$$\frac{dG}{dt} = -\int_A \mathbf{j}_G \cdot d\mathbf{A} + \int_V \phi_G \, dV, \tag{6.2.3}$$

where the first integral is over the entire surface A bounding the volume V. In the special case when G is carried only by convection due to actual flow of the medium,

$$\mathbf{j}_G = \rho_m g \mathbf{u}, \tag{6.2.4}$$

with $\mathbf{u}$ the fluid velocity.

The two expressions for (dG/dt) may be equated, and if the surface integral of equation (6.2.3) is converted to a volume integral by use of Gauss' theorem, one finds

$$\int_V \left[\frac{\partial}{\partial t}(\rho_m g) + \nabla \cdot \mathbf{j}_G - \phi_G\right] dV = 0. \tag{6.2.5}$$

Since V is arbitrary, the integrand of (6.2.5) must vanish, whereupon

$$\frac{\partial}{\partial t}(\rho_m g) + \nabla \cdot \mathbf{j}_G - \phi_G = 0, \tag{6.2.6}$$

which is a statement of a general condition of conservation.

If G is taken to be the mass, then $g = 1$, and assuming conservation of mass $\phi_G = 0$, so that equation (6.2.6) reduces to the equation of continuity:

$$\frac{\partial \rho_m}{\partial t} + \nabla \cdot (\rho_m \mathbf{u}) = 0. \tag{6.2.7}$$

The force on a fixed but arbitrary volume V consists of two parts, a volume force and a surface force. Let $\mathbf{f}$ be the external force density and $\boldsymbol{\sigma}$ the stress tensor: the volume force on V is just $\int_V \mathbf{f}\, dV$, and the surface force is $\int_A \boldsymbol{\sigma} \cdot d\mathbf{A}$.

The stress tensor comprises a set of nine components, σ_{ij}, where i, j take on any of the values 1, 2, 3, corresponding to the Cartesian axes $x_1(\equiv x)$, $x_2(\equiv y)$, $x_3(\equiv z)$. σ_{ij} is the i component of the force transmitted in the j direction. If $d\mathbf{A}$ is a vector element of area, the i component of force transmitted across $d\mathbf{A}$ is

$$dF_i = \sigma_{ij}\, dA_j \qquad \text{(Summation convention)} \tag{6.2.8a}$$

or, in vector notation, the force transmitted across $d\mathbf{A}$ is

$$d\mathbf{F} = \boldsymbol{\sigma} \cdot d\mathbf{A}. \tag{6.2.8b}$$

For an element of the fluid which is in static equilibrium or is moving with constant velocity, the total force is

$$\int_{V'} \mathbf{f}\, dV + \int_{A'} \boldsymbol{\sigma} \cdot d\mathbf{A} = 0,$$

and the total torque is

$$\int_{V'} \mathbf{r} \times \mathbf{f}\, dV + \int_{A'} \mathbf{r} \times (\boldsymbol{\sigma} \cdot d\mathbf{A}) = 0,$$

where V' and A' are the volume and area of the elements. It follows* that $\boldsymbol{\sigma}$ is symmetric.

The total momentum carried by the volume V may also be written in the form

$$\mathbf{P} = \int_V \rho_m \mathbf{u}\, dV, \tag{6.2.9}$$

and since V is fixed,

$$\frac{d\mathbf{P}}{dt} = \int_V \frac{\partial}{\partial t}(\rho_m \mathbf{u})\, dV. \tag{6.2.10}$$

But $\mathbf{u} \cdot d\mathbf{A}$ is the volume of fluid crossing $d\mathbf{A}$ in unit time, and since each unit of volume carries out with it a momentum $\rho_m \mathbf{u}$, the total momentum transferred out through the surface A per unit time is $\int_A \rho_m \mathbf{uu} \cdot d\mathbf{A}$. This momentum transfer rate, when added to $(d\mathbf{P}/dt)$, must equal the force acting on V. By combination of (6.2.10) and the definition of the total force acting on V, one finds

$$\int_V \mathbf{f}\, dV + \int_A \boldsymbol{\sigma} \cdot d\mathbf{A} = \int_V \frac{\partial}{\partial t}(\rho_m \mathbf{u})\, dV + \int_A \rho_m \mathbf{uu} \cdot d\mathbf{A}. \tag{6.2.11}$$

Again converting the surface integrals to volume integrals and noting that V is arbitrary,

$$\frac{\partial}{\partial t}(\rho_m \mathbf{u}) + \nabla \cdot (\rho_m \mathbf{uu}) = \mathbf{f} + \nabla \cdot \boldsymbol{\sigma}, \tag{6.2.12}$$

which is the equation of motion of the fluid.

* This statement can be proved as follows. A vector product $\mathbf{y} \times \mathbf{x}$ may be replaced by the matrix product $\mathbf{Y} \cdot \mathbf{x}$, where $\mathbf{Y}$ is the skew symmetric matrix whose elements are $Y_{ij} = \epsilon_{ijk} y_k$; ϵ_{ijk} is $+1$ or -1 according as (i,j,k) is an even or an odd permutation of (1,2,3), and zero otherwise. Using the divergence theorem for the total force relation, we obtain

$$\int_{V'} [\mathbf{f} + \nabla \cdot \boldsymbol{\sigma}]\, dV = 0, \qquad \text{or} \qquad f_i = -\frac{\partial}{\partial x_j} \sigma_{ij}, \tag{1}$$

since V' is arbitrary. For the torque relation we obtain, in a similar way,

$$\epsilon_{ijk} x_k f_j + \frac{\partial}{\partial x_j}(\epsilon_{ikl} x_l \sigma_{kj}) = 0. \tag{2}$$

Expanding the differentiation in (2) and substituting from (1) now gives

$$\sigma_{kj} \frac{\partial}{\partial x_j}(\epsilon_{ikl} x_l) = \sigma_{kj} \epsilon_{ikl} \delta_{jl} = \sigma_{kj} \epsilon_{ikj} = 0.$$

Hence, from the defined properties of ϵ_{ijk}, we obtain

$$\sigma_{kj} - \sigma_{jk} = 0.$$

Associated with each element of mass of the fluid, $\rho_m \, dV$, is an internal energy $e\rho_m \, dV$, where e is the internal energy per unit mass. In addition, the motion of the fluid causes the mass element to have kinetic energy $(u^2/2)\rho_m \, dV$. Thus, the total energy in the volume V is

$$\int_V [e + (u^2/2)]\rho_m \, dV,$$

and its rate of change is

$$\int_V \frac{\partial}{\partial t}\{[e + (u^2/2)]\rho_m\} \, dV.$$

The energy current consists of two parts: the convection current $[e + (u^2/2)]\rho_m\mathbf{u}$ and the conduction current $\mathbf{q}$. Thus, the rate of loss of energy due to currents through A is

$$\int_A [\mathbf{q} + \{e + (u^2/2)\}\rho_m\mathbf{u}] \cdot d\mathbf{A}.$$

Finally, the work done per unit time on the fluid in V consists again of two contributions: that done by the volume force $\mathbf{f}$ and that done by the surface force $\boldsymbol{\sigma} \cdot d\mathbf{A}$.

Since the total work done on the volume V must equal the rate of increase of the energy contained in V plus the energy transported out through the surface A by convection and conduction currents, we are led to the relation

$$\int_V \mathbf{u} \cdot \mathbf{f} \, dV + \int_A \mathbf{u} \cdot \boldsymbol{\sigma} \cdot d\mathbf{A} = \int_V \frac{\partial}{\partial t}\{[e + (u^2/2)]\rho_m\} \, dV + \int_A [\mathbf{q} + \{e + (u^2/2)\}\rho_m\mathbf{u}] \cdot d\mathbf{A}. \quad (6.2.13)$$

Converting the surface integrals to volume integrals and using the fact that V is arbitrary, we find

$$\mathbf{u} \cdot \mathbf{f} + \nabla \cdot (\boldsymbol{\sigma} \cdot \mathbf{u}) - \nabla \cdot \mathbf{q} = \frac{\partial}{\partial t}\{[e + (u^2/2)]\rho_m\} + \nabla \cdot \{[e + (u^2/2)]\rho_m\mathbf{u}\}, \quad (6.2.14)$$

which is the energy transport equation.

Equation (6.2.14) may be considerably simplified by use of the continuity equation (6.2.7) and the equation of motion (6.2.12). The right-hand side of equation (6.2.14) may be transformed as follows:

$$\frac{\partial}{\partial t}\{[e + (u^2/2)]\rho_m\} + \nabla \cdot \{[e + (u^2/2)]\rho_m \mathbf{u}\}$$

$$= [e + (u^2/2)]\left[\frac{\partial \rho_m}{\partial t} + \nabla \cdot (\rho_m \mathbf{u})\right]$$

$$+ \rho_m\left[\frac{\partial}{\partial t}\{e + (u^2/2)\} + \mathbf{u} \cdot \nabla\{e + (u^2/2)\}\right]$$

$$= \rho_m \frac{D}{Dt}[e + (u^2/2)] = \rho_m\left[\frac{De}{Dt} + \mathbf{u} \cdot \frac{D\mathbf{u}}{Dt}\right], \quad (6.2.15)$$

where

$$\frac{D}{Dt} = \frac{\partial}{\partial t} + \mathbf{u} \cdot \nabla. \quad (6.2.16)$$

The first brace on the second line of (6.2.15) vanishes by virtue of (6.2.7). The term $\nabla \cdot (\boldsymbol{\sigma} \cdot \mathbf{u})$ may be transformed as follows:

$$\nabla \cdot (\boldsymbol{\sigma} \cdot \mathbf{u}) = \frac{\partial}{\partial x_i}(\sigma_{ij} u_j)$$

$$= u_j \frac{\partial}{\partial x_i} \sigma_{ij} + \sigma_{ij} \frac{\partial}{\partial x_i} u_j$$

$$= \mathbf{u} \cdot (\nabla \cdot \boldsymbol{\sigma}) + \boldsymbol{\sigma} : \nabla \mathbf{u}, \quad (6.2.17)$$

whereupon the use of (6.2.15) and (6.2.17) reduces (6.2.14) to

$$\mathbf{u} \cdot \left[\mathbf{f} + \nabla \cdot \boldsymbol{\sigma} - \rho_m \frac{D\mathbf{u}}{Dt}\right] + \boldsymbol{\sigma} : \nabla \mathbf{u} - \nabla \cdot \mathbf{q} - \rho_m \frac{De}{Dt} = 0. \quad (6.2.18)$$

Using now the equation of motion, equation (6.2.12), the energy-transport equation assumes the form

$$\rho_m \frac{De}{Dt} + \nabla \cdot \mathbf{q} - \boldsymbol{\sigma} : \nabla \mathbf{u} = 0. \quad (6.2.19)$$

Alternatively, equation (6.2.19) may be rewritten in terms of the internal energy density $\mathscr{E} = \rho_m e$ as

$$\frac{\partial \mathscr{E}}{\partial t} + \nabla \cdot (\mathscr{E} \mathbf{u}) = \boldsymbol{\sigma} : \nabla \mathbf{u} - \nabla \cdot \mathbf{q}. \quad (6.2.20)$$

Since e is the *internal* energy, neither equations (6.2.19) nor (6.2.20) involve the external potential, or the external force density. Equation

(6.2.20) is slightly more convenient for comparison with the statistical mechanical expressions of the next section.

The equations just derived represent a mechanical description of the fluid and in themselves do not display dissipative behavior. In order to describe irreversible phenomena it is necessary to establish relationships between $\boldsymbol{\sigma}$, $\mathbf{q}$, etc., and the macroscopic variables defining the non-equilibrium state of the fluid. In the phenomenological approach these relations are determined experimentally and are used, in differential equation form, to describe the properties of the fluid. Indeed, the usual classification and description of non-equilibrium behavior is in terms of the phenomenological relations and coefficients thereby determined.

For the stress-strain relationship of a fluid we introduce the Newtonian law

$$\begin{aligned} \boldsymbol{\sigma} &= -(p + [\tfrac{2}{3}\eta - \phi]\nabla \cdot \mathbf{u})\mathbf{I} + 2\eta\boldsymbol{\epsilon} \\ \boldsymbol{\epsilon} &= \mathrm{Sym}\,(\nabla\mathbf{u}) = \tfrac{1}{2}(\nabla\mathbf{u} + \widetilde{\nabla\mathbf{u}}), \\ (\widetilde{\nabla\mathbf{u}})_{ij} &= (\nabla\mathbf{u})_{ji}, \end{aligned} \tag{6.2.21}$$

with p the equilibrium pressure, η the coefficient of shear viscosity, and ϕ the coefficient of bulk (dilatational) viscosity. The experimental determination of η or ϕ depends on the solution of equation (6.2.21) for the boundary conditions and geometry of the particular experiment. As a phenomenological law, equation (6.2.21) is extremely accurate for the case of simple fluids. Indeed, in this monograph we shall not be at all concerned with failure of (6.2.21).

Equation (6.2.21) can be brought into a different form. Using the definition of tensor divergence,

$$\nabla \cdot \boldsymbol{\sigma} = -\nabla p + (\phi - \tfrac{2}{3}\eta)\nabla(\nabla \cdot \mathbf{u}) + \eta\nabla^2\mathbf{u} + \eta\nabla(\nabla \cdot \mathbf{u}), \tag{6.2.22}$$

so that the equation of motion becomes

$$\rho_m \frac{D\mathbf{u}}{Dt} = -\nabla p + (\tfrac{1}{3}\eta + \phi)\,\nabla(\nabla \cdot \mathbf{u}) + \eta\,\nabla^2\mathbf{u} + \mathbf{f}, \tag{6.2.23}$$

which is the Navier-Stokes equation.

Given the Newtonian stress tensor, what form does the energy transport equation take? Noting that $\mathbf{I}:\nabla\mathbf{u} = \nabla \cdot \mathbf{u}$, and substituting equation (6.2.21) into (6.2.19),

$$\rho_m \frac{De}{Dt} + \nabla \cdot \mathbf{q} + [p + (\tfrac{2}{3}\eta - \phi)\,\nabla \cdot \mathbf{u}]\,\nabla \cdot \mathbf{u} - 2\eta\boldsymbol{\epsilon}:\nabla\mathbf{u} = 0. \tag{6.2.24}$$

For very small gradients in the velocity components, one may neglect all terms in (6.2.24) which involve the product of two gradients. Dividing through by ρ_m,

$$\frac{De}{Dt} + \frac{1}{\rho_m}\nabla\cdot\mathbf{q} + \frac{p}{\rho_m}\nabla\cdot\mathbf{u} = 0. \tag{6.2.25}$$

But

$$\frac{1}{\rho_m}\nabla\cdot\mathbf{u} = \frac{1}{\rho_m^{\,2}}\nabla\cdot(\rho_m\mathbf{u}) - \frac{\mathbf{u}}{\rho_m^{\,2}}\cdot\nabla\rho_m, \tag{6.2.26}$$

and from the equation of continuity,

$$\nabla\cdot(\rho_m\mathbf{u}) = -\frac{\partial\rho_m}{\partial t},$$

so that

$$\begin{aligned}\frac{1}{\rho_m}\nabla\cdot\mathbf{u} &= -\frac{1}{\rho_m^{\,2}}\frac{\partial\rho_m}{\partial t} - \mathbf{u}\cdot\left(\frac{1}{\rho_m^{\,2}}\nabla\rho_m\right)\\ &= \frac{\partial}{\partial t}\left(\frac{1}{\rho_m}\right) + \mathbf{u}\cdot\nabla\left(\frac{1}{\rho_m}\right)\\ &= \frac{D}{Dt}\left(\frac{1}{\rho_m}\right) = \frac{Dv}{Dt},\end{aligned} \tag{6.2.27}$$

where $v = \rho_m^{-1}$ is the specific volume. Under the assumption of local thermodynamic equilibrium, the combination of equations (6.2.27) and (6.2.25) gives directly

$$\frac{D}{Dt}(e + pv)_p + \frac{1}{\rho_m}\nabla\cdot\mathbf{q} = 0, \tag{6.2.28}$$

or from the first and second laws of thermodynamics,

$$\rho_m T\frac{DS}{Dt} + \nabla\cdot\mathbf{q} = 0, \tag{6.2.29}$$

which is an equation of continuity for entropy.

Now, the internal energy e may be considered to be a function of v and T, whereupon

$$\begin{aligned}\frac{De}{Dt} &= \left(\frac{\partial e}{\partial T}\right)_v\frac{DT}{Dt} + \left(\frac{\partial e}{\partial v}\right)_T\frac{Dv}{Dt}\\ &= C_V\frac{DT}{Dt} + \left(\frac{\partial e}{\partial v}\right)_T\frac{Dv}{Dt},\end{aligned} \tag{6.2.30}$$

where C_V is the specific heat at constant volume. By substitution of equations (6.2.27) and (6.2.30) into equation (6.2.25), we find

$$C_V \frac{DT}{Dt} + \frac{1}{\rho_m} \nabla \cdot \mathbf{q} + \left[\left(\frac{\partial e}{\partial v} \right)_T + p \right] \frac{Dv}{Dt} = 0. \tag{6.2.31}$$

Under almost all experimental conditions, (Dv/Dt) is negligibly small, so that

$$C_V \frac{DT}{Dt} + \frac{1}{\rho_m} \nabla \cdot \mathbf{q} = 0. \tag{6.2.32}$$

When the fluid is at rest, then $(D/Dt) \to (\partial/\partial t)$, and it is found empirically that

$$\mathbf{q} = -\varkappa \nabla T, \tag{6.2.33}$$

in a frame of reference moving with the local center of mass of the fluid. Substitution of (6.2.33) into (6.2.32) leads to the heat conduction equation:

$$\frac{\partial T}{\partial t} = \frac{\varkappa}{\rho_m C_V} \nabla^2 T, \tag{6.2.34}$$

where $\varkappa$ is the coefficient of thermal conduction.

6.2.B. *The Molecular Theory* (1)

In order that we may finally obtain expressions for the transport coefficients in terms of molecular variables, we must develop statistical mechanical analogs to the phenomenological laws such as the Newtonian stress tensor (6.2.21) and the Fourier conduction law (6.2.33). We follow the procedure of Irving and Kirkwood; this is quite general and consists simply in defining molecular equivalents of, for instance, mass, momentum, and energy densities, and establishing their equations of motion by suitable contractions of the Liouville equation (3.2.20) or (6.2.37).

As in our earlier analysis, we consider N monatomic molecules contained in a volume V. For convenience, we introduce the notation

$$\langle \alpha; f^{(N)} \rangle = \int \alpha(\Gamma_N) f^{(N)}(\Gamma_N; t)\, d\Gamma_N. \tag{6.2.35}$$

Providing that α is not an explicit function of time,

$$\frac{\partial}{\partial t}\langle\alpha;f^{(N)}\rangle = \left\langle\alpha;\frac{\partial f^{(N)}}{\partial t}\right\rangle. \tag{6.2.36}$$

Multiplication of the Liouville equation,

$$\frac{\partial f^{(N)}}{\partial t} = [H,f^{(N)}], \tag{6.2.37}$$

by α and integration over phase space gives

$$\begin{aligned}\frac{\partial}{\partial t}\langle\alpha;f^{(N)}\rangle &= \langle\alpha;[H,f^{(N)}]\rangle \\ &= -\langle[H,\alpha];f^{(N)}\rangle \\ &= \sum_{k=1}^{N}\left\langle\frac{1}{m}\mathbf{p}_k\cdot\nabla_k\alpha + \mathbf{F}_k\cdot\nabla_{p_k}\alpha;f^{(N)}\right\rangle,\end{aligned} \tag{6.2.38}$$

after a partial integration and use of the self-adjoint properties of the linear operator $[H,\cdots]$. Contrary to statements sometimes made, equation (6.2.38) is not restricted to position dependent forces in its validity. Equation (6.2.38) expresses the rate of change of the expectation of α as the expectation of $[\alpha,H]$.

Since the phenomenological equations derived in the previous section are expressed in terms of densities of mass, momentum, and energy, we introduce the definitions

$$\rho_m(\mathbf{r};t) = \sum_{k=1}^{N} m\langle\delta(\mathbf{R}_k-\mathbf{r});f^{(N)}\rangle, \tag{6.2.39}$$

$$\rho_m(\mathbf{r};t)\mathbf{u}(\mathbf{r};t) = \sum_{k=1}^{N}\langle\mathbf{p}_k\,\delta(\mathbf{R}_k-\mathbf{r});f^{(N)}\rangle, \tag{6.2.40}$$

$$E_K(\mathbf{r};t) = \sum_{k=1}^{N}\left\langle\frac{1}{2m}\,p_k^{\,2}\,\delta(\mathbf{R}_k-\mathbf{r});f^{(N)}\right\rangle, \tag{6.2.41}$$

for the mass, momentum and kinetic energy densities, as can be readily verified by substitution in the definition of average value. Equations (6.2.39), (6.2.40), and (6.2.41) merely state that molecule k has directly associated with it mass, m, momentum, $\mathbf{p}_k$, and kinetic energy, $(p_k^2/2m)$. The density at the point $\mathbf{r}$ is just the ensemble average of the relevant molecular function, conditional on molecule k being at the point $\mathbf{r}$.

The total potential energy of the system will be assumed to be of the form

$$U = \sum_{k=1}^{N} \psi(\mathbf{R}_k) + \tfrac{1}{2} \sum_{j \neq k=1}^{N}\sum u_{jk}, \tag{6.2.42}$$

where $\psi(\mathbf{R}_k)$ is the potential energy of the kth molecule in an external force field. The potential energy $\psi(\mathbf{R}_k)$ may quite naturally be localized at $\mathbf{R}_k$ and associated directly with particle k, whereupon

$$\begin{aligned} E_\psi(\mathbf{r};t) &= \sum_{k=1}^{N} \langle \psi(\mathbf{R}_k)\, \delta(\mathbf{R}_k - \mathbf{r}); f^{(N)} \rangle \\ &= \sum_{k=1}^{N} \psi(\mathbf{r}) \langle \delta(\mathbf{R}_k - \mathbf{r}); f^{(N)} \rangle, \end{aligned} \tag{6.2.43}$$

$$\begin{aligned} \mathbf{f}(\mathbf{r};t) &= \sum_{k=1}^{N} \langle -\nabla_k \psi(\mathbf{R}_k)\, \delta(\mathbf{R}_k - \mathbf{r}); f^{(N)} \rangle \\ &= -\sum_{k=1}^{N} \nabla \psi(\mathbf{r}) \langle \delta(\mathbf{R}_k - \mathbf{r}); f^{(N)} \rangle, \end{aligned} \tag{6.2.44}$$

with $\mathbf{f}$ the external force density. In contrast to the preceding one molecule functions, the intermolecular pair potential u_{jk} depends on the positions of both molecules j and k. Although u_{jk} may be considered localized only in the six-dimensional configuration space of the pair of molecules, it may be precisely though arbitrarily localized in ordinary three-dimensional space. We define the total interaction potential energy residing in the kth molecule by

$$\tfrac{1}{2} \sum_{j=1(\neq k)}^{N} u_{jk},$$

corresponding to the assumption that half of the energy u_{jk} resides in each molecule. With this definition,

$$E_V(\mathbf{r};t) = \tfrac{1}{2} \sum_{j \neq k=1}^{N}\sum \langle u_{jk}\, \delta(\mathbf{R}_k - \mathbf{r}); f^{(N)} \rangle. \tag{6.2.45}$$

Finally, we shall have occasion to use the density of molecules in pair space,

$$\rho^{(2)}(\mathbf{r},\mathbf{r}';t) = \sum_{j \neq k=1}^{N}\sum \langle \delta(\mathbf{R}_k - \mathbf{r})\, \delta(\mathbf{R}_j - \mathbf{r}'); f^{(N)} \rangle, \tag{6.2.46}$$

the particle current density in pair space,

$$\mathbf{j}^{(2)}(\mathbf{r},\mathbf{r}';t) = \tfrac{1}{2} \sum_{j \neq k=1}^{N}\sum \left\langle \frac{1}{m} (\mathbf{p}_k \oplus \mathbf{p}_j)\, \delta(\mathbf{R}_k - \mathbf{r})\, \delta(\mathbf{R}_j - \mathbf{r}'); f^{(N)} \right\rangle, \tag{6.2.47}$$

and the particle current density in ordinary three-dimensional space, conditional on the presence of a second particle at a selected point, multiplied by the particle density at that selected point,

$$\mathbf{j}_1^{(2)}(\mathbf{r},\mathbf{r}';t) = \sum_{k\neq j=1}^{N}\sum \left\langle \frac{1}{m}\,\mathbf{p}_k\,\delta(\mathbf{R}_k - \mathbf{r})\,\delta(\mathbf{R}_j - \mathbf{r}'); f^{(N)} \right\rangle. \quad (6.2.48)$$

In equation (6.2.47) the symbol $\oplus$ indicates the direct sum, i.e., the two vectors are added to generate a six-dimensional space and *are not* added in the same three-dimensional space. The reader should note that $\rho^{(2)}(\mathbf{r},\mathbf{r}';t)$ and $\mathbf{j}^{(2)}(\mathbf{r},\mathbf{r}';t)$ are symmetric on interchange of $\mathbf{r}$ and $\mathbf{r}'$, whereas $\mathbf{j}_1^{(2)}$ does not have this symmetry.

The first phenomenological equation derived, equation (6.2.7), was an expression of the conservation of mass. If in the statistical theory we set

$$\alpha_m \equiv \sum_{j=1}^{N} m\,\delta(\mathbf{R}_j - \mathbf{r}), \quad (6.2.49)$$

then starting with the result

$$\frac{1}{m}\,\mathbf{p}_k \cdot \nabla_k \alpha_m + \mathbf{F}_k \cdot \nabla_{p_k} \alpha_m = \mathbf{p}_k \cdot \nabla_k\,\delta(\mathbf{R}_k - \mathbf{r}) = -\nabla \cdot [\mathbf{p}_k\,\delta(\mathbf{R}_k - \mathbf{r})]$$

and taking the ensemble average, using equations (6.2.39) and (6.2.40) for the two terms on the right-hand side of equation (6.2.38), we find

$$\frac{\partial}{\partial t}\langle \alpha_m; f^{(N)}\rangle = \sum_{k=1}^{N}\langle -\nabla \cdot [\mathbf{p}_k\,\delta(\mathbf{R}_k - \mathbf{r})]; f^{(N)}\rangle,$$

or

$$\frac{\partial}{\partial t}\,\rho_m(\mathbf{r};t) = -\nabla \cdot [\rho_m(\mathbf{r};t)\mathbf{u}(\mathbf{r};t)], \quad (6.2.50)$$

which will be recognized to be identical with equation (6.2.7).

As in the phenomenological case, to obtain the equation of motion of the fluid, we must examine the transport of momentum. In this case we define

$$\boldsymbol{\alpha}_p \equiv \sum_{j=1}^{N} \mathbf{p}_j\,\delta(\mathbf{R}_j - \mathbf{r}). \quad (6.2.51)$$

The reader should note that $\boldsymbol{\alpha}_p$ is a vector quantity. The appropriate generalization of equation (6.2.37) is

$$\frac{\partial}{\partial t}\langle \boldsymbol{\alpha}_p ; f^{(N)}\rangle = \sum_{k=1}^{N}\left\langle \frac{1}{m}\,\mathbf{p}_k\cdot\nabla_k\boldsymbol{\alpha}_p + \mathbf{F}_k\cdot\nabla_{p_k}\boldsymbol{\alpha}_p ; f^{(N)}\right\rangle, \quad (6.2.52)$$

as may be easily verified by writing equation (6.2.38) for each of the components of $\boldsymbol{\alpha}_p$. Again, starting with the result

$$\begin{aligned}\frac{1}{m}\,\mathbf{p}_k\cdot\nabla_k\boldsymbol{\alpha}_p + \mathbf{F}_k\cdot\nabla_{p_k}\boldsymbol{\alpha}_p &= \frac{1}{m}\,\mathbf{p}_k\cdot\nabla_k\mathbf{p}_k\,\delta(\mathbf{R}_k-\mathbf{r}) + \mathbf{F}_k\cdot\nabla_{p_k}\mathbf{p}_k\,\delta(\mathbf{R}_k-\mathbf{r})\\ &= -\nabla\cdot\left[\frac{1}{m}\,\mathbf{p}_k\mathbf{p}_k\,\delta(\mathbf{R}_k-\mathbf{r})\right] + \mathbf{F}_k\,\delta(\mathbf{R}_k-\mathbf{r}),\end{aligned} \quad (6.2.53)$$

and using the decomposition of the intermolecular potential,

$$\mathbf{F}_k = -\nabla_k\psi(\mathbf{R}_k) - \sum_{j=1(\neq k)}^{N}\nabla_k u_{jk}, \quad (6.2.54)$$

together with the definition (6.2.40) of the momentum density,

$$\langle \boldsymbol{\alpha}_p ; f^{(N)}\rangle = \rho_m(\mathbf{r};t)\mathbf{u}(\mathbf{r};t), \quad (6.2.55)$$

leads directly to

$$\begin{aligned}\frac{\partial}{\partial t}(\rho_m\mathbf{u}) = -\nabla\cdot\sum_{k=1}^{N}&\left\langle\frac{1}{m}\,\mathbf{p}_k\mathbf{p}_k\,\delta(\mathbf{R}_k-\mathbf{r}) ; f^{(N)}\right\rangle\\ &+ \mathbf{f}(\mathbf{r};t) - \sum_{j\neq k=1}^{N}\sum\langle(\nabla_k u_{jk})\,\delta(\mathbf{R}_k-\mathbf{r}) ; f^{(N)}\rangle.\end{aligned} \quad (6.2.56)$$

To proceed, we introduce the difference between the mean velocity, $\mathbf{u}$, and the molecular velocity, $(\mathbf{p}_k/m)$, and note that

$$\begin{aligned}\sum_{k=1}^{N} m\langle(\mathbf{p}_k/m-\mathbf{u})(\mathbf{p}_k/m-\mathbf{u})\,\delta(\mathbf{R}_k-\mathbf{r}) ; f^{(N)}\rangle\\ = \sum_{k=1}^{N}\left\langle\frac{1}{m}\,\mathbf{p}_k\mathbf{p}_k\,\delta(\mathbf{R}_k-\mathbf{r}) ; f^{(N)}\right\rangle - \mathbf{u}\sum_{k=1}^{N}\langle\mathbf{p}_k\,\delta(\mathbf{R}_k-\mathbf{r}) ; f^{(N)}\rangle\\ - \sum_{k=1}^{N}\langle\mathbf{p}_k\,\delta(\mathbf{R}_k-\mathbf{r}) ; f^{(N)}\rangle\mathbf{u} + \mathbf{u}\mathbf{u}\sum_{k=1}^{N}\langle m\,\delta(\mathbf{R}_k-\mathbf{r}) ; f^{(N)}\rangle\\ = \sum_{k=1}^{N}\left\langle\frac{1}{m}\,\mathbf{p}_k\mathbf{p}_k\,\delta(\mathbf{R}_k-\mathbf{r}) ; f^{(N)}\right\rangle - \rho_m\mathbf{u}\mathbf{u}.\end{aligned} \quad (6.2.57)$$

Because the potential u_{jk} is symmetric in the positions of molecules j and k, it is convenient to symmetrize the last term of equation (6.2.56) with respect to j and k (k appears only as a dummy index). Rewriting the last term of (6.2.56) in terms of a summation over j, summing the two equations and introducing a factor of one half, and using the identity $\nabla_j u_{jk} = -\nabla_k u_{jk}$, leads to

$$-\sum_{j\neq k=1}^{N}\sum \langle(\nabla_k u_{jk})\,\delta(\mathbf{R}_k - \mathbf{r}); f^{(N)}\rangle$$
$$= -\tfrac{1}{2}\sum_{j\neq k=1}^{N}\sum \langle(\nabla_k u_{jk})[\delta(\mathbf{R}_k - \mathbf{r}) - \delta(\mathbf{R}_j - \mathbf{r})]; f^{(N)}\rangle. \quad (6.2.58)$$

The difference between the delta functions in equation (6.2.58) may be developed in a Taylor's series in the vector separation $\mathbf{R}_{jk} = \mathbf{R}_k - \mathbf{R}_j$ about $\delta(\mathbf{R}_j - \mathbf{r})$, and in a dense liquid only the first term need be kept. With this expansion, a commutation of ∇ and the integration over phase space, the insertion of equation (6.2.58) into (6.2.56) leads to the equation of motion

$$\frac{\partial}{\partial t}(\rho_m \mathbf{u}) + \nabla \cdot (\rho_m \mathbf{u}\mathbf{u})$$
$$= \mathbf{f} + \nabla \cdot \left[-\sum_{k=1}^{N} m\left\langle\left(\frac{\mathbf{p}_k}{m} - \mathbf{u}\right)\left(\frac{\mathbf{p}_k}{m} - \mathbf{u}\right)\delta(\mathbf{R}_k - \mathbf{r}); f^{(N)}\right\rangle\right.$$
$$\left. + \tfrac{1}{2}\sum_{j\neq k=1}^{N}\sum \langle(\nabla_k u_{jk})\mathbf{R}_{jk}\,\delta(\mathbf{R}_j - \mathbf{r}); f^{(N)}\rangle\right]. \quad (6.2.59)$$

By neglecting higher order terms in the expansion of the difference of delta functions in equation (6.2.58), we restrict (6.2.59) to the case of the dense fluid. For, in the liquid the pair density $\rho^{(2)}(\mathbf{r}, \mathbf{r} + \mathbf{R}; t)$ is only a very slowly varying function of $\mathbf{r}$ but a very rapidly varying function of $\mathbf{R}$. Thus, we expect that $\mathbf{R} \cdot \nabla\rho^{(2)}$ is negligible relative to $\rho^{(2)}(\mathbf{r}, \mathbf{r} + \mathbf{R}; t)$ for all values of R comparable with the range of the intermolecular potential. Of course, in the limit of the infinitely dilute gas the contribution due to the potential energy of interaction vanishes as ρ^2. It is only for the first potential energy correction to the stress tensor of a gas, when, because of the low density, the collision cylinder is very long and hence R is large, that the neglected derivative terms need be introduced. We emphasize that at liquid densities, equation (6.2.59) is very accurate.

A comparison of equations (6.2.12) and (6.2.59) shows that the stress tensor is defined by

$$\boldsymbol{\sigma} = \boldsymbol{\sigma}_K + \boldsymbol{\sigma}_V,$$

$$\boldsymbol{\sigma}_K = -\sum_{k=1}^{N} m\left\langle\left(\frac{\mathbf{p}_k}{m} - \mathbf{u}\right)\left(\frac{\mathbf{p}_k}{m} - \mathbf{u}\right) \delta(\mathbf{R}_k - \mathbf{r}); f^{(N)}\right\rangle,$$

$$\boldsymbol{\sigma}_V = \tfrac{1}{2}\sum_{j\neq k=1}^{N}\sum \left\langle \frac{\mathbf{R}_{jk}\mathbf{R}_{jk}}{R_{jk}} u_{jk}' \, \delta(\mathbf{R}_j - \mathbf{r}); f^{(N)}\right\rangle,$$

where

$$\nabla_k u_{jk} = \nabla_{jk} u_{jk} = (\mathbf{R}_{jk}/R_{jk})(du_{jk}/dR_{jk}) = (\mathbf{R}_{jk}/R_{jk})u_{jk}'. \quad (6.2.60)$$

Strictly speaking, since $\boldsymbol{\sigma}$ appears in equation (6.2.12) as $\nabla \cdot \boldsymbol{\sigma}$, the form of $\boldsymbol{\sigma}$ given in equation (6.2.60) is determined only to within the curl of an arbitrary vector function of $\mathbf{r}$. However, we shall show later [Eq. (6.2.79)] that this is the correct form. The separation of $\boldsymbol{\sigma}$ in equation (6.2.60) into $\boldsymbol{\sigma}_K$ and $\boldsymbol{\sigma}_V$ has a well-known physical significance: $\boldsymbol{\sigma}_K$ represents the momentum flux due to the translation of individual molecules, while $\boldsymbol{\sigma}_V$ represents the momentum flux arising from intermolecular forces. Both $\boldsymbol{\sigma}_K$ and $\boldsymbol{\sigma}_V$ are referred to a coordinate system moving with the local fluid velocity $\mathbf{u}$. In the dilute gas $\boldsymbol{\sigma}_K$ gives the dominant contribution, while in a dense gas or liquid translation of individual molecules is inhibited and $\boldsymbol{\sigma}_V$ gives the dominant contribution.

It is of interest to show that the stress tensor defined by equation (6.2.60) properly relates the pressure to the pair distribution function. To express $\boldsymbol{\sigma}_V$ directly in terms of the pair distribution function we introduce an integral relation involving the delta function, $\delta(\mathbf{R}_{jk} - \mathbf{R})$, defined such that equation (6.2.60) is preserved. This relation is

$$\boldsymbol{\sigma}_V(\mathbf{r};t) = \frac{1}{2}\sum_{j\neq k=1}^{N}\sum \left\langle \int \delta(\mathbf{R}_{jk} - \mathbf{R}) \frac{\mathbf{R}\mathbf{R}}{R} u'(R)\, \delta(\mathbf{R}_j - \mathbf{r})\, d\mathbf{R}; f^{(N)}\right\rangle. \quad (6.2.61)$$

Since the integration over phase space does not involve the dummy variable $\mathbf{R}$, the integration over $\mathbf{R}$ may be commuted with the integration over phase and the summation over j and k. We are thereby led to

$$\boldsymbol{\sigma}_V(\mathbf{r}\cdot t) = \frac{1}{2}\int \frac{\mathbf{R}\mathbf{R}}{R} u'(R) \sum_{j\neq k=1}^{N}\sum \langle \delta(\mathbf{R}_{jk} - \mathbf{R})\, \delta(\mathbf{R}_j - \mathbf{r}); f^{(N)}\rangle \, d\mathbf{R}. \quad (6.2.62)$$

By the definition of the expectation value and of the delta function, $\delta(\mathbf{R}_{jk} - \mathbf{R})\, \delta(\mathbf{R}_j - \mathbf{r})$ in the integrand is equivalent to

$$\delta(\mathbf{R}_j - \mathbf{r})\, \delta(\mathbf{R}_k - \mathbf{r} - \mathbf{R}),$$

whereupon the use of definition (6.2.46) enables us to express $\boldsymbol{\sigma}_V$ in the form

$$\boldsymbol{\sigma}_V(\mathbf{r};t) = \frac{1}{2}\int \frac{\mathbf{RR}}{R} u'(R)\rho^{(2)}(\mathbf{r}, \mathbf{r} + \mathbf{R}; t)\, d\mathbf{R}$$
$$= \frac{\rho^2}{2}\int \frac{\mathbf{RR}}{R} u'(R) g^{(2)}(\mathbf{r},\mathbf{R};t)\, d\mathbf{R}. \tag{6.2.63}$$

The reader should note that our derivation is valid only for the case of a continuous differentiable potential. We shall have occasion to modify equation (6.2.63) for the case that $u(R)$ represents a discontinuous rigid core repulsion.

To obtain the pressure we note that from equation (6.2.21)

$$p = -\tfrac{1}{3} Tr\boldsymbol{\sigma} \tag{6.2.64}$$

when $\nabla\mathbf{u} = \boldsymbol{\epsilon} = 0$. The kinetic contribution to p is just

$$p_K = -\tfrac{1}{3} Tr\boldsymbol{\sigma}_K = \frac{2}{3}\sum_{j=1}^{N}\left\langle \frac{m}{2}\left(\frac{\mathbf{p}_k}{m} - \mathbf{u}\right)^2 \delta(\mathbf{R}_k - \mathbf{r}); f^{(N)}\right\rangle = \rho kT, \tag{6.2.65}$$

since the average kinetic energy per particle in an equilibrium ensemble is just $\frac{3}{2}kT$. For the intermolecular force contribution we find

$$p_V = -\tfrac{1}{3} Tr\boldsymbol{\sigma}_V = -\frac{\rho^2}{6}\int R u'(R) g^{(2)}(\mathbf{r},\mathbf{R})\, d\mathbf{R}, \tag{6.2.66}$$

since the diagonal terms of $\mathbf{RR}$ just give $(R^2/3)\mathbf{I}$. In an equilibrium ensemble, ρ and $g^{(2)}$ are independent of $\mathbf{r}$. By combination of equations (6.2.65) and (6.2.66), we find for the equilibrium pressure

$$p = \rho kT - \frac{2\pi\rho^2}{3}\int_0^\infty u'(R) g_0^{(2)}(R) R^3\, dR, \tag{6.2.67}$$

in complete agreement with equation (2.4.49).

We turn now to a derivation of the energy transport equation using techniques identical with those introduced above. It is convenient to proceed by deriving the two separate contributions to the internal energy density. Consider first the internal kinetic energy density $\mathscr{E}_K$, for which

$$\alpha_K = \sum_{j=1}^{N} \frac{m}{2}\left(\frac{\mathbf{p}_j}{m} - \mathbf{u}\right)^2 \delta(\mathbf{R}_j - \mathbf{r}), \tag{6.2.68}$$

and

$$\mathscr{E}_K = \langle \alpha_K; f^{(N)}\rangle.$$

Now,

$$\frac{1}{m}\mathbf{p}_k\cdot\nabla_k\alpha_k+\mathbf{F}_k\cdot\nabla_{p_k}\alpha_K$$

$$=\frac{1}{m}\mathbf{p}_k\cdot\left[\frac{m}{2}\left(\frac{\mathbf{p}_k}{m}-\mathbf{u}\right)^2\nabla_k\,\delta(\mathbf{R}_k-\mathbf{r})\right]$$

$$-\left[\nabla_k\left(\sum_{j(\neq k)}^{N}u_{kj}+\psi(\mathbf{R}_k)\right)\right]\cdot\left(\frac{\mathbf{p}_k}{m}-\mathbf{u}\right)\delta(\mathbf{R}_k-\mathbf{r})\Bigg]$$

$$=-\nabla\cdot\left[\tfrac{1}{2}\mathbf{p}_k\left(\frac{\mathbf{p}_k}{m}-\mathbf{u}\right)^2\delta(\mathbf{R}_k-\mathbf{r})\right]-\nabla\mathbf{u}:\left(\frac{\mathbf{p}_k}{m}-\mathbf{u}\right)\mathbf{p}_k\,\delta(\mathbf{R}_k-\mathbf{r})$$

$$-\left\{\nabla_k\left[\sum_{j(\neq k)}^{N}u_{jk}+\psi(\mathbf{R}_k)\right]\right\}\cdot\left(\frac{\mathbf{p}_k}{m}-\mathbf{u}\right)\delta(\mathbf{R}_k-\mathbf{r}),\qquad(6.2.69)$$

so that equation (6.2.38) for $\mathscr{E}_K$ becomes

$$\frac{\partial\mathscr{E}_k}{\partial t}=-\nabla\cdot\left\langle\tfrac{1}{2}\sum_{k=1}^{N}\mathbf{p}_k\left(\frac{\mathbf{p}_k}{m}-\mathbf{u}\right)^2\delta(\mathbf{R}_k-\mathbf{r});f^{(N)}\right\rangle$$

$$-\nabla\mathbf{u}:\left\langle\sum_{k=1}^{N}\mathbf{p}_k\left(\frac{\mathbf{p}_k}{m}-\mathbf{u}\right)\delta(\mathbf{R}_k-\mathbf{r});f^{(N)}\right\rangle$$

$$-\left\langle\sum_{j\neq k=1}^{N}\sum\nabla_k u_{jk}\cdot\left(\frac{\mathbf{p}_k}{m}-\mathbf{u}\right)\delta(\mathbf{R}_k-\mathbf{r});f^{(N)}\right\rangle,\qquad(6.2.70)$$

with

$$\left\langle\sum_{k=1}^{N}\nabla_k\psi(\mathbf{R}_k)\cdot\left(\frac{\mathbf{p}_k}{m}-\mathbf{u}\right)\delta(\mathbf{R}_k-\mathbf{r});f^{(N)}\right\rangle$$

$$=\nabla\psi(\mathbf{r})\cdot\left\langle\sum_{k=1}^{N}\left(\frac{\mathbf{p}_k}{m}-\mathbf{u}\right)\delta(\mathbf{R}_k-\mathbf{r});f^{(N)}\right\rangle\equiv 0,\quad(6.2.71)$$

which follows from equation (6.2.40). By expressing all velocities in equation (6.2.70) with respect to the local fluid velocity $\mathbf{u}$, we obtain

$$\frac{\partial\mathscr{E}_K}{\partial t}=-\nabla\cdot\left\langle\sum_{k=1}^{N}\frac{m}{2}\left(\frac{\mathbf{p}_k}{m}-\mathbf{u}\right)^2\left(\frac{\mathbf{p}_k}{m}-\mathbf{u}\right)\delta(\mathbf{R}_k-\mathbf{r});f^{(N)}\right\rangle$$

$$-\nabla\cdot(\mathscr{E}_K\mathbf{u})+\nabla\mathbf{u}:\boldsymbol{\sigma}_K$$

$$-\left\langle\sum_{j\neq k=1}^{N}\sum\nabla_k u_{jk}\cdot\left(\frac{\mathbf{p}_k}{m}-\mathbf{u}\right)\delta(\mathbf{R}_k-\mathbf{r});f^{(N)}\right\rangle.\qquad(6.2.72)$$

As in the study of momentum transport, the treatment of the intermolecular potential contribution is more complex. Once again defining the intermolecular potential energy associated with molecule j as

$$\tfrac{1}{2} \sum_{k(\neq j)}^{N} u_{jk}$$

the microscopic density at $\mathbf{r}$ is

$$\alpha_V = \tfrac{1}{2} \sum_{j\neq k=1}^{N}\sum u_{jk}\, \delta(\mathbf{R}_j - \mathbf{r}). \tag{6.2.73}$$

Now,

$$\begin{aligned}
&\frac{1}{m}\mathbf{p}_k \cdot \nabla_k \alpha_V + \mathbf{F}_k \cdot \nabla_{p_k}\alpha_V \\
&= \frac{1}{m}\mathbf{p}_k \cdot \nabla_k \left[\frac{1}{2} \sum_{j\neq i=1}^{N}\sum u_{ji}\, \delta(\mathbf{R}_j - \mathbf{r})\right] \\
&= \frac{1}{2m}\mathbf{p}_k \cdot \left[\sum_{j(\neq k)=1}^{N} \nabla_k u_{kj}\, \delta(\mathbf{R}_j - \mathbf{r}) + \sum_{i(\neq k)=1}^{N} \nabla_k u_{ik}\, \delta(\mathbf{R}_k - \mathbf{r}) \right. \\
&\qquad \left. + \sum_{i(\neq k)=1}^{N} u_{ik}\, \nabla_k\, \delta(\mathbf{R}_k - \mathbf{r})\right] \\
&= \frac{1}{2m}\mathbf{p}_k \cdot \left[\sum_{j(\neq k)=1}^{N} \nabla_k u_{jk}\{\delta(\mathbf{R}_j - \mathbf{r}) + \delta(\mathbf{R}_k - \mathbf{r})\}\right] \\
&\qquad - \frac{1}{2m}\nabla \cdot \left[\sum_{j(\neq k)=1}^{N} u_{jk}\mathbf{p}_k\, \delta(\mathbf{R}_k - \mathbf{r})\right],
\end{aligned} \tag{6.2.74}$$

whence, from equation (6.2.38),

$$\begin{aligned}
\frac{\partial \mathscr{E}_V}{\partial t} &= \frac{1}{2m}\left\langle \sum_{j\neq k=1}^{N}\sum \mathbf{p}_k \cdot \nabla_k u_{jk}\{\delta(\mathbf{R}_j - \mathbf{r}) + \delta(\mathbf{R}_k - \mathbf{r})\}; f^{(N)}\right\rangle \\
&\quad - \frac{1}{2m}\nabla \cdot \left\langle \sum_{j\neq k=1}^{N}\sum u_{jk}\mathbf{p}_k\, \delta(\mathbf{R}_k - \mathbf{r}); f^{(N)}\right\rangle \\
&= \frac{1}{2}\left\langle \sum_{j\neq k=1}^{N}\sum \left(\frac{\mathbf{p}_k}{m} - \mathbf{u}\right) \cdot \nabla_k u_{jk}\{\delta(\mathbf{R}_j - \mathbf{r}) + \delta(\mathbf{R}_k - \mathbf{r})\}; f^{(N)}\right\rangle \\
&\quad - \tfrac{1}{2}\nabla \cdot \left\langle \sum_{j\neq k=1}^{N}\sum u_{jk}\left(\frac{\mathbf{p}_k}{m} - \mathbf{u}\right) \delta(\mathbf{R}_k - \mathbf{r}); f^{(N)}\right\rangle - \nabla \cdot (\mathscr{E}_V \mathbf{u}),
\end{aligned} \tag{6.2.75}$$

since

$$\left\langle \sum_{j\neq k=1}^{N}\sum \nabla_k u_{jk}\{\delta(\mathbf{R}_k - \mathbf{r}) + \delta(\mathbf{R}_j - \mathbf{r})\}; f^{(N)}\right\rangle$$

vanishes identically. Combining equations (6.2.72) and (6.2.75), we obtain

$$\frac{\partial \mathscr{E}}{\partial t} + \nabla \cdot (\mathbf{u}\mathscr{E}) = -\nabla \cdot \left\langle \sum_{k=1}^{N} \frac{m}{2} \left(\frac{\mathbf{p}_k}{m} - \mathbf{u}\right)^2 \left(\frac{\mathbf{p}_k}{m} - \mathbf{u}\right) \delta(\mathbf{R}_k - \mathbf{r}); f^{(N)} \right\rangle$$
$$+ \frac{1}{2} \left\langle \sum_{j \neq k=1}^{N}\sum \left(\frac{\mathbf{p}_k}{m} - \mathbf{u}\right) \cdot \nabla_k u_{jk} \{\delta(\mathbf{R}_j - \mathbf{r}) - \delta(\mathbf{R}_k - \mathbf{r})\}; f^{(N)} \right\rangle$$
$$- \tfrac{1}{2}\nabla \cdot \left\langle \sum_{j \neq k=1}^{N}\sum u_{jk} \left(\frac{\mathbf{p}_k}{m} - \mathbf{u}\right) \delta(\mathbf{R}_k - \mathbf{r}); f^{(N)} \right\rangle. \quad (6.2.76)$$

Using the relation

$$\delta(\mathbf{R}_j - \mathbf{r}) = \delta(\mathbf{R}_k + (\mathbf{R}_j - \mathbf{R}_k) - \mathbf{r})$$
$$= \delta(\mathbf{R}_k - \mathbf{r}) + \mathbf{R}_{kj} \cdot \nabla_k \, \delta(\mathbf{R}_k - \mathbf{r}) + \cdots, \quad (6.2.77)$$

the second term on the right hand side of equation (6.2.76) may be transformed to

$$\frac{1}{2} \left\langle \sum_{j \neq k=1}^{N}\sum \left(\frac{\mathbf{p}_k}{m} - \mathbf{u}\right) \cdot \nabla_k u_{jk} \{\delta(\mathbf{R}_j - \mathbf{r}) - \delta(\mathbf{R}_k - \mathbf{r})\}; f^{(N)} \right\rangle$$
$$= -\frac{1}{2} \left\langle \sum_{j \neq k=1}^{N}\sum \left(\frac{\mathbf{p}_k}{m} - \mathbf{u}\right) \cdot \mathbf{R}_{kj} \frac{u_{jk}'}{R_{kj}} \{\mathbf{R}_{kj} \cdot \nabla_k \, \delta(\mathbf{R}_k - \mathbf{r}) + \cdots\}; f^{(N)} \right\rangle$$
$$= \tfrac{1}{2}\nabla \cdot \left\langle \sum_{j \neq k=1}^{N}\sum \mathbf{R}_{kj}\mathbf{R}_{kj} \cdot \left(\frac{\mathbf{p}_k}{m} - \mathbf{u}\right) \frac{u_{jk}'}{R_{kj}} \delta(\mathbf{R}_k - \mathbf{r}); f^{(N)} \right\rangle + \boldsymbol{\sigma}_V : \nabla \mathbf{u},$$
$$(6.2.78)$$

where we have again neglected higher derivatives of $\delta(\mathbf{R}_k - \mathbf{r})$. Equation (6.2.76) becomes

$$\frac{\partial \mathscr{E}}{\partial t} + \nabla \cdot (\mathbf{u}\mathscr{E})$$
$$= \boldsymbol{\sigma} : \nabla \mathbf{u} - \nabla \cdot \left[\left\langle \sum_{k=1}^{N} \frac{m}{2} \left(\frac{\mathbf{p}_k}{m} - \mathbf{u}\right)^2 \left(\frac{\mathbf{p}_k}{m} - \mathbf{u}\right) \delta(\mathbf{R}_k - \mathbf{r}); f^{(N)} \right\rangle \right.$$
$$\left. + \frac{1}{2} \left\langle \sum_{j \neq k=1}^{N}\sum \left(u_{kj}\mathbf{I} - \frac{\mathbf{R}_{kj}\mathbf{R}_{kj}}{R_{kj}} u_{kj}'\right) \cdot \left(\frac{\mathbf{p}_k}{m} - \mathbf{u}\right) \delta(\mathbf{R}_k - \mathbf{r}); f^{(N)} \right\rangle \right],$$
$$(6.2.79)$$

and upon comparison of equation (6.2.79) with (6.2.20) the heat flux vector $\mathbf{q}$ may be identified as

$$\mathbf{q} = \mathbf{q}_K + \mathbf{q}_V,$$

$$\mathbf{q}_K = \left\langle \sum_{k=1}^{N} \frac{m}{2}\left(\frac{\mathbf{p}_k}{m} - \mathbf{u}\right)^2 \left(\frac{\mathbf{p}_k}{m} - \mathbf{u}\right) \delta(\mathbf{R}_k - \mathbf{r}); f^{(N)} \right\rangle,$$

$$\mathbf{q}_V = \frac{1}{2}\left\langle \sum_{j \neq k=1}^{N}\sum \left(u_{kj}\mathbf{1} - \frac{\mathbf{R}_{kj}\mathbf{R}_{kj}}{R_{kj}} u_{kj}'\right) \cdot \left(\frac{\mathbf{p}_k}{m} - \mathbf{u}\right) \delta(\mathbf{R}_k - \mathbf{r}); f^{(N)} \right\rangle, \tag{6.2.80}$$

apart from the curl of an arbitrary vector. The comparison also yields a completely determined expression for $\boldsymbol{\sigma}$, which is identical with the form given in equation (6.2.60), as may be seen by comparison of equations (6.2.70) and (6.2.72), and of the two lines of equation (6.2.78). The confirmation of equation (6.2.60) for $\boldsymbol{\sigma}$ encourages us to believe that equation (6.2.80) for $\mathbf{q}$ is also complete. This hope is supported by a calculation of the equation of change of the quantity

$$\left\langle \sum_{k=1}^{N} \left\{ \frac{m}{2}\left(\frac{\mathbf{p}_k}{m} - \mathbf{u}\right)^2 \mathbf{l} + \frac{1}{2} \sum_{j(\neq k)=1}^{N} \left(u_{kj}\mathbf{l} - \frac{\mathbf{R}_{kj}\mathbf{R}_{kj}}{R_{kj}} u_{kj}'\right)\right\} \cdot (\mathbf{p}_k/m - \mathbf{u}); f^{(N)} \right\rangle = \mathbf{q}$$

in which $\mathbf{q}$ appears directly, for the same reason that $\boldsymbol{\sigma}$, which appears in $\nabla \cdot \boldsymbol{\sigma}$ in the momentum equation, appears in $\boldsymbol{\sigma}:\nabla\mathbf{u}$ in the internal energy equation. Unfortunately, the equation of change of the heat flow vector has no phenomenological meaning, so that the expression for $\mathbf{q}$ cannot be established by comparison of a statistical mechanical equation with a phenomenological equation. For many purposes the possibility that equation (6.2.80) is incomplete does not matter because calculations are usually made with equation (6.2.32) or (6.2.34), in which only $\nabla \cdot \mathbf{q}$ appears.

It is convenient for future calculations, as it was with $\boldsymbol{\sigma}_V$, to express $\mathbf{q}_V$ in terms of quantities associated with a pair of molecules. To this end we introduce the dummy variable $\mathbf{R}$ by means of an integration over the delta-function $\delta(\mathbf{R}_{kj} - \mathbf{R})$. The product $\delta(\mathbf{R}_k - \mathbf{r})\,\delta(\mathbf{R}_{kj} - \mathbf{R})$ is, by virtue of the singular properties of the delta-function, equivalent to $\delta(\mathbf{R}_k - \mathbf{r})\,\delta(\mathbf{R}_j - \mathbf{r} - \mathbf{R})$. After a little manipulation the result

$$\mathbf{q}_V = \frac{1}{2}\int \left[u(R)\mathbf{l} - \frac{\mathbf{RR}}{R} u'(R)\right] \cdot [\mathbf{j}_1^{(2)}(\mathbf{r}, \mathbf{r} + \mathbf{R}; t) - \mathbf{u}(\mathbf{r};t)\rho^{(2)}(\mathbf{r}, \mathbf{r} + \mathbf{R}; t)]\, d\mathbf{R} \tag{6.2.81}$$

is obtained.

The heat flux $\mathbf{q}_K$ arises from the net transport of kinetic energy across an arbitrary reference plane in the fluid, while the heat flux $\mathbf{q}_V$ arises from the net transport of potential energy across the same reference plane by virtue of the current of potential energy [term proportional to $u(R)$] and the work done by the molecules on one side of the plane on the molecules on the other side of the plane. (Work is done when molecules move in the force field of other molecules.) In dilute gases, $\mathbf{q}_K$ makes the dominant contribution, whereas in liquids $\mathbf{q}_V$ dominates the total heat flux. As in the case of the stress tensor, equation (6.2.81) is valid for a continuous potential and must be modified for the case of a discontinuous intermolecular interaction. An alternative expression for the heat flow vector may be obtained by a transformation to center of mass and relative coordinates, which are perhaps more natural for the discussion of the motion of a pair of molecules. Since the expression for $\mathbf{q}_V$ in equation (6.2.80) is invariant under an interchange of the subscripts j, k, it can be written as

$$\mathbf{q}_V = \frac{1}{4}\left\langle \sum_{j\neq k=1}^{N}\sum \left(u_{kj}\mathbf{I} - \frac{\mathbf{R}_{kj}\mathbf{R}_{kj}}{R_{kj}}u_{kj}'\right) \cdot\left\{\left(\frac{\mathbf{p}_k}{m} - \mathbf{u}\right)\delta(\mathbf{R}_k - \mathbf{r}) + \left(\frac{\mathbf{p}_j}{m} - \mathbf{u}\right)\delta(\mathbf{R}_j - \mathbf{r})\right\}; f^{(N)}\right\rangle. \quad (6.2.82)$$

We now introduce the new variables

$$\begin{aligned}\mathbf{r}_{kj} &= \tfrac{1}{2}(\mathbf{R}_k + \mathbf{R}_j)\\ \mathbf{R}_{kj} &= \mathbf{R}_j - \mathbf{R}_k,\end{aligned} \quad (6.2.83)$$

so that

$$\begin{aligned}\mathbf{R}_j &= \mathbf{r}_{kj} + \tfrac{1}{2}\mathbf{R}_{kj}\\ \mathbf{R}_k &= \mathbf{r}_{kj} - \tfrac{1}{2}\mathbf{R}_{kj}.\end{aligned} \quad (6.2.84)$$

Both delta-functions are now expanded about $\delta(\mathbf{r}_{kj} - \mathbf{r})$, and equation (6.2.82) becomes*

$$\mathbf{q}_V = \tfrac{1}{4}\left\langle \sum_{j\neq k=1}^{N}\sum \left(u_{kj}\mathbf{I} - \frac{\mathbf{R}_{kj}\mathbf{R}_{kj}}{R_{kj}}u_{kj}'\right)\cdot\left(\frac{\mathbf{p}_k}{m} + \frac{\mathbf{p}_j}{m} - 2\mathbf{u}\right)\delta(\mathbf{r}_{kj} - \mathbf{r}); f^{(N)}\right\rangle + \tfrac{1}{8}\nabla\cdot\left\langle \sum_{j\neq k=1}^{N}\sum \mathbf{R}_{kj}\left(u_{kj}\mathbf{I} - \frac{\mathbf{R}_{kj}\mathbf{R}_{kj}}{R_{kj}}u_{kj}'\right) \cdot\left(\frac{\mathbf{p}_k}{m} - \frac{\mathbf{p}_j}{m} - \mathbf{R}_{kj}\cdot\nabla\mathbf{u}\right)\delta(\mathbf{r}_{kj} - \mathbf{r}); f^{(N)}\right\rangle + \cdots \quad (6.2.85)$$

* It is not necessary to introduce the new variables $\mathbf{r}_{kj}$,$\mathbf{R}_{kj}$, only at this stage; it could equally well have been done in equation (6.2.77).

By our earlier arguments, the second term in equation (6.2.85) will be negligible in a dense fluid; it can be seen to involve $\nabla^2 T$ and $(\nabla T)^2$ since that part of the distribution function which gives rise to a non-vanishing heat flux is already proportional to ∇T. Introduction of the dummy variable $\mathbf{R}$ by means of an integration over the delta-function $\delta(\mathbf{R}_{kj} - \mathbf{r})$ now puts equation (6.2.85) in the form (2)

$$\mathbf{q}_V = \frac{1}{2}\int \left[u(R)\mathbf{I} - \frac{\mathbf{RR}}{R}u'(R)\right] \cdot [\mathbf{j}^{(2)}(\mathbf{r},\mathbf{R};t) - \mathbf{u}(\mathbf{r};t)\rho^{(2)}(\mathbf{r},\mathbf{R};t)]\,d\mathbf{R}, \quad (6.2.86)$$

where $\rho^{(2)}$ and $\mathbf{j}^{(2)}$ are defined by equations (6.2.46) and (6.2.47), and we have ignored non-uniformities in the velocity gradient. If we were to adopt the viewpoint that the heat flux is not measured as a point function in practice, but in terms of the heat passing between the two opposite end faces of a sample, then the quantity we relate to the thermal conductivity is a volume average $\mathbf{Q}$ of $\mathbf{q}(\mathbf{r}; t)$:

$$\mathbf{Q} = \frac{1}{V}\int \mathbf{q}(\mathbf{r}; t)\,d\mathbf{r}, \quad (6.2.87)$$

where V is the volume of the system. Thus, from equations (6.2.86) and (6.2.87), we see that the quantity to be calculated is

$$\mathbf{Q} = \frac{1}{2V}\iint \left[u(R)\mathbf{I} - \frac{\mathbf{RR}}{R}u'(R)\right] \cdot [\mathbf{j}^{(2)}(\mathbf{r}, \mathbf{R}; t) - \mathbf{u}(\mathbf{r}; t)\rho^{(2)}(\mathbf{r}, \mathbf{R}; t)]\,d\mathbf{R}\,d\mathbf{r}. \quad (6.2.88)$$

Equation (6.2.88) was first obtained by Eisenschitz (2) by a different method.

Having obtained formulas for the stress tensor and heat flux in terms of molecular variables, it is pertinent to remark on the difference between the macroscopic and microscopic theories. In the molecular theory the densities defined are all point functions, having been defined as ensemble averages with the complete distribution function, $f^{(N)}$. On the other hand, the derivation of the equations of macroscopic hydrodynamics makes use of continuity assumptions which identify the variables as macroscopic observables. The relationship between the microscopic and macroscopic variables is not defined entirely by the ensemble average. For, the statistical formulas permit fluctuations which are inadmissible in the mechanical description. Thus, the equations of macroscopic hydrodynamics describe the mechanical behavior of volume elements large enough to contain many molecules but small enough to represent a point in terms of the size of the measuring instruments. In this sense, the equations of macroscopic hydrodynamics represent a coarse grained description of the system.

We have already noted that the description of dissipative processes in macroscopic terms requires the introduction of relationships between $\boldsymbol{\sigma},\mathbf{q}$ and the macroscopic variables defining the departure from equilibrium. It is interesting that the point functions defined by the statistical theory satisfy equations identical in form to the hydrodynamic equations despite the difference in the domains to which the point functions refer, but the reader should not be misled into believing that the statistical formulas as derived describe irreversible phenomena. Just as in the macroscopic case, relations between $\boldsymbol{\sigma},\mathbf{q}$ and variables such as $\nabla\mathbf{u}$, ∇T, etc., must be established by supplementary means. In the statistical theory, the description of irreversible processes enters when the distribution function is specified in terms of the variables $\nabla\mathbf{u}$, ∇T, etc., and it is the introduction of irreversibility into the equation for the distribution function which enables us to derive the Newtonian stress tensor, the Fourier law, and the corresponding transport coefficients.

We have not mentioned the interesting (but to some extent irrelevant) fact that the macroscopic observables are also dependent on spatial and temporal averages defined by the size and relaxation time of the measuring instruments. Changes in resolution of the measuring instruments are reflected primarily in the relationships between the stress tensor (or heat flux) and pertinent macroscopic variables. For example, the shear viscosity of complex liquids may be frequency dependent. In these cases, it is not the fundamental hydrodynamic equations which change, but rather the nature of the phenomenological relations such as (6.2.21) and (6.2.33), and the coefficients which appear therein. Only when the external conditions are such that the spatial variation or temporal variation of some force is comparable with molecular separations or molecular frequencies must we seek new macroscopic mechanical descriptions. An example of one such phenomenon is the absorption of sound by a gas under conditions where the frequency of the sound wave is comparable to the inverse of the time between collisions. Under these conditions the Navier-Stokes equation is invalid, as indeed are the continuity assumptions leading to the equation of motion (6.2.12). The forces inside any volume large enough to have small fluctuations in density, etc., vary rapidly and it is not clear that a meaningful stress tensor can be defined. Indeed, under extreme conditions it may be necessary to abandon the concept of a macroscopic equation and work entirely with statistical molecular methods.

In principle, the statistical formulas derived can be reduced to the appropriate hydrodynamic description by suitable space and time averaging. For this to be meaningful, the distribution function must be defined under the same conditions. Thus, any restrictions on the domain of validity of a kinetic equation defining the behavior of a distribution function will ultimately restrict the range of possible hydrodynamic behavior describable. It is clear that different approximate kinetic equations may have to be used in the several ranges of physical interest, if no one equation is accurate over the entire range.

In the remainder of this chapter we shall discuss the molecular theory of steady-state transport phenomena on the basis of the kinetic equations introduced earlier.

6.3. THE MOMENTUM AND ENERGY FLUXES IN A DENSE FLUID

We come now to the calculation of the momentum and energy fluxes in a dense fluid in terms of the properties of the constituent molecules. Our starting point is, of course, the expression for these quantities developed in the preceding section. As we have already mentioned, the momentum and energy equations (6.2.12) and (6.2.19–20) respectively, do not exhibit irreversible behavior until the stress tensor and heat flux are replaced by empirical dissipative expressions [the Newtonian stress tensor, Eq. (6.2.21) and the Fourier law, Eq. (6.2.33)]. Also, the microscopic expressions for the stress tensor, equations (6.2.60) and (6.2.62), and the heat flux, equations (6.2.80) and (6.2.81), do not have the dissipative form as they stand. The N-molecule distribution function $f^{(N)}$ has, since it is a solution of the Liouville equation (6.2.37), simultaneously the property of time reversibility and the property of exhibiting an approach to equilibrium for the "short" time intervals of interest in the evolution of the universe. It is not possible at the present stage of the theory of irreversible processes (Chapter 7) to distinguish in a systematic way those features of $f^{(N)}$ which give the approach to equilibrium for the systems in which we are interested. Therefore, it is necessary to replace the correct $f^{(N)}$, or equivalently $f^{(1)}$ and $f^{(2)}$ in equations (6.2.60) and (6.2.80), by distribution functions which we have purposely constructed to exhibit this property. It was the purpose of Chapter 5 to develop differential equations for these distribution functions, and we use the solution of these equations to calculate the dissipative forms of the stress tensor and heat flux in this section.

6.3.A. *The Coefficients of Viscosity* (3)

Consider first the kinetic contribution. The form given in equation (6.2.60) may be written, after integration over the phase space of $(N-1)$ molecules, as

$$\boldsymbol{\sigma}_K = -m \int \left(\frac{\mathbf{p}_1}{m} - \mathbf{u}\right)\left(\frac{\mathbf{p}_1}{m} - \mathbf{u}\right) \bar{f}^{(1)}(1)\, d\mathbf{p}_1, \qquad (6.3.1)$$

where $\bar{f}^{(1)}(1)$ is the solution of the kinetic equation (5.3.69) (4), and is

$$\bar{f}^{(1)}(1) = \bar{f}_0^{(1)}\left(1 + \left(\frac{2kT}{m}\right)^{1/2} \frac{15}{4} \frac{[(1/\rho g(\sigma)) + (2\pi\sigma^3/5)]}{[4\Omega^{(2,2)} + (45\zeta_S/4\rho m g(\sigma))]}\right.$$
$$\times (\tfrac{5}{2} - W_1^2)\mathbf{W}_1 \cdot \nabla \ln T - 5\, \frac{[(1/\rho g(\sigma)) + (4\pi\sigma^3/15)]}{[4\Omega^{(2,2)} + (5\zeta_S/\rho m g(\sigma))]}$$
$$\left.\times (\mathbf{W}_1\mathbf{W}_1 - \tfrac{1}{3}W_1^2\mathbf{I}):\nabla\mathbf{u}\right),$$

$$\bar{f}_0^{(1)} = \frac{\rho}{(2\pi m k T)^{3/2}} \exp\left(-\frac{(\mathbf{p}_1 - m\mathbf{u})^2}{2mkT}\right),$$

$$\Omega^{(2,2)} = \left(\frac{4\pi k T}{m}\right)^{1/2} \sigma^2,$$

$$\mathbf{W}_1 = (2mkT)^{-1/2}(\mathbf{p}_1 - m\mathbf{u}). \qquad (6.3.2)$$

In equation (6.3.2) we have written $g_0^{(2)}(R_{12} = \sigma) = g(\sigma)$ for brevity.

The integrand of equation (6.3.1) is proportional to the tensor $\mathbf{W}_1\mathbf{W}_1$, so that terms in equation (6.3.2) which are odd in $\mathbf{W}_1$ will not contribute to $\boldsymbol{\sigma}_K$. Of course, the term unity gives the kinetic contribution to the pressure [see Eq. (6.2.65)]. If equation (6.3.2) is substituted in equation (6.3.1) there remain only quadratures to perform. From the vector theorem

$$\int F(x)\mathbf{xx}[\mathbf{xx} - \tfrac{1}{3}x^2\mathbf{I}]:\nabla\mathbf{u}\, d\mathbf{x} = \frac{8\pi}{15}[\boldsymbol{\epsilon} - \tfrac{1}{3}\nabla\cdot\mathbf{u}\mathbf{I}]\int F(x)x^6\, dx, \quad (6.3.3)$$

and remembering the definition

$$\boldsymbol{\sigma} = [-p + (\phi - \tfrac{2}{3}\eta)\nabla\cdot\mathbf{u}]\mathbf{I} + 2\eta\boldsymbol{\epsilon}, \quad (6.2.21)$$

we find after identification of terms in the Newtonian stress tensor deduced,

$$\eta_K = \frac{5kT}{8g(\sigma)}\frac{[1 + (4\pi\rho\sigma^3 g(\sigma)/15)]}{\{\Omega^{(2,2)} + [5\zeta_S/4\rho m g(\sigma)]\}},$$
$$\phi_K = 0, \quad (6.3.4)$$

for the kinetic contributions to the shear and bulk viscosities.

To calculate the intermolecular force contribution to the shear viscosity we start from the exact equation (6.2.60) which may be readily reduced to the form

$$\boldsymbol{\sigma}_V = \frac{1}{2}\int \mathbf{R}_{12}\,\nabla_{12}u(\mathbf{R}_{12})f^{(2)}(1,2)\, d\mathbf{R}_{12}\, d\mathbf{p}_1\, d\mathbf{p}_2. \quad (6.3.5)$$

The transfer of momentum which occurs during a rigid core encounter must be treated carefully because of the discontinuous nature of the potential. Consider the kinematics of a rigid core encounter. The change of momentum takes place along the line joining the centers of the spheres at contact, if the spheres are smooth. If the relative momentum before collision is $\mathbf{p}_{12}$ then the transfer of momentum, $\Delta\mathbf{p}_{12}$, is

$$\Delta\mathbf{p}_{12} = -2\mathbf{kk}\cdot\mathbf{p}_{12}; \qquad \mathbf{k}\cdot\mathbf{p}_{12} < 0, \quad (6.3.6)$$

where $\mathbf{k}$ is the unit vector pointing from molecule 1 to molecule 2 and parallel to the line joining their centers at the instant of contact. A collision occurs only if $\mathbf{k}\cdot\mathbf{p}_{12} < 0$. If the rigid core is regarded as a limit of some suitable continuous potential of finite range, then the transfer of momentum which occurs at collision may be calculated as the time-integral of the force along the trajectory at each stage of the limiting process. In order to calculate the change of momentum correctly the time integration must cover the interval during which the molecules are within the finite range of the potential. If, at some stage of the limiting process the range of the force is small compared to the (final) rigid core diameter, then the integration interval τ may be chosen so that for most of the interval the trajectory is linear while the molecules are outside the range, and the actual collision occurs in a small portion of τ. The $\mathbf{R}_{12}$ integration in equation (6.3.5) is taken over the region of space in which a molecule must lie if it undergoes the collision sometime during τ. If we erect a system of cylindrical polar coordinates with radius b and azimuth ϵ and z-axis parallel to $\mathbf{p}_{12}$ then, because of the linear character of the trajectory except at collision, the volume element $d\mathbf{R}_{12}$ takes the form of a cylinder of length $(p_{12}/m)\tau$ and cross section $b\,db\,d\epsilon$. Since the force differs from zero only for a very small variation of $\mathbf{R}_{12}$ (i.e., the range) then equation (6.3.5) may be written with negligible error as

$$\boldsymbol{\sigma}_V(\sigma) = \frac{1}{2\tau}\int_0^\tau \int \mathbf{R}_{12}\,\nabla_{12}u(R_{12}(s))\bar{f}^{(2)}(1,2)\,d\mathbf{R}_{12}\,d\mathbf{p}_1\,d\mathbf{p}_2\,ds, \quad (6.3.7)$$

where $\mathbf{R}_{12}(s)$ is the separation as a function of the time variable s. For a continuous potential $u(R)$, the change of momentum $\Delta\mathbf{p}_{12}$* is given by

$$\Delta\mathbf{p}_{12} = -2\int_0^\tau \nabla_{12}u[R_{12}(s)]\,ds, \quad (6.3.8)$$

when τ covers the interval during which the molecules are within range of each other. Assuming that the limiting process applied to the potential can be interchanged with the time integration, equation (6.3.7) becomes

$$\boldsymbol{\sigma}_V(\sigma) = \frac{\sigma}{2m}\int_{(\mathbf{k}\cdot\mathbf{p}_{12}<0)} \mathbf{kkk}\cdot\mathbf{p}_{12}\bar{f}^{(2)}(1,2)p_{12}b\,db\,d\epsilon\,d\mathbf{p}_1\,d\mathbf{p}_2, \quad (6.3.9)$$

where we have used equation (6.3.6). If, as in the present case, there is a soft potential superimposed on the rigid core then the interval τ must be small enough that the molecules do not experience significant changes in the soft potential during τ. Since in the limit, the range of the rigid core potential is zero, τ may be allowed to approach arbitrarily close to zero, and equation (6.3.9) is rigorously correct for the rigid core contribution even when a superimposed soft potential is present.

* The factor 2 in equation (6.3.8) arises because both molecules are moving freely under their mutual force. Thus,

$$\begin{aligned}\frac{d}{dt}\mathbf{p}_{12} &= \frac{d}{dt}\mathbf{p}_2 - \frac{d}{dt}\mathbf{p}_1\\ &= -\nabla_2 u(R_{12}) + \nabla_1 u(R_{12})\\ &= -2\nabla_{12}u(R_{12}).\end{aligned}$$

In order to calculate $\boldsymbol{\sigma}_V(\sigma)$ the non-equilibrium pair distribution function $\bar{f}^{(2)}$ is required (5). $\bar{f}^{(2)}$ has been calculated in Chapter 5 and the solution is equation (5.4.165); for convenience we rewrite it here:

$$\bar{f}^{(2)}(1,2) = \bar{f}_0^{(2)}\Big(1 - \sum_{j=1,2} \{A_{1_j}(\tfrac{5}{2} - W_j^2)\mathbf{W}_j \cdot \nabla_j \ln T_j + B_{0j}^{(1)}(\mathbf{W}_j\mathbf{W}_j - \tfrac{1}{3}W_j^2\mathbf{I}) : \nabla_j \mathbf{u}_j + C_{0j}\mathbf{W}_j \cdot {}^{(2)}\mathbf{G}_j^F\}\Big), \quad (6.3.10)$$

where

$$\bar{f}_0^{(2)} = \frac{\rho^{(2)}(1,2)}{(2\pi mk)^3[T(\mathbf{R}_1)]^{3/2}[T(\mathbf{R}_2)]^{3/2}} \times \exp\left(-\frac{[\mathbf{p}_1 - m\mathbf{u}(\mathbf{R}_1)]^2}{2mkT(\mathbf{R}_1)} - \frac{[\mathbf{p}_2 - m\mathbf{u}(\mathbf{R}_2)]^2}{2mkT(\mathbf{R}_2)}\right) \quad (6.3.11)$$

is the local equilibrium distribution function, and

$$A_{1_j} = -\left(\frac{2kT}{m}\right)^{1/2} \frac{15}{4\rho} \frac{[g(\sigma)^{-1} + (2\pi\rho\sigma^3/5)]}{[8\Omega^{(2,2)} + (45\zeta_S/4\rho m g(\sigma))]} \times \left[1 + \frac{4\Omega^{(2,2)}}{4\Omega^{(2,2)} + (45\zeta_S/4\rho m g(\sigma))}\right]$$

$$B_{0j}^{(1)} = \frac{5}{\rho} \frac{[g(\sigma)^{-1} + (4\pi\rho\sigma^3/15)]}{[8\Omega^{(2,2)} + (5\zeta_S/\rho m g(\sigma))]} \left[1 + \frac{4\Omega^{(2,2)}}{4\Omega^{(2,2)} + (5\zeta_S/\rho m g(\sigma))}\right]$$

$$C_{0j} = -\left(\frac{2m}{kT(\mathbf{R}_j)}\right)^{1/2} \frac{1}{\zeta_S(\mathbf{R}_j)}$$

$$\begin{aligned} {}^{(2)}\mathbf{G}_j^F &= \mathbf{F}_j^{(2)} - \mathbf{F}_j^* - kT(\mathbf{R}_j)\nabla_j \ln g^{(2)}(1,2) \\ &= {}^{(2)}\langle\mathbf{F}_j\rangle^0 + {}^{(2)}\mathbf{F}_j^\dagger - {}^{(1)}\langle\mathbf{F}_j\rangle^0 - {}^{(1)}\mathbf{F}_j^\dagger - kT(\mathbf{R}_j)\nabla_j \ln g^{(2)}(1,2) \end{aligned}$$

$$g^{(2)}(1,2) = g^{(2)}(\mathbf{R}_{12}). \quad (6.3.12)$$

It is convenient now to introduce the center of mass and relative reduced peculiar velocities $\mathbf{W}$, $\mathbf{w}$, respectively defined by*

$$\mathbf{W} = \tfrac{1}{2}(\mathbf{W}_1 + \mathbf{W}_2); \qquad \mathbf{w} = (2mkT)^{-1/2}\mathbf{p}_{12}, \quad (6.3.13)$$

* Neglecting terms of the order of the velocity gradient,

$$\mathbf{w} = \mathbf{W}_2 - \mathbf{W}_1 = (2mkT)^{-1/2}\,\mathbf{p}_{12} + \mathcal{O}(\nabla\mathbf{u}).$$

We use the form cited in equation (6.3.13) for ease of reduction, since the filamentary volume element contains the factor $\mathbf{p}_{12}$. Note that only $\mathbf{ww}$ or $\mathbf{w} \cdot \mathbf{G}$ appears in equation (6.3.15), so that the neglected terms in equation (6.3.15) are of order $(\nabla\mathbf{u})^2$.

from which it follows that

$$\mathbf{W}_1 = \mathbf{W} - \tfrac{1}{2}\mathbf{w}; \qquad \mathbf{W}_2 = \mathbf{W} + \tfrac{1}{2}\mathbf{w}$$
$$d\mathbf{W}_1\, d\mathbf{W}_2 = d\mathbf{W}\, d\mathbf{w}. \tag{6.3.14}$$

Since A_{1j} and $B_{0j}^{(1)}$ are the same for $j = 1$ and 2, equation (6.3.10) may be written

$$\begin{aligned} \bar{f}^{(2)} = \bar{f}_0^{(2)}[1 &- A_{1j}(-\mathbf{ww} + \{5 - 2W^2 - \tfrac{1}{2}w^2\}\mathbf{I})\mathbf{:}\mathbf{W}\,\nabla \ln T \\ &- B_0^{(1)}(2\{\mathbf{WW} - \tfrac{1}{3}W^2\mathbf{I}\} + \tfrac{1}{2}\{\mathbf{ww} - \tfrac{1}{3}w^2\mathbf{I}\})\mathbf{:}\nabla\mathbf{u} \\ &- (\mathbf{W}\cdot\{C_{01}^{(2)}\mathbf{G}_1{}^F + C_{02}^{(2)}\mathbf{G}_2{}^F\} - \tfrac{1}{2}\mathbf{w}\cdot\{C_{02}^{(2)}\mathbf{G}_2{}^F - C_{01}^{(2)}\mathbf{G}_1{}^F\})]. \end{aligned} \tag{6.3.15}$$

It is seen from equation (6.3.13) that the definitions of $\mathbf{w}$ and $\mathbf{p}_{12}$ are not consistent, in that while

$$\mathbf{p}_{12} = \mathbf{p}_2 - \mathbf{p}_1, \qquad \mathbf{w} \neq (2mkT)^{-1/2}[\mathbf{p}_2 - \mathbf{p}_1 + m\{\mathbf{u}(\mathbf{R}_1) - \mathbf{u}(\mathbf{R}_2)\}].$$

This situation may easily be rectified by expanding the position-dependent quantities in $\bar{f}_0^{(2)}$ in Taylor series about the center of mass of the pair of molecules. Thus, if $\mathbf{r} = \frac{1}{2}(\mathbf{R}_1 + \mathbf{R}_2)$,

$$\begin{aligned} \mathbf{u}(\mathbf{R}_1) &\simeq \mathbf{u}(\mathbf{r}) + (\mathbf{R}_1 - \mathbf{r})\cdot\nabla\mathbf{u} = \mathbf{u} - \tfrac{1}{2}\mathbf{R}_{12}\cdot\nabla\mathbf{u}, \\ T(\mathbf{R}_1) &\simeq T(\mathbf{r}) + (\mathbf{R}_1 - \mathbf{r})\cdot\nabla T = T(1 - \tfrac{1}{2}\mathbf{R}_{12}\cdot\nabla \ln T). \end{aligned} \tag{6.3.16}$$

Similar equations apply for $\mathbf{u}(\mathbf{R}_2)$, $T(\mathbf{R}_2)$ but with the sign of $\mathbf{R}_{12}$ changed. It is found that $\bar{f}_0^{(2)}$ may be written as

$$\bar{f}_0^{(2)} = \bar{f}_{\mathrm{eq}}^{(2)} + \Delta \bar{f}_0^{(2)},$$

$$\Delta \bar{f}_0^{(2)} = -\,\bar{f}_{\mathrm{eq}}^{(2)}\left(\left(\frac{m}{2kT}\right)^{1/2}\mathbf{wR}_{12}\mathbf{:}\nabla\mathbf{u} + \mathbf{w}\cdot\mathbf{WR}_{12}\cdot\nabla \ln T + \cdots\right), \tag{6.3.17}$$

where $\bar{f}_{\mathrm{eq}}^{(2)}$ is the *true* equilibrium distribution function, dependent only on the flow and temperature at $\mathbf{r}$, and may be written as

$$\bar{f}_{\mathrm{eq}}^{(2)} = \rho^{(2)}(1,2)(2\pi mkT)^{-3}\exp(-2W^2 - \tfrac{1}{2}w^2). \tag{6.3.17a}$$

We now turn to the evaluation of $\boldsymbol{\sigma}_V(\sigma)$. Terms linear in the gradients arise in three ways. The first kind, whose contribution is denoted $\boldsymbol{\sigma}_V^{(1)}$, arises from the distortion of the momentum dependence of the local equilibrium distribution function [i.e., Eq. (6.3.10)]. The second kind $\boldsymbol{\sigma}_V^{(2)}$ arises from the correction (6.3.17) to $\bar{f}_{\mathrm{eq}}^{(2)}$. The third kind $\boldsymbol{\sigma}_V^{(3)}$ arises from a distortion to the pair correlation function. The calculation of this distortion is dealt with in equation (6.3.49), and after. It is sufficient here to write down the definition of the distortion. Thus,

$$\rho^{(2)}(1,2) = \rho^2 g^{(2)}(1,2)$$
$$= \rho^2 g_0^{(2)}(1,2)\left(1 + \frac{\zeta_S}{2kT}\left\{\left[\frac{\mathbf{R}_{12}\cdot\boldsymbol{\epsilon}\cdot\mathbf{R}_{12}}{R_{12}{}^2} - \tfrac{1}{3}\nabla\cdot\mathbf{u}\right]\psi_2(R_{12}) + \tfrac{1}{3}\nabla\cdot\mathbf{u}\psi_0(R_{12})\right\}\right). \quad (6.3.18)$$

For the purpose of calculating $\boldsymbol{\sigma}_V(\sigma)$, equation (6.3.18) can be reduced to

$$\rho^{(2)}(1,2) = \rho^2 g(\sigma)\left(1 + \frac{\zeta_S}{2kT}\{[\mathbf{kk}:\boldsymbol{\epsilon} - \tfrac{1}{3}\nabla\cdot\mathbf{u}]\psi_2(\sigma) + \tfrac{1}{3}\nabla\cdot\mathbf{u}\psi_0(\sigma)\}\right). \quad (6.3.19)$$

The first contribution to $\boldsymbol{\sigma}_V(\sigma)$ is given by

$$\boldsymbol{\sigma}_V^{(1)} = \frac{\sigma\rho^2 g(\sigma)kT}{\pi^3}\int_{(\mathbf{k}\cdot\mathbf{w}<0)}\iint \mathbf{kkk}\cdot\mathbf{w}\exp(-2W^2 - \tfrac{1}{2}w^2)$$
$$\times [1 - A_1(R_{12}=\sigma)(\mathbf{ww} + \{5 - 2W^2 - \tfrac{1}{2}w^2\}\mathbf{I}):\mathbf{W}\,\nabla \ln T$$
$$- B_0^{(1)}(R_{12}=\sigma)(2\{\mathbf{WW} - \tfrac{1}{3}W^2\mathbf{I}\} + \tfrac{1}{2}\{\mathbf{ww} - \tfrac{1}{3}w^2\mathbf{I}\}):\nabla\mathbf{u}]$$
$$\times\, w\, d\mathbf{w}\, d\mathbf{W} b\, db\, d\epsilon$$
$$= \frac{\sigma\rho^2 g(\sigma)kT}{(2\pi)^{3/2}}\int_{(\mathbf{k}\cdot\mathbf{w}<0)}\int \mathbf{kkk}\cdot\mathbf{w}\exp(-\tfrac{1}{2}w^2)$$
$$\times [1 - \tfrac{1}{2}B_0^{(1)}(\sigma)(\mathbf{ww} - \tfrac{1}{3}w^2\mathbf{I}):\nabla\mathbf{u}]w\, d\mathbf{w} b\, db\, d\epsilon. \quad (6.3.20)$$

Equation (6.3.20) arises from equation (6.3.9) by substitution of the equilibrium pair-distribution function (6.3.17*a*) with the distortion of $g^{(2)}(1,2)$ excluded, and of the asymmetric momentum dependent factor (in square brackets) from equation (6.3.15). We take ${}^{(2)}\mathbf{G}_j{}^F = 0$ at $R_{12} = \sigma$, and an integration over $\mathbf{W}$ eliminates all other terms except those displayed in the final line.

The $\mathbf{k}$ integration is taken over the surface of a hemisphere (because $\mathbf{k}\cdot\mathbf{w} < 0$) of radius σ, and it is convenient to treat $\mathbf{w}$ as a reference vector lying along the z-axis:

$$\mathbf{w} = w\mathbf{h}. \quad (6.3.21)$$

Denoting the angle between $\mathbf{k}$ and $\mathbf{w}$ as Φ (co-latitude), we have

$$\mathbf{k}\cdot\mathbf{w} = \cos\Phi; \qquad b = \sigma\sin\Phi; \qquad db = \sigma\cos\Phi\, d\Phi, \quad (6.3.22)$$

since b is the radial coordinate in the azimuthal plane. From equation (6.3.20), the **k** integration is

$$w \int_{(\mathbf{k}\cdot\mathbf{w}<0)} \mathbf{kkk}\cdot\mathbf{w} b\, db\, d\epsilon = w^2\sigma^2 \int_0^{2\pi}\int_{\pi/2}^{\pi} \mathbf{kk}\cos^2\Phi \sin\Phi\, d\Phi\, d\epsilon. \quad (6.3.23)$$

The cartesian decomposition of **k** is

$$\mathbf{k} = \mathbf{i}\sin\Phi\cos\epsilon + \mathbf{j}\sin\Phi\,\sin\epsilon + \mathbf{h}\cos\Phi, \quad (6.3.24)$$

so that

$$\begin{aligned}\mathbf{kk} = {} & \mathbf{ii}\sin^2\Phi\cos^2\epsilon + \mathbf{jj}\sin^2\Phi\sin^2\epsilon + \mathbf{hh}\cos^2\Phi \\ & + (\mathbf{ij}+\mathbf{ji})\sin^2\Phi\sin\epsilon\cos\epsilon + (\mathbf{ih}+\mathbf{hi})\sin\Phi\cos\Phi\cos\epsilon \\ & + (\mathbf{jh}+\mathbf{hj})\sin\Phi\cos\Phi\sin\epsilon. \quad (6.3.25)\end{aligned}$$

It is clear that integration over ϵ causes the off-diagonal elements of **kk** in equation (6.3.25) to vanish. Equation (6.3.23) becomes

$$\begin{aligned} w \int_{(\mathbf{k}\cdot\mathbf{w}<0)} & \mathbf{kkk}\cdot\mathbf{w}\, b\, db\, d\epsilon \\ &= \pi\sigma^2 w^2 \int_{\pi/2}^{\pi} [(\mathbf{ii}+\mathbf{jj})\sin^2\Phi + 2\mathbf{hh}\cos^2\Phi]\cos^2\Phi\sin\Phi\, d\Phi \\ &= -\pi\sigma^2 w^2[(\mathbf{ii}+\mathbf{jj})\tfrac{2}{15} + \tfrac{2}{5}\mathbf{hh}] \\ &= -\pi\sigma^2 w^2[\tfrac{4}{15}\mathbf{hh} + \tfrac{2}{15}\mathbf{I}] \\ &= -\frac{2\pi\sigma^2}{15}[2\mathbf{ww} + w^2\mathbf{I}], \end{aligned} \quad (6.3.26)$$

where we have used equation (6.3.21) in associating each factor w with a unit vector **h** to retrieve **w**.

$\boldsymbol{\sigma}_V^{(1)}$ may be conveniently separated into equilibrium and non-equilibrium parts, $\boldsymbol{\sigma}_{V\,\mathrm{eq}}^{(1)}$ and $\boldsymbol{\sigma}_{V\,\mathrm{neq}}^{(1)}$, respectively. Thus,

$$\begin{aligned}\boldsymbol{\sigma}_{V\,\mathrm{eq}}^{(1)} &= -\frac{2\pi\sigma^3\rho^2 g(\sigma)kT}{15(2\pi)^{3/2}}\int [2\mathbf{ww} + w^2\mathbf{I}]\exp(-\tfrac{1}{2}w^2)\, d\mathbf{w} \\ &= -(\tfrac{2}{3}\pi\rho\sigma^3 g(\sigma))\rho kT\mathbf{I}, \end{aligned} \quad (6.3.27)$$

where we have used the integral theorems

$$\int [2\mathbf{ww} + w^2\mathbf{I}]F(w)\, d\mathbf{w} = \frac{20\pi}{3}\mathbf{I}\int_0^{\infty} F(w)w^4\, dw,$$

$$\int_0^{\infty} w^r\exp(-\alpha w^2)\, dw = \tfrac{1}{2}\alpha^{-(r+1)/2}\,\Gamma\left(\frac{r+1}{2}\right), \quad (6.3.28)$$

and

$$\boldsymbol{\sigma}_{V\,\mathrm{neq}}^{(1)} = \frac{\pi\sigma^3\rho^2 g(\sigma)kT}{15(2\pi)^{3/2}} B_0^{(1)}(\sigma) \times \int [2\mathbf{ww} + w^2\mathbf{I}][\mathbf{ww} - \tfrac{1}{3}w^2\mathbf{I}]:\nabla\mathbf{u} \exp(-\tfrac{1}{2}w^2)\, d\mathbf{w}$$
$$= \tfrac{2}{15}\pi\sigma^3\rho^2 g(\sigma)kTB_0^{(1)}(\sigma)(2\boldsymbol{\epsilon} - \tfrac{2}{3}\nabla\cdot\mathbf{uI}). \quad (6.3.29)$$

To obtain equation (6.3.29), the additional vector theorems

$$\int \mathbf{wwww}:\nabla\mathbf{u}F(w)\, d\mathbf{w} = \frac{4\pi}{15}(2\boldsymbol{\epsilon} + \nabla\cdot\mathbf{uI})\int_0^\infty F(w)w^6\, dw,$$
$$\int w^2(\mathbf{ww} - \tfrac{1}{3}w^2\mathbf{I})F(w)\, d\mathbf{w} = 0, \quad (6.3.30)$$

were needed.

From equations (6.3.29) and (6.3.12) we obtain

$$\eta_V^{(1)} = \frac{5kT}{8g(\sigma)}\left(\frac{2\pi\rho\sigma^3}{15}\right)\{1 + [4\pi\rho\sigma^3 g(\sigma)/15]\}D$$
$$D = \{\Omega^{(2,2)} + [5\zeta_S/8\rho m g(\sigma)]\}^{-1}\left\{1 + \frac{4\Omega^{(2,2)}}{4\Omega^{(2,2)} + [5\zeta_S/\rho m g(\sigma)]}\right\},$$
$$\phi_V^{(1)} = 0, \quad (6.3.31)$$

for the first collisional contributions to the shear and bulk viscosities.

The expression for $\boldsymbol{\sigma}_V^{(2)}$ is obtained from equations (6.3.9) and (6.3.17) by noting that since $\mathbf{k}$ is directed from molecule 1 to molecule 2, $\mathbf{R}_{12} = \sigma\mathbf{k}$, at contact. Thus,

$$\boldsymbol{\sigma}_V^{(2)} = -\frac{\sigma^2\rho^2 g(\sigma)kT}{\pi^3}\int_{(\mathbf{k}\cdot\mathbf{w}<0)}\iint \mathbf{kkk}\cdot\mathbf{w}\exp(-2W^2 - \tfrac{1}{2}w^2)$$
$$\times\left[\left(\frac{m}{2kT}\right)^{1/2}\mathbf{wk}\cdot\nabla\mathbf{u} + \mathbf{w}\cdot\mathbf{Wk}\cdot\nabla\ln T\right] w\, d\mathbf{w}\, d\mathbf{W}\, b\, db\, d\epsilon. \quad (6.3.32)$$

Upon integrating equation (6.3.32) over $\mathbf{W}$ using equation (6.3.28), it is found that

$$\boldsymbol{\sigma}_V^{(2)} = \left(\frac{mkT}{\pi}\right)^{1/2}\frac{\sigma^2\rho^2 g(\sigma)}{4\pi}\int \mathbf{H}\exp(-\tfrac{1}{2}w^2)w\, d\mathbf{w}, \quad (6.3.33)$$

where

$$\mathbf{H} = \int_{(\mathbf{k}\cdot\mathbf{w}<0)} \mathbf{kkk}\cdot\mathbf{wk}\cdot\nabla\mathbf{u}\cdot\mathbf{w}\, b\, db\, d\epsilon. \quad (6.3.34)$$

$\mathbf{H}$ is evaluated by a method similar to that used for equation (6.3.23). Again using $\mathbf{w}$ as the reference z-axis [Eq. (6.3.21)] and denoting $\nabla\mathbf{u}\cdot\mathbf{w}$ by $\mathbf{F}$, so that

$$\mathbf{k}\cdot\mathbf{F} = F_1 \sin\Phi \cos\epsilon + F_2 \sin\Phi \sin\epsilon + F_3 \cos\Phi,$$

it is found that

$$\begin{aligned}\mathbf{H} &= -w\sigma^2 \int_{(\mathbf{k}\cdot\mathbf{w}<0)} \mathbf{kkk}\cdot\mathbf{F}\cos^2\Phi \sin\Phi\, d\Phi\, d\epsilon \\ &= \frac{\pi\sigma^2 w}{12}[F_1(\mathbf{ih}+\mathbf{hi}) + F_2(\mathbf{jh}+\mathbf{hj}) + F_3(\mathbf{ii}+\mathbf{jj}+4\mathbf{hh})] \\ &= \frac{\pi\sigma^2}{12}\left[\mathbf{F}\cdot\mathbf{w}\mathbf{l} + \mathbf{Fw} + \mathbf{wF} + \frac{\mathbf{ww}}{w^2}\mathbf{w}\cdot\mathbf{F}\right]. \end{aligned} \tag{6.3.35}$$

$\mathbf{H}$ is now substituted in equation (6.3.33) from equation (6.3.35) and the integration over $\mathbf{w}$ carried out. Using the vector integral theorems (6.3.28) and (6.3.30) we find that

$$\boldsymbol{\sigma}_V^{(2)} = \left(\frac{mkT}{\pi}\right)^{1/2} \frac{4\pi}{15}\rho^2\sigma^4 g(\sigma)[2\boldsymbol{\epsilon} + \nabla\cdot\mathbf{u}\mathbf{l}]. \tag{6.3.36}$$

Upon introducing the reduced hard sphere cross section $\Omega^{(2,2)}$ from equation (6.3.2), the coefficients of shear and bulk viscosity are found to be (3,6)

$$\begin{aligned}\eta_V^{(2)} &= \frac{8\pi}{15}\frac{\rho^2\sigma^6 g(\sigma)kT}{\Omega^{(2,2)}}, \\ \phi_V^{(2)} &= \tfrac{5}{3}\eta_V^{(2)}.\end{aligned} \tag{6.3.37}$$

The expression for $\boldsymbol{\sigma}_V^{(3)}$ is obtained by substituting the distortion part of equation (6.3.19) into equation (6.3.9). After integration over $\mathbf{W}$ we obtain

$$\boldsymbol{\sigma}_V^{(3)} = -\frac{\sigma^3\rho^2 g(\sigma)\zeta_S}{4\pi(2\pi)^{1/2}}\int \mathbf{I}\exp(-\tfrac{1}{2}w^2)w^2\, d\mathbf{w}, \tag{6.3.38}$$

where

$$\mathbf{I} = -\int_{(\mathbf{k}\cdot\mathbf{w}<0)} \mathbf{kk}\big(\mathbf{kk}:\boldsymbol{\epsilon}\psi_2(\sigma) + \tfrac{1}{3}\nabla\cdot\mathbf{u}\mathbf{l}\{\psi_0(\sigma) - \psi_2(\sigma)\}\big) \times \cos^2\Phi \sin\Phi\, d\Phi\, d\epsilon. \tag{6.3.39}$$

Using the techniques previously described, **I** is found to be

$$\mathbf{I} = \frac{2\pi}{105}\left(2\left[\boldsymbol{\epsilon} + \frac{\boldsymbol{\epsilon}:\mathbf{ww}}{w^2}\mathbf{I} + \frac{2}{w^2}\mathbf{w}\{\boldsymbol{\epsilon}\cdot\mathbf{w} + \mathbf{w}\cdot\boldsymbol{\epsilon}\} + \frac{\mathbf{ww}}{w^4}\mathbf{ww}:\boldsymbol{\epsilon}\right] + \nabla\cdot\mathbf{u}\mathbf{I}\right)\psi_2(\sigma)$$
$$+ \frac{2\pi}{45}\left(2\frac{\mathbf{ww}}{w^2} + \mathbf{I}\right)\nabla\cdot\mathbf{u}[\psi_0(\sigma) - \psi_2(\sigma)]. \quad (6.3.40)$$

Substitution of equation (6.3.40) in equation (6.3.38) and integration over **w**-space now leads to

$$\boldsymbol{\sigma}_V^{(3)} = -\frac{37}{70}\left(\frac{2\pi\rho\sigma^3}{15}\right)\rho g(\sigma)\zeta_S$$
$$\times\left[2\psi_2(\sigma)\boldsymbol{\epsilon} + \left(\frac{175\psi_0(\sigma) - 94\psi_2(\sigma)}{111}\right)\nabla\cdot\mathbf{u}\mathbf{I}\right], \quad (6.3.41)$$

from which we obtain the results

$$\eta_V^{(3)} = -\frac{37}{70}\left(\frac{2\pi\rho\sigma^3}{15}\right)\rho g(\sigma)\zeta_S\psi_2(\sigma),$$
$$\phi_V^{(3)} = \left(\frac{2\pi\rho\sigma^3}{15}\right)\rho g(\sigma)\zeta_S\left[\frac{4\psi_2(\sigma) - 35\psi_0(\sigma)}{42}\right]. \quad (6.3.42)$$

Equations (6.3.42) represent a result peculiar to the present theory. It appears neither in the pure Fokker-Planck theory of Kirkwood (7,8) (which does not consider the rigid core), nor in the Enskog theory (in which the range of the intermolecular force is supposed short compared to the intermolecular separation). Since $\eta_V^{(3)}$ and $\phi_V^{(3)}$ are proportional to the soft friction coefficient ζ_S, these contributions may best be described as a cross effect.

The total contribution to the viscosity from the collisional transfer process is the sum of the three contributions evaluated in equations (6.3.31), (6.3.37), and (6.3.42):

$$\theta_V(\sigma) = \sum_{i=1}^{3}\theta_V^{(i)}; \qquad \theta = \eta,\phi. \quad (6.3.43)$$

We come now to the calculation of the contribution due to the soft part of the intermolecular force, which is given by equation (6.2.63). In this case the molecules of a pair are separated by distances greater than σ, and the kinetic equation reduces to a simpler form. Since it is necessary to know only the distribution of distances between the two molecules of the pair, the kinetic equation is projected onto the pair configuration space. It was shown in Chapter 5 that the pair configuration distribution function $\rho^{(2)}$ satisfies, under reasonable assumptions, the Smoluchowski equation [see also Eq. (4.4.86)] (7,8)

$$\frac{\partial \rho^{(2)}}{\partial t} = \sum_{i=1,2} \left[\nabla_i \cdot \left(\frac{kT}{\zeta_S} \nabla_i \rho^{(2)} - \frac{\mathbf{F}_i^{(2)}}{\zeta_S} \rho^{(2)} \right) - \nabla_i \cdot (\mathbf{u}_i \rho^{(2)}) \right]. \quad (6.3.44)$$

Equation (6.3.44) may be cast into the form of an equation for $g^{(2)}$ by eliminating the time derivatives of the singlet densities using

$$\frac{\partial \rho^{(1)}(i)}{\partial t} + \nabla_i \cdot [\mathbf{u}_i \rho^{(1)}(i)] = 0; \quad i = 1, 2. \quad (6.3.45)$$

It is envisaged that forces giving rise to the velocity gradients are so small and slowly varying that, although the density may change with time, the system is spatially uniform at any instant. Upon eliminating the singlet densities by means of equation (6.3.45) and transforming to center of mass $\mathbf{r}$, and relative $\mathbf{R}_{12}$ coordinates, according to

$$\mathbf{r} = \tfrac{1}{2}(\mathbf{R}_1 + \mathbf{R}_2); \qquad \mathbf{R}_{12} = \mathbf{R}_2 - \mathbf{R}_1,$$
$$\nabla \equiv \partial/\partial \mathbf{r}; \qquad \nabla_{12} \equiv \partial/\partial \mathbf{R}_{12},$$

we obtain the equation

$$\begin{aligned}\frac{\partial g^{(2)}}{\partial t} = 2\nabla_{12} \cdot \left[\frac{kT}{\zeta_S} \nabla_{12} g^{(2)} + \frac{(\mathbf{F}_1^{(2)} - \mathbf{F}_2^{(2)})}{2\zeta_S} g^{(2)} \right] - (\mathbf{u}_2 - \mathbf{u}_1) \cdot \nabla_{12} g^{(2)} \\ + \tfrac{1}{2}\nabla \cdot \left[\frac{kT}{\zeta_S} \nabla g^{(2)} - \frac{(\mathbf{F}_1^{(2)} + \mathbf{F}_2^{(2)})}{2\zeta_S} g^{(2)} \right] \\ - \tfrac{1}{2}(\mathbf{u}_1 + \mathbf{u}_2) \cdot \nabla g^{(2)}. \quad (6.3.46)\end{aligned}$$

From equilibrium statistical mechanics, the mean forces $\mathbf{F}_i^{(2)}$ are related to the potential of the mean (pair) force $W^{(2)}(R_{12})$ by

$$\tfrac{1}{2}(\mathbf{F}_2^{(2)} - \mathbf{F}_1^{(2)}) = -\nabla_{12} W^{(2)} = kT\, \nabla_{12} \ln g_0^{(2)}. \quad (6.3.47)$$

In the absence of a temperature gradient (and an external field) neither $g^{(2)}$ nor the mean forces will depend on the position of the center of mass, so that with equation (6.3.47), equation (6.3.46) becomes

$$\frac{\partial g^{(2)}}{\partial t} = \frac{2kT}{\zeta_S} \nabla_{12} \cdot \left[\nabla_{12} g^{(2)} + \frac{\nabla_{12} W^{(2)}}{kT} g^{(2)} \right] - \mathbf{R}_{12} \cdot \nabla \mathbf{u} \cdot \nabla_{12} g^{(2)}. \quad (6.3.48)$$

Equation (6.3.48) is solved by what is essentially a perturbation procedure. Assuming that for small rates of strain, $\boldsymbol{\epsilon}$, a solution can be obtained which is linear in $\boldsymbol{\epsilon}$, we write*

$$g^{(2)} = g_0^{(2)}\left\{1 + \frac{\zeta_S}{2kT}\left[\left(\frac{\mathbf{R}_{12}\cdot\boldsymbol{\epsilon}\cdot\mathbf{R}_{12}}{{R_{12}}^2} - \tfrac{1}{3}\nabla\cdot\mathbf{u}\right)\psi_2(R_{12}) + \tfrac{1}{3}\nabla\cdot\mathbf{u}\psi_0(R_{12})\right]\right\}. \tag{6.3.49}$$

ψ_0 and ψ_2 are radial functions only, associated with the dilational and shear parts of $\boldsymbol{\epsilon}$, respectively. Upon substituting equation (6.3.49) into (6.3.48), it is found that the last term on the right-hand side of the latter contains a term non-linear in $\nabla\mathbf{u}$. The perturbation procedure consists of neglecting this nonlinearity by replacing $g^{(2)}$ by $g_0^{(2)}$ in this term. Since

$$\nabla_{12}g_0^{(2)} = \frac{\mathbf{R}_{12}}{R_{12}}\frac{dg_0^{(2)}}{dR_{12}},$$

the cited term becomes

$$\frac{\mathbf{R}_{12}\cdot\nabla\mathbf{u}\cdot\mathbf{R}_{12}}{R_{12}}\frac{dg_0^{(2)}}{dR_{12}} = \frac{\mathbf{R}_{12}\cdot\boldsymbol{\epsilon}\cdot\mathbf{R}_{12}}{R_{12}}\frac{dg_0^{(2)}}{dR_{12}}.$$

Equation (6.3.48) is solved for the steady state. However, the existence of a steady dilation implies that the density is a function of time. Now, the pair correlation function is very sensitive to density, so that

$$\begin{aligned}\frac{\partial g^{(2)}}{\partial t} &= \frac{\partial}{\partial \rho^{(1)}}g^{(2)}(\mathbf{R}_{12};\rho^{(1)})\frac{\partial \rho^{(1)}}{\partial t}\\ &\simeq -\frac{\partial g_0^{(2)}}{\partial \ln \rho}\nabla\cdot\mathbf{u}.\end{aligned} \tag{6.3.50}$$

Substitution of equations (6.3.49) and (6.3.50) into equation (6.3.48) yields an equation which can be separated into two independent equations for ψ_0 and ψ_2, when use is made of the fact that the dilational and shear parts of $\nabla\mathbf{u}$ are independent. Thus, equating the coefficients of $\nabla\cdot\mathbf{u}$ and $({R_{12}}^{-2}\mathbf{R}_{12}\cdot\boldsymbol{\epsilon}\cdot\mathbf{R}_{12} - \tfrac{1}{3}\nabla\cdot\mathbf{u})$, we obtain

$$\frac{d}{dR_{12}}\left({R_{12}}^2 g_0^{(2)}\frac{d\psi_0}{dR_{12}}\right) = {R_{12}}^3\frac{dg_0^{(2)}}{dR_{12}} - 3{R_{12}}^2\frac{dg_0^{(2)}}{d\ln\rho}, \tag{6.3.51}$$

$$\frac{d}{dR_{12}}\left({R_{12}}^2 g_0^{(2)}\frac{d\psi_2}{dR_{12}}\right) - 6\psi_2 g_0^{(2)} = {R_{12}}^3\frac{dg_0^{(2)}}{dR_{12}}. \tag{6.3.52}$$

* The notation ψ_n is associated with an expansion in spherical harmonics; ψ_n is found to be the coefficient of the harmonic of order n.

The boundary conditions on the solutions of equations (6.3.51) and (6.3.52) are deduced from the requirements that the excess relative flow $\mathbf{j}_{12}$ (excess) must vanish as $R_{12} \to \infty$ and that its normal component must vanish at the rigid core. The excess flows are defined from equation (6.3.44) in the following way: The general form of equation (6.3.44) is that of an equation of continuity in pair space (see Chapter 5):

$$\frac{\partial \rho^{(2)}}{\partial t} = -\sum_{i=1,2} \nabla_i \cdot \mathbf{j}_i^{(2)}. \tag{6.3.53}$$

The excess flow is defined as

$$\mathbf{j}_i(\text{excess}) = \mathbf{j}_i^{(2)} - \rho^{(2)}\mathbf{u}_i; \qquad i = 1,2,$$

so that from equation (6.3.44) we find that

$$\mathbf{j}_i(\text{excess}) = -\frac{kT}{\zeta_S}\nabla_i \rho^{(2)} + \frac{\mathbf{F}_i^{(2)}}{\zeta_S}\rho^{(2)}. \tag{6.3.54}$$

The relative excess flow is, therefore,

$$\mathbf{j}_{12}(\text{excess}) = -\frac{2kT}{\zeta_S}\left[\nabla_{12}g^{(2)} + \frac{\nabla_{12}W^{(2)}}{kT}g^{(2)}\right]. \tag{6.3.55}$$

The requirements on $\mathbf{j}_{12}$(excess) then lead to

$$\begin{aligned}
&\lim_{R_{12}\to\sigma} g_0^{(2)} \frac{d\psi_0}{dR_{12}} = 0,\\
&\lim_{R_{12}\to\infty} \frac{d\psi_0}{dR_{12}} = 0,\\
&\lim_{R_{12}\to\sigma} g_0^{(2)} \frac{d\psi_2}{dR_{12}} = 0,\\
&\lim_{R_{12}\to\infty} \psi_2 = 0.
\end{aligned} \tag{6.3.56}$$

Expressions for the contributions of the soft force to the viscosity coefficients are obtained by substituting equation (6.3.44) in (6.2.63). After integrating over angles we obtain

$$\begin{aligned}
\eta_V(R_{12} > \sigma) &= \frac{\pi\zeta_S}{15kT}\rho^2\int_\sigma^\infty u'(R_{12})g_0^{(2)}(R_{12})\psi_2(R_{12})R_{12}^{\,3}\,dR_{12},\\
\phi_V(R_{12} > \sigma) &= \frac{\pi\zeta_S}{9kT}\rho^2\int_\sigma^\infty u'(R_{12})g_0^{(2)}(R_{12})\psi_0(R_{12})R_{12}^{\,3}\,dR_{12}.
\end{aligned} \tag{6.3.57}$$

Note the similarity of these integral forms to equation (6.2.66) determining the pressure in terms of $g_0^{(2)}$; we may anticipate that equation (6.3.57) will be as sensitive to the relative positions of the minimum of u and the first maximum of $g_0^{(2)}$ as is the pressure integral.

The total viscosity coefficients are now determined by the sums of the contributions from equations (6.3.4), (6.3.43), and (6.3.57):

$$\theta = \theta_K + \theta_V(\sigma) + \theta_V(R_{12} > \sigma); \qquad \theta = \eta,\phi. \tag{6.3.58}$$

6.3.B. *The Coefficient of Thermal Conductivity* (9)

The kinetic (i.e., single molecule translation) contribution to the heat flux is obtained in a suitable form by integrating the appropriate expression in equation (6.2.80) over the phase of $(N - 1)$ molecules:

$$\mathbf{q}_K = \frac{m}{2}\int \left(\frac{\mathbf{p}_1}{m} - \mathbf{u}\right)^2 \left(\frac{\mathbf{p}_1}{m} - \mathbf{u}\right) \bar{f}^{(1)}(1)\, d\mathbf{p}_1. \tag{6.3.59}$$

Insertion of the solution (6.3.2) of the singlet kinetic equation into equation (6.3.59) and integration over the angles of $\mathbf{W}_1$ leaves only the term in $\nabla \ln T$, all others being odd functions of $\mathbf{W}_1$. After a comparison of the resulting expression with the phenomenological Fourier heat-conduction law

$$\mathbf{q} = -\varkappa \nabla T, \tag{6.3.60}$$

where $\varkappa$ is the coefficient of thermal conductivity, it is found that the kinetic contribution to the thermal conductivity is given by

$$\varkappa_K = \frac{75k^2T}{32mg(\sigma)} \frac{\{1 + [2\pi\rho\sigma^3 g(\sigma)/5]\}}{\{\Omega^{(2,2)} + [45\zeta_S/16\rho m g(\sigma)]\}}. \tag{6.3.61}$$

The contribution to the heat flux vector from hard core collisions is evaluated in the same way as the corresponding contribution to the stress tensor in Section 6.3.A. We note that the direct potential part of the intermolecular force term in equation (6.2.80) is not concerned in the *transfer* at collision. Upon integrating over the phase of $(N - 2)$ molecules it is consequently found that

$$\mathbf{q}_V(\sigma) = -\frac{1}{2}\int \mathbf{R}_{12}\, \nabla_{12} u \cdot \left(\frac{\mathbf{p}_1}{m} - \mathbf{u}\right) \bar{f}^{(2)}(1,2)\, d\mathbf{p}_1\, d\mathbf{p}_2\, d\mathbf{R}_{12}. \tag{6.3.62}$$

Insertion of equations (6.3.8) and (6.3.6) in equation (6.3.62) leads to

$$\mathbf{q}_V(\sigma) = -\frac{\sigma}{2m}\int_{(\mathbf{k}\cdot\mathbf{p}_{12}<0)} \mathbf{k}(\mathbf{k}\cdot\mathbf{p}_{12})\left[\mathbf{k}\cdot\left(\frac{\mathbf{p}_1}{m}-\mathbf{u}\right)\right]\bar{f}^{(2)}(1,2)\,d\mathbf{p}_1\,d\mathbf{p}_2 b\,db\,d\epsilon. \tag{6.3.63}$$

The first collisional contribution $\mathbf{q}_V^{(1)}$ arises from the distortion of $\bar{f}^{(2)}$ from the local equilibrium form $\bar{f}_0^{(2)}$. This contribution may be expressed entirely in terms of the reduced peculiar velocities $\mathbf{w},\mathbf{W}$; after substitution of equation (6.3.15) and use of equation (6.3.14) in equation (6.3.63), we find

$$\begin{aligned}\mathbf{q}_V^{(1)} &= \tfrac{1}{2}m\sigma\rho^2 g(\sigma)\left(\frac{2kT}{m\pi^2}\right)^{3/2} A_1 \int_{(\mathbf{k}\cdot\mathbf{w}<0)}\iint \mathbf{k}(\mathbf{k}\cdot\mathbf{w})(\mathbf{k}\cdot[\mathbf{W}-\tfrac{1}{2}\mathbf{w}])\\ &\quad\times(-\mathbf{w}\mathbf{w}+[5-2W^2-\tfrac{1}{2}w^2]\mathbf{I})\!:\!\mathbf{W}\,\nabla\ln T\\ &\quad\times\exp(-2W^2-\tfrac{1}{2}w^2)w\,d\mathbf{w}\,d\mathbf{W}b\,db\,d\epsilon. \end{aligned}\tag{6.3.64}$$

Two other non-vanishing contributions arise, due respectively to the deviation of $\bar{f}_0^{(2)}$ from $\bar{f}_{\text{eq}}^{(2)}$ [Eq. (6.3.17)], and to the distortion of the pair correlation function at the surface of the hard core. These are denoted $\mathbf{q}_V^{(2)}$ and $\mathbf{q}_V^{(3)}$ in conformity with the notation introduced in the previous section. No contribution arises from the term in $\nabla\mathbf{u}$, since it consists of a linear combination of odd functions of $\mathbf{W}$.

Equation (6.3.64) may be simplified immediately by carrying out the integration over $\mathbf{W}$ space, giving

$$\begin{aligned}\mathbf{q}_V^{(1)} &= \frac{\sqrt{2}}{32}m\sigma\rho^2 g(\sigma)\left(\frac{2kT}{m\pi}\right)^{3/2} A_1\\ &\quad\times\int_{(\mathbf{k}\cdot\mathbf{w}<0)}\int \mathbf{k}(\mathbf{k}\cdot\mathbf{w})\{\mathbf{k}\cdot(-\mathbf{w}\mathbf{w}+[\tfrac{5}{2}-\tfrac{1}{2}w^2]\mathbf{I})\cdot\nabla\ln T\}\\ &\quad\times\exp(-\tfrac{1}{2}w^2)w\,d\mathbf{w}b\,db\,d\epsilon. \end{aligned}\tag{6.3.65}$$

The integral over the collision hemisphere may be separated into two parts. For any vector $\mathbf{B}$ (independent of $\mathbf{k}$ and $\mathbf{w}$) we have, using the notation and methods of the preceding section,

$$\begin{aligned}\int_{(\mathbf{k}\cdot\mathbf{w}<0)} \mathbf{k}(\mathbf{k}\cdot\mathbf{w})^2\mathbf{w}\cdot\mathbf{B}b\,db\,d\epsilon &= \sigma^2 w^2\mathbf{w}\cdot\mathbf{B}\mathbf{h}\int_0^{2\pi}\int_{\pi/2}^{\pi}\cos^4\Phi\sin\Phi\,d\Phi\,d\epsilon\\ &= \frac{2\pi}{5}\sigma^2 w\mathbf{w}\cdot\mathbf{B}\mathbf{w}, \end{aligned}\tag{6.3.66a}$$

and

$$\int_{(\mathbf{k}\cdot\mathbf{w}<0)} \mathbf{k}(\mathbf{k}\cdot\mathbf{w})(\mathbf{k}\cdot\mathbf{B})(\tfrac{5}{2} - \tfrac{1}{2}w^2)b\,db\,d\epsilon$$

$$= \frac{2\pi}{15}\sigma^2(\tfrac{5}{2} - \tfrac{1}{2}w^2)w(B_1\mathbf{i} + B_2\mathbf{j} + 3B_3\mathbf{h})$$

$$= \frac{2\pi}{15}\frac{\sigma^2}{w}(\tfrac{5}{2} - \tfrac{1}{2}w^2)(2\mathbf{ww} + w^2\mathbf{I})\cdot\mathbf{B}. \quad (6.3.66b)$$

The integration over the angles of $\mathbf{w}$ can be performed directly on equations (6.3.66), giving

$$\int \frac{2\pi}{15}\sigma^2 w\left[-3\mathbf{ww} + \frac{1}{w^2}(\tfrac{5}{2} - \tfrac{1}{2}w^2)(2\mathbf{ww} + w^2\mathbf{I})\right]\cdot\mathbf{B}\,d\Omega_w$$

$$= \frac{4\pi^2\sigma^2}{45}w[25 - 11w^2]\mathbf{B}. \quad (6.3.67)$$

Insertion of equation (6.3.67) into (6.3.65) with $\mathbf{B} = \nabla \ln T$ and integration over w now leads to

$$\mathbf{q}_V^{(1)} = \tfrac{1}{4}\pi\sigma^3\rho^2 g(\sigma)m\left(\frac{2kT}{m}\right)^{3/2} A_1 \nabla \ln T, \quad (6.3.68)$$

which yields the result

$$\varkappa_V^{(1)} = \frac{75k^2T}{32mg(\sigma)}\left(\frac{2\pi\rho\sigma^3}{5}\right)\frac{\{1 + [2\pi\rho\sigma^3 g(\sigma)/5]\}}{\{2\Omega^{(2,2)} + [45\zeta_S/16\rho m g(\sigma)]\}}$$

$$\times \left\{1 + \frac{\Omega^{(2,2)}}{\Omega^{(2,2)} + [45\zeta_S/16\rho m g(\sigma)]}\right\} \quad (6.3.69)$$

upon substitution of the expression for the factor A_1.

The second contribution to collisional transfer is obtained upon substitution of equation (6.2.17) in (6.3.63). The term proportional to $\mathbf{W}_1$ does not contribute because it is odd in $\mathbf{W}_1$, so that we obtain

$$\mathbf{q}_V^{(2)} = \frac{\rho^2\sigma^2 g(\sigma)kT}{\pi^3}\left(\frac{2kT}{m}\right)^{1/2}\int_{(\mathbf{k}\cdot\mathbf{w}<0)}\iint(\mathbf{k}\cdot\mathbf{w})(\mathbf{k}\cdot\mathbf{W})(\mathbf{w}\cdot\mathbf{W})\mathbf{kk}\cdot\nabla \ln T$$

$$\times \exp(-2W^2 - \tfrac{1}{2}w^2)w\,d\mathbf{w}\,d\mathbf{W}\,b\,db\,d\epsilon. \quad (6.3.70)$$

As before, an integration over $\mathbf{W}$ space simplifies the expression to

$$\mathbf{q}_V^{(2)} = \frac{\rho^2\sigma^2 g(\sigma)kT}{8\pi^2}\left(\frac{\pi kT}{m}\right)^{1/2}\int_{(\mathbf{k}\cdot\mathbf{w}<0)}\int(\mathbf{k}\cdot\mathbf{w})^2\mathbf{kk}\cdot\nabla \ln T$$

$$\times \exp(-\tfrac{1}{2}w^2)w\,d\mathbf{w}\,b\,db\,d\epsilon. \quad (6.3.71)$$

Integration over the collision hemisphere leads to the expression

$$\int_{(\mathbf{k}\cdot\mathbf{w}<0)} (\mathbf{k}\cdot\mathbf{w})^2\mathbf{kk}\cdot\mathbf{B}\, b\, db\, d\epsilon = \frac{\pi\sigma^2}{12}[3\mathbf{ww} + w^2\mathbf{I}]\cdot\mathbf{B}, \quad (6.3.72)$$

and when equation (6.3.72) is substituted in equation (6.3.71), and the integration over $\mathbf{w}$ space performed, it is found that

$$\mathbf{q}_V^{(2)} = -\frac{4\rho^2\sigma^6 g(\sigma)\sqrt{\pi}}{3\Omega^{(2,2)}}\frac{k^2T}{m}\nabla T. \quad (6.3.73)$$

The expression for $\varkappa_V^{(2)}$ obtained by comparison of equation (6.3.73) with the Fourier law (6.3.60) is, after a rearrangement of the factors,

$$\varkappa_V^{(2)} = \frac{75k^2Tg(\sigma)}{32m\Omega^{(2,2)}}\left(\frac{2\pi\rho\sigma^3}{5}\right)^2\left(\frac{32}{9\pi^{3/2}}\right). \quad (6.3.74)$$

Recall now the equivalence, to $\mathscr{O}[(\nabla T)^2]$, of the conditional excess particle current $(\mathbf{j}_1^{(2)} - \rho^{(2)}\mathbf{u}_1)$ at $\mathbf{R}_1$, and the excess center of mass current

$$\mathbf{j}^{(2)} - \rho^{(2)}\mathbf{u} = \tfrac{1}{2}\sum_{i=1,2}(\mathbf{j}_i^{(2)} - \rho^{(2)}\mathbf{u}_i), \quad (6.3.75)$$

which was demonstrated in Section 6.2.B [see Eqs. (6.2.81) and (6.2.86)]. This equivalence is clearly borne out in the foregoing calculations of $\varkappa_V^{(1)}$ and $\varkappa_V^{(2)}$. The factors $(\mathbf{W} - \tfrac{1}{2}\mathbf{w})$ in equations (6.3.64) and (6.3.70) arise from the factor $\left(\frac{\mathbf{p}_1}{m} - \mathbf{u}\right)$ in equation (6.3.62), and are seen, in the course of the analysis, to contribute only through the term $\mathbf{W}$; the term $-\tfrac{1}{2}\mathbf{w}$ vanishes in each case because it is coupled with an odd function of $\mathbf{W}$. We shall now *invoke* this equivalence to simplify the calculation of $\varkappa_V^{(3)}$ and $\varkappa_V(R_{12} > \sigma)$. Indeed, we shall see that if the steady-state pair correlation function is written as

$$g^{(2)} = g_0^{(2)}(T) + \Delta g^{(2)}, \quad (6.3.76)$$

where $g_0^{(2)}(T)$ is the equilibrium radial distribution function, T the temperature at the center of mass, and $\Delta g^{(2)}$ is a distortion due to the presence of a temperature gradient, then explicit calculation of $\Delta g^{(2)}$ can be avoided.

Consider the third collisional contribution to the heat flux, $\mathbf{q}_V^{(3)}$. Since the forces ${}^{(2)}\mathbf{G}_i^F$ vanish by definition at the surface of the rigid core, the contribution arises from the distortion of the factor $g^{(2)}$ in $\bar{f}^{(2)}_{\text{eq}}$ [cf. Eq. (6.3.17*a*)]. From equation (6.3.63) we obtain in this case

$$\begin{aligned}
\mathbf{q}_V^{(3)} &= -\frac{\sigma\rho^2}{2m(2\pi mkT)^3}\int\limits_{(\mathbf{k}\cdot\mathbf{p}_{12}<0)}\iint \mathbf{k}(\mathbf{k}\cdot\mathbf{p}_{12})\left(\mathbf{k}\cdot\left[\frac{\mathbf{p}_1}{m}-\mathbf{u}\right]\right)\\
&\quad\times \Delta g^{(2)}(\sigma)\exp\left(-2W^2-\tfrac{1}{2}w^2\right)p_{12}\,d\mathbf{p}_1\,d\mathbf{p}_2 b\,db\,d\epsilon\\
&= -\frac{m\sigma\rho^2}{2}\left(\frac{2kT}{m\pi^2}\right)^{3/2}\int\limits_{(\mathbf{k}\cdot\mathbf{w}<0)}\iint \mathbf{k}(\mathbf{k}\cdot\mathbf{w})(\mathbf{k}\cdot[\mathbf{W}-\tfrac{1}{2}\mathbf{w}])\\
&\quad\times \Delta g^{(2)}(\sigma)\exp\left(-2W^2-\tfrac{1}{2}w^2\right)w\,d\mathbf{w}\,d\mathbf{W}b\,db\,d\epsilon\\
&\cong -\frac{m\sigma\rho^2}{2}\left(\frac{2kT}{m\pi^2}\right)^{3/2}\int\limits_{(\mathbf{k}\cdot\mathbf{w}<0)}\iint \mathbf{k}(\mathbf{k}\cdot\mathbf{w})(\mathbf{k}\cdot\mathbf{W})\\
&\quad\times \Delta g^{(2)}(\sigma)\exp\left(-2W^2-\tfrac{1}{2}w^2\right)w\,d\mathbf{w}\,d\mathbf{W}b\,db\,d\epsilon\\
&= 0.
\end{aligned}\tag{6.3.77}$$

The third member of equation (6.3.77) follows from the second by invoking the equivalence equation (6.3.75) and vanishes because the integrand is an odd function integrated over an even interval. As already noted, this is correct to terms linear in the gradients. Consequently,

$$\varkappa_V^{(3)} = 0,\tag{6.3.78}$$

and the collisional contribution to the heat flux is given by

$$\varkappa_V(\sigma) = \varkappa_V^{(1)} + \varkappa_V^{(2)}\tag{6.3.79}$$

where $\varkappa_V^{(1)}$ and $\varkappa_V^{(2)}$ are displayed in equations (6.3.69) and (6.3.74).

We come now to the calculation of the soft force contribution. From equilibrium statistical mechanics we find that the net mean force on a molecule at $\mathbf{R}_i$ when another is at $\mathbf{R}_j$ $(i,j = 1,2)$ is*

$${}^{(2)}\langle\mathbf{F}_i\rangle^0 - {}^{(1)}\langle\mathbf{F}_i\rangle^0 = kT_i\,\nabla_i \ln g_0^{(2)}(T_i),\tag{6.3.80}$$

where $g_0^{(2)}(T_i)$ is the *equilibrium* radial distribution function for the (uniform) temperature $T_i = T(\mathbf{R}_i)$. The forces ${}^{(2)}\mathbf{G}_i^F$ may, therefore, be written

$${}^{(2)}\mathbf{G}_i^F = kT_i[\nabla_i \ln g_0^{(2)}(T_i) - \nabla_i \ln g^{(2)}].\tag{6.3.81}$$

* The forces $\mathbf{F}_i^\dagger$ in equation (6.3.12), due to the deviation of the higher order-distribution functions from equilibrium, are considered negligible.

Introduction of the relative and center-of-mass coordinates requires the expression of the net mean forces at temperatures T_i in terms of the temperature $T = \frac{1}{2}(T_1 + T_2)$ at the center of mass. We, therefore, have* (10)

$$kT_i \nabla_i \ln g_0^{(2)}(T_i) = kT\nabla_i \ln g_0^{(2)} \pm \tfrac{1}{2}\mathbf{R}_{12} \cdot \nabla T \left\{\frac{\partial}{\partial T} [kT\nabla_i \ln g_0^{(2)}]\right\}_p$$

$$= kT\nabla_i \ln g_0^{(2)} \pm \frac{k}{2} \mathbf{R}_{12} \cdot \nabla T \nabla_i \ln g_0^{(2)}$$

$$\pm \frac{kT}{2} \mathbf{R}_{12} \cdot \nabla T \left(\frac{\partial}{\partial T} \nabla_i \ln g_0^{(2)}\right)_p, \qquad (6.3.82)$$

where the lower and upper signs apply for $i = 1,2$, respectively, and suppression of the temperature in the argument of $g_0^{(2)}$ implies the temperature at the center of mass. Transformation of the differential operators is accomplished by means of the relations

$$\nabla_i = \pm\nabla_{12} + \tfrac{1}{2}\nabla$$
$$= \pm\nabla_{12} + \tfrac{1}{2}\nabla T \left(\frac{\partial}{\partial T}\right)_p, \qquad (6.3.83)$$

where the upper and lower signs have the same meaning as before. It must be borne in mind, however, that the net mean force is defined in terms of $g_0^{(2)}$, which is not a function of the position of the center of mass. For the actual pair correlation function for the fluid supporting a temperature gradient, we have the following transformation:

$$kT_i \nabla_i \ln g^{(2)} = k(T \pm \tfrac{1}{2}\mathbf{R}_{12} \cdot \nabla T)\left[\pm\nabla_{12} + \tfrac{1}{2}\nabla T \left(\frac{\partial}{\partial T}\right)_p\right] \ln g^{(2)}$$

$$= \pm kT\nabla_{12} \ln g^{(2)} + \frac{k}{2} \mathbf{R}_{12} \cdot \nabla T \nabla_{12} \ln g^{(2)}$$

$$+ \frac{kT}{2} \nabla T \left[\frac{\partial \ln g^{(2)}}{\partial T}\right]_p + \mathcal{O}[(\nabla T)^2]. \qquad (6.3.84)$$

* If the fluid is in a quasi-stationary state (so that we are not concerned with, for instance, the simultaneous propagation of sound waves) the temperature derivative is properly taken at constant pressure.

Upon introducing the distortion defined in equation (6.3.76), this becomes

$$kT_i \nabla_i \ln g^{(2)} = \pm kT\nabla_{12}\left[\ln g_0^{(2)} + \frac{\Delta g^{(2)}}{g_0^{(2)}}\right] + \frac{k}{2}\mathbf{R}_{12}\cdot\nabla T\nabla_{12}\ln g_0^{(2)} + \frac{kT}{2}\nabla T\left[\frac{\partial}{\partial T}\ln g_0^{(2)}\right]_p + \mathcal{O}[(\nabla T)^2], \quad (6.3.85)$$

where we have assumed that $\Delta g^{(2)} \sim \nabla T$ and $|\Delta g^{(2)}| \ll g_0^{(2)}$. Substitution of equations (6.3.82) and (6.3.85) in equation (6.3.81) leads immediately to

$$^{(2)}\mathbf{G}_i^F = kT\left\{\mp\nabla_{12}\left[\frac{\Delta g^{(2)}}{g_0^{(2)}}\right] + \tfrac{1}{2}\mathbf{R}_{12}\cdot\nabla T\left[\frac{\partial}{\partial T}\nabla_{12}\ln g_0^{(2)}\right]_p - \tfrac{1}{2}\nabla T\left[\frac{\partial \ln g_0^{(2)}}{\partial T}\right]_p\right\}. \quad (6.3.86)$$

Invoking now the equivalence, equation (6.3.75), it follows that the relevant part of the distribution function in equation (6.3.15) is*

$$\bar{f}^{(2)} = \bar{f}_0^{(2)}C_0\mathbf{W}\cdot[^{(2)}\mathbf{G}_1^F + {}^{(2)}\mathbf{G}_2^F]$$
$$= \bar{f}_0^{(2)}\frac{(2mkT)^{1/2}}{\zeta_S}\mathbf{W}\cdot\left\{\mathbf{R}_{12}\cdot\nabla T\left[\frac{\partial}{\partial T}\nabla_{12}\ln g_0^{(2)}\right]_p - \nabla T\left[\frac{\partial}{\partial T}\ln g_0^{(2)}\right]_p\right\}. \quad (6.3.87)$$

The contribution to the heat flux due to the soft forces is now obtained by integration of equation (6.2.80) over the phase of $(N-2)$ molecules, which yields

$$\mathbf{q}_V(R_{12} > \sigma) = \tfrac{1}{2}\int\left(u\mathbf{I} - \frac{\mathbf{R}_{12}\mathbf{R}_{12}}{R_{12}}u'\right)\cdot\left(\frac{\mathbf{p}_1}{m} - \mathbf{u}\right)\bar{f}^{(2)}(1,2)\,d\mathbf{p}_1\,d\mathbf{p}_2\,d\mathbf{R}_{12}. \quad (6.3.88)$$

* It is easily verified that the coefficients of A_1 and $B_0^{(1)}$ vanish identically upon integration over both $\mathbf{w}$ and $\mathbf{W}$ space.

The equivalence condition also implies that

$$C_0\mathbf{w}\cdot[^{(2)}\mathbf{G}_2^F - {}^{(2)}\mathbf{G}_1^F] = 0,$$

i.e., that $^{(2)}\mathbf{G}_2^F = {}^{(2)}\mathbf{G}_1^F$ when expressed in terms of the temperature at the center of mass. This in turn implies that $\Delta g^{(2)}$ vanishes identically to $\mathcal{O}[(\nabla T)^2]$, which result is in agreement with the discussion of Zwanzig et al. (10). These workers choose to expand all quantities in terms of T_1 rather than T, and obtain as a result

$$g^{(2)} = g_0^{(2)}(T_1) + \tfrac{1}{2}\mathbf{R}_{12}\cdot\nabla T\left[\frac{\partial g_0^{(2)}}{\partial T_1}(T_1)\right]_p,$$

which is identical with our formulation.

After the introduction of reduced variables equation (6.3.88) becomes

$$\mathbf{q}_V(R_{12} > \sigma) = \frac{kT\rho^2}{\zeta_S \pi^3} \iiint \left(u\mathbf{I} - \frac{\mathbf{R}_{12}\mathbf{R}_{12}}{R_{12}} u' \right) \cdot \mathbf{WW}$$

$$\cdot \left\{ \mathbf{R}_{12} \cdot \nabla T \left[\frac{\partial}{\partial T} \nabla_{12} \ln g_0^{(2)} \right]_p - \nabla T \left[\frac{\partial \ln g_0^{(2)}}{\partial T} \right]_p \right\} g_0^{(2)}$$

$$\times \exp(-\tfrac{1}{2}W^2 - \tfrac{1}{2}w^2)\, d\mathbf{w}\, d\mathbf{W}\, d\mathbf{R}_{12}$$

$$= \frac{kT\rho^2}{4\zeta_S} \int \left(u\mathbf{I} - \frac{\mathbf{R}_{12}\mathbf{R}_{12}}{R_{12}} u' \right) \cdot \left\{ \mathbf{R}_{12} \cdot \nabla T \left[\frac{\partial}{\partial T} \nabla_{12} \ln g_0^{(2)} \right]_p - \nabla T \left[\frac{\partial \ln g_0^{(2)}}{\partial T} \right]_p \right\} g_0^{(2)}\, d\mathbf{R}_{12}$$

$$= \frac{\pi k T \rho^2}{3\zeta_S} \int_\sigma^\infty (u - R_{12}u') \left(\frac{d}{dR_{12}} \left[\frac{\partial \ln g_0^{(2)}}{\partial T} \right]_p \right) g_0^{(2)} R_{12}^{\ 3}\, dR_{12} \nabla T$$

$$- \frac{\pi k T \rho^2}{\zeta_S} \int_\sigma^\infty (u - \tfrac{1}{3}R_{12}u') \left[\frac{\partial g_0^{(2)}}{\partial T} \right]_p R_{12}^{\ 2}\, dR_{12} \nabla T. \quad (6.3.89)$$

The second member of equation (6.3.89) follows from the first by an integration over $\mathbf{w}$ and $\mathbf{W}$ space, and the third by an integration over the angles of $\mathbf{R}_{12}$. It follows from equation (6.3.89) that the soft force contribution to the coefficient of thermal conductivity is

$$\varkappa_V(R_{12} > \sigma) = \frac{\pi k T \rho^2}{3\zeta_S} \int_\sigma^\infty (R_{12}u' - u) \left\{ \frac{d}{dR_{12}} \left[\frac{\partial \ln g_0^{(2)}}{\partial T} \right]_p \right\} g_0^{(2)} R_{12}^{\ 3}\, dR_{12}$$

$$+ \frac{\pi k T \rho^2}{\zeta_S} \int_\sigma^\infty (u - \tfrac{1}{3}R_{12}u') \left[\frac{\partial g_0^{(2)}}{\partial T} \right]_p R_{12}^{\ 2}\, dR_{12}. \quad (6.3.90)$$

The total coefficient of thermal conductivity is, therefore, given by

$$\varkappa = \varkappa_K + \varkappa_V(\sigma) + \varkappa_V(R_{12} > \sigma), \quad (6.3.91)$$

the three contributions being displayed in equations (6.3.61), (6.3.79), and (6.3.90), respectively.

6.4. CALCULATION OF THE COEFFICIENTS OF VISCOSITY AND THERMAL CONDUCTIVITY (3,6–11)

The calculation of the transport coefficients from the equations given in the preceding section presents no difficulties in principle. However, several difficulties are met with in practice, particularly in the computation of the friction coefficient and radial distribution function. While a well defined relationship for the friction coefficient was obtained in Chapter 5, we shall see in Section 6.5.C that this formalism introduces an aspect of the N-body problem which cannot be adequately treated at present. Indeed, although numerical calculations lead to values of the self-diffusion coefficient within 30% of experiment, in this section we choose to test the structure of the theory and, therefore, use accurate values of the friction coefficient deduced from experimental data. It will be demonstrated in Section 6.5 that the diffusion coefficient, D, is related to the friction coefficient by

$$D = \frac{kT}{\zeta}, \tag{6.4.1}$$

where

$$\zeta = \zeta_H + \zeta_S; \qquad \zeta_H = \tfrac{8}{3}\rho\sigma^2 g(\sigma)(\pi mkT)^{1/2}, \tag{6.4.2}$$

and ζ_H is the hard core friction coefficient defined in, for instance, equation (6.5.39). In Table 6.1 are displayed ζ, ζ_H, and the soft-friction coefficient ζ_S for four temperatures for liquid Argon.

In the following sections it will be evident that the presence of rigid cores does not contribute very much *directly* to the total transport coefficients, because the kinetic contribution and first two collisional contributions are generally much smaller than the soft force contribution. Nevertheless, ζ_H is comparable in magnitude with ζ_S, with the result that the presence of the rigid cores has a considerable influence on the soft-force contribution through the value of ζ_S.

TABLE 6.1

Values of ζ_H and ζ_S for Liquid Ar[a]

T(°K)	ρ_m (g. cm.$^{-3}$)	p (atm.)	$\zeta \times 10^{10}$ (g. sec.$^{-1}$)	$\zeta_H \times 10^{10}$ (g. sec.$^{-1}$)	$\zeta_S \times 10^{10}$ (g. sec.$^{-1}$)
90	1.38	1.3	5.11	0.64	4.47
128	1.12	50	2.94	0.94	2.00
133.5	1.12	100	3.13	1.00	2.13
185.5	1.12	500	3.20	1.52	1.68

[a] The total friction coefficient is estimated from the self-diffusion measurements of Naghizadeh and Rice(11).

Our intended use of only four sets of values for the friction coefficients requires comment. The number of points at which we can calculate the transport coefficients is in the first place limited by the availability of appropriate radial distribution functions; these have been calculated for only two densities for the liquid phase (for all T). We are limited in the second place by the availability of data on self-diffusion.

Certainly, the more serious problem is that of obtaining accurate radial distribution functions. It is clear from the discussion of Sections 2.6 and 2.7 that, at present, exact radial distribution functions cannot be calculated, and the plain fact is that at liquid densities the approximate radial distribution functions known at present do not predict good values of the pressure and internal energy. It is possible to make a partial improvement of this situation by the intuitive process of "scaling," which we shall discuss in detail in the following sections.

6.4.A. *The Coefficient of Shear Viscosity* (3,7,8)

To compute the shear viscosity we must solve equation (6.3.52) for the function ψ_2. It is easily verified that the differential equation for ψ_2 and its boundary conditions are equivalent to the integral equation

$$-\psi_2(x) = 6\int_x^\infty \frac{1}{s^2 g(s)} \int_1^s g(u)\psi_2(u)\,du\,ds + \int_x^\infty \frac{1}{s^2 g(s)} \int_1^s u^3 \frac{dg(u)}{du}\,du\,ds. \quad (6.4.3)$$

In equation (6.4.3) we have introduced $g(x)$ for $g_0^{(2)}(R_{12})$ for simplicity, since we are no longer concerned with the *physical* significance of the original symbols.

With the definitions

$$a(x) = \int_x^\infty \frac{ds}{s^2 g(s)}; \qquad \lim_{x\to\infty} a(x) = 0,$$

$$b(x) = \int_x^\infty s^2[g(s) - 1]\,ds; \qquad \lim_{x\to\infty} b(x) = 0,$$

$$c(x) = \int_x^\infty s^2[g(s) - 1]a(s)\,ds,$$

$$d(x) = \int_x^\infty s[g(s)^{-1} - 1]\,ds,$$

$$\int_x^\infty h(s)\int_s^\infty k(u)\,du\,ds = \int_x^\infty h(s)\,ds\int_x^\infty k(u)\,du - \int_x^\infty k(s)\int_s^\infty h(u)\,du\,ds,$$

(for any $h(x)$, $k(x)$) (6.4.4)

and eliminating the derivative terms by partial integration

$$\int_s^\infty u^3 \frac{dg(u)}{du}\, du = \{u^3[g(u) - 1]\}_s^\infty - 3\int_s^\infty u^2[g(u) - 1]\, du, \quad (6.4.5)$$

it is found that

$$\psi_2(x) = d(x) - 3a(x)b(x) + 3c(x) + 6\int_x^\infty [a(x) - a(s)]g(s)\psi_2(s)\, ds. \quad (6.4.6)$$

We have made use of the fact that $[g(u) - 1] \to 0$ faster than u^{-3} as $u \to \infty$. Also note that [cf. Eq. (6.4.7)] $\lim_{u\to\infty} u^2[d\psi_2(u)/du] = 0$, so that $6\int_1^\infty g(u)\psi_2(u)\, du = -\int_1^\infty u^3[dg(u)/du]\, du$. Equation (6.4.6) was solved numerically using the asymptotic condition

$$\lim_{x\to\infty} \psi_2(x) = \frac{P}{x^3}, \quad (6.4.7)$$

where P is a constant. Since a, b, c, and d are known functions of x, it is clear that equations (6.4.6) and (6.4.7) will give a family of solutions $\psi_2(x;P)$. The correct value of P will be that for which $\psi_2(x;P)$ satisfies the boundary conditions at $x = \infty$. From the relations displayed following equation (6.4.6), we obtain

$$\int_1^\infty g(x)\psi_2(x;P)\, dx = \tfrac{1}{6}[g(1) - 1] + \tfrac{1}{2}b(1). \quad (6.4.8)$$

The right-hand side of this equation is known. Since every value of $\psi_2(x;P)$ is linear in P, the left-hand side of the equation is linear in P. This then gives us a method of finding the value of P which will satisfy the boundary conditions. The procedure is as follows: two values of P are chosen and the corresponding $\psi_2(x;P)$ computed and used to evaluate the integral on the left-hand side of the equation. The computed values are then compared with the value on the right-hand side and a linear interpolation leads to the correct value of P.

Numerical calculations have been made by Lowry, Rice, and Gray (3) using a digital computer. The data from Kirkwood, Lewinson, and Alder (12) were introduced along with the appropriate temperatures. The machine computed and stored in memory $a(x)$, $b(x)$, $c(x)$, $d(x)$, and $g(x)$ at intervals of 0.005 for $1 \leqslant x \leqslant 7$; $\psi_2(x;P)$ was evaluated for $P = 1$ and $P = 2$. These functions were used to compute the integral of equation (6.4.8) and the correct value of P. $\psi_2(x;P)$ was recomputed and then, if the left-hand side of equation (6.4.8) agreed with the right-hand side to within 0.1%, the machine used these $\psi_2(x)$ functions to evaluate the integral of equation (6.4.6) using the trapezoidal rule and a mesh of 0.005. In Table 6.2 are displayed the values of P and $\psi_2(\sigma)$ thus obtained for the same physical conditions as in Table 6.1. It should be noted that all the values of $\psi_2(\sigma)$ in Table 6.2 are negative, consistent with a positive value of $\eta_V^{(3)}$.

TABLE 6.2

Values of P and $\psi_2(\sigma)$ in the Solution of equation (6.4.6)

T(°K)	p(atm.)	P	$\psi_2(\sigma)/\sigma^2$
90	1.3	3.96	−0.129
128	50	4.39	−0.106
133.5	100	4.44	−0.103
185.5	500	5.16	−0.080

A close examination of the integration is discouraging. All the functions $g(x)$,* $\psi_2(x)$ and $u'(x)$ vary widely, and both $\psi_2(x)$ and $u'(x)$ can be positive and negative. The negative contributions to the integral tend to cancel the positive contributions and the computation is extremely sensitive to the relative shapes and positions of $g(x)$, $\psi_2(x)$ and $u(x)$.

* The Kirkwood theory of the pair correlation function involves an expansion in powers of ϵ/kT where ϵ is the depth of the Lennard-Jones potential describing the interaction between molecules. At the normal boiling point of Ar, (ϵ/kT) exceeds unity, but the theoretical function appears to agree with the observed radial distribution function when ϵ is taken to be somewhat smaller than the value characteristic of the gas phase interaction (Kirkwood compares a function calculated for $(\epsilon/kT) = 1.2$ with experiment for which $(\epsilon/kT) = 1.34$ based on ϵ taken from second virial coefficient measurements). This decrease in ϵ is predicted by theory when the effects of the fluctuating fields of other molecules on a given pair interaction are considered. In any event, to minimize the danger of nonconvergence, $g(x)$ was computed for $(\epsilon/kT) < 1$ and for a density somewhat less than the normal liquid density (but in the liquid phase). The computations were made from the expansion published by Kirkwood, Lewinson, and Alder using $\epsilon = 171 \times 10^{-16}$ ergs and $\sigma = 3.418 \times 10^{-8}$ cm, as found by Naghizadeh and Rice to fit corresponding states self-diffusion data.

A similar situation is apparent when we examine the equation of state for the fluid. This is

$$\frac{p}{\rho kT} = 1 + \frac{2\pi\rho\sigma^3}{3} g(\sigma) - \frac{8\pi\rho\sigma^3\epsilon}{3kT}\int_1^\infty u'(x)g(x)x^3\,dx. \quad (6.4.9)$$

Direct calculations of the pressure with equation (6.4.8) from the distribution functions used to compute ψ_2 lead to negative pressures (see also Section 2.7.B). This is a symptom of the errors in our knowledge of $u(x)$ and $g(x)$. It is interesting that a shift of the relative positions of $u'(x)$ and $g(x)$ by only 2% suffices to obtain the correct pressure. This change in relative position is most easily effected by replacing $u'(x)$ by $u'(cx)$. Then the values of c found are 0.9705, 0.9819, 0.9827, and 0.9887 for the set of conditions for which we quoted values of P before (13). Noting the similarity in structure between equations (6.4.9) and (6.3.57), we use the same correction in the calculation of the viscosity and find for $\eta_V(R_{12} > \sigma)$:

1.3 atm., 90°K	0.9258 → 1.2560
50 atm., 128°K	0.1844 → 0.2224
100 atm., 133.5°K	0.1898 → 0.2228
500 atm., 185.5°K	0.1114 → 0.1214.

Both scaled and unscaled values are displayed in Table 6.3. It should be noted that the required change in potential is well within the experimental uncertainties. Also displayed in Table 6.3 are values of η ($T = 185.5°$; $\rho_m = 1.12$ g. cm.$^{-3}$) for which $g(\sigma) = 1$. Although the calculated value of $g(\sigma)$ is 1.255, an extrapolation of lower temperature values leads smoothly to $g(\sigma) = 1$. Its relevance will be discussed in Section 6.4.D.

6.4.B. *The Coefficient of Bulk Viscosity* (6,8)

To compute the bulk viscosity, equation (6.3.51) must be solved. The integral equation equivalent to equation (6.3.51) and the boundary condition (6.3.56) is

$$\psi_0(x) = a(x)[Q - 3b(x)] + 3c(x) + d(x) + 3f(x), \quad (6.4.10)$$

in the notation of equation (6.4.4), and where

$$f(x) = \int_x^\infty [a(u) - a(x)]\frac{dg(u)}{d\ln\rho}u^2\,du. \quad (6.4.11)$$

The asymptotic solution of equation (6.3.51) is

$$\lim_{x \to \infty} \psi_0(x) = \frac{Q}{x}, \tag{6.4.12a}$$

where it can easily be verified that

$$Q = \sigma^3 \int_1^\infty \left(3x^2 \frac{dg(x)}{d \ln \rho} - x^3 \frac{dg(x)}{dx} \right) dx. \tag{6.4.12b}$$

TABLE 6.3

Shear Viscosity of Liquid Argon in Millipoise

T°K p atm.	90 1.3	128 50	133.5 100	185.5 500
η_K	0.031	0.059	0.059	0.095 0.110[a]
$\eta_V^{(1)}$	0.012	0.058	0.036	0.076 0.076[a]
$\eta_V^{(2)}$	0.282	0.330	0.350	0.532 0.424[a]
$\eta_V^{(3)}$	0.155	0.058	0.042	0.050
$\eta_V(R_{12} > \sigma)$	0.926 1.256[b]	0.184 0.222[b]	0.190 0.223[b]	0.111 0.121[b]
$\eta_{\text{calc.}}$	1.21	0.692	0.701	0.864 0.874[b]
	1.74[b]	0.727[b]	0.730[b]	0.771[a] 0.781[a,b]

[a] $g(\sigma) = 1$.
[b] Scaled values of $\eta_V(R_{12} > \sigma)$.

The computation of the bulk viscosity also suffers from the numerical difficulties described in the previous section as regards the uncertainties in $u(x)$ and $g(x)$, although equation (6.4.10) does not involve an iteration. However, it suffers in addition from the inaccuracies introduced in the determination of $[dg(x)/d \ln \rho]$. Since $g(x)$ has only been calculated for four different densities, the reader will immediately appreciate the fact that the calculation of the bulk viscosity is probably not accurate* to better than 20%, and is certainly less reliable than the shear viscosity.

The values of $[dg(x)/d\ln\rho]$ were obtained for each x using the differentiated form of the Lagrangian interpolation formula. The resultant functions were not particularly smooth, owing to the inaccuracies in the radial distribution functions, and were smoothed by means of Spencer's analytic smoothing formula (14). In practice, the calculated values of Q conflict strongly with experiment. For, after a partial integration, equation (6.4.13) may be written

$$Q = \frac{3\sigma^3}{4\pi}\int\left[g(x) - 1 + \frac{dg(x)}{d\ln\rho}\right]d\mathbf{x} + \sigma^3[g(\sigma) - 1]$$

$$= -\frac{3kT}{4\pi}\rho^2\kappa_T^{\,2}\left(\frac{\partial^2 p}{\partial\rho^2}\right)_T + \sigma^3[g(\sigma) - 1], \tag{6.4.13}$$

where κ_T is the isothermal compressibility.

While experimental data are inadequate to estimate Q accurately, they show clearly that $(\partial^2 p/\partial\rho^2)_T > 0$ at liquid densities. Consequently, since $g(\sigma) < 1$ for all thermodynamic states considered except one, we should expect that $Q \leqslant 0$. However, the calculated values of Q are found to be strongly positive. At the present time this situation cannot be remedied, but a provisional estimate is obtained by adopting the value $Q = 0$ for all calculations. It is a feature of the calculation that the value of Q dominates the final value of the soft force contribution $\phi_V(R_{12} > \sigma)$, and also determines the value of $\psi_0(\sigma)$. It is found that if Q is less than some small positive value the third collisional contribution $\phi_V^{(3)}$ is non-negative. Thus, the experimental value of $(\partial^2 p/\partial\rho^2)_T$ (and the chosen value of Q) can be said to be consistent with physical experience to the extent that the dissipation is a source, and not a sink of entropy.

In Table 6.4 are displayed the values of Q calculated directly from equation (6.4.13) (denoted Q'), the maximum values of Q for $\phi_V^{(3)}$ to be non-negative (denoted Q''), and the values of $\psi_0(\sigma)$ for $Q = 0$.

In Table 6.5 are displayed the numerical values of the various contributions to ϕ. It should be noted that scaling induces a swing

* By "accurate" we mean in comparison to that value obtainable from a (hypothetical) correct radial distribution function, its density derivative, and the pair potential. A similar conclusion is justified with regard to the thermal conductivity (see next section).

irregularities in the parent function. However, this difficulty can be somewhat reduced by a partial integration (analytic) which leads to a small end point contribution at $R = \sigma$; the derivative is then found to be much less erratic in behavior. As in the case of bulk viscosity just discussed, Lagrangian interpolation and Spencer's smoothing formula were used to obtain smooth values of $(\partial \ln g/\partial \rho)_T$. The results of the calculations are displayed in Table 6.6.

6.4.D. *Comparison with Experiment*

In this section only the shear viscosity and thermal conductance will be discussed; no accurate measurements of the bulk viscosity of simple liquids have yet been made.*

The shear viscosity of liquid argon has been measured for several temperatures and pressures. Rudenko and Schubnikov (15) made measurements at five points in a temperature range of 3°K. Zhdanova (16) and Scott (17) have made measurements over a considerable range of pressure and temperature. Finally, Lowry, Rice and Gray (LRG) (3) have reported measurements at two temperatures for the pressure range 50–500 atm.

An examination of Figure 6.4.1 shows that the data of Zhdanova agree better with that obtained by LRG than do the data of Scott. Indeed, the agreement is quite good. At 128°K, both the data of Zhdanova and Scott disagree with that obtained in the experiments of LRG in that the pressure dependence of the viscosity is smaller than they observe. If we accept the measurements reported by LRG, the computed and observed viscosities are in good agreement at 128°K and 50 atm. (see Table 6.7). On the other hand, at 90°K and 1.3 atm. there remains a discrepancy between theory and experiment of about 35%.

To examine the temperature dependence of the viscosity, we assume that the data of Zhdanova give the correct slope at constant density, even though the absolute value may be in error (at 128°K and 50 atm. Zhdanova reports $\eta = 1.02 \times 10^{-3}$ poise, whereas LRG find $\eta = 0.835 \times 10^{-3}$ poise). The results of this comparison are displayed in

* Professor C. Squire, of the Texas A. and M. University, has informed us of new measurements of the bulk viscosity of liquid argon. The preliminary data give $0.8 < (\phi/\eta) < 1.4$, in good agreement with the prediction $(\phi/\eta) \simeq 1.3$.

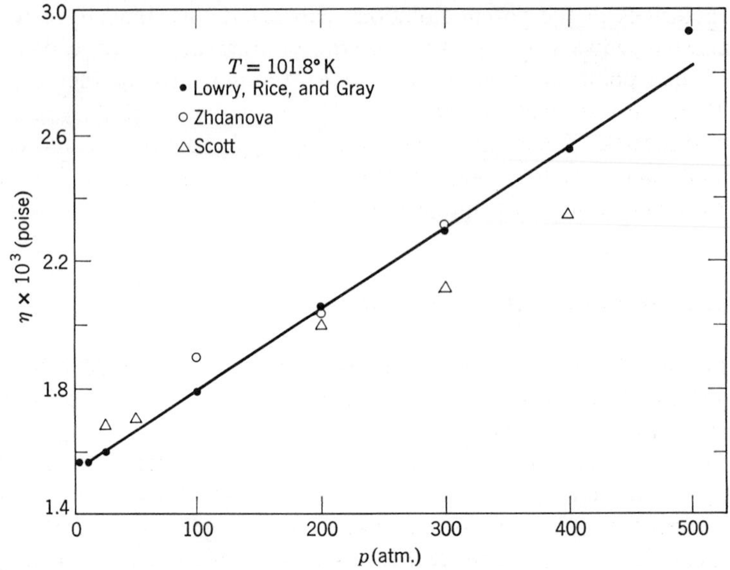

Fig. 6.4.1. The shear viscosity of liquid argon at 101.8°K as a function of pressure.

Table 6.8. In view of the sensitivity of the theory to the imperfectly known radial distribution function, we consider the agreement between theory and experiment to be quite good. The theory correctly predicts that at constant density the shear viscosity is little affected by changes

TABLE 6.7

Comparison of Computed and Measured Values of the Shear Viscosity of Liquid Argon (Units are Millipoise)[a,b]

State	90°K 1.3 atm.	128°K 50 atm.	133.5°K 100 atm.	185.5°K 500 atm.
$\eta_{calc.}$	1.74	0.727	0.730	0.771 0.781[c]
$\eta_{obs.}$	2.39	0.835	0.843	0.869

[a] The measurements at the three higher temperatures are at the constant density $\rho_m = 1.12$g./cm³.

[b] The computed values are scaled.

[c] $g(\sigma) = 1$.

in temperature, the sign of the small temperature change is computed correctly, and the computed slope is only slightly larger than the observed slope if the Kirkwood value of $g(\sigma)$ is used. If we assume that $g(\sigma) = 1$ at $T = 185.5$°K and $p = 500$ atm., then the computed and observed slopes are still in very good agreement, but the very small slope is overestimated. Given the uncertainty of the experimental data, it is likely that the difference between the computed and experimental temperature derivatives of the shear viscosity is not significant.

TABLE 6.8

Comparison of Computed and Measured Temperature Dependence of the Shear Viscosity of Liquid Argon of Constant Density, $\rho_m = 1.12$ g./cm.$^{-3}$

State	128°K 50 atm.	133.5°K 100 atm.	185.5°K 500 atm.
$\dfrac{\eta_{calc}(T)}{\eta_{calc}(128)}$	1.00	1.005	1.06 1.08[a]
$\dfrac{\eta_{obs}(T)}{\eta_{obs}(128)}$	1.00	1.01	1.04

[a] $g(\sigma) = 1$.

Measurements of the thermal conductivity of liquid argon have been reported by Uhlir (18), by Ziebland and Burton (19), and by Keyes (20). Measurements over extensive ranges of temperature and pressure have been reported by Ikenberry and Rice (IR) (9).

The comparison of the computed values of thermal conductivity with the data of IR in Table 6.9 exhibits features very similar to those for the shear viscosity. The computed value at 90°K and 1.3 atm. is again about 40% low, while those at the higher temperatures and constant density of $\rho_m = 1.12$ gm. cm.$^{-3}$ are within 10% of the observed values. Again, the important features of the temperature dependence are correctly predicted. However, the theory exaggerates the dip in $\varkappa$ at 133.5°K and 100 atm.* As in the case of the shear viscosity, (see

* The assumption that $g(\sigma) = 1$ at $T = 185.5$°K, $p = 500$ atm. in this case somewhat worsens the agreement.

TABLE 6.9

Comparison of Computed and Measured Values of the Thermal Conductivity of Liquid Argon (Units are 10^{-4} cal./cm. sec. deg.)[a,b]

State	90°K 1.3 atm.	128°K 50 atm.	133.5°K 100 atm.	185.5°K 500 atm.
$\varkappa_{\text{calc}}$	1.645	1.692	1.589	1.696 1.580[c]
$\varkappa_{\text{obs}}$	2.96	1.89	1.86	1.87

[a] The measurements at the three higher temperatures are at constant density, $\rho_m = 1.12$ g./cm.^{3}

[b] The computed values are scaled.

[c] $g(\sigma) = 1$.

Table 6.7), because of the uncertainties in $g(x)$ it is unlikely that the remaining discrepancies between observed and computed values of $(\partial\varkappa/\partial T)_p$ are physically significant.

A question which must be discussed after examination of our arguments is the following: Is the overall agreement (or disagreement) between theory and experiment significant? This question is very difficult to answer. We have repeatedly remarked that at present the available radial distribution functions and potential functions for a

TABLE 6.10

Comparison of Computed and Measured Temperature Dependence of the Thermal Conductivity of Liquid Argon at Constant Density $\rho_m = 1.12.$ g./cm.^{3}

State	128°K 50 atm.	133.5°K 100 atm.	185.5°K 500 atm.
$\dfrac{\varkappa_{\text{calc}}(T)}{\varkappa_{\text{calc}}(128°\text{K})}$	1.00	0.939	1.010 0.935[a]
$\dfrac{\varkappa_{\text{obs}}(T)}{\varkappa_{\text{obs}}(128°\text{K})}$	1.00	0.983	0.989

[a] $g(\sigma) = 1$.

dense fluid are extremely poor, and have already noted that at liquid densities it is not uncommon to have the predicted pressure be negative. Moreover, the pressure is so sensitive to the relative positions of the minimum of $u(R)$ and the first maximum of $g_0^{(2)}(R)$ that a $2\frac{1}{2}\%$ relative shift can change the predicted pressure from -1000 atm. to $+1$ atm. An examination of the scale factors used in Section 6.4.A shows that the equilibrium theory is worst at high densities and low temperatures (c furthest from unity). It is to be expected that the predicted values of η and $\varkappa$ at low temperatures and high densities will be furthest from the experimental values, especially since ψ_2 depends on $g_0^{(2)}$ through equation (6.3.52), $\varkappa_V(R > \sigma)$ depends on g and dg/dT, and $\eta_V(R_{12} > \sigma)$ depends in turn on both ψ_2 and $g_0^{(2)}$.

There are at least two other sources of large uncertainty in the above calculations. It is difficult to estimate how accurately ϵ is known (or if it should be density dependent), and there is at least a 5% variation in the literature values for σ. The uncertainty in σ is particularly important because σ^6 and σ^{12} are required in the computation of the shear viscosity. These factors also enter in the determination of $g_0^{(2)}$. It is our opinion that most of the observed disagreement could be accounted for by the present inadequacies of the available pair potential and radial distribution function.

We therefore conclude that the practical utility of the theory cannot be adequately assessed at the present time. Complete testing of the theory awaits the determination of accurate potential functions and radial distribution functions. The present extent of agreement between the Rice-Allnatt theory and experiment does, however, suggest that the theory gives a good first order description of liquids.

6.4.E. *The High-Density, High-Temperature Limit*

Inspection of Table 6.1 indicates that the hard core friction coefficient, ζ_H, increases at the expense of the soft friction coefficient ζ_S as the temperature is increased. That is, the importance of the soft attractive–repulsive potential diminishes as (ϵ/kT) becomes smaller. At sufficiently high temperatures

$$\zeta_H \gg \zeta_S, \qquad T \gg \epsilon/k. \tag{6.4.15}$$

In this limit the Fokker-Planck operators on the right-hand sides of the kinetic equations become small and the transport coefficients are given by

$$\eta = \eta_K + \sum_{i=1,2} \eta_V^{(i)} + \eta_V(R_{12} > \sigma),$$
$$\phi = \phi_V^{(2)} + \phi_V(R_{12} > \sigma),$$
$$\varkappa = \varkappa_K + \sum_{i=1,2} \varkappa_V^{(i)} + \varkappa_V(R_{12} > \sigma), \quad (6.4.16)$$

where the argument $R_{12} > \sigma$ now implies a weak perturbation by the soft potential.

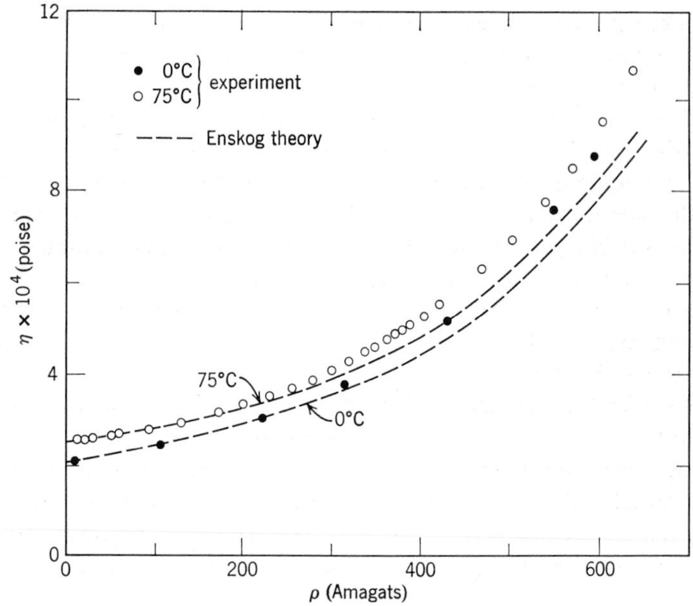

Fig. 6.4.2. Comparison of the Enskog theory with experiment for the shear viscosity of argon at 0° and 75°C as a function of density.

The values* of $\eta_V(R_{12} > \sigma)$ and $\varkappa_V(R_{12} > \sigma)$ can, in principle, be calculated directly from the radial distribution functions of Kirkwood, Lewinson, and Alder, already used for the low-temperature computations. Unfortunately, no data on self-diffusion exist at high temperatures and high densities, so that ζ_S cannot be easily estimated. We content ourselves with simple (and therefore crude) extrapolations from the

* No bulk viscosity measurements exist in this p, T region and we therefore do not discuss the limiting behavior of this quantity.

scaled values of $\eta_V(R_{12} > \sigma)$ and $\varkappa_V(R_{12} > \sigma)$ at $\rho_m = 1.12$ gm. cm.$^{-3}$ given in Tables 6.3 and 6.6. It is thereby estimated that at 348°K (65°C)

$$\left.\begin{aligned} \eta_V(R_{12} > \sigma) &\sim 0.04\text{–}0.06 \quad \text{millipoise} \\ \varkappa_V(R_{12} > \sigma) &\sim 0.4\text{–}0.6 \quad 10^{-4}\ \text{cal./cm. sec. deg.} \end{aligned}\right\} T = 348°\text{K}°.$$

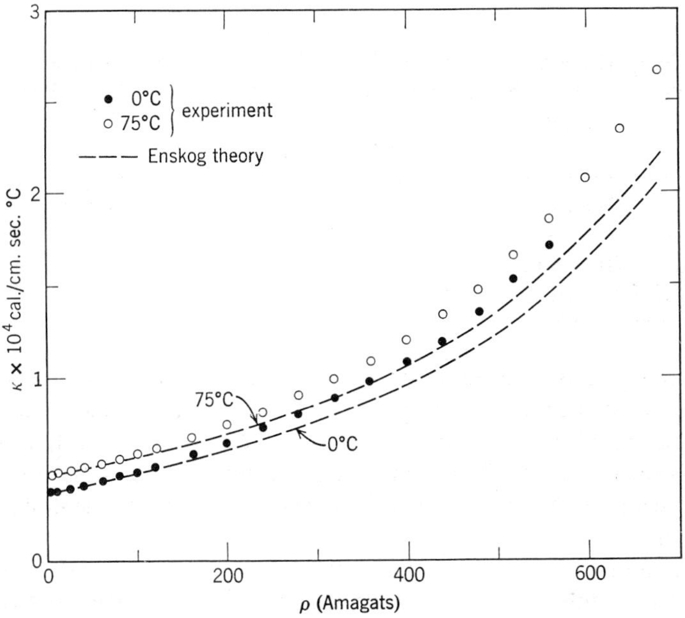

Fig. 6.4.3. Comparison of the Enskog theory with experiment for the thermal conductivity of argon at 0° and 75°C as a function of density.

These values are to be compared with the deviations of the Enskog curves from experiment at 620 Amagats, in Figures 6.4.2 and 6.4.3, respectively (21). This comparison yields the results displayed in Table 6.11, and it appears that more detailed computations may give good agreement with experiment.

6.5. THE FLUX OF MATTER IN A LIQUID

In this section we discuss the transport of matter in a liquid. This may arise in two ways. If a liquid system is subjected to an external field, such as an electric field, any ions present will drift through the liquid in, or against, the direction of the field according to the signs of the electric charges they carry. Alternatively, if a concentration of some molecules different from the liquid molecules in size or structure is introduced at some point in the liquid, they will be found at some

TABLE 6.11

Comparison of the Estimated Soft Force Contribution to Shear Viscosity and Thermal Conductance, with Experimentally Determined(21) Deviations from the Enskog Theory, at $T = 348°K$, $\rho_m = 620$ Amagats

Quantity θ	$\theta_V(R_{12} > \sigma)$	$\Delta\theta$ (expt)
η (10^{-3} poise)	0.04–0.06	0.11
$\varkappa$ (10^{-4} cal./cm. sec. deg.)	0.4–0.6	0.50

later time to have moved to other regions. In this case the average flux can be related to the density gradient of the foreign molecules and they can be regarded as moving under the influence of an effective force field which is essentially entropic in character. We shall discuss both these cases within the same theoretical formalism in the following section.

We can envisage the situation that would obtain if we undertook to describe the flux in cases where the guest molecules became successively more and more like the molecules of the host liquid. Eventually, the "foreign" molecules would be indistinguishable from those of the "host" liquid, and we would be discussing the phenomenon of self-diffusion. We shall see that, in fact, these two phenomena arise from the same mechanism; namely, random motions in the foreign molecule induced by interaction with the molecules of the host liquid.

6.5.A. *Ion Mobility and Tracer Diffusion* (22)

We now turn to the general theory of the flux of foreign molecules in a host liquid. The situation envisaged is one in which the foreign molecules are very dilute, so that they do not interact with each other, and do not disturb the equilibrium state of the host liquid.

It is convenient to rewrite the kinetic equation in such a way as to distinguish between the foreign molecules, and the molecules of the host liquid. Thus, quantities referring to the host molecules will have the subscript 2, while those referring to the foreign molecules will have subscript 1:

$$\frac{\partial \bar{f}_1^{(1)}}{\partial t} + \mathbf{X}_1 \cdot \nabla_{p_1} \bar{f}_1^{(1)} = \zeta_S \mathscr{A}_1^{(1)} \bar{f}_1^{(1)} + J_1(\bar{f}_1^{(1)}, \bar{f}_2^{(1)}), \qquad (6.5.1)$$

where ζ_S is the soft-force friction experienced by a foreign molecule due to host molecules, and

$$J_1 = g_{12}(\sigma) \int [\bar{f}_1^{(1)*} \bar{f}_2^{(1)*} - \bar{f}_1^{(1)} \bar{f}_2^{(1)}] \left| \frac{\mathbf{p}_1}{m_1} - \frac{\mathbf{p}_2}{m_2} \right| b \, db \, d\epsilon \, d\mathbf{p}_2. \quad (6.5.2)$$

In equation (6.5.2) $g_{12}(\sigma)$ is the radial distribution function at hard core contact between foreign and host molecules, $\sigma = \frac{1}{2}(\sigma_{\text{foreign}} + \sigma_{\text{host}})$ is the separation of centers at contact, and $\mathbf{X}_1$ is an as yet unspecified mean force on the foreign molecule. It should be noted that, in accordance with our assumption that the foreign molecules are dilute, no account is taken of the spatial variations of $\bar{f}_1^{(1)}$. $\bar{f}_2^{(1)}$ is, as has been mentioned, the equilibrium distribution function for the host molecules, $\bar{f}_{20}^{(1)}$.

Equation (6.5.1) is solved in the linear approximation

$$\bar{f}_1^{(1)} = \bar{f}_{10}^{(1)}(1 + \Phi_1),$$
$$\bar{f}_{10}^{(1)} = \rho_1 (2\pi m k T)^{-3/2} \exp\left(-\frac{p_1^2}{2mkT}\right). \qquad (6.5.3)$$

Substitution of equation (6.5.3) in equation (6.5.1) yields

$$\mathbf{X}_1 \cdot \nabla_{p_1} \bar{f}_1^{(1)} = g_{12}(\sigma) \bar{f}_{10}^{(1)} \int \bar{f}_{20}^{(1)} [\Phi_1^* - \Phi_1] \left| \frac{\mathbf{p}_1}{m_1} - \frac{\mathbf{p}_2}{m_2} \right| b \, db \, d\epsilon \, d\mathbf{p}_2$$
$$+ kT\zeta_S \nabla_{p_1} \cdot (\bar{f}_{10}^{(1)} \nabla_{p_1} \Phi_1). \quad (6.5.4)$$

It is convenient to define linear operators J_2, J_3 by*

$$J_2 \Phi_1 = \frac{1}{\rho_2} \int \bar{f}_{20}^{(1)} [\Phi_1 - \Phi_1^*] \left| \frac{\mathbf{p}_1}{m_1} - \frac{\mathbf{p}_2}{m_2} \right| b \, db \, d\epsilon \, d\mathbf{p}_2,$$
$$J_3 \Phi_1 = m_1 k T \bar{f}_{10}^{(1)-1} \nabla_{p_1} \cdot (\bar{f}_{10}^{(1)} \nabla_p \Phi_1) = \bar{f}_{10}^{(1)-1} \mathscr{A}_1^{(1)} \bar{f}^{(1)}, \quad (6.5.5)$$

so that equation (6.5.4) may be rewritten as

* The reader should note the distinction between Φ, J_2, J_3, and the quantities $\Phi^{(1)}(1), J_1^{(1)}, J_2^{(1)}$, defined in Chapter 5.

$$\mathbf{X}_1 \cdot \nabla_{p_1} \bar{f}_1^{(1)} = -\rho_2 g_{12}(\sigma) \bar{f}_{10}^{(1)} J_2 \Phi_1 + \frac{\zeta_S}{m_1} \bar{f}_{10}^{(1)} J_3 \Phi_1. \tag{6.5.6}$$

If we define the inner product of two functions $\phi(\mathbf{p}_1)$ and $\psi(\mathbf{p}_1)$ by

$$(\phi,\psi) = \frac{1}{\rho_1} \int \bar{f}_{10}^{(1)} \phi(\mathbf{p}_1) \psi(\mathbf{p}_1) \, d\mathbf{p}_1, \tag{6.5.7}$$

then it follows from the definitions (6.5.5) of J_2 and J_3 that*

$$(\psi,J_2\phi) = (\phi,J_2\psi)$$
$$(\psi,J_3\phi) = (\phi,J_3\psi). \tag{6.5.8}$$

Multiplication of equation (6.5.6) by $\phi_1(\mathbf{p}_1)$ and integration over $\mathbf{p}_1$ now leads to

$$\mathbf{X}_1 \cdot \langle \nabla_{p_1} \phi_1 \rangle = \rho_2 g_{12}(\sigma) \langle J_2 \phi_1 \rangle - \frac{\zeta_S}{m_1} \langle J_3 \phi_1 \rangle, \tag{6.5.9}$$

where we have used the result

$$(\psi,J\phi) = (\psi,J[1+\phi])$$

and

$$\langle \phi_1 \rangle = \frac{1}{\rho_1} \int \bar{f}_1^{(1)} \phi_1(\mathbf{p}_1) \, d\mathbf{p}_1. \tag{6.5.10}$$

To proceed further, we introduce the Kihara functions (23)

$$\psi_l^{(r)} = \left(\frac{p_1^{\,2}}{2m_1kT}\right)^{l/2} P_l\left(\frac{q_1}{p_1}\right) S_{l+\frac{1}{2}}^{(r)}\left(\frac{p_1^{\,2}}{2m_1kT}\right), \tag{6.5.11}$$

where P_l and $S_{l+\frac{1}{2}}^{(r)}$ are Legendre and Sonine polynomials, respectively, and q_1 is the component of $\mathbf{p}_1$ in the direction of $\mathbf{X}_1$. By direct differentiation the $\psi_l^{(r)}$ can be shown to be eigenfunctions of the Fokker-Planck operator J_3:

$$J_3 \psi_l^{(r)} = -(2r + l) \psi_l^{(r)}. \tag{6.5.12}$$

If the molecular interactions were given by the Maxwell potential $u \sim R_{12}^{-4}$, then the $\psi_l^{(r)}$ would also be eigenfunctions of J_2. This is not the case, however, because the interaction envisaged is that of rigid cores. Thus,

$$J_2 \psi_l^{(r)} = \sum_s a_l^{(r,s)} \psi_l^{(s)}. \tag{6.5.13}$$

* The first of these results follows by changing the variables of integration from $(\mathbf{p}_1,\mathbf{p}_2)$ to $(\mathbf{p}_1^*,\mathbf{p}_2^*)$ and using the fact that the elementary collision cylinder is invariant to this transformation. Since the variables of integration are dummy variables, starred and unstarred variables are thereby interchanged in the kernel. The second result follows after two partial integrations (since J_3 is a second-order differential operator) from which the resulting surface terms vanish.

Since the Kihara functions satisfy the orthogonality relation

$$(\psi_l^{(r)},\psi_{l'}^{(r')}) = \frac{2}{2l+1}\frac{1}{\pi^{1/2}}\frac{1}{r!}\Gamma(l+r+\tfrac{3}{2})\,\delta_{ll'}\,\delta_{rr'}, \qquad (6.5.14)$$

the coefficients $a_l^{(r,s)}$ are given by

$$a_l^{(r,s)} = (\psi_l^{(s)},J_2\psi_l^{(r)})/(\psi_l^{(s)},\psi_l^{(s)}). \qquad (6.5.15)$$

From the recursion formulas for Legendre and Sonine polynomials (see Chapter 5), it is easily verified that

$$(l+\tfrac{1}{2})(2m_1kT)^{1/2}\frac{\partial\psi_l^{(r)}}{\partial q_1} = l(l+r+\tfrac{1}{2})\psi_{l-1}^{(r)} - (l+1)\psi_{l+1}^{(r-1)}. \qquad (6.5.16)$$

If in equation (6.5.9) we set $\phi_1 = \psi_l^{(r)}$, we obtain

$$(l+\tfrac{1}{2})\left[\rho_2 g_{12}(\sigma)\sum_s a_l^{(r,s)}\langle\psi_l^{(s)}\rangle + (2r+l)\frac{\zeta_S}{m_1}\langle\psi_l^{(r)}\rangle\right]$$
$$= \mathscr{X}[l(l+r+\tfrac{1}{2})\langle\psi_{l-1}^{(r)}\rangle - (l+1)\langle\psi_{l+1}^{(r-1)}\rangle], \qquad (6.5.17)$$

where

$$\mathscr{X} = \frac{X_1}{(2m_1kT)^{1/2}}. \qquad (6.5.18)$$

Equation (6.5.17) may be solved for the $a_l^{(r,s)}$ by successive approximations, since the off-diagonal coefficients ($r \neq s$) represent the deviation of the $\psi_l^{(r)}$ from the eigenfunctions of J_2. Denoting the first approximation by $\langle\psi_l^{(r)}\rangle_I$, we have

$$(l+\tfrac{1}{2})\left[\rho_2 g_{12}(\sigma)a_l^{(r,r)} + (2r+l)\frac{\zeta_S}{m}\right]\langle\psi_l^{(r)}\rangle_I$$
$$= \mathscr{X}[l(l+r+\tfrac{1}{2})\langle\psi_{l-1}^{(r)}\rangle_I - (l+1)\langle\psi_{l+1}^{(r-1)}\rangle_I]. \qquad (6.5.19)$$

In order to obtain an expression for the drift velocity due to $\mathbf{X}_1$, we must evaluate the quantity $\langle q_1\rangle_I$. Now

$$\psi_1^{(0)} = \frac{q_1}{(2m_1kT)^{1/2}} = \left(\frac{m_1}{2kT}\right)^{1/2} v, \qquad (6.5.20)$$

where v is the drift velocity in the direction of $\mathbf{X}_1$. Using the identity $\psi_l^{(-1)} = 0$ for all l, we obtain the result*

$$\langle v\rangle_I = \frac{X_1}{(m_1\rho_2 g_{12}(\sigma)a_1^{(0,0)} + \zeta_S)}. \qquad (6.5.21)$$

* The reader should note that the self-diffusion coefficient defined by the complete weak coupling operator with momentum dependent friction coefficients is still $D = kT/(\zeta_H + \zeta_S)$ where ζ_H is the usual hard core friction coefficient and ζ_S is

The second approximation to $\langle v \rangle$ can be obtained by substituting the first approximation for $\langle \psi_l^{(r)} \rangle$ into the off-diagonal terms in equation (6.5.17). If $A_l^{(r)}$ is defined by

$$A_l^{(r)} = (l + \tfrac{1}{2})\left[\rho_2 g_{12}(\sigma) a_l^{(r,r)} + (2r + l)\frac{\zeta_S}{m} \right], \qquad (6.5.22)$$

---

the quantity evaluated by Helfand, namely, a diagonal element of the equilibrium average of the friction tensor $\langle \boldsymbol{\zeta} \rangle = \zeta_S \mathbf{I}$. In the following we outline the proof which follows from a minor modification of Section 6.5.A.

Let the new operator be $\Omega_S^{(1)}$, where

$$\Omega_S^{(1)} = \nabla_{p_1} \cdot \boldsymbol{\zeta} \cdot \left(\frac{\mathbf{p}_1}{m} + kT \nabla_{p_1} \right) f^{(1)},$$

$$= kT \nabla_{p_1} \cdot \boldsymbol{\zeta} f_0^{(1)} \cdot \nabla_{p_1} \Phi_1$$

and

$$f^{(1)} = f_0^{(1)}(1 + \Phi_1).$$

Define now a new operator, J_4, by

$$J_4 \Phi_1 = \frac{1}{f_0^{(1)}} \nabla_{p_1} \cdot \boldsymbol{\zeta} f_0^{(1)} \cdot \nabla_{p_1} \Phi_1,$$

in analogy with equation (6.5.5). Equation (6.5.6) now becomes

$$\mathbf{X} \cdot \nabla_{p_1} f^{(1)} = -\rho_2 g_{12}(\sigma) f_0^{(1)} J_2 \Phi_1 + kT f_0^{(1)} J_4 \Phi_1.$$

Obviously, J_4 satisfies

$$(\psi, J_4 \phi) = (\phi, J_4 \psi),$$

and if we define $a_l^{(r,s)}, b_l^{(r,s)}$ by

$$a_l^{(r,s)} = (\psi_l^{(s)}, J_2 \psi_l^{(r)})/(\psi_l^{(s)}, \psi_l^{(s)}),$$

$$b_l^{(r,s)} = (\psi_l^{(s)}, J_4 \psi_l^{(r)})/(\psi_l^{(s)}, \psi_l^{(s)}),$$

we find that the field-independent approximation $\langle v \rangle_I$ [Eq. (6.5.21)] is given by

$$\langle v \rangle_I = \frac{X_1}{m[\rho_2 g_{12}(\sigma) a_1^{(0,0)} - kT b_1^{(0,0)}]}.$$

But

$$b_1^{(0,0)} = (\psi_1^{(0)}, J_4 \psi_1^{(0)})/(\psi_1^{(0)}, \psi_1^{(0)})$$

$$= 2 \int d\mathbf{p}_1 f_0^{(1)} \psi_1^{(0)} \left[\frac{1}{f_0^{(1)}} \nabla_{p1} \cdot \boldsymbol{\zeta} f_0^{(1)} \cdot \nabla_{p1} \psi_1^{(0)} \right]$$

$$= -2 \int d\mathbf{p}_1 (\nabla_{p1} \psi_1^{(0)}) \cdot \boldsymbol{\zeta} f_0^{(1)} \cdot (\nabla_{p1} \psi_1^{(0)})$$

$$= -\frac{\langle \zeta_{zz} \rangle}{mkT} = -Tr \left(\frac{\langle \boldsymbol{\zeta} \rangle}{3mkT} \right).$$

This yields the required result when substituted in the equation for $\langle v \rangle_I$.

then

$$\langle\psi_l^{(r)}\rangle_I A_l^{(r)} = \mathscr{X}[l(l + r + \tfrac{1}{2})\langle\psi_{l-1}^{(r)}\rangle_I - (l + 1)\langle\psi_{l+1}^{(r-1)}\rangle_I], \quad (6.5.23)$$

so that

$$\langle\psi_1^{(0)}\rangle_{II}\left[\rho_2 g_{12}(\sigma) \sum_s a_1^{(0,s)}(\langle\psi_1^{(s)}\rangle_I/\langle\psi_1^{(0)}\rangle_I) + \frac{\zeta_S}{m_1}\right] = \mathscr{X}. \quad (6.5.24)$$

The coefficients $a_1^{(0,s)}$ have been evaluated by Kihara, who found

$$(\psi_1^{(r)}, J_2\psi_1^{(0)}) = \frac{8m_2}{m_1 + m_2}\frac{(-)^r}{r!}\left(\frac{m_2 T}{m_1 + m_2}\right)^r\left(\frac{d}{dT}\right)^r \Omega^{(1,1)}, \quad (6.5.25)$$

where

$$(a)\ \Omega^{(l,r)} = \pi^{\frac{1}{2}}\int_0^\infty \phi^{(l)} V^{2r+2} e^{-V^2}\, dV, \quad (6.5.26)$$

$$(b)\quad V = (2\mu_r kT)^{-\frac{1}{2}} p_{12},$$

$$(c)\quad \phi^{(l)} = \frac{g_{12}(\sigma)\sigma^2}{2}\left(1 - \frac{\{1 + (-)^l\}}{2(l + 1)}\right), \qquad \text{for rigid spheres,}$$

where μ_r is the reduced mass ($\mu_r = m_1 m_2/(m_1 + m_2)$). Inspection of equation (6.5.23) shows that

$$\langle\psi_l^{(r)}\rangle_I \sim \mathscr{X}^{r+1},$$

so that in order to obtain a field-independent drift velocity $\langle v\rangle_{II}$ we retain only the leading term $a_1^{(0,0)}$ in equation (6.5.24). From equations (6.5.14), (6.5.15), (6.5.26), and (6.5.27), it is found that

$$a_1^{(0,0)} = \frac{8}{3}\frac{m_2}{m_1 + m_2}\sigma^2\left(\frac{2\pi kT}{\mu_r}\right)^{\frac{1}{2}}, \quad (6.5.27)$$

so that equation (6.5.21) becomes, finally,

$$\langle v\rangle_I = \frac{X_1}{\frac{8}{3}\rho_2 g_{12}(\sigma)\sigma^2(2\pi\mu_r kT)^{\frac{1}{2}} + \zeta_S}. \quad (6.5.28)$$

The two cases which we wish to consider are, as mentioned at the beginning of this section, ion motion and tracer diffusion. If the system comprises a host liquid, with a small number of ions in it, subjected to an external electric field **E**, the force on an ion is

$$\mathbf{X}_{\text{ion}} = e\mathbf{E}, \quad (6.5.29)$$

where e is the charge on the ion. The mobility μ is defined by

$$\langle v\rangle_I = \mu E,$$

so that from equations (6.5.28) and (6.5.29) we find

$$\mu = \frac{e}{\frac{8}{3}\rho_2 g_{12}(\sigma)\sigma^2(2\pi\mu_r kT)^{1/2} + \zeta_S}. \tag{6.5.30}$$

In the case of a diffusion process, the force is due to the concentration gradient. If C_1 is the concentration of foreign molecules, then Bearman, Kirkwood, and Fixman (24) have shown that on thermodynamic grounds the external force per molecule required to balance a diffusion process is

$$\mathbf{X}_1 = \nabla_1\mu_1, \tag{6.5.31}$$

where μ_1 is the chemical potential per foreign molecule. If the concentration of foreign molecules is small,

$$\lim_{\rho_1\to 0} \mu_1 = kT \ln \rho_1 + \text{constant}. \tag{6.5.32}$$

Under the same circumstances, the concentration C_1 of foreign molecules is given by

$$C_1 = \frac{\rho_1}{\rho_1 + \rho_2} \simeq \frac{\rho_1}{\rho_2}, \tag{6.5.33}$$

while

$$\nabla_1\rho_2 \simeq 0. \tag{6.5.34}$$

Thus, since the force per molecule inducing diffusion is the negative of equation (6.5.31), we have

$$\mathbf{X}_1 = -\frac{kT}{\rho_1}\nabla_1\rho_1 \simeq -\frac{kT}{C_1}\nabla_1 C_1. \tag{6.5.35}$$

The diffusion coefficient of the foreign molecules immersed in the host liquid, D_{12}, is defined by

$$C_1\langle\mathbf{v}\rangle_I = -D_{12}\nabla_1 C_1 = \frac{D_{12}C_1}{kT}\mathbf{X}_1, \tag{6.5.36}$$

whence we find, from equation (6.5.28),

$$D_{12} = \frac{kT}{\frac{8}{3}\rho_2 g_{12}(\sigma)\sigma^2(2\pi\mu_r kT)^{1/2} + \zeta_S}. \tag{6.5.37}$$

Thus, the self-diffusion coefficient of the host liquid molecules, as measured by the tracer diffusion of foreign molecules of the same diameter and mass m, is

$$D = \frac{kT}{\zeta_H + \zeta_S}, \tag{6.5.38}$$

where

$$\zeta_H = \tfrac{8}{3}\rho g(\sigma)\sigma^2(\pi mkT)^{1/2} \tag{6.5.39}$$

is the hard core friction coefficient.

In order to obtain numerical values for μ and D the friction coefficients must be calculated. We take up this problem in Section 6.5.C after a digression on the theory of molten salts.

6.5.B. *The Ideal Ionic Melt* (25,26)

In this section we digress to examine an example of the qualitative information and the physical insight which can be obtained from an application of the formal kinetic theory to the description of a class of liquids.

Except for the condensed phases of Ne, Ar, Kr, and Xe, the simplest dense fluids are the molten alkali halides. As in the case of the noble gases, the intermolecular pair potential is spherically symmetric. Moreover, from studies of ionic crystals and of gaseous diatomic molecules, the parameters of the Coulomb portion of the pair potential and the parameters describing the pairwise repulsive interaction are moderately well known.

From the experimental evidence accumulated in the last decade it has become apparent that many of the properties of ionic melts are similar to the corresponding properties of dense fluids composed of molecules which interact with a short range intermolecular potential. The long range nature of the Coulomb potential, the dominant term in the intermolecular pair potential, does not seem to confer any radically different properties on the dense fluid. This remark is not so surprising as it may seem at first sight in view of the considerable differences in behavior between plasmas and dilute gases, and between dilute solutions of electrolytes and of non-electrolytes. The following brief qualitative discussion suffices to demonstrate that the observed properties are in fact simply explained in terms of the relative strengths of the Coulomb (long range) and van der Waals (short range) interparticle forces. The Coulomb potential differs from van der Waals type potentials in three respects:

(*a*) The range of the potential is infinite (that is, $4\pi R_{12}^2 u(R_{12})_{\text{Coulomb}} \nrightarrow 0$ as $R_{12} \rightarrow \infty$);

(*b*) The Coulomb interaction may be either attractive or repulsive dependent only on the signs of the pair of charges;

(*c*) The Coulomb potential is very much greater in strength than ordinary van der Waals potentials.

As a consequence of characteristics (*b*) and (*c*), it is impossible to have macroscopic deviations from electroneutrality. Moreover, the structural polarization in a fluid of positive and negative charges implied by conditions (*b*) and (*c*) is such as to screen the Coulomb potential, decreasing the effective range to the order of molecular dimensions. As a consequence of this polarization and shielding, the divergence catastrophes implied in (*a*) are avoided. From (*b*) and (*c*) it also follows that, on average, a positive ion is surrounded by negative ions, and vice versa. Indeed, we can make the stronger statement that the approach of like ions to within core* distances is extremely unlikely energetically. Likewise, close approach of unlike ions is energetically favored.

We therefore introduce the following physical notions which are taken to define an ideal ionic melt. The ideal ionic melt is a fluid consisting of (equal numbers of positive and negative) spherically symmetric ions, interacting pairwise with a potential consisting of a rigid impenetrable core, a short range van der Waals potential, and a long range Coulomb potential. Oppositely charged ions are of identical size and otherwise identical electronic properties. Rigid core encounters between like ions are considered sufficiently unfavorable (energetically) as to make a negligible contribution to transport. It is seen immediately from the formula for the friction coefficient (Section 6.5.C) that the Coulombic contribution vanishes identically. We therefore assume as part of our model that the role of the Coulomb potential is indirect in determining the transport properties, in that its primary role is that of determining the local geometry through energetic considerations. This assumption allows us to consider the ideal ionic melt as a pseudo one component fluid.

* Core has its usual meaning; namely, the repulsive part of the short-range potential.

Proceeding further, the preceding assumptions allow the derivation of an integro-differential equation using the methods described in Chapter 5. In this case the analysis proceeds by first deriving the equations appropriate to a binary mixture and then specializing them to the ideal ionic melt. The resulting equations for the singlet distribution function are formally identical to those for a pure fluid. The distribution function for species α, $\bar{f}^{(1)}(\alpha)$, satisfies the equation

$$\mathscr{D}_{\alpha}^{(1)}\bar{f}^{(1)}(\alpha 1) = [J_{1\alpha\beta}^{(1)} + J_{2\alpha\beta}^{(1)} + (\zeta_{\alpha\alpha} + \zeta_{\alpha\beta})\mathscr{A}_{\alpha 1}^{(1)}]\bar{f}^{(1)}(\alpha 1), \quad (6.5.40)$$

with

$$(a) \qquad \mathscr{D}_{\alpha}^{(1)} = \frac{\partial}{\partial t} + \frac{1}{m_{\alpha}}\mathbf{p}_{\alpha 1}\cdot\nabla_{\alpha 1} + \mathbf{F}_{\alpha 1}^{*}\cdot\nabla_{p_{\alpha 1}},$$

$$(b) \qquad \mathscr{A}_{\alpha 1}^{(1)} = \nabla_{p_{\alpha 1}}\cdot\left[\frac{1}{m_{\alpha}}\mathbf{p}_{\alpha 1} + kT\,\nabla_{p_{\alpha 1}}\right],$$

$$(c) \qquad \mathbf{F}_{\alpha 1}^{*} = {}^{(1)}\langle\mathbf{F}_{\alpha 1}^{(S)}\rangle^{0} + \mathbf{F}_{\alpha 1}^{\dagger}, \quad (6.5.41)$$

$$(d) \quad J_{1\alpha\beta}^{(1)}\bar{f}^{(1)}(\alpha 1) = g_{0}^{(2)}(\sigma_{\alpha\beta})\int\cdots\int[\bar{f}^{(1)}(\mathbf{R}_{\alpha 1}, \mathbf{p}_{\alpha 1} - \Delta\mathbf{p}_{\alpha 1}; t)$$
$$\times\,\bar{f}^{(1)}(\mathbf{R}_{\alpha 1}, \mathbf{p}_{\beta 1} - \Delta\mathbf{p}_{\beta 1}; t) - \bar{f}^{(1)}(\mathbf{R}_{\alpha 1}, \mathbf{p}_{\alpha 1}; t)\bar{f}^{(1)}(\mathbf{R}_{\alpha 1}, \mathbf{p}_{\beta 1}; t)]$$
$$\times\left|\frac{\mathbf{p}_{\alpha 1}}{m_{\alpha}} - \frac{\mathbf{p}_{\beta 1}}{m_{\beta}}\right| b\,db\,d\epsilon\,d\mathbf{p}_{\beta 1},$$

$$(e) \quad J_{2\alpha\beta}^{(1)}\bar{f}^{(1)}(\alpha 1) = \sigma_{\alpha\beta}g_{0}^{(2)}(\sigma_{\alpha\beta})\int\cdots\int[\bar{f}^{(1)}(\mathbf{R}_{\alpha 1}, \mathbf{p}_{\alpha 1} - \Delta\mathbf{p}_{\alpha 1}; t)$$
$$\times\,\mathbf{k}\cdot\nabla_{\alpha 1}\bar{f}^{(1)}(\mathbf{R}_{\alpha 1}, \mathbf{p}_{\beta 1} - \Delta\mathbf{p}_{\beta 1}; t) +$$
$$\bar{f}^{(1)}(\mathbf{R}_{\alpha 1}, \mathbf{p}_{\alpha 1}; t)\,\mathbf{k}\cdot\nabla_{\alpha 1}\bar{f}^{(1)}(\mathbf{R}_{\alpha 1}, \mathbf{p}_{\beta 1}: t)]$$
$$\times\left|\frac{\mathbf{p}_{\alpha 1}}{m_{\alpha}} - \frac{\mathbf{p}_{\beta 1}}{m_{\beta}}\right| b\,db\,d\epsilon\,d\mathbf{p}_{\beta 1},$$

where α,β refer to positive and negative ions. In equation (6.5.41), $g^{(2)}(\sigma_{\alpha\beta})$ is the pair correlation function evaluated at the point of contact when the pair separation is just the ion core diameter $\sigma_{\alpha\beta}$. Collisions between like ions have been neglected, and the equation for $\bar{f}^{(1)}(\beta 1)$ is obtained simply by interchanging α and β. The friction coefficients $\zeta_{ij}(i,j = \alpha,\beta)$ are defined in terms of the correlations of the corresponding soft forces.

Equation (6.5.41) has been solved by Berne and Rice (26) and the solution used in conjunction with the Bearman-Kirkwood (27) representation of the stress tensor and energy flux in a binary mixture to calculate formulas for the shear viscosity and thermal conductivity.

These formulas are very similar to those obtained in Section 6.3 for a one component fluid, a feature which is a direct consequence of the assumptions made in defining the ideal ionic melt. So little is known about the nature of the short range forces between ions, and about the pair correlation functions, that it is not possible to obtain numerical estimates at the present time.

A more interesting application of the general theory arises when we consider a phenomenon which is qualitatively different in the molten salt and in the simple liquid. For this reason we now study the electrical conductivity of a molten salt.

For ions in a simple fluid, $\mathbf{F}_1^*$ must vanish at least as E^2, but this need not be true if the fluid surrounding a selected ion is itself charged. When the surrounding particles are uncharged, to first order the external electric field does not induce a distortion from spherical symmetry, and hence $\mathbf{F}_1^*$ vanishes. On the other hand, when the surrounding particles have charge opposite in sign to that of the central ion, as in a molten salt, the external electric field exerts forces of opposite sign on the central ion and its first neighbors, leading to a deviation from spherical symmetry. Because of this distortion there is an internal electric field exerted on the selected ion which is opposed (antiparallel) to the external field. Since the net field exerted on the ion is thereby less than the applied field, the diffusion mobility is expected to exceed the conductance mobility. We shall attempt to compute this difference and compare theory with experiment wherever possible.

The calculation of the electrical conductivity (or the mobility of an ion) in a molten salt can be formulated just as in the previous section. By using the properties of the ideal ionic melt, an analysis almost identical with that presented in the previous section leads to the following formula for the z component of the velocity of an ion of species α [cf. Eq. (6.5.28)]:

$$\langle v_\alpha \rangle_I = \frac{e_\alpha E + (\mathbf{F}_{\alpha 1}^*)_z}{\frac{8}{3}\rho_\beta g^{(2)}(\sigma_{\alpha\beta})\sigma_{\alpha\beta}^2(2\pi\mu_r kT)^{1/2} + \zeta_{\alpha\alpha} + \zeta_{\alpha\beta}}, \tag{6.5.42}$$

where

$$\mu_r = \frac{m_\alpha m_\beta}{m_\alpha + m_\beta}, \tag{6.5.43}$$

e_α is the charge on ions of type α, and $\rho_i (i = \alpha, \beta)$ is the number density of type i ions. The small asymmetry imposed by the external field causes $\mathbf{F}_{\alpha 1}^*$ to be nonvanishing. The definition of $\mathbf{F}_{\alpha 1}^*$ is

$$(\mathbf{F}_{\alpha 1}^*)_z = +\int (\nabla_{12} u_{\alpha\beta})_z\, \rho^{(2/1)}(\alpha 1, \beta 2 \mid \alpha 1)\, d\mathbf{R}_{12}, \tag{6.5.44}$$

where

$$\begin{aligned}\rho^{(2/1)}(\alpha 1, \beta 2 \mid \alpha 1) &= \frac{\rho^{(2)}(\alpha 1,\beta 2)}{\rho^{(1)}(\alpha 1)} \\ &= \frac{(\rho_\beta \rho_\alpha g_0^{(2)}(\alpha 1,\beta 2) \exp[-\beta\{\phi(\mathbf{R}_1) + \phi(\mathbf{R}_2)\}])}{\{\rho_\alpha \exp[-\beta\phi(\mathbf{R}_1)]\}},\end{aligned} \tag{6.5.45}$$

and $u_{\alpha\beta}$ is the short-range potential between unlike ions. The natural reference point for the calculation of $\mathbf{F}_{\alpha 1}^*$ is the point $\mathbf{R}_1$ (since we are considering the distribution around $\alpha 1$). That is, the pair distribution function refers to two points in space with nominal external potentials $\phi(\mathbf{R}_1)$ and $\phi(\mathbf{R}_2)$. The distortion in the distribution function arises solely from the nonvanishing potential gradient. Thus, the Taylor expansion

$$\phi(\mathbf{R}_2) = \phi(\mathbf{R}_1) + \mathbf{R}_{12} \cdot \nabla_1 \phi(\mathbf{R}_1) + \cdots \tag{6.5.46}$$

leads to

$$\begin{aligned}\rho^{(2/1)}(\alpha 1, \beta 2 \mid \alpha 1) &= \rho_\beta \exp(-\beta\phi(\mathbf{R}_1)) g_0^{(2)}(\alpha 1,\beta 2) \exp(-\beta \mathbf{R}_{12} \cdot \nabla\phi) \\ &= \rho_\beta^* g_0^{(2)}(\alpha 1,\beta 2) \exp(-\beta \mathbf{R}_{12} \cdot \nabla_1 \phi),\end{aligned} \tag{6.5.47}$$

where ρ_β^* is the number density scaled with the Boltzmann factor for the external field at $\mathbf{R}_1$. Now, for all practically attainable field strengths, $|\mathbf{R}_{12} \cdot \nabla_1 \phi| \ll kT$ and we may expand the right-hand exponential factor, retaining only the first non-vanishing term linear in $\nabla_1 \phi$†:

$$\rho^{(2/1)}(\alpha 1, \beta 2 \mid \alpha 1) = \rho_\beta^* g_0^{(2)}(\alpha 1,\beta 2) \left[1 - \frac{e_\alpha \mathbf{E} \cdot \mathbf{R}_{12}}{kT}\right]. \tag{6.5.48}$$

Substitution of equation (6.5.48) in equation (6.5.44) now gives

$$\mathbf{F}_{1\alpha}^* = -\frac{4\pi e_\alpha \rho_\beta^*}{3kT} \int_{\sigma_{\alpha\beta}}^{\infty} \frac{du_{\alpha\beta}}{dR_{12}}\, g_0^{(2)}(\alpha 1,\beta 2) R_{12}^3\, dR_{12} \mathbf{E}. \tag{6.5.49}$$

† The sign of the field dependent term in equation (6.5.48) is determined by the fact that the charge on a β ion is $e_\beta = -e_\alpha$.

Substitution of equation (6.5.49) in (6.5.42) yields an equation for the mobility of α ions:

$$(\mu_\alpha)_I = \frac{e_\alpha}{\zeta_H{}^{\alpha\beta} + \zeta_{\alpha\alpha} + \zeta_{\alpha\beta}}\left[1 - \frac{4\pi\rho_\beta{}^*}{3kT}\int_{\sigma_{\alpha\beta}}^{\infty} \frac{du_{\alpha\beta}}{dR_{12}}\, g_0^{(2)}(\alpha 1,\beta 2)R_{12}{}^3\, dR_{12}\right]. \tag{6.5.50}$$

Introducing the diffusion coefficient D_α of α ions we find

$$(\mu_\alpha)_I = \frac{e_\alpha D_\alpha}{kT}[1 - \Delta], \tag{6.5.51}$$

so that the calculation predicts a deviation, Δ, from the Nernst-Einstein relation, where

$$\Delta = \frac{4\pi\rho_\beta{}^*}{3kT}\int_{\sigma_{\alpha\beta}}^{\infty} \frac{du_{\alpha\beta}}{dR_{12}}\, g_0^{(2)}(\alpha 1,\beta 2)R_{12}{}^3\, dR_{12}. \tag{6.5.52}$$

It will be noted that Δ is very similar in structure to the integral defining the pressure in a simple fluid and the calculation is therefore very sensitive to the relative positions of the minimum of $u_{\alpha\beta}$ and the first peak of $g_0^{(2)}$. Calculation of Δ requires that $u_{\alpha\beta}$ and $g_0^{(2)}$ be known. To estimate the magnitude of Δ we assume that $g_0^{(2)}$ is the same as that for liquid Ar at the same number density, and that the potential is of a depth determined by the ionization potentials and polarizabilities of the ions but scaled to the depth of the Ar–Ar potential. This procedure leads to $\epsilon_{\mathrm{KCl}} = 96 \times 10^{-16}$ ergs compared to $\epsilon_{\mathrm{Ar}} = 171 \times 10^{-16}$ ergs. While these approximations are admittedly crude, no better potentials or radial distribution functions are currently available. In the simplest estimate we put $g_0^{(2)} = 1$ for all $(R_{12}/\sigma_{\alpha\beta}) \geqslant 1$, and $g_0^{(2)} = 0$ for $(R_{12}/\sigma_{\alpha\beta}) < 1$. This leads to $\Delta \simeq 0.48$ at 1100°K for KCl using the 6–12 potential with parameters $\epsilon = 96 \times 10^{-16}$ ergs and $\sigma_{\alpha\beta} = 3.14 \times 10^{-8}$ cm. This is certainly a crude value of Δ because $g_0^{(2)}$ rises appreciably above unity in the first peak and it is just this region of the integrand that contributes heavily to Δ. However, because of the opposite signs of the attractive and repulsive forces, it is not clear whether this value of Δ is large or small. For a comparison, we use the function $g_0^{(2)}$ relevant to liquid Ar at the constant density 1.68×10^{22} cm.$^{-3}$ and for several different temperatures and pressures. This integration leads to $\Delta \simeq$ 0.28–0.30, a value sensibly independent of the variations in $g_0^{(2)}$ over the range studied. For Ar, these variations correspond to the temperatures 128, 133.5, and 185.5°K with pressures of 50, 100, and 500 atm., all at the constant density cited.

The predicted deviations from the Nernst-Einstein relation are of the order of 10–40%, a range which is in agreement with the experimental data presently available (see Table 6.12). Clearly, the calculation of a precise value of Δ will require much more accurate pair potentials and pair correlation functions than have been used here. Nevertheless,

TABLE 6.12

Experimental Deviations from the Nernst-Einstein Relation in Molten Salts (28)

		Diffusion coefficients $\times 10^4$ cm.^{2}/sec.$^{-1}$		
Salt	Temp. °K	From ion mobility	From tracer diffusion	Δ
NaCl	1111	1.39	1.63	0.17
	1250	1.82	2.47	0.36
RbCl	1010	0.75	0.88	0.17
	1163	1.17	1.46	0.24
CsCl	943	0.60	0.73	0.21
	1063	0.93	1.15	0.23
NaI	943	1.05	1.13	0.08
	1067	1.44	1.47	0.01_4

the order of magnitude agreement suggests that the theory provides a qualitative understanding of the relevant physical processes.

6.5.C. *Self-Diffusion and Molecular Friction*

It has been pointed out in previous sections that, although prescriptions exist for the calculation of the friction coefficient ζ_S, the numerical accuracy so far attainable from theory is not as good as that attainable from the use of self-diffusion data and the established relationship equation (6.5.38) between D and ζ_H and ζ_S.

In this section we shall explore the three (essentially) independent methods by which the friction coefficient may be calculated. First, however, it is necessary to discuss some important properties of the momentum correlation function and its relation to the diffusion coefficient (29).

The momentum correlation function of a particle is denoted by [see Eq. (4.2.13)]

$$\langle \mathbf{p}(t) \cdot \mathbf{p}(t+s) \rangle$$

where $\langle \cdots \rangle$ represents an average over an ensemble appropriate to the state of the system containing the particle and $\mathbf{p}(t)$ is the momentum of the particle at time t. Clearly, $\mathbf{p}(t)$ is a function of the phase of the system, and hence implicitly a function of the time. If the state is a stationary one, the choice of the origin of time is arbitrary and, therefore,

$$\frac{\partial}{\partial t} \langle \mathbf{p}(t) \cdot \mathbf{p}(t+s) \rangle = 0; \qquad \text{(stationary state)},$$

so that

$$\langle \dot{\mathbf{p}}(t) \cdot \mathbf{p}(t+s) \rangle = -\langle \mathbf{p}(t) \cdot \dot{\mathbf{p}}(t+s) \rangle. \tag{6.5.53}$$

When $s = 0$ in equation (6.5.53) we have

$$\langle \dot{\mathbf{p}}(t) \cdot \mathbf{p}(t) \rangle = 0. \tag{6.5.54}$$

If we define the normalized momentum correlation function $\psi(s)$ by

$$\langle p(t)^2 \rangle \psi(s) = \langle \mathbf{p}(t) \cdot \mathbf{p}(t+s) \rangle, \tag{6.5.55}$$

where

$$\langle p(t)^2 \rangle = \langle p^2 \rangle \qquad (= 3\,mkT, \text{ the equipartition value}),$$

then equations (6.5.54) and (6.5.55) give

$$(a)\ \psi(0) = 1,$$
$$(b)\ \dot{\psi}(0) = 0, \tag{6.5.56}$$

as initial conditions on $\psi(s)$, since

$$\left[\frac{\partial}{\partial s} \langle \mathbf{p}(t) \cdot \mathbf{p}(t+s) \rangle \right]_{s=0} = \langle \mathbf{p}(t) \cdot \dot{\mathbf{p}}(t) \rangle.$$

The foregoing does not constitute a proof of equation (6.5.56*b*), but merely illustrates the underlying ideas. A proof within the framework of classical statistical mechanics is given in Appendix 6.A. It is shown that exceptions can occur when the particles are rigid spheres since then the momentum is not differentiable during a collision and the proof cannot be carried through. Equation (6.5.56*b*) can be understood intuitively in the following way. The temporal extent of the flat top of $\psi(s)$, τ_c, the existence of which is implied by equation (6.5.56*b*), is a measure of the time for which the motion of the particles is coherent.

Thus, if the force on the particle is known at the initial instant $s = 0$, then the way in which the momentum will change in the short period following is predictable with certainty if the force is not liable to discontinuous changes. The rate of loss of correlation is, therefore, initially zero. It becomes different from zero when the predictability of the motion is lost as the particle moves to a region where the force is different, and when the positions of the other particles responsible for the force have changed. Alternatively, equation (6.5.56*b*) may be interpreted as the assertion that the instantaneous force on, and momentum of, a particle are uncorrelated in a stationary system. This is most easily seen when the force is a function of position only, because then $\dot{\psi}(0)$ becomes the product of the average momentum and the average force. In the case of Brownian particles the coherence time is finite (essentially that of the liquid molecules in which they are immersed), but the particles are so massive compared to the liquid molecules that their initial momenta persist for times long compared to the coherence time, which can then be neglected to a good approximation, and the flat top of $\psi(s)$ replaced by the cusp of $\exp\left(-\frac{\zeta}{m}|s|\right)$.* Conversely, the motion of a liquid molecule has comparatively little persistence, since its mass is the same as the mass of the molecules with which it is interacting. Indeed, it seems likely that the momentum of a liquid molecule will exhibit a succession of positive and negative correlations. Later in this section we shall describe a model which has just this feature.

Similarly, we may show, by differentiating $\langle \mathbf{p}(t) \cdot \mathbf{p}(t + s)\rangle$ twice with respect to t, that [see Eq. (6.A.25)]

$$\frac{\partial^2}{\partial s^2}\langle \mathbf{p}(t) \cdot \mathbf{p}(t + s)\rangle = -\langle \mathbf{F}(t) \cdot \mathbf{F}(t + s)\rangle \tag{6.5.57}$$

in a stationary state.

The relation (6.5.57) is useful in discussing the validity of the Fokker-Planck equation. Kirkwood originally showed that the friction coefficient could be defined as

$$\zeta = \frac{1}{3kT\tau}\int_0^\tau\int_0^s \langle \mathbf{F}(t) \cdot \mathbf{F}(t + s')\rangle_1\, ds'\, ds, \tag{6.5.58}$$

* This property is typical of Brownian particles: see, for instance, equations (4.4.69*a*) and (4.5.29).

where the average is taken in an ensemble in which the $(N - 1)$ molecule environment of the specified molecule is in a stationary state independent of the phase of that molecule. We may apply equation (6.5.57) to this situation, with the result

$$\zeta/m = -\frac{1}{\tau}\int_0^\tau\int_0^s \ddot{\psi}(s')\,ds'\,ds$$
$$= \frac{1 - \psi(\tau)}{\tau}. \tag{6.5.59}$$

In order that ζ should be independent of τ, or at least insensitive to its value, there must be a range of values of τ such that

$$1 - \psi(\tau) \simeq \mathcal{O}(\tau).$$

Since $\dot{\psi}(\tau) \sim 0$ for $\tau \sim \tau_c$, the coherence time referred to above, and since τ must also satisfy $\tau \ll m\zeta^{-1}$ (cf., the discussion of Section 4.4.B), $\psi(\tau)$ must have the form

$$\psi(\tau) \simeq 1 - \zeta\tau/m; \qquad \tau_c \ll \tau \ll m\zeta^{-1}.$$

It is clear, therefore, that for this range of its argument, $\psi(\tau)$ must be close to the exponential function:

$$\psi(\tau) \simeq \exp(-\zeta\tau/m); \qquad \tau_c \ll \tau \ll m\zeta^{-1}. \tag{6.5.60}$$

It is easy to see that equation (6.5.60) is just a restatement of equation (4.5.1). Thus, we have

$$\langle \Delta\mathbf{p}\rangle_1 = \langle \mathbf{p}(\tau) - \mathbf{p}(0)\rangle_1 = \langle \mathbf{p}(\tau)\rangle_1 - \mathbf{p}_1(0)$$
$$= [\psi(\tau) - 1]\mathbf{p}(0) = -\frac{1}{m}\zeta\mathbf{p}_1(0) + \mathcal{O}(\tau^2). \tag{6.5.61}$$

Equation (6.5.61) states that the *average* increments in momentum in a short time τ must be proportional to τ. This is almost trivially true for colloidal particles, since these are so massive compared to the molecules with which they interact that the behavior of individual particles is close to the average behavior. On the other hand, these relations should be satisfied for other systems provided that two time scales, which differ by some orders of magnitude and possess similar physical significance to τ_c and $m\zeta^{-1}$, can be identified.

As an example, consider the dilute gas. Here two widely different time scales are easily identified as the duration of a collision, τ_c, and the mean free time, τ_f, so that an interval, τ, may be chosen to satisfy

$$\tau_c \ll \tau \ll \tau_f.$$

The duration of a collision, τ_c, may be interpreted in much the same way as before; namely, as a time in which the motion of a molecule is predictable from a knowledge of its initial momentum and the force on it at the initial instant. For times longer than τ_c, a second collision may occur, completely uncorrelated with the first, so that the extent of the flat top of ψ will be defined by τ_c. At the other end of the scale, the mean free time τ_f may be interpreted as the decay time of ψ, since the momentum after a second collision is almost uncorrelated with its initial value, except for a small persistence effect, and the free time has a probability distribution similar to that for free paths,

$$\tau_f^{-1} \exp(-\tau/\tau_f).$$

A number of authors have calculated the friction coefficient from equation (6.5.59), or, what is equivalent if the time scales τ_c and $m\zeta^{-1}$ are widely separated, from the formula

$$\begin{aligned} \zeta/m &= -\int_0^{\tau_1} \ddot{\psi}(s')\, ds' \\ &= -\dot{\psi}(\tau_1), \end{aligned} \tag{6.5.62}$$

where τ_1 satisfies the same inequalities. Calculations of the friction coefficient from equation (6.5.59), or of the mean and mean square momentum increments, have been made for the case that the environment of the particle is a dilute gas. It is found that the two moments are extremely complicated functions of the momentum of the particle when this is of comparable mass to the gas particles,* but do lead to a momentum independent friction coefficient [(cf., Eqs. (4.4.31) and (4.4.33)] when the particle is heavy compared to the gas particles. Berne and Gray (29) have solved the singlet kinetic equation by approximating the spatially homogeneous collision operator by a Fokker-Planck operator with constant friction coefficient ζ_H. The solution differs from the original only in simple numerical factors multiplying ζ_H, which are indicative of the momentum dependence of the friction implicit in the collision integral, and ignored in the approximate treatment.

* These functions, and their compatibility with equation (4.4.28), are discussed in Appendix 6.B.

The situation in dense fluids is certainly not the simple one described before. From an intuitive understanding of the structure of a liquid or dense gas, one expects $\psi(s)$ to exhibit a succession of oscillations, so that no separation between a coherence time and a relaxation time is apparent. This view is borne out by estimates of velocity spectra from neutron scattering. The caging effect of neighboring molecules, which gives rise to the oscillations of $\psi(s)$, is due to the strong repulsive encounters, and has already been discussed in Chapter 5. What remains when the repulsive forces due to one or two close neighbors are separated out is the relatively weak, rapidly fluctuating force due the ten or twelve neighbors in the first coordination shell. These soft forces are not separately subject to relations such as (6.5.56) and (6.5.57), and consequently the representation of the dissipative effect of these forces by Fokker-Planck operators is much more reasonable than a similar representation of the total forces. The subsequent treatment of the repulsive forces as rigid core encounters does not imply the existence of a cusp to $\psi(s)$ at $s = 0$, although this feature is exploited in the calculation of ζ_H.

The friction coefficient may be calculated by three independent methods, and we shall give examples of each. The first is the most direct in that the correlation function of the soft forces is calculated according to the linear trajectory prescription derived in Chapter 5. The second method makes use of the phenomenological relation between the frictional force on a particle of one species due to its non-vanishing average motion relative to other species present in a fluid mixture.* The third method attempts a direct calculation of the momentum correlation function. From equation (4.4.16), the self-diffusion coefficient is defined by

$$\begin{aligned} D &= \lim_{t\to\infty} \frac{\langle[\Delta\mathbf{R}(t)]^2\rangle}{6t} \\ &= \lim_{t\to\infty} \frac{1}{6m^2t}\int_0^t\int_0^t \langle \mathbf{p}(s)\cdot\mathbf{p}(s')\rangle\, ds'\, ds \\ &= \frac{kT}{m}\int_0^\infty \psi(s)\, ds, \end{aligned} \tag{6.5.63}$$

* For self-diffusion this case is, of course, specialized to that of tracer diffusion in a binary mixture.

so that ζ is given by

$$\zeta = m\left[\int_0^\infty \psi(s)\,ds\right]^{-1}. \tag{6.5.64}$$

The first two methods calculate the friction coefficient directly, and can therefore be applied to the hard core and soft friction coefficients separately; the third cannot. The hard core friction coefficient has already been calculated [see Eq. (6.5.39)]. An alternative method, first used by Longuet-Higgins and Pople (30), is (essentially) to calculate the mean momentum increment as in equation (6.5.61). Since, as already mentioned, the friction coefficient so obtained is a complicated function of the momentum,* we calculate the *average*, which is the quantity associated with diffusion. The existence of the cusp in $\psi(s)$ at $s = 0$ (because of the rigid core) allows the calculation of ζ_H from

$$\begin{aligned} 3kT\zeta_H &= -\frac{d}{ds}\langle \mathbf{p}_1(0)\cdot \mathbf{p}_1(s)\rangle\Big|_{s=0} \\ &= -\lim_{\tau\to 0}\frac{1}{\tau}\langle \mathbf{p}_1(0)\cdot \Delta\mathbf{p}_1(\tau)\rangle. \end{aligned} \tag{6.5.65}$$

$\Delta\mathbf{p}_1(\tau)$, the increment of momentum of molecule 1 due to the single collision isolated in the interval $\tau \to 0$, is half the momentum transfer given in equation (6.3.6). Extending the length of the collision cylinder to $p_{12}\tau/m$ in the usual way, and introducing distribution function for the momenta of molecules 1 and 2 conditional on the presence of molecule 1 at $\mathbf{R}_1$,

$$f_0^{(2/1)}(\mathbf{p}_1,\mathbf{p}_2,\mathbf{R}_1,\mathbf{R}_2) = \rho^{-1} f_0^{(2)}, \tag{6.5.66}$$

equation (6.5.65) becomes

$$3kT\zeta_H = \frac{1}{m}\int_{(\mathbf{k}\cdot\mathbf{p}_{12}<0)} (\mathbf{p}_1\cdot\mathbf{k})(\mathbf{p}_{12}\cdot\mathbf{k}) f_0^{(2/1)} p_{12} b\, db\, d\epsilon\, d\mathbf{p}_1\, d\mathbf{p}_2. \tag{6.5.67}$$

The integrations in equation (6.5.67) are simply performed and lead to the result

$$\zeta_H = \tfrac{8}{3}\rho g(\sigma)\sigma^2(\pi mkT)^{1/2}, \tag{6.5.68}$$

as obtained in equation (6.5.39).

* See Appendix 6.B.

We discuss now the calculation of the soft-friction coefficient by the linear trajectory method (49). ζ_S is defined as

$$\zeta_S = \frac{1}{kT\tau}\int_0^\tau\int_{-s}^0 \langle \mathbf{F}_{12}^{(S)}\mathbf{F}_1^{(S)}[\mathbf{R}_1 + (s + s')\mathbf{p}_1/m]\rangle_1 \, ds' \, ds, \quad (6.5.69)$$

where the average is over the initial phase of the other $(N - 1)$ molecules, and the correlation function is calculated with all molecules restricted *by definition* to the linear motions corresponding to the initial phase. Consider the separation of forces already achieved. The total intermolecular force correlation function is

$$\langle \mathbf{F}_1(0)\mathbf{F}_1(s)\rangle = \langle \mathbf{F}_1^{(H)}(0)\mathbf{F}_1^{(H)}(s)\rangle + \langle \mathbf{F}_1^{(H)}(0)\mathbf{F}_1^{(S)}(s)\rangle + \langle \mathbf{F}_1^{(S)}(0)\mathbf{F}_1^{(H)}(s)\rangle + \langle \mathbf{F}_1^{(S)}\mathbf{F}_1^{(S)}(s)\rangle. \quad (6.5.70)$$

Only the first and last terms on the right-hand side of equation (6.5.70) are retained in the kinetic equation. If, however, we also include the second term with the last, the correlation function appearing in the definition of ζ_S can be written $\langle \mathbf{F}_1(0)\mathbf{F}_1^{(S)}(s)\rangle$, so that it involves the initial total force. Only the third part $\langle \mathbf{F}_1^{(S)}(0)\mathbf{F}_1^{(H)}(s)\rangle$ is now neglected; since the relaxation induced by the soft forces has been shown (cf. Section 5.4.B) to be rapid compared to the average time between hard core collisions, it follows that this particular correlation should be small. Given this redefinition, the product of the initial total force and the interaction part of the $(N - 1)$ molecule distribution function may be written

$$\mathbf{F}_1(\mathbf{R}^{(N)}(0)) \exp[-\beta U(\{N\})] = -[\nabla_1 U(\{N\})] \exp[-\beta U(\{N\})] = \beta^{-1}\nabla_1 \exp[-\beta U(\{N\})], \quad (6.5.71)$$

where we have used $\beta^{-1} = kT$, to avoid confusion with the wave vector $\mathbf{k}$ in equation (6.5.72). A partial integration now introduces the second derivative of the soft potential at time $(s + s')$.* The time

* This is strictly analogous to the well-known result

$$\begin{aligned}\langle \mathbf{F}(0) \cdot \mathbf{F}(s)\rangle\big|_{s=0} &= -\langle \mathbf{p}(0) \cdot \dot{\mathbf{p}}(s)\rangle\big|_{s=0} \\ &= -\langle \mathbf{p}(0) \cdot (i\mathscr{L})^2 \exp(i\mathscr{L}s)\mathbf{p}(0)\rangle\big|_{s=0} \\ &= (N - 1)kT\langle \nabla_{12}{}^2 u(R_{12})\rangle.\end{aligned}$$

integrations are conveniently performed after a spatial Fourier analysis of the pair potential. If

$$\tilde{u}(k) = \int u(R_{12}) \exp(i\mathbf{k} \cdot \mathbf{R}_{12})\, d\mathbf{R}_{12}, \tag{6.5.72}$$

then

$$\int u(|\mathbf{R}_{12} + (s + s')\mathbf{p}_{12}/m|) \exp(i\mathbf{k} \cdot \mathbf{R}_{12})\, d\mathbf{R}_{12} = \tilde{u}(k) \exp(-i\mathbf{k} \cdot \mathbf{p}_{12}(s + s')/m). \tag{6.5.73}$$

Upon introducing the inverse form of equation (6.5.73) into

$$\langle \nabla_{12}\nabla_{12} u(|\mathbf{R}_{12} + (s + s')\mathbf{p}_{12}/m|)\rangle_1$$

we obtain

$$\langle \nabla_{12}\nabla_{12} u(|\mathbf{R}_{12} + (s + s')\mathbf{p}_{12}/m|)\rangle_1 = -\frac{1}{(2\pi)^3}\int k^2\tilde{u}(k) \times \langle \exp(-i\mathbf{k} \cdot \mathbf{p}_{12}(s + s')/m)\rangle\langle \exp(-i\mathbf{k} \cdot \mathbf{R}_{12})\rangle\, d\mathbf{k}. \tag{6.5.74}$$

The exact definition of $\boldsymbol{\zeta}_S$ requires that the average of

$$\exp(-i\mathbf{k} \cdot \mathbf{p}_{12}(s + s')/m)$$

be taken over $\mathbf{p}_2$ only. The result is then a (complex) function of $\mathbf{p}_1$, and has already been given in equation (5.3.66). However, we have already shown (see p. 427) that the quantity associated with diffusion is $\frac{1}{3} Tr\, \boldsymbol{\zeta}_S$, i.e., the average of $\boldsymbol{\zeta}_S$ over $\mathbf{p}_1$. Hence,

$$\langle \exp(-i\mathbf{k} \cdot \mathbf{p}_{12}(s + s')/m)\rangle = \rho^{(2)-1}\int \exp(-i\mathbf{k} \cdot \mathbf{p}_{12}(s + s')/m) \bar{f}_0^{(2)}\, d\mathbf{p}_{12}\, d\mathbf{P} = \exp(-k^2(s + s')^2/m\beta). \tag{6.5.75}$$

The quantity $\langle \exp(-i\mathbf{k} \cdot \mathbf{R}_{12})\rangle$ is defined by

$$\langle \exp(-i\mathbf{k} \cdot \mathbf{R}_{12})\rangle = V^{-1}\left[\int \exp(-i\mathbf{k} \cdot \mathbf{R}_{12})(g_0^{(2)}(R_{12}) - 1)\, d\mathbf{R}_{12} + (2\pi)^3\, \delta(\mathbf{k})\right] = V^{-1}[G(k) + (2\pi)^3\, \delta(\mathbf{k})]. \tag{6.5.76}$$

Insertion of equations (6.5.74), (6.5.75), and (6.5.76) in equation (6.5.69) now yields

$$\zeta_S = -\frac{2\rho}{3\tau(2\pi)^2}\int_0^\tau\int_{-s}^0 \exp\,[-k^2(s+s')^2/m\beta]k^4\tilde{u}(k)G(k)\,d\mathbf{k}\,ds'\,ds. \tag{6.5.77}$$

The physical significance of the linear trajectory approximation now comes into play. The neglect of the effect of the soft forces on the trajectories of the molecules means that there is essentially no feedback between the motion and the forces. Thus, the integral of the force-correlation function does not vanish as the upper limit of integration tends to infinity, as in equations (4.5.21) and (6.5.59). Alternatively, one might say that the negative part of the correlation function (region B in Fig. 4.5.2) is excluded from consideration. Upon changing the sign of s', and recognizing the resulting domain of integration as the triangular half of the square domain as in Figure 4.5.1, equation (6.5.77) is found to be

$$\zeta_S = -\frac{(\pi m\beta)^{1/2}\rho}{3(2\pi)^2}\int_0^\infty k^3\tilde{u}(k)G(k)\,dk. \tag{6.5.78}$$

Helfand has also inverted equation (6.5.78) for the modified Lennard-Jones 6-12 potential

$$\begin{aligned} u(\sigma x) &= 4\epsilon[x^{-12}-x^{-6}]; \qquad & x \geqslant 1 \\ &= 0; & x < 1. \end{aligned} \tag{6.5.79}$$

The result is

$$\zeta_S = \tfrac{8}{3}\rho\sigma^2(\pi m\beta)^{1/2}\epsilon\int_1^\infty [g_0^{(2)}(\sigma x)-1][11h_{12}(x)-5h_6(x)]\,dx, \tag{6.5.80}$$

where

$$h_n(x) = 2\sum_{l=1}^{n/2}(2l-1)^{-1}x^{2l-n} - x^{1-n}\ln\left(\frac{x+1}{x-1}\right). \tag{6.5.81}$$

Davis, Rice, and Sengers (31) have derived a formula for ζ_S for the special case of a square-well fluid by comparing the exact kinetic equation for the square-well fluid and the Fokker-Planck version of the kinetic equation for the same case. Correlation effects are properly included but the final result must be numerically integrated because of its complex form. The result is

$$\zeta_S = \frac{m}{\rho}\int M\, d\mathbf{p}_1;$$

$$M = \sigma_2{}^2 g_0^{(2)}(\sigma_2)(N-1)$$

$$\times \int_{(\mathbf{g}\cdot\mathbf{k}>0)} \Big[\bar{f}^{(1)}(1)\{\Delta\mathbf{p}_2^{(2)}\cdot\nabla_{p_2}\bar{f}^{(1)}(2) + \tfrac{1}{2}(\Delta p_2^{(2)})^2\,\nabla_{p_2}{}^2\bar{f}^{(1)}(2)\}$$

$$+ m\sigma_2 \bar{f}_0^{(1)}(1)\bar{f}_0^{(1)}(2)\mathbf{k}\cdot\nabla_1\left\{\frac{\Delta\mathbf{p}_2^{(2)}}{mkT}\cdot\left(\frac{\mathbf{p}_2}{m}-\mathbf{u}\right)\right\}$$

$$+ \{1-e^{-s^2}\}\bar{f}^{(1)}(1)\bar{f}^{(1)}(2)\Big]\mathbf{g}\cdot\mathbf{k}\, d\mathbf{k}\, d\mathbf{p}_2 + e^{-s^2}\sigma_2{}^2 g_0^{(2)}(\sigma_2)(N-1)$$

$$\times \int_{\left[\mathbf{g}\cdot\mathbf{k}<-\left(\frac{4\epsilon}{m}\right)^{1/2}\right]} \Big[\bar{f}^{(1)}(1)\{\Delta\mathbf{p}_2^{(3)}\cdot\nabla_{p_2}\bar{f}^{(1)}(2) + \tfrac{1}{2}[\Delta p_2^{(3)}]^2\,\nabla_{p_2}{}^2\bar{f}^{(1)}(2)\}$$

$$+ m\sigma_2 \bar{f}_0^{(1)}(1)\bar{f}_0^{(1)}(2)\mathbf{k}\cdot\nabla_1\left\{\frac{\Delta\mathbf{p}_2^{(3)}}{mkT}\cdot\left(\frac{\mathbf{p}_2}{m}-\mathbf{u}\right)\right\}$$

$$+ \{1-e^{-s^2}\}\bar{f}^{(1)}(1)\bar{f}^{(1)}(2)\Big]\mathbf{g}\cdot\mathbf{k}\, d\mathbf{k}\, d\mathbf{p}_2$$

$$+ \sigma_2{}^2 g_0^{(2)}(\sigma_2)(N-1)$$

$$\times \int_{\left(-\left(\frac{4\epsilon}{m}\right)^{1/2}<\mathbf{g}\cdot\mathbf{k}<0\right)} \Big[\bar{f}^{(1)}(1)\{\Delta\mathbf{p}_2^{(4)}\cdot\nabla_{p_2}\bar{f}^{(1)}(2) + \tfrac{1}{2}[\Delta p_2^{(4)}]^2\,\nabla_{p_2}{}^2\bar{f}^{(1)}(2)\}$$

$$+ m\sigma_2 \bar{f}_0^{(1)}(1)\bar{f}_0^{(1)}(2)\mathbf{k}\cdot\nabla_1\left\{\frac{\Delta\mathbf{p}_2^{(4)}}{mkT}\cdot\left(\frac{\mathbf{p}_2}{m}-\mathbf{u}\right)\right\}\Big]\mathbf{g}\cdot\mathbf{k}\, d\mathbf{k}\, d\mathbf{p}_2$$

$$s^2 = \epsilon/kT,$$

$$\mathbf{g} = \frac{1}{m}(\mathbf{p}_2 - \mathbf{p}_1),$$

$$\Delta\mathbf{p}_2^{(2)} = m\{-\mathbf{g}\cdot\mathbf{k} + [(\mathbf{g}\cdot\mathbf{k})^2 + (4\epsilon/m)]^{1/2}\}\mathbf{k},$$

$$\Delta\mathbf{p}_2^{(3)} = m\{-\mathbf{g}\cdot\mathbf{k} - [(\mathbf{g}\cdot\mathbf{k})^2 - (4\epsilon/m)]^{1/2}\}\mathbf{k},$$

$$\Delta\mathbf{p}_2^{(4)} = -2m\mathbf{g}\cdot\mathbf{k}\mathbf{k}. \tag{6.5.82}$$

The details of this calculation are tedious but straightforward and we omit them here.

The second method of calculating the friction coefficient uses the relation between the mean velocity of a molecule with respect to its surroundings and the force it experiences (32). This definition automatically averages over all momenta of the observed particle (in order to define its average velocity). Bearman and Kirkwood have shown that the phenomenological relations relating the mass fluxes to the concentration gradients through the diffusion coefficients may be inverted to relate the mean force on a particle to its average velocity relative to the surroundings through the friction coefficients. It is sufficient for our purposes to use the result already established in equation (6.5.28). Writing $\langle \mathbf{v} \rangle_I$ as $\mathbf{u}$, we have

$$\mathbf{X}_1 = -(\zeta_H + \zeta_S)\mathbf{u}. \tag{6.5.83}$$

The change in sign from equation (6.5.28) is due to the fact that in that equation $\mathbf{X}_1$ is the force required to keep molecule 1 in motion; we are now interested in calculating the force it experiences when it is constrained to steady motion. Since the hard core friction has already been dealt with, we concern ourselves only with the soft force. The time smoothed distribution function

$$\bar{f}^{(N)} = \frac{1}{\tau}\int_0^\tau f^{(N)}(\Gamma_N; t + s)\, ds$$

is introduced in the definition of the average:

$$\mathbf{X}_1 = \langle \mathbf{F}_1 \rangle = \langle \mathbf{F}_1; \bar{f}^{(N)} \rangle. \tag{6.5.84}$$

The average is taken over all phase space, although we are observing a particular molecule. This procedure is justified by the fact we are not interested in where the molecule is, nor in its instantaneous momentum. Applying the transformation theory discussed in detail in Chapter 5, we time smooth the force instead, so that

$$\langle \mathbf{F}_1 \rangle = \langle \overline{\mathbf{F}}_1; f^{(N)} \rangle, \tag{6.5.85}$$

where

$$\overline{\mathbf{F}}_1 = \frac{1}{\tau}\int_0^\tau \mathbf{F}_1[\mathbf{R}^{(N)}(t + s)]\, ds. \tag{6.5.86}$$

The full expression for equation (6.5.85) is

$$\langle \mathbf{F}_1^{(S)} \rangle = \frac{\displaystyle\int \left[\frac{1}{\tau} \int_0^\tau \int \sum_{j=2}^{N} \nabla_{ij} u^{(S)}[R_{ij}(t + s)] f^{(N)}(\Gamma_N; t)\, \Delta_{1j}^{(2)}\, d\Gamma_N\, ds \right] d\mathbf{R}_j^0}{\displaystyle\sum_{j=2}^{N} \int f^{(N)}(\Gamma_N; t)\, \delta(\mathbf{R}_1^0 - \mathbf{R}_1)\, \delta(\mathbf{R}_j^0 - \mathbf{R}_j)\, d\Gamma_N\, d\mathbf{R}_j^0}, \tag{6.5.87}$$

which is equivalent to the use of the conditional configuration distribution function $\rho^{(2)}/\rho^{(1)}$. When the distribution functions are normalized such that

$$f^{(n)}(\Gamma_n;t) = \frac{N!}{(N-n)!}\int f^{(N)}(\Gamma_{N-n},\Gamma_n;f)\,d\Gamma_{N-n}, \quad (6.5.88)$$

then equation (6.5.87) assumes the form

$$\rho\langle \mathbf{F}_1^{(S)}\rangle = \int\left[\frac{1}{\tau}\int_0^\tau\int \nabla_{12}u^{(S)}(R_{12}(t+s))f^{(N)}(\Gamma_N;t)\right.$$
$$\left.\times\,\delta(\mathbf{R}_1{}^0-\mathbf{R}_1)\,\delta(\mathbf{R}_2{}^0-\mathbf{R}_2)\,d\Gamma_N\,ds\right]d\mathbf{R}_2{}^0. \quad (6.5.89)$$

The potential energy is not an explicit function of the time, but depends on it through the change in intermolecular separation with time. Since we have separated off the large repulsive force, a Taylor expansion may be truncated after only a few terms:

$$\nabla_{12}u^{(S)}[R_{12}(t+s)] = \nabla_{12}u^{(S)}[R_{12}(t)] + \Delta\mathbf{R}_{12}(s)\cdot\nabla_{12}\nabla_{12}u^{(S)}[R_{12}(t)] + \cdots$$
$$\mathbf{R}_{12}(t+s) = \mathbf{R}_{12}(t) + \Delta\mathbf{R}_{12}(s). \quad (6.5.90)$$

We now assume that the pair distribution function of the liquid is adequately approximated as the product of the local equilibrium, configuration distribution function and a momentum distribution function which is Maxwellian about the mean velocity of molecule 1. This assumption permits us to write

$$f^{(2)}(\Gamma_2) = \frac{\rho^2 g_0^{(2)}(R_{12})}{(2\pi mkT)^3}\exp\left[-\frac{(\mathbf{p}_1-m\mathbf{u}_1)^2+\mathbf{p}_2{}^2}{2mkT}\right]. \quad (6.5.91)$$

If we introduce the new variables $2\mathbf{P} = \mathbf{p}_1 + \mathbf{p}_2$ and $2\boldsymbol{\pi}_{12} = \mathbf{p}_2 - \mathbf{p}_1$, followed by integration over $d\mathbf{P}$, expansion of the term involving $\boldsymbol{\pi}_{12}\cdot\mathbf{u}_1$, and neglecting terms of order $u_1{}^2$, equation (6.5.91) becomes

$$f^{(2)}(\Gamma_2) = \frac{\rho^2 g_0^{(2)}(R_{12})}{(2\pi mkT)^3}\exp\left[-\frac{(\pi_{12}{}^2+P^2)}{2mkT}\right]\left[1+\frac{(\mathbf{P}-\boldsymbol{\pi}_{12})\cdot\mathbf{u}_1}{kT}+\cdots\right]. \quad (6.5.92)$$

The distribution function (6.5.92) is introduced into equation (6.5.89) by noting that $f^{(N)}$ can be written in the form $f^{(2)}[f^{(N)}/f^{(2)}]$.

Using the transformation of $f^{(N)}$ cited, and equations (6.5.90) and (6.5.92), equation (6.5.89) becomes

$$\langle \mathbf{F}_1^{(S)} \rangle = -\frac{1}{\rho k T \tau} \int_0^\tau \int \mathbf{u}_1 \cdot \langle \boldsymbol{\pi}_{12}\, \Delta\mathbf{R}_{12}(s) \rangle^{1,2} \cdot \nabla_{12}\nabla_{12} u(R_{12}) \times f_0^{(2)}(\Gamma_2)\, d\mathbf{p}_1\, d\mathbf{p}_2\, d\mathbf{R}_{12}\, ds, \quad (6.5.93)$$

where

$$\langle \boldsymbol{\pi}_{12}\, \Delta\mathbf{R}_{12}(s) \rangle^{1,2} = \int \boldsymbol{\pi}_{12}\, \Delta\mathbf{R}_{12}(s) \frac{f^{(N)}(\Gamma_N)}{f^{(2)}(\Gamma_2)}\, d\Gamma_{N-2}. \quad (6.5.94)$$

In equation (6.5.93) we have not displayed the terms that vanish on integration. These include the two terms resulting from the product of the local equilibrium part of $f^{(2)}$ (namely $f_0^{(2)}$) and the expansion of the gradient of the potential energy, since the average soft force acting on a molecule at equilibrium is zero. The integral of the product of $\boldsymbol{\pi}_{12}$ and the first term in the expansion of equation (6.5.90) also vanishes because $\nabla_{12} u(R_{12})$ is independent of momentum, and the integrand is then an odd function integrated over an even interval. The term containing the product of $\mathbf{P}$ and $\Delta\mathbf{R}_{12}(s)$ vanishes because the relative displacement is assumed independent of the motion of the center of mass.

In the following we shall introduce the hypothesis of molecular chaos in the form of the assumption that a time τ exists which is short enough that the change in relative displacement, $\Delta\mathbf{R}_{12}(s)$, is small [permitting truncation of the Taylor expansion (6.5.90)], but nevertheless long enough that $\langle \Delta\mathbf{R}_{12}(\tau)\Delta\mathbf{R}_{12}(\tau)\rangle^{1,2}$ reaches the asymptotic form $2\mathbf{D}_S^{(2)}\tau$, with $\mathbf{D}_S^{(2)}$, the relative pair diffusion tensor,

$$\mathbf{D}_S^{(2)} = \frac{\langle \Delta\mathbf{R}_{12}(\tau)\, \Delta\mathbf{R}_{12}(\tau) \rangle^{1,2}}{2\tau}. \quad (6.5.95)$$

We have previously seen (Chapter 4) that the definition of a diffusion coefficient involves a time scale long compared to times in which the momentum retains significant correlations with its initial value. To convert (6.5.93) to a more useful form we note that (13)

$$\frac{m}{2}\, d[\Delta\mathbf{R}_{12}(s)] = \boldsymbol{\pi}_{12}(s)\, ds. \quad (6.5.96)$$

From the relation

$$\zeta = \zeta_H + \zeta_S$$

$$\langle \mathbf{F}_1 \rangle = \langle \mathbf{F}_1^{(H)} + \mathbf{F}_1^{(S)} \rangle = -(\zeta_H + \zeta_S)\mathbf{u}_1 \quad (6.5.97)$$

and equation (6.5.93), by elimination of the vector $\mathbf{u}_1$ we obtain a relationship for ζ_S. Using (6.5.96), equation (6.5.94) is converted to

$$\frac{1}{\tau}\int_0^\tau \langle \boldsymbol{\pi}_{12}(s)\,\Delta\mathbf{R}_{12}(s)\rangle^{1,2}\,ds = \frac{1}{\tau}\int_0^\tau \langle \boldsymbol{\pi}_{12}(0)\,\Delta\mathbf{R}_{12}(s)\rangle^{1,2}\,ds + \frac{1}{\tau}\int_0^\tau \langle \Delta\boldsymbol{\pi}_{12}(s)\,\Delta\mathbf{R}_{12}(s)\rangle^{1,2}\,ds. \quad (6.5.98)$$

It is possible to show that the second term on the right-hand side of equation (6.5.98) is zero under certain circumstances. Put

$$\Delta\mathbf{R}_{12}(s) = \frac{2}{m}\int_0^s \boldsymbol{\pi}_{12}(s')\,ds', \quad (6.5.99)$$

so that

$$\langle \Delta\boldsymbol{\pi}_{12}(s)\,\Delta\mathbf{R}_{12}(s)\rangle^{1,2} = \frac{2}{m}\int_0^\tau [\langle \boldsymbol{\pi}_{12}(s)\boldsymbol{\pi}_{12}(s')\rangle^{1,2} - \langle \boldsymbol{\pi}_{12}(0)\boldsymbol{\pi}_{12}(s')\rangle^{1,2}]\,ds'. \quad (6.5.100)$$

The reader should recall that the average used here is for the case that both the initial positions and momenta of molecules 1 and 2 are held fixed. If the momentum changes characterize a stationary random process,

$$\langle \boldsymbol{\pi}_{12}(0)\boldsymbol{\pi}_{12}(s')\rangle^{1,2} = \tfrac{1}{3}\pi_{12}(0)^2\psi(s')\mathbf{I}. \quad (6.5.101)$$

On the other hand, calculation of $\langle \boldsymbol{\pi}_{12}(s)\boldsymbol{\pi}_{12}(s')\rangle^{1,2}$ requires a knowledge of the trivariate distribution for $\boldsymbol{\pi}_{12}(0)$, $\boldsymbol{\pi}_{12}(s)$, and $\boldsymbol{\pi}_{12}(s')$. Consider the case in which the momentum is a Gaussian process, though not necessarily Markovian. Then it can be shown that

$$\langle \boldsymbol{\pi}_{12}(s)\boldsymbol{\pi}_{12}(s')\rangle^{1,2} = [\tfrac{1}{3}\langle \pi_{12}{}^2\rangle(\psi(s-s') - \psi(s)\psi(s')) + \tfrac{1}{3}\pi_{12}(0)^2\psi(s)\psi(s')]\mathbf{I}. \quad (6.5.102)$$

If we now average over the initial momentum, $\boldsymbol{\pi}_{12}(0)$, it is found that

$$\langle\langle \boldsymbol{\pi}_{12}(s)\boldsymbol{\pi}_{12}(s')\rangle^{1,2}\rangle = \tfrac{1}{3}\langle \pi_{12}{}^2\rangle\psi(s-s')\mathbf{I}, \quad (6.5.103)$$

whereupon

$$\langle\langle \Delta\boldsymbol{\pi}_{12}(s)\,\Delta\mathbf{R}_{12}(s)\rangle^{1,2}\rangle = \frac{2}{3m}\langle \pi_{12}{}^2\rangle\mathbf{I}\int_0^s [\psi(s-s') - \psi(s')]\,ds' = 0, \quad (6.5.104)$$

because the integrand of (6.5.104) vanishes identically upon a change of variable. Therefore, provided that only the initial positions of the pair of molecules are fixed, and that the initial momenta are averaged over an ensemble, it is valid to write

$$\frac{m}{2}\, d[\Delta \mathbf{R}_{12}(s)] = \boldsymbol{\pi}_{12}(0)\, ds. \tag{6.5.105}$$

It should be noted that equation (6.5.105) is of the same form as a linear trajectory approximation, although in fact it is considerably more general than such an approximation. Returning to equation (6.5.94) it is seen that $\langle \boldsymbol{\pi}_{12}(0)\Delta\mathbf{R}_{12}(s)\rangle^{1,2}$ could equally well have been defined with respect to the distribution function $(f^{(N)}/\rho^{(2)})$, whereupon the use of (6.5.105) in the following is validated. Inspection of equation (6.5.93) shows that $\langle \mathbf{F}_1^{(S)}\rangle$ is not parallel to $\mathbf{u}_1$ unless $\mathbf{D}_S^{(2)}$ is isotropic. It has already been pointed out in Chapter 5 that this must be the case for different reasons. Equation (6.5.95) is, therefore, written

$$\mathbf{D}_S^{(2)} = D_S^{(2)}\mathbf{I} = \frac{\langle(\Delta R_{12}(s))^2\rangle}{6\tau}\,\mathbf{I}. \tag{6.5.106}$$

Clearly $D_S^{(2)}$ is a function of R_{12}. The simplest assumption which can be made is that the motions of molecules 1 and 2 are independent at all separations, so that

$$D_S^{(2)} = 2D_S^{(1)}, \qquad \text{(independent molecules)}. \tag{6.5.107}$$

In order to obtain a closed expression this approximation is, in fact, the only one known at the present time. It is not good because it is obviously worst for precisely those separations for which the most significant contributions to the integral in equation (6.5.93) arise. Equation (6.5.107) is inserted in equation (6.5.93) and yields, after an integration over the R_{12}-angles,*

$$\zeta_S^{(1)} = \left[\frac{4\pi m\rho}{3}\int_\sigma^\infty \nabla_{12}{}^2 u^{(S)}(R_{12})g_0^{(2)}(R_{12})R_{12}{}^2\, dR_{12}\right]^{\frac{1}{2}}. \tag{6.5.108}$$

It is pertinent at this point to remark that equation (6.5.108) has been derived by several investigators using different approaches. The assumptions we have used may be summarized as follows:

(*a*) The average displacement of a pair of molecules in time τ is small compared to the intermolecular spacing.

* This model is known as the small-step diffusion model. It has been used by Rice and Kirkwood (32) to calculate the stress tensor and heat flux, with considerable success.

(*b*) The distribution function in pair space can be approximated as the product of the local equilibrium distribution function in configuration space and a momentum distribution function Maxwellian about the mean velocity.

(*c*) The pair diffusion coefficient can be approximated *at all distances* as the sum of singlet diffusion coefficients.

It is also interesting that, aside from a factor of $(2/\pi)^{1/2}$, equation (6.5.108) can be derived on the assumption that the autocorrelation function of momentum is gaussian in the time (33), and Collins and Raffel (34) derived equation (6.5.108) by assuming that the momentum of a molecule as a function of time can be represented as having equal but opposite curvatures in the steady state and in the initial decay of the fluctuation.

If the interaction between a given molecule and the rest of the system is represented by a model in which the molecule is in contact with a continuum, then the correlation between particles will be overestimated (35). The reason for this is easy to see, since the use of boundary conditions of a mechanical nature at the surface between the selected molecule and the continuum requires complete coherence between medium and molecule. That is, such conditions preclude all possible fluctuations which are characteristic of the real, molecularly coarse, fluid. It is, of course, just the existence of these fluctuations in the real system which limit the extent, both spatial and temporal, of possible intermolecular correlations. The model to be described now attempts to incorporate into a continuum the essential features of a real molecular system. Thus, the density of matter as a function of distance from the molecule is taken to agree with the pair correlation function, and the molecule and the accompanying density variations about it will be taken to constitute a distributed force field affecting the amplitude and propagation of acoustic waves.

The starting point for our considerations is the time averaged soft force acting on a given molecule. We write this force in the form

$$\langle \mathbf{F}_1^{(S)} \rangle = \frac{\rho}{\tau} \int_0^{\tau} \nabla_{12} u^{(S)}[R_{12}(t + s)] g_0^{(2)}(R_{12}) \, d\mathbf{R}_{12} \, ds, \quad (6.5.109)$$

which is essentially the same as equation (6.5.89). As in earlier work, the force acting at time $t + s$ is expanded about the force acting at time t, in the form presented in equation (6.5.90). After inserting equation (6.5.90) in equation (6.5.109), we find

$$\langle \mathbf{F}_1^{(S)} \rangle = \frac{\rho_m}{m\tau} \int_0^\tau \int \Delta\mathbf{R}_{12}(s) \cdot \nabla_{12} \nabla_{12} u^{(S)}(R_{12}) g_0^{(2)}(R_{12})\, d\mathbf{R}_{12}, \quad (6.5.110)$$

with ρ_m the mass density of the fluid.

We now consider the transformation to the continuum model. We interpret $u^{(S)}(R_{12})/m$ as the potential of the soft force acting between a molecule and a unit mass of the surrounding medium. Further, the density variation of the medium surrounding the molecule is described by $g_0^{(2)}(R_{12})$, now interpreted in terms of the mass density of the continuum.

The time smoothing appears automatically in this model. Suppose that the molecule is instantaneously at some point $\mathbf{R}_1(t + s) = \mathbf{R}_1(t) + \mathbf{u}_1 s$ at time $t + s$. The fluid at some point $\mathbf{R}_2$ reacts almost instantaneously to the potential of the molecule, but since density fluctuations propagate at a speed c* the actual density at $\mathbf{R}_2$ is that corresponding to the radial distribution function centered on the molecule at an earlier time t, such that

$$|\mathbf{R}_2 - \mathbf{R}_1(t)| = cs. \quad (6.5.111)$$

In the continuum model, the relative displacement $\Delta\mathbf{R}_{12}(s)$ can be thought of as arising from a variation in density accompanying an acoustic wave. However, the presence of a molecule at the origin modifies the acoustic field by generating a force per unit mass, $-\nabla_{12} u^{(S)}(R_{12})/m$, and we may, therefore, regard the molecule as a distributed force center. Under these circumstances, the displacement of an element of the continuum satisfies the inhomogeneous wave equation

$$\frac{1}{c^2}\frac{\partial^2}{\partial s^2} \Delta\mathbf{R}_{12} - \nabla^2(\Delta\mathbf{R}_{12}) = -\frac{g_0^{(2)}(R_{12})}{mc^2} \nabla_{12} u^{(S)}[R_{12}(t + s)], \quad (6.5.112)$$

with c the velocity of propagation of high frequency density fluctuations in the medium. We take as our boundary conditions that the displacement and its first derivative with respect to time both vanish at the surface of the containing volume, i.e., in the limit as $R_{12} \to \infty$. Under

* Since the distances of interest are of the order of the molecular separations in a real fluid, c is not necessarily the velocity of low frequency sound waves normally associated with the propagation of density fluctuations (36–38).

these circumstances, the solution of equation (6.5.112) can be shown to be (39)

$$\Delta\mathbf{R}_{12}(s) = -\frac{1}{4\pi mc^2}\int \frac{g_0^{(2)}(R_{12})}{R_{12}} \nabla_{12}u^{(S)}(R_{12}{}^*)\, d\mathbf{R}_{12}, \quad (6.5.113)$$

where the asterisk refers to the retarded value of R_{12}, i.e.,

$$R_{12}{}^* = R_{12}[t + s - (R_{12}/c)]. \quad (6.5.114)$$

The expansion of equation (6.5.113) using equation (6.5.90) gives

$$\Delta\mathbf{R}_{12}(s) = -\frac{1}{4\pi mc^2}\int \frac{g_0^{(2)}(R_{12})}{R_{12}} \Delta\mathbf{R}_{12}{}^* \cdot \nabla_{12}\nabla_{12}u^{(S)}(R_{12})\, d\mathbf{R}_{12}, \quad (6.5.115)$$

to terms of the same order as retained in equation (6.5.110). With the expansion

$$\Delta\mathbf{R}_{12}{}^* = \Delta\mathbf{R}_{12}(s) - \frac{R_{12}}{c}\frac{\partial\,\Delta\mathbf{R}_{12}(s)}{\partial s} + \cdots$$

and substitution of equations (6.5.115) and (6.5.116) into equation (6.5.110), we obtain for the mean force the relation

$$\langle\mathbf{F}_1^{(S)}\rangle = \frac{\rho_m}{4\pi m^2c^3\tau}\int_0^\tau \left[\int g_0^{(2)}(R_{12})\frac{\partial\,\Delta\mathbf{R}_{12}(s)}{\partial s} \cdot \nabla_{12}\nabla_{12}u^{(S)}(R_{12})\, d\mathbf{R}_{12}\right] \cdot \left[\int g_0^{(2)}(R_{12})\nabla_{12}\nabla_{12}u^{(S)}(R_{12})\, d\mathbf{R}_{12}\right] ds. \quad (6.5.116)$$

In equation (6.5.116) the only term dependent on s is the time derivative. With the identification

$$\frac{1}{\tau}\int_0^\tau \frac{\partial\,\Delta\mathbf{R}_{12}(s)}{\partial s}\, ds = -\mathbf{u}_1, \quad (6.5.117)$$

where $\mathbf{u}_1$ is the mean velocity of the molecule relative to the medium, and the definition of the friction coefficient (6.5.28) we find, after integration over angles,

$$\zeta_S = \frac{4\pi\rho_m}{9m^2c^3}\left[\int_\sigma^\infty \nabla_{12}{}^2u^{(S)}(R_{12})g_0^{(2)}(R_{12})R_{12}{}^2\, dR_{12}\right]^2. \quad (6.5.118)$$

The model discussed is very simple and its physical interpretation is clear. The real molecular coarse fluid is replaced by an acoustic continuum with a distributed force field. The distributed force field, representing the interaction between a molecule and the medium, is chosen to duplicate the local mean density variations of a real fluid. The uncertainties involved in the definition of a proper molecular size and in the use of macroscopic boundary conditions at a surface of molecular dimensions have been avoided by using conditions on the wave amplitude and its derivative in the limit as $R_{12} \to \infty$.

In the model discussed a strong correlation is always maintained between the origin of the distributed force and fluid displacements, independent of the separation of the displacement from the origin. This correlation arises from the coherence of the acoustic wave, which we have taken to be non-dissipatively propagated. The natural damping of correlations by intervening fluctuations is thereby destroyed, and the molecular friction overestimated.

We consider, finally, a simple model designed to elucidate the qualitative features of $\psi(s)$ for all values of s (40). The momentum correlation function is related to the conditionally averaged momentum, $\langle \mathbf{p}(s) \rangle_1$, by [cf. Eq. (6.5.61)]

$$\langle \mathbf{p}(s) \rangle_1 = \mathbf{p}(0)\psi(s;\mathbf{p}(0)), \tag{6.5.119}$$
$$\langle \mathbf{p}(0)\langle \mathbf{p}(s) \rangle_1 \rangle = \langle \mathbf{p}(0)\mathbf{p}(0)\psi(s;\mathbf{p}(0)) \rangle = mkT\mathbf{1}\psi(s).$$

Here, $\psi(s;\mathbf{p}(0))$ is the momentum correlation function for a *given initial momentum* $\mathbf{p}(0)$, and in general depends upon $\mathbf{p}(0)$. $\psi(s)$ is obtained from $\psi(s;\mathbf{p}(0))$ by the indicated average over the initial momenta.* The relaxation model we consider here yields an equation linear in $\langle \mathbf{p}(s) \rangle_1$, however, and hence an equation for $\psi(s)$ can be obtained upon multiplication by $\mathbf{p}(0)$ and averaging as above. The conditional average represents a process of selecting from the ensemble all those replicas for which the observed molecule is initially at $\mathbf{R}_1^0$ with momentum $\mathbf{p}(0)$. This sub-ensemble is not stationary, even if the full ensemble is stationary. If $\mathbf{F}_1$ is the instantaneous force exerted on the observed molecule, then the conditional average force is

$$\langle \mathbf{F}_1 \rangle = \left\langle \frac{d\mathbf{p}}{ds} \right\rangle_1 = \frac{d}{ds} \langle \mathbf{p} \rangle_1. \tag{6.5.120}$$

That the commutation of the time derivative and the conditional average is correct is demonstrated in Appendix 6.A. Of course,

$$\langle \mathbf{F}_1 \rangle = \int \nabla_{12} u \frac{\rho^{(2)}}{\rho^{(1)}} \, d\mathbf{R}_{12}, \tag{6.5.121}$$

* The authors are indebted to Dr. P. Schofield for drawing their attention to this feature.

and since $\mathbf{F}_1$ is not an explicit function of the time,

$$\int \mathbf{F}_1 \frac{\partial}{\partial s}\left(\frac{\rho^{(2)}}{\rho^{(1)}}\right) d\mathbf{R}_{12} = \frac{d}{ds}\int \mathbf{F}_1 \frac{\rho^{(2)}}{\rho^{(1)}}\, d\mathbf{R}_{12}$$

$$= \frac{d^2}{ds^2}\langle \mathbf{p}\rangle_1. \tag{6.5.122}$$

The reader should note that $\mathbf{F}_1 = -\nabla_1 u = \nabla_{12} u$, a fact which has been used in equation (6.5.121). Now, under conditions of local equilibrium, the relative flux $\mathbf{j}_{12} = \mathbf{j}_2^{(2)} - \mathbf{j}_1^{(2)}$ is just

$$\mathbf{j}_{12} = -\frac{\rho^{(2)}}{m}\langle \mathbf{p}\rangle_1. \tag{6.5.123}$$

The equation of continuity

$$\frac{\partial \rho^{(2)}}{\partial t} + \nabla_1 \cdot \mathbf{j}_1^{(2)} + \nabla_2 \cdot \mathbf{j}_2^{(2)} = 0 \tag{6.5.124}$$

may be rewritten in terms of the relative flux $\mathbf{j}_{12}$ and the center of mass flux, $\mathbf{J}$, in the form

$$\frac{\partial \rho^{(2)}}{\partial t} + \nabla_{12} \cdot \mathbf{j}_{12} + \nabla \cdot \mathbf{J} = 0. \tag{6.5.125}$$

The simple model we shall consider replaces the last term of equation (6.5.125) with a relaxation term. This should be a satisfactory approximation for many purposes since the transport of mass, momentum, and energy depend on the relative motion of a pair of particles and not on the center of mass motion. It should be noted, however, that the introduction of a space and momentum independent relaxation time leads to normalization inconsistencies. These inconsistencies can be removed if the relaxation time is allowed to depend on R_{12}, but that will not be done herein. With these preliminary remarks, we rewrite equation (6.5.125) in the approximate form

$$\frac{\partial \rho^{(2)}}{\partial t} + \nabla_{12} \cdot \mathbf{j}_{12} = -\gamma[\rho^{(2)} - \rho_0^{(2)}]. \tag{6.5.126}$$

To a first approximation the pair distribution function appearing in (6.5.123) may be replaced by its local equilibrium value, so that

$$\frac{\partial \rho^{(2/1)}}{\partial s} + \gamma[\rho^{(2/1)} - \rho_0^{(2/1)}] - \frac{1}{m}\langle \mathbf{p}\rangle_1 \cdot \nabla_{12}\rho_0^{(2/1)} = 0. \tag{6.5.127}$$

In equation (6.5.127) we have also changed to the conditional distribution function, $\rho^{(2/1)} = (\rho^{(2)}/\rho^{(1)})$. If equation (6.5.127) is multiplied by $\nabla_{12}u$ and integrated over the variable $\mathbf{R}_{12}$, then the first term on the left-hand side gives equation (6.5.122) and the term $\gamma\rho_0^{(2/1)}$ gives the equilibrium average force, which is zero. The last term is simply transformed:

$$\frac{1}{m}\int \nabla_{12}u\langle\mathbf{p}\rangle_1 \cdot \nabla_{12}\rho_0^{(2/1)}\, d\mathbf{R}_{12} = -\frac{4\pi}{3m}\langle\mathbf{p}\rangle_1 \int \nabla_{12}{}^2 u\rho_0^{(2/1)} R_{12}{}^2\, dR_{12}$$
$$= -\gamma\alpha\langle\mathbf{p}\rangle_1, \qquad (6.5.128)$$

by partial integration. In equation (6.5.128) we have also used the fact that

$$\int_0^{2\pi}\int_0^{\pi} \mathbf{R}_{12}\mathbf{R}_{12} \sin\theta d\,\theta\, d\Phi = \frac{4\pi}{3} R_{12}{}^2\mathbf{I},$$

and defined α by comparison of the two lines of the equation. By combination of equations (6.5.128), (6.5.120), and (6.5.122) with (6.5.119) we find the differential equation

$$\ddot{\psi} + \gamma\dot{\psi} + \alpha\gamma\psi = 0, \qquad (6.5.129)$$

which must be solved subject to the boundary conditions (6.5.56) (continuous potential). The solution is*

$$\psi(s) = \frac{1}{\theta_+ - \theta_-}[\theta_+ \exp(\theta_- s) - \theta_- \exp(\theta_+ s)], \qquad (6.5.130)$$

where θ_+ and θ_- are the roots of the auxiliary equation

$$\theta_{\mp} = -\frac{\gamma}{2} \mp \left(\frac{\gamma^2}{4} - \alpha\gamma\right)^{1/2}. \qquad (6.5.131)$$

* By a simple extension of the analysis of Appendix 6.A which leads to equation (6.5.56), it may be shown that [see Eq. (6.A.25)]

$$\frac{\partial^2}{\partial s^2}\langle\mathbf{p}(t)\cdot\mathbf{p}(t+s)\rangle = -\langle\mathbf{F}(t)\cdot\mathbf{F}(t+s)\rangle.$$

Thus,

$$\ddot{\psi}(0) = -(3mkT)^{-1}\langle\mathbf{F}(t)^2\rangle.$$

It is interesting to note that the solution of equation (6.5.129) given in equation (6.5.130) satisfies this condition, since it can be shown that

$$\theta_+\theta_- = \alpha\gamma = (3mkT)^{-1}\langle\mathbf{F}^2\rangle.$$

From the Einstein relation, equation (6.5.63), using equation (6.5.130) for $\psi(s)$, it is easily found that

$$D = \frac{kT}{m\alpha}, \tag{6.5.132}$$

so that $\zeta = m\alpha$, the friction coefficient introduced earlier.

It is interesting that equation (6.5.130) has the proper limiting form for a Brownian particle. For a massive particle, $\alpha \ll \gamma$, since γ is presumed to be a constant characteristic of the liquid, whereas the interaction between a particle and the surrounding fluid per unit mass of the particle decreases as the particle size increases. That α decreases as stated can be seen from Stokes law, since if $\zeta = 6\pi\eta\sigma$, then α is proportional to $m^{-4/3}$. For sufficiently large particles, the stated inequality must hold. When $\alpha \ll \gamma$, the roots of equation (6.5.131) become

$$\theta_+ \simeq -\alpha,$$
$$\theta_- \simeq -\gamma,$$

so that

$$\psi(s) = \left(1 - \frac{\alpha}{\gamma}\right)^{-1}\left[\exp(-\alpha s) - \frac{\alpha}{\gamma}\exp(-\gamma s)\right],$$

and for times long compared to γ^{-1},

$$\psi(s) \simeq \exp(-\alpha s), \tag{6.5.133}$$

which is the expected correlation function for Brownian particles.

Under conditions appropriate to liquid Ar, equation (6.5.130) displays damped oscillations, as conjectured in the discussion at the beginning of this section. It has been made clear that negative contributions to $\psi(s)$ are to be expected in a liquid. Such contributions arise because the most likely displacement following an initial displacement away from a position of symmetry relative to the close neighbors of a molecule is antiparallel to the initial displacement. When the density is low and there is no cage of neighbors to force a rebound, the negative contributions to $\psi(s)$ vanish and exponential or near exponential behavior of $\psi(s)$ is expected.

Equations (6.5.132) and (6.5.128) give a relationship for $\gamma\zeta$ in terms of the intermolecular potential and the pair correlation function, but not for γ and ζ separately. One possible method of obtaining a molecular formula for ζ would be to guess the form of $\psi(s)$ using such guidance as is available from the exact series expansion of $\psi(s)$.

Alternatively, the consistency of the model can be tested by calculating other transport coefficients (40). If the shear viscosity is calculated one has then the Einstein relation (6.5.132), equation (6.5.128) for the product $\alpha\zeta^{(1)}$, and a viscosity formula involving γ and known thermodynamic functions.

In the next section we shall discuss the comparison of these various models for the friction coefficient, and also the ion mobility, with experiment.

6.5.D. *Comparison with Experiment* (11,22)

It has already been pointed out that the calculation of the friction coefficient from first principles requires, essentially, the solution of the N-body problem. However, the deduction of the relationships between the friction coefficient and other coefficients describing dissipative processes is a comparatively simple problem. Indeed, it is this problem which is solved by the kinetic theory. Therefore, we expect to find that given the correct friction coefficient the values of other transport coefficients will be in good agreement with observation.

In this section we shall first examine the various *a priori* calculations of the friction coefficient and then conclude with a comparison of the theoretical predictions of the coefficient of self-diffusion and the ion mobility with experiments.

In the previous section five independent calculations of the friction coefficient were developed. The results of calculations for liquid argon, and the corresponding experimental values, are compared in Table 6.11. The best calculation, in the sense that it comes nearest to a proper solution of the N-body problem, is that due to Helfand and based upon the exact prescription for the friction coefficient developed in Chapter 5 from the weak interaction model of the soft forces. The resulting formula is given in equation (6.5.80). In this model the hard and soft friction coefficients are calculated separately. A calculation has been made for liquid argon at the single temperature 84°K and density $\rho_m = 1.374$ g. cm.$^{-3}$. The theoretical value quoted is probably within 30% of the value which would be obtained with a radial distribution function yielding the correct pressure.

The square well model [Eq. (6.5.82)] is evaluated by fitting the parameters σ_1, σ_2, ϵ to gas data; it is seen to give better agreement with experiment than any of the other calculations. Although the values are 30% low if the autocorrelation function is assumed to decay exponentially, the temperature dependence is very close to the observed value. Moreover, even the discrepancy in magnitude is removed when the assumption that the momentum autocorrelation function is adequately given by a simple exponential decay is removed. The general formula derived by Davis, Rice, and Sengers [Eq. (6.5.82)] is cumbersome to use but does lead to very good agreement with experiment.

The small step diffusion model [Eq. (6.5.108)] has been formulated in terms of a rigid core and a soft friction coefficient, as was Helfand's calculation. However, the radial distribution function for this temperature and density yields a poor value of the pressure, and numerical values can be obtained by a different method but with probably greater reliability. If the qualitative distinction between the rigid core and the soft forces is ignored it is found that the friction coefficient is given in terms of the average of the Laplacian of the total potential energy:

$$\zeta^2 = \frac{m}{3}\langle \nabla_1{}^2 U(\{N\})\rangle. \tag{6.5.134}$$

Now, the quantity $\langle \nabla_1{}^2 U(\{N\})\rangle$ may be shown to be related to the mean-square force by

$$\langle[\nabla_1 U(\{N\})]^2\rangle = kT\langle \nabla_1{}^2 U(\{N\})\rangle. \tag{6.5.135}$$

The mean-square force may be measured directly by studying isotope separation. The separation factor can readily be shown to arise from a first-order quantum correction to the classical description of equilibrium, and is directly related to $\langle \nabla_1{}^2 U(\{N\})\rangle$. ζ has been calculated from equations (6.5.134) and (6.5.135) using the data of Boato et al. (41). It is seen from Table 6.13 that, while the numerical values of the diffusion coefficient are fairly good, the temperature dependence is too small. Alternatively, a direct calculation of ζ_S may be made using the radial distribution function of Kirkwood, Lewinson, and Alder. In accounting for the temperature dependence of the self-diffusion coefficients of Ar, Kr, and Xe, Naghizadeh and Rice have argued that, at constant pressure, the variation in $g_0^{(2)}(R_{12})$ with temperature arises from thermal expansion causing the average height of the maxima in $g_0^{(2)}(R_{12})$ to decrease and the positions of the peaks to shift. To a first approximation the peak shift is $\frac{1}{3}\alpha(T - T_0)R_{12}$ and the amplitude is decreased by a factor of $[1 + \alpha(T - T_0)]^{-1}$, where α is the coefficient of thermal expansion.

TABLE 6.13

Values of the Self-Diffusion Coefficient for Liquid Argon from the Several Friction Coefficient Formulas[a]

Source	$D \times 10^5$ cm.^{2} sec.$^{-1}$ 84°K	90°K	100°K
Helfand			
Equation (6.5.80)	3.0	—	—
Square Well			
Equation (6.5.82)			
Exponentially decaying			
correlation function	1.43	1.8	2.25
Square Well			
Equation (6.5.82)			
Davis, Rice, and Sengers	1.81	2.31	3.39
Small Step			
Equation (6.5.108)			
with Isotope Separation	2.25	2.49	2.92
Small Step			
Equations (6.5.108) and (6.5.136)			
Direct Calculation	—	2.22	3.22
Acoustic Continuum			
Equation (6.5.118)	—	0.84	—
Relaxation Model			
Equation (6.5.132)	0.84	1.16	1.69
Experiment (11)	1.84	2.35	3.45

[a] The experimental values are for states along the vaporization curve (11).

Thus, if $g_0^{(2)}(R_{12};T_0)$ is the pair correlation function at T_0, then the pair correlation function at T is given by

$$g_0^{(2)}(R_{12};T) = [1 + \alpha(T - T_0)]^{-1} g_0^{(2)}\left(\frac{R_{12}}{1 + \frac{1}{3}\alpha(T - T_0)}\,;\,T_0\right).$$

With the aid of this approximation for $g_0^{(2)}(R_{12};T)$ the temperature dependence of the self-diffusion coefficient is quantitatively predicted.

A calculation based on the acoustic continuum model, equation (6.5.118), is given for the only temperature for which the low frequency velocity of sound is known. (The data from isotope separation are also used.) It is apparent from Table 6.13 that the velocity of propagation of the high frequency density fluctuations must be approximately

$3^{1/3}$ times as high as that of low frequency sound, if this model is to be a quantitatively correct description of a fluid.

The calculations for the relaxation model [Eq. (6.5.132)] again use the isotope separation data. From equation (6.5.128) it is seen that

$$\alpha\gamma = \frac{\langle \nabla_1{}^2 U(\{N\})\rangle}{3m}. \tag{6.5.136}$$

The model contains one undetermined parameter, which must be evaluated by comparison of some formula predicted by the model with experiment. If it is assumed that the intermolecular forces are responsible for the total viscous effect, γ may be estimated from the known value of the shear viscosity. Use of the data of Boato et al. then leads to values of α and the self-diffusion coefficient displayed in Table 6.13. It is seen that not only are the absolute values one-half the measured values, but the temperature dependence is too large. On the other hand, if the value of α is deduced from the self-diffusion coefficient, and γ from the data of Boato et al. through equation (6.5.136), a lower value of η_V is obtained, which is consistent with calculations of Section 6.4.A. Also, as discussed below, the momentum correlation function is very close to that calculated by Rahman(42).

It is of interest now to discuss the molecular dynamics exhibited by liquid argon molecules. In deriving the kinetic equations it was postulated that following a rigid core collision a molecule would execute a quasi-Brownian motion in the field of the soft forces of its neighbors for a sufficiently long time before undergoing a second rigid core collision that its initial momentum would have almost relaxed to equilibrium. On average the impulse of a second rigid core collision will be antiparallel to the initial motion and will, therefore, tend to reverse the direction of motion. That is, the momentum correlation function will become negative; this is known as the "caging effect." However, if the soft forces cause a sufficiently rapid regression, the *extent* to which the correlation function becomes negative will be small. The momentum correlation function calculated for liquid argon at 90°K and $\rho_m = 1.374$ g. cm.$^{-3}$ by the method of molecular dynamics (42)* is displayed in Figure 6.5.1. For comparison, the correlation

* The molecular dynamics method consists in solving the equations of motion of a number (in this case 864) of molecules step by step numerically, in a computer. For the present purposes the result may be regarded as exact.

functions given by the gaussian and relaxation models are also displayed. The important feature of the exact correlation function is that it is very similar to what is expected from the foregoing qualitative argument. The correlation function predicted by the relaxation model (α, γ deduced from self-diffusion and isotope separation data) lies close to the exact curve. In particular, the decay constant is the same, but the oscillations are, of course, regular, and the extent of the first negative peak is slightly overestimated. On the other hand, the gaussian model displays no caging effect.* The success of the latter model in making a reasonably good prediction of the self-diffusion coefficient is due to the fact that the area under the peak is determined mainly by the curvature at $t = 0$, i.e., by $\ddot{\psi}(0)$ or the mean-square force.

Finally, we turn to the computation of the ionic mobility from equation (6.5.30). It is readily seen that the critical problem is again the evaluation of ζ_S. In this case, electrostriction causes the distribution of molecules about a neutral molecule to differ from the distribution of molecules about an ion.

It has been established spectroscopically that the positive species M_2^+ is stable in the gas phase, where M represents an He, Ne, Ar, Kr, or Xe atom. Davis, Rice, and Meyer assume that the positive charge carrier in these fluids is M_2^+ and that the ion-molecule interaction can be represented by the following spherically symmetric potential:

$$u(R_{12}) = \infty; \qquad R_{12} \leqslant \sigma,$$

$$u(R_{12}) = 4\epsilon\left[\left(\frac{\sigma}{R_{12}}\right)^{12} - \left(\frac{\sigma}{R_{12}}\right)^{6}\right] - \frac{\alpha}{2}\left(\frac{\mathscr{D}+2}{3\mathscr{D}}\right)^{2}\frac{e^2}{R_{12}^{4}}, \qquad (6.5.137)$$

with α the polarizability and $\mathscr{D}$ the static dielectric constant. This form assumes rapid and free rotation of M_2^+ in the liquid, a supposition which is likely to be correct because of the small size of M_2^+ ions. Moreover, since the ions are assumed to be diatomic, Davis, Rice, and Meyer took as a first approximation $\epsilon_{M_2^+} \simeq 2\epsilon_M$. Detailed calculations have been made, in the classical case, for Ar_2^+ in Ar, where the parameter σ may be obtained from the experimental data of Biondi and Chanin.

* By the central limit theorem, the gaussian correlation function may be interpreted as characteristic of a succession of many independent, random, momentum changes, subject only to the given initial conditions.

To a first approximation we can treat the short range and long range correlations separately. That is, the total correlation function is given by

$$g^{(2)}(R_{12}) = g_0^{(2)}(R_{12}) + g_p^{(2)}(R_{12}), \tag{6.5.138}$$

where $g_0^{(2)}(R)$ is the correlation function due to the Lennard-Jones potential, ignoring the polarization forces, and $g_p^{(2)}(R)$ is the added correlation due to the polarization forces ignoring the short range interactions.

To obtain the polarization contribution $g_p^{(2)}(R)$, the fluid is treated as a dielectric continuum in contact with a static ion. Simple thermodynamic arguments (as presented by Atkins (43)) lead to

$$\int_{p_0}^{p(R_{12})} v\,dp = \tfrac{1}{2}N\alpha(E')^2, \tag{6.5.139}$$

where $N\alpha$ is the molar polarizability of the liquid, v the molar volume, p_0 the unperturbed hydrostatic pressure of the liquid, $p(R_{12})$ the pressure at a distance R_{12} from the ion due to the electrostrictive density increase, and $\mathbf{E}'$ the electric field at a distance R_{12} from the ion. Assuming the ion to have an excluded volume of diameter σ the electric field is given by

$$E' = \frac{e}{\mathscr{D}{R_{12}}^2}; \qquad R_{12} \geqslant \sigma,$$

$$E' = 0; \qquad R_{12} < \sigma. \tag{6.5.140}$$

From equation of state data and equation (6.5.139) the density increase due to electrostriction can be found as a function of the distance from the ion. Then the correlation function $g_p^{(2)}(R_{12})$, defined by

$$g_p^{(2)}(R_{12}) = \frac{\rho_{m_1}(R_{12}) - \rho_{m_1}(\infty)}{\rho_{m_1}(\infty)}, \tag{6.5.141}$$

can be calculated. $\rho_{m_1}(\infty)$ in equation (6.5.141) is the unperturbed mean density and $\rho_{m_1}(R_{12})$ is the perturbed density at a distance R_{12} from the ion. In obtaining $g_0^{(2)}(R)$ at 90°K from the calculations of Kirkwood et al. we have used values of ϵ, α, σ, $\mathscr{D}$, and density appropriate to argon, namely,

$$\epsilon = 2\epsilon_0 = 3.30 \times 10^{-14}\ \text{erg (44)}$$
$$\alpha = 1.7 \times 10^{-24}\ \text{cm.}^3\text{/molecule (45)}$$

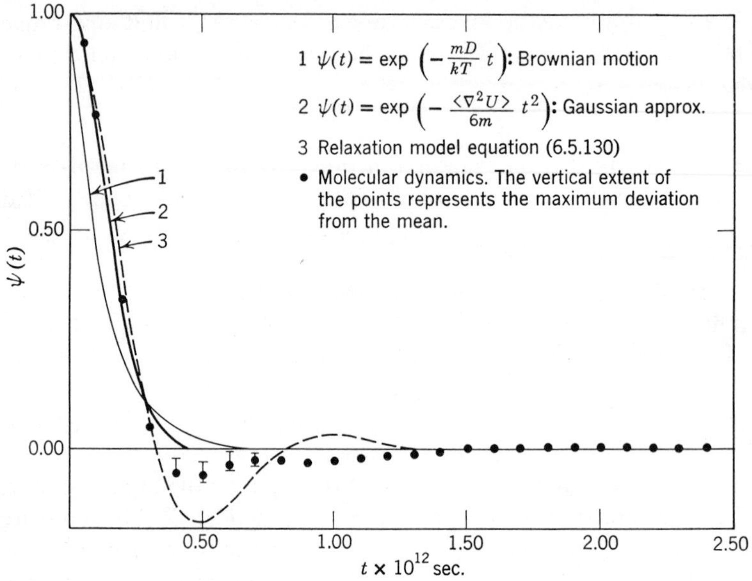

Fig. 6.5.1. Calculated normalized momentum autocorrelation functions $\psi(t)$ for argon molecules in the liquid at $\rho_m = 1.374$ g. cm.$^{-3}$, $T = 90$°K. The following experimental data were used in calculating curves 1, 2, and 3: $D = 2.72\ 10^{-5}$ cm.^{2} sec.$^{-1}$ (Naghizadeh and Rice), $\langle\nabla^2 U\rangle = 11.25\ 10^3$ erg. cm.$^{-3}$ (Boato et al.). The molecular dynamics points are those calculated by Rahman.

$$\sigma = 4.3 \times 10^{-8} \text{ cm.}$$
$$\mathscr{D}(90°\text{K}) = 1.53$$
$$\mathscr{D}(120°\text{K}) = 1.43$$
$$\rho_{m_1}(90°\text{K}) = 1.386 \text{ g. cm.}^{-3}$$
$$\rho_{m_1}(120°\text{K}) = 1.170 \text{ g. cm.}^{-3}$$

The temperature dependence of the pair correlation function is calculated by means of equation (6.5.136). Because the increase in density arising from electrostriction is small (extrapolating past the phase change) this continuum approximation is probably not too bad. It is found that the electrostrictive perturbation leads to an increase of $g^{(2)}(R)$ for $R < 2\sigma$. In this region both the peak values and minimum values of $g^{(2)}(R)$ are increased, but by $R > 2\sigma$ the pair correlation function is essentially indistinguishable from that of the pure fluid.

TABLE 6.14

Theoretical and Experimental Positive Ion Mobility in Liquid Ar (22)

	90°K	120°K
μ_+(calc)	5.93[a]	24
μ_+(obs)	6.10	17

[a] Units are 10^{-4} cm.^{2} v.$^{-1}$ sec.$^{-1}$

We see, from the entries in Table 6.14, that at 90°K the theory is in quantitative agreement with experiment. At 120°K, the agreement is satisfactory in view of the approximation to $g^{(2)}(R_{12})$.

In order to obtain insight into the role of the long range polarization interaction in irreversible processes it is important at this point to compare the observed self-diffusion coefficients D_0 of Ar, Kr, and Xe and the ionic diffusion coefficients (D_i). The ionic diffusion coefficients are obtained from the mobility data with the aid of the Einstein relation. In Table 6.15 we compare D_0 with D_i for the three liquids at 15 atm. and at the temperatures given in the second column of the table. As is shown by the ratio D_0/D_i in the last column of Table 6.15, the ionic diffusion coefficients are substantially smaller (from three to six times) than the self-diffusion coefficients for the liquids. Using the friction coefficient formula given in equations (6.5.68) and (6.5.118), both D_0 and D_i have been calculated for argon at 15 atm. and 90°K. The predicted ratio of the coefficients is $D_0/D_i = 4.8$ as compared to the observed ratio of 5 given in Table 6.15. D_i is smaller than D_0 as a result of both the polarization interaction and the larger size of the diatomic ion. The hard core radius $\frac{1}{2}\sigma_i$ of the ion M_2^+ is larger than

TABLE 6.15

Comparison of D_s and D_0 for the Three Liquids at 15 atm. (22)

Substance	(°K)	$D_0 \times 10^5$ cm.^{2} sec.$^{-1}$	$D_i \times 10^5$ cm.^{2} sec.$^{-1}$	D_0/D_i
Argon	90.1	2.35	0.474	5.0
Krypton	145.0	2.78	0.875	3.2
Xenon	184.3	2.48	0.442	5.6

that of the neutral molecule M by a factor of about 1.5, so that the ion-molecule collision diameter $\sigma = \frac{1}{2}(\sigma_i + \sigma_0)$, is larger than the molecule–molecule collision diameter by a factor of about 1.25.

From the preceding observations we conclude that the polarization interaction makes a significant contribution to the friction experienced by a moving ion and, therefore, significantly alters the magnitude of the mobility.

In calculating the friction coefficient we see that the polarization force contributes in two ways: (*1*) The density is increased in the vicinity of the ion by the Coulomb field, and (*2*) there is a contribution $\nabla^2 u_p(R_{12})$ arising from the polarization potential, u_p. However, direct calculation shows the contribution of $\nabla^2 u_p$ to the integral for ζ_S to be very small compared to the contribution of the Lennard-Jones term $\nabla^2 u_{LJ}^{(S)}$. From this we conclude that the primary effect of u_p is to bring the molecules closer together in the vicinity of the ions while the short-range forces provide the dissipative interactions. Similarly, in the treatment of the transport properties of molten salts it was concluded that the chief effect of the Coulomb potential is to maintain electroneutrality; that is, to surround each positive ion with negative ions and to increase the total density of the system, while the dissipation of energy arises primarily from the short-range forces.

To examine this notion further let us proceed with the observation that $g_p^{(2)}(R)$, defined by equation (6.5.141), decreases as the temperature increases at constant pressure. In the case of the neutral molecule the correlation function $g_0^{(2)}(R)$ decreases with increasing temperature at constant pressure, thereby decreasing the friction coefficient correspondingly. But in the case of the ion there is an additional decrease in $g^{(2)}(R)$ since $g^{(2)}(R) = g_0^{(2)}(R) + g_p^{(2)}(R)$. As a result, one would predict the temperature dependence of the ion mobility to be greater than that of the self-diffusion coefficient. This prediction is borne out by the data recorded in Table 6.16. The temperature dependence of the mobility can be represented adequately by the form $D_i = A \exp[-B/T]$. This was also the case for the self-diffusion data of Naghizadeh and Rice. All values entered in the figure are for a pressure of 20 atm. Table 6.16 is a comparison of the parameters B_i for the ions and B_0 for the molecules. We note that the listed values confirm the preceding arguments.

We can make one more observation in the comparison of D_0 and D_i. Again by direct calculation one can show that at constant temperature

$g_p^{(2)}(R)$ is changed negligibly in the vicinity of the ion by an increase in the external pressure (at least within the range of pressures considered herein). The pressure dependences of D_0 and D_i at constant temperature would then be expected to be the same. This is found to be the case within the sum of the uncertainties in each experiment.

The study of negative ions is more difficult than the study of positive ions because of impurity effects. Indeed, Davis, Rice, and Meyer (46) interpret their mobility data in terms of the properties of the O_2^- ion.

TABLE 6.16

Comparison of the Temperature Dependence of D_0 with D_i at 20 atm. (11,22)

Substance	B_i °K	B_0 °K
Argon	468	358
Krypton	553	408
Xenon	960	610

Because such high purity is required (carrier densities are only of order 10^5 cm.$^{-3}$) it is almost impossible to eliminate all impurities. If it be assumed that the negative charge carriers in liquid Ar, Kr, and Xe are indeed O_2^- ions, then an analysis similar to that described before may be used.

The determination of the parameters of the Lennard-Jones part of the potential is difficult. For the neutral molecules, O_2 and N_2, the parameters ϵ and σ are about equal to the corresponding parameters for the Ar–Ar interaction. For the ions, σ_i of O_2^- is known to be about 6% larger than σ of O_2, but the depth of the potential well, ϵ_i, is not known. It might be expected that the parameter ϵ will scale with the polarizability, but the polarizability of O_2^- is also unknown. In view of the situation sketched, Davis, Rice, and Meyer have considered ϵ to be adjustable and have fitted theory to experiment.

As already noted, it is expected that the interaction of an ion with an atom is considerably stronger than the interaction between the parent atoms. Resulting from the increased interaction is an enhancement and sharpening of the first peak of $g^{(2)}(R)$. Superimposed on this density distribution is the local density increase due to electrostriction.

We have calculated the effect of electrostriction on $g^{(2)}(R)$ by the method outlined previously. The chief difficulty in the analysis arises from the difficulty of calculating that part of $g^{(2)}(R)$ arising from the Lennard-Jones portion of $u^{(S)}(R)$. In the case considered herein, the parameter (ϵ/kT) is about 4, and the utility of the Kirkwood expansion for $g_0^{(2)}(R)$ may be seriously questioned. Nevertheless, the Kirkwood theory is the only formulation permitting a calculation of $g_0^{(2)}(R)$ from a knowledge of $u^{(S)}(R)$, and we have, perforce, used it in the following analysis.

Consider now, as an example, the mobility of the negative ion in liquid argon at 90°K and about 5 atm. Using the values displayed in Table 6.17, quantitative agreement between experiment and theory is

TABLE 6.17

Parameters of the Ion-Molecule Pair Potential (44)[a, b, c]

	A		°K
$\sigma(O_2)$	3.43	$\epsilon(O_2)/k$	113
$\sigma(N_2)$	3.68	$\epsilon(N_2)/k$	91.5
$\sigma(Ar)$	3.47	$\epsilon(Ar)/k$	116

[a] $\sigma_i = 3.63$ A.
[b] $\epsilon_i/k = 384$°K.
[c] $\alpha(Ar) = 1.7$A^3-molecule^{-1} (45).

obtained; the value of ϵ_i required is a factor of 3.4 greater than the depth of the Lennard-Jones potential well for neutral O_2. Since the ion O_2^- must have a very much larger polarizability α than O_2, this value for ϵ_i appears reasonable.

The calculated mobility is quite sensitive to the magnitude of ϵ_i. We have made calculations also for values of (ϵ_i/k) of 113 and 339°K, in each case computing the function $g^{(2)}(R)$ for $T = 90$°K. The mobilities corresponding to these choices for (ϵ_i/k) are 8.6×10^{-3} and 1.23×10^{-3} cm.^{2} v.$^{-1}$/sec.$^{-1}$, both clearly very much larger than the experimental value which is 8×10^{-4} cm.^{2} v.$^{-1}$ sec.$^{-1}$. In view of the uncertainties in $g^{(2)}(R)$ we have not, in this case, computed the temperature dependence of μ. Estimates of $(d\mu/dT)_p$ (using a reduction of the 90°K calculations) indicate that the same choice of ϵ_i suffices to account for the observed temperature dependence of μ.

APPENDIX 6.A

Properties of Autocorrelation Functions in Stationary Ensembles (40)

Let $A(\Gamma)$ be a function of the phase Γ of an N-molecule system.* The averaging operation in the definition of the correlation function can be divided into two parts. Thus,

$$\langle A(\Gamma_0)A(\Gamma_s)\rangle = \langle A(\Gamma_0)\langle A(\Gamma_s)\rangle_1\rangle_A, \tag{6.A.1}$$

where Γ_0 is the phase of the system at time t, and Γ_s is the phase at time $t + s$. The average $\langle A(\Gamma_s)\rangle_1$ represents the average value of the variable A at time $t + s$, given its value at time t. The second average $\langle\cdots\rangle_A$ is an average over all possible initial values of A for the particular ensemble. Thus, while the left-hand side of equation (6.A.1) is defined in the original ensemble, $\langle A(\Gamma_s)\rangle_1$ is defined in a sub-ensemble, in all members of which $A(\Gamma_0)$ has the same value. It follows that the essential time dependence is contained in the sub-ensemble. Thus,

$$\langle A(\Gamma_s)\rangle_1 = A(\Gamma_0)\psi_A(s; A(\Gamma_0)), \tag{6.A.2}$$

where $\psi(s; A(\Gamma_0))$ is the normalized autocorrelation function of A for a fixed initial value $A(\Gamma_0)$.† We are interested in the properties of $\psi_A(s; A(\Gamma_0))$ when the system is in a stationary state.

Let $A(\Gamma)$ be a continuous function of the phase Γ of a system; then its time derivative at a time t is defined by its Poisson bracket with the Hamiltonian $H(\Gamma_0)$:

$$\frac{dA}{dt} = \dot{A} = [A(\Gamma_0),H(\Gamma_0)]. \tag{6.A.3}$$

If $\dot{A}$ is also a continuous function of the phase,

$$\begin{aligned}\lim_{s\to 0} \dot{A}(\Gamma_s) &= \lim_{s\to 0} \dot{A}(\Gamma_0 + \Delta\Gamma_s)\\ &= \dot{A}(\Gamma_0),\end{aligned} \tag{6.A.4}$$

where $\Delta\Gamma_s$ is the change in phase of the system, according to the equations of motion, which takes place in a time interval s. If the

* For convenience here we have suppressed the subscript N on Γ_N.

† See footnote on p. 465.

phase is a continuous function of the time,

$$\lim_{s\to 0} \Gamma_s = \lim_{s\to 0} (\Gamma_0 + \Delta\Gamma_s)$$
$$= \Gamma_0. \tag{6.A.5}$$

If, for instance, A is the momentum of a particle, then A and $\dot{A}$ are continuous if the interparticle forces are continuous functions of position.

At time t select from the ensemble of replica systems all those members for which $A(\Gamma_0)$ has some given initial value A_0. Then the phase space distribution of the sub-ensemble is

$$W(A_0)^{-1}\, \delta(A(\Gamma_0) - A_0), \tag{6.A.6}$$

where

$$W(A_0) = \int d\Gamma_0\, \delta(A(\Gamma_0) - A_0), \tag{6.A.7}$$

and δ is the Dirac delta function. The distribution at a time s later is accordingly

$$W(A_0)^{-1} \int d\Gamma_0\, \delta(A(\Gamma_0) - A_0) K^{(N)}(\Gamma_s \mid \Gamma_0; s), \tag{6.A.8}$$

where $d\Gamma_0$ is a volume element in the phase space, and $K^{(N)}(\Gamma_s | \Gamma_0; s)$ is the phase space transition probability for the transition $\Gamma_0 \to \Gamma_s$ in a time s [cf. Chapter 5, Eq. (5.3.7)]. $K^{(N)}$ satisfies Liouville's equation

$$\frac{dK^{(N)}}{dt} = [K^{(N)}, H] + \frac{\partial K^{(N)}}{\partial t} = 0, \tag{6.A.9}$$

with the initial condition

$$K^{(N)}(\Gamma \mid \Gamma_0; 0) = \delta(\Gamma - \Gamma_0), \tag{6.A.10}$$

where $\delta(\Gamma - \Gamma_0)$ is a $6N$-dimensional Dirac delta function. The formal solution of equation (6.A.9) is

$$K^{(N)}(\Gamma_s \mid \Gamma_0; s) = \delta(\Gamma_s - \Gamma_0 - \Delta\Gamma_s). \tag{6.A.11}$$

The conditional average of $A(\Gamma_s)$ calculated from the sub-ensemble is, from equation (6.A.8),

$$\langle A(\Gamma_s)\rangle_1 = W(A_0)^{-1} \int d\Gamma_0 \int d\Gamma_s\, \delta(A(\Gamma_0) - A_0) A(\Gamma_s) K^{(N)}(\Gamma_s \mid \Gamma_0; s). \tag{6.A.12}$$

According to equation (6.A.2) $\langle A(\Gamma_s)\rangle_1$ is proportional to the correlation function of A, and depends explicitly on time s. The explicit time dependence of the right-hand side of equation (6.A.12) is contained in $K^{(N)}$, and thus, from equation (6.A.9),

$$\frac{d}{ds}\langle A(\Gamma_s)\rangle_1 = W(A_0)^{-1}\int d\Gamma_0\int d\Gamma_s \times \delta(A(\Gamma_0) - A_0)A(\Gamma_s)\left[\frac{\partial}{\partial s}K^{(N)}(\Gamma_s\,|\,\Gamma_0; s)\right]$$
$$= -W(A_0)^{-1}\int d\Gamma_0\int d\Gamma_s\,\delta(A(\Gamma_0) - A_0)A(\Gamma_s) \times [K^{(N)}(\Gamma_s\,|\,\Gamma_0{:}\ s), H(\Gamma_s)]. \quad (6.A.13)$$

Assuming that $K^{(N)}$ vanishes sufficiently rapidly towards the boundaries of the phase space, partial integration of equation (6.A.13) gives

$$\frac{d}{ds}\langle A(\Gamma_s)\rangle_1 = W(A_0)^{-1}\int d\Gamma_0\int d\Gamma_s \times \delta(A(\Gamma_0) - A_0)[A(\Gamma_s),H(\Gamma_s)]K^{(N)}(\Gamma_s\,|\,\Gamma_0; s)$$
$$= \langle \dot{A}(\Gamma_s)\rangle_1. \quad (6.A.14)$$

Equation (6.A.14) proves equation (6.5.120).

The correlation function of A is obtained from equation (6.A.1), by an average of $A(\Gamma_0)\langle A(\Gamma_s)\rangle_1$ over all initial values of $A(\Gamma_0)$. The distribution function of $A_0 = A(\Gamma_0)$ is

$$f(A_0;t) = \int d\Gamma_0'\ \delta(A(\Gamma_0') - A_0)f^{(N)}(\Gamma_0';t), \quad (6.A.15)$$

where $f^{(N)}(\Gamma_0';t)$ is the distribution function characterizing the whole ensemble, and is also a solution of Liouville's equation. Thus, from equation (6.A.12) and (6.A.15),

$$\langle A(\Gamma_0)A(\Gamma_s)\rangle = \int dA_0 f(A_0;t)A_0\langle A(\Gamma_s)\rangle_1$$
$$= \int W(A_0)^{-1}\,dA_0\int d\Gamma_0'\int d\Gamma_0\int d\Gamma_s\,\delta(A(\Gamma_0') - A_0) \times \delta(A(\Gamma_0) - A_0)A(\Gamma_0')A(\Gamma_s)K^{(N)}(\Gamma_s\,|\,\Gamma_0; s)f^{(N)}(\Gamma_0';t). \quad (6.A.16)$$

Upon integrating equation (6.A.16) over A_0 and Γ_0' we obtain

$$\begin{aligned}\langle A(\Gamma_0)A(\Gamma_s)\rangle &= \int d\Gamma_0' \int d\Gamma_0 \int d\Gamma_s W(A(\Gamma_0))^{-1}\,\delta(A(\Gamma_0') - A(\Gamma_0))\\ &\quad\times A(\Gamma_0)A(\Gamma_s)K^{(N)}(\Gamma_s \mid \Gamma_0; s)f^{(N)}(\Gamma_0;t)\\ &= \int d\Gamma_0 \int d\Gamma_s A(\Gamma_0)A(\Gamma_s)K^{(N)}(\Gamma_s \mid \Gamma_0; s)f^{(N)}(\Gamma_0;t),\end{aligned} \tag{6.A.17}$$

since

$$\int d\Gamma_0'\,\delta(A(\Gamma_0') - A(\Gamma_0)) = W(A(\Gamma_0)).$$

From equation (6.A.14), equation (6.A.17) can be seen to become, on differentiation with respect to s,

$$\begin{aligned}\frac{d}{ds}\langle A(\Gamma_0)A(\Gamma_s)\rangle &= \int d\Gamma_0 \int d\Gamma_s A(\Gamma_0)A(\Gamma_s)\left[\frac{\partial}{\partial s}K^{(N)}(\Gamma_s \mid \Gamma_0; s)\right]f^{(N)}(\Gamma_0;t)\\ &= \langle A(\Gamma_0)\dot{A}(\Gamma_s)\rangle.\end{aligned} \tag{6.A.18}$$

Using the formal solution equation (6.A.11) for $K^{(N)}$, and integrating over Γ_s, this becomes

$$\langle A(\Gamma_0)\dot{A}(\Gamma_s)\rangle = \int d\Gamma_0 A(\Gamma_0)\dot{A}(\Gamma_0 + \Delta\Gamma_s)f^{(N)}(\Gamma_0;t), \tag{6.A.19}$$

and proceeding to the limit $s = 0$ we have, from equation (6.A.4),

$$\langle A(\Gamma_0)\dot{A}(\Gamma_0)\rangle = \int d\Gamma_0 A(\Gamma_0)\dot{A}(\Gamma_0)f^{(N)}(\Gamma_0;t).$$

If the whole ensemble is stationary we have, from equation (6.A.9),

$$[f^{(N)}(\Gamma_0),H(\Gamma_0)] = 0,$$

so that, upon performing a partial integration as with equation (6.A.13), we find

$$\begin{aligned}\langle A(\Gamma_0)\dot{A}(\Gamma_0)\rangle &= -\int d\Gamma_0 A\ \Gamma_0)[A(\Gamma_0)f^{(N)}(\Gamma_0),H(\Gamma_0)]\\ &= -\int d\Gamma_0 A(\Gamma_0)\dot{A}(\Gamma_0)f^{(N)}(\Gamma_0;t)\\ &= -\langle A(\Gamma_0)\dot{A}(\Gamma_0)\rangle\\ &= 0,\end{aligned} \tag{6.A.20}$$

and equation (6.A.20) proves equation (6.5.56*b*).

The second derivative of equation (6.A.17) is, following the manipulation leading to equation (6.A.18),

$$\frac{d^2}{ds^2}\langle A(\Gamma_0)A(\Gamma_s)\rangle = \langle A(\Gamma_0)\ddot{A}(\Gamma_s)\rangle. \tag{6.A.21}$$

We now introduce the linear Liouville operator

$$\mathscr{L}\phi = i[H,\phi]. \tag{6.A.22}$$

If $B(\Gamma)$ is a function of the phase only, then the operator $\exp(i\mathscr{L}s)$* is a time displacement, or projection operator:

$$\exp(i\mathscr{L}s)B(\Gamma_0) = B(\Gamma_s), \tag{6.A.23}$$

with $i\mathscr{L}$ playing the role of a time differentiation

$$i\mathscr{L}B(\Gamma_0) = \dot{B}(\Gamma_0). \tag{6.A.24}$$

Using equations (6.A.23) and (6.A.24) with equation (A6.1.21), it is easily shown that

$$\langle A(\Gamma_0)\ddot{A}(\Gamma_s)\rangle = -\langle \dot{A}(\Gamma_0)\dot{A}(\Gamma_s)\rangle. \tag{6.A.25}$$

APPENDIX 6.B

Moments of the Momentum Increments for a Particle in a Gas

Consider a rigid, spherical test particle of mass M, diameter σ_1, and velocity $\mathbf{v}_1$, immersed in a gas of non-interacting, rigid, spherical particles of mass m, diameter σ_2, and velocities $\mathbf{v}_2$. At the instant of collision between the test particle and a particle of the gas, their centers are separated by $\sigma = \frac{1}{2}(\sigma_1 + \sigma_2)$. If $\mathbf{k}$ is the unit vector from the test particle to the gas particle, the change in momentum of the test particle due to a collision with a gas particle of initial velocity $\mathbf{v}_2$ is

$$\Delta\mathbf{p}_1 = -2\mu\mathbf{k}\mathbf{k}\cdot\mathbf{v}_{12}, \tag{6.B.1}$$

where

$$\mu = \frac{mM}{m + M}$$

and

$$\mathbf{v}_{12} = \mathbf{v}_2 - \mathbf{v}_1.$$

* $\exp(i\mathscr{L}s)$ is defined by its series expansion.

In order to develop a differential representation of the collision operator (see Section 4.3.C) we must evaluate the quantities

$$\mathbf{a}^{(n)} = \lim_{\tau \to 0} \frac{1}{\tau} \langle (\Delta \mathbf{p}_1)^{(n)} \rangle_1, \tag{6.B.2}$$

where the superscript (n) denotes the nth rank tensor formed from the appropriate vector. The average is the combined average over the collision parameters and the initial velocity $\mathbf{v}_2$ of the gas particle. Since the filamentary volume element of the collision cylinder is extended to a length $v_{12}\tau$, it is clear that $\mathbf{a}^{(n)}$ approaches a limit independent of τ for all n. Thus, in general, the differential operator equivalent to the collision integral is of infinite order; it has the form*

$$\sum_{n=1}^{\infty} \frac{1}{n!} (\nabla_{p_1})^{(n)} \,\|\, [\mathbf{a}^{(n)} f(\mathbf{p}_1)] = \langle f(\mathbf{p}_1 + \Delta \mathbf{p}_1) \rangle - f(\mathbf{p}_1). \tag{6.B.3}$$

In equation (6.B.3) the heavy vertical bar denotes the fact that the nth order tensor gradient and the nth rank tensor $\mathbf{a}^{(n)} f(\mathbf{p}_1)$ is contracted n-fold to yield a scalar quantity. The average indicated by $\langle \cdots \rangle$ in equation (6.B.3) is the same as that represented in equation (6.B.2).

The complete expression for $\mathbf{a}^{(n)}$ is

$$\mathbf{a}^{(n)} = \rho g(\sigma) \int_{(\mathbf{k}\cdot\mathbf{v}_{12}<0)} \iint (\Delta \mathbf{p}_1)^{(n)} \frac{\exp(-[m\mathbf{v}_2^{\,2}/2kT])}{(2\pi kT/m)^{3/2}} V_{12}\, d\mathbf{v}_2\, b\, db\, d\epsilon. \tag{6.B.4}$$

We now introduce the dimensionless velocities

$$\mathbf{w} = \left(\frac{m}{2kT}\right)^{1/2} \mathbf{v}_{12}, \text{ etc.,}$$

and write also,

$$\mathbf{v}_2 = \mathbf{v}_{12} + \mathbf{v}_1; \qquad d\mathbf{v}_2 = d\mathbf{v}_{12},$$

so that equation (6.B.5) becomes

$$\mathbf{a}^{(n)} = (-)^n \frac{\rho g(\sigma)}{2\pi^{3/2}\mu} \left(\frac{8\mu^2 kT}{m}\right)^{(n+1)/2} \int \iint_{(\mathbf{k}\cdot\mathbf{w}<0)} (\mathbf{k})^{(n)} (\mathbf{k}\cdot\mathbf{w})^n \times \exp(-[\mathbf{w} + \mathbf{w}_1]^2) w\, d\mathbf{w} b\, db\, d\epsilon. \tag{6.B.5}$$

* The right-hand side of equation (6.B.3) is, of course, just the Boltzmann collision integral. Alternatively, the average may be regarded as that appearing in equation (4.3.59).

In the limit that the test particle becomes very massive compared to the gas particles, we find

$$\mathbf{w}_1 = \left(\frac{m}{2kT}\right)^{1/2} \mathbf{v}_1 \sim \mathcal{O}\left[\left(\frac{m}{M}\right)^{1/2}\right] \to 0. \qquad (6.B.6)$$

In the limit $\mathbf{w}_1 \to 0$, we may write

$$\exp(-[\mathbf{w} + \mathbf{w}_1]^2) \simeq \exp(-w^2)(1 - 2\mathbf{w} \cdot \mathbf{w}_1 + \cdots), \quad (6.B.7)$$

and it is apparent that the limiting form of $\mathbf{a}^{(n)}$ as $(m/M) \to 0$ is either independent of $\mathbf{w}_1$ or linear in $\mathbf{w}_1$. Moreover, as $M \to \infty$, $\mu \to m$, and the magnitude of the nth term in the series in equation (6.B.3) is

$$(\nabla_{p_1})^{(n)} \,|\, [\mathbf{a}^{(n)} f(\mathbf{p}_1)] = (2MkT)^{-n/2} (\nabla_{w_1})^{(n)} \,|\, [\mathbf{a}^{(n)} f(\mathbf{p}_1)]$$
$$\simeq \mathcal{O}\left[\left(\frac{m}{M}\right)^{n/2}\right], \qquad (6.B.8)$$

since

$$f(\mathbf{p}_1) = F\left(\frac{\mathbf{p}_1}{(2MkT)^{1/2}}\right) = F(\mathbf{w}_1). \qquad (6.B.9)$$

Hence, nth order terms vanish as $(m/M)^{n/2}$, and in the limit it is necessary to retain only the first two terms, i.e., the Fokker-Planck operator.

The detailed forms of the first two moments have been worked out by several authors (47–49). They are

$$\mathbf{a}^{(1)} = -\tfrac{1}{2}\rho g(\sigma)\sigma^2(\mu/m)(2\pi mkT)^{1/2} \phi_1(w_1)\mathbf{v}_1$$
$$\mathbf{a}^{(2)} = \tfrac{16}{3}kT\rho g(\sigma)\sigma^2(2\mu/m)^2(\pi mkT)^{1/2}$$
$$\times \left[\phi_2(w_1)\mathbf{I} + \phi_3(w_1)\frac{\mathbf{w}_1\mathbf{w}_1}{w_1^{\,2}}\right], \qquad (6.B.10)$$

where

$$\phi_1(x) = (2 + x^{-2})e^{-x^2} + (4x + 4x^{-1} - x^{-3})\frac{\pi^{1/2}}{2}\operatorname{erf}(x),$$

$$\phi_2(x) = \frac{2^{1/2}}{32}\left[(x^2 + 4 + \tfrac{3}{4}x^{-2})e^{-x^2} \right.$$
$$\left. + (2x^3 + 9x + \tfrac{9}{2}x^{-1} - \tfrac{3}{4}x^{-3})\frac{\pi^{1/2}}{2}\operatorname{erf}(x)\right],$$

$$\phi_3(x) = \frac{2^{1/2}}{32}\left[(3x^2 + 3 - \tfrac{9}{4}x^{-2})e^{-x^2} \right.$$
$$\left. + (6x^3 + 9x - \tfrac{9}{2}x^{-1} + \tfrac{9}{4}x^{-3})\frac{\pi^{1/2}}{2}\operatorname{erf}(x)\right]. \qquad (6.B.11)$$

In the limit $x \to 0$, the functions $\phi_i(x)$ tend to the values

$$\phi_1(x \to 0) = \frac{16}{3}\,; \qquad \phi_2(x \to 0) = \frac{2^{1/2}}{4}\,; \qquad \phi_3(x \to 0) = 0,$$

and the moments become

$$\mathbf{a}^{(1)} = -\zeta \mathbf{v}_1,$$
$$\mathbf{a}^{(2)} = 2kT\zeta\mathbf{I}, \tag{6.B.12}$$

where ζ is given by

$$\zeta = \tfrac{8}{3}\rho g(\sigma)\sigma^2(2\pi mkT)^{1/2}. \tag{6.B.13}$$

It will be seen that ζ, in equation (6.B.13), is not the same as ζ_H [see Eq. (6.5.68)]. This is because ζ_H applies to particles of the *same* size. If $\mathbf{a}^{(2)}$ in equation (6.B.10) is averaged over all $\mathbf{w}_1$, as was done to obtain equation (6.5.68), one obtains (the quantity in square brackets is normalized to unity) again equation (6.5.68), remembering that in this case $\mu = \dfrac{m}{2}$.

APPENDIX 6.C

A Simple Model Fluid—The Square Well Fluid

It is sometimes advantageous to examine the properties of simple model systems so as to obtain insight into the relative contributions of different components of a physical process. For example, we have emphasized the very important role of the strongly repulsive forces in determining the pair correlation function, as well as pointing out that because of the small free volume available in the liquid collisions characterized by a small impact parameter are relatively very important. In this appendix we examine the interplay between the attractive and repulsive portions of the intermolecular pair potential by comparing the results of an analysis of the transport coefficients of a simple model fluid with experiment. For this purpose we consider a system characterized by an intermolecular pair potential of the form

$$\begin{aligned} u(R) &= \infty, & R &< \sigma, \\ u(R) &= -\epsilon, & \sigma_1 &\leqslant R \leqslant \sigma_2, \\ u(R) &= 0, & R &> \sigma_2. \end{aligned} \tag{6.C.1}$$

We shall not repeat the analysis required to obtain the results quoted below. It suffices to remark that the techniques employed are identical with those discussed in Chapters 5 and 6. The interested reader is referred to the work of Davis, Rice, and Sengers (31) for the computational details.

Let $g^{(2)}(\sigma_1)$ and $g^{(2)}(\sigma_2)$ be the values of the pair correlation function at the two discontinuities in the intermolecular potential. Then, it may be shown that the shear viscosity, dilatational viscosity, and thermal conductivity of this fluid are:

$$\eta = \frac{5}{16\sigma_1^{\,2}}\left(\frac{mkT}{\pi}\right)^{1/2}\left\{\frac{[1 + \frac{2}{5}b\rho(g^{(2)}(\sigma_1) + y^3 g^{(2)}(\sigma_2)\psi)]^2}{g^{(2)}(\sigma_1) + y^2 g^{(2)}(\sigma_2)\left[\Xi + \frac{1}{6}\left(\frac{\epsilon}{kT}\right)^2\right]} + \frac{48}{25\pi}(b\rho)^2(g^{(2)}(\sigma_1) + y^4 g^{(2)}(\sigma_2)\Xi)\right\}, \tag{6.C.2}$$

$$\phi = \frac{(b\rho)^2}{\pi\sigma_1^{\,2}}\left(\frac{mkT}{\pi}\right)^{1/2}(g^{(2)}(\sigma_1) + y^4 g^{(2)}(\sigma_2)\Xi), \tag{6.C.3}$$

$$\varkappa = \frac{75}{64\sigma_1^{\,2}}\left(\frac{k^3T}{\pi m}\right)^{1/2}\left\{\frac{[1 + \frac{3}{5}b\rho(g^{(2)}(\sigma_1) + y^3 g^{(2)}(\sigma_2)\psi)]^2}{g^{(2)}(\sigma_1) + y^2 g^{(2)}(\sigma_2)\left[\Xi + \frac{11}{16}\left(\frac{\epsilon}{kT}\right)^2\right]} + \frac{32}{25\pi}(b\rho)^2(g^{(2)}(\sigma_1) + y^4 g^{(2)}(\sigma_2)\Xi)\right\}, \tag{6.C.4}$$

where

$$\begin{aligned}
\psi &= 1 - e^{\epsilon/kT} + \frac{\epsilon}{2kT}\left[1 + \frac{4}{\sqrt{\pi}}e^{\epsilon/kT}\int_{(\epsilon/kT)^{1/2}}^{\infty} e^{-x^2}x^2\,dx\right],\\
\Xi &= e^{\epsilon/kT} - \frac{\epsilon}{2kT} - 2\int_0^{\infty} x^2\left(x^2 + \frac{\epsilon}{kT}\right)^{1/2} e^{-x^2}\,dx,\\
b &= \frac{2\pi\sigma_1^{\,3}}{3},\\
y &= \frac{\sigma_2}{\sigma_1}.
\end{aligned} \tag{6.C.5}$$

To make numerical calculations we require both the parameters of the intermolecular potential $(\sigma_1, \sigma_2, \epsilon)$ and the radial distribution function at the two points $R = \sigma_1$ and $R = \sigma_2$. The pair correlation function is most simply obtained by application of the perturbation analysis described in Chapter 2, Section 2.5.C. For the unperturbed component of the pair correlation function, it is convenient to choose the equilibrium pair correlation function for the rigid sphere fluid, and to use

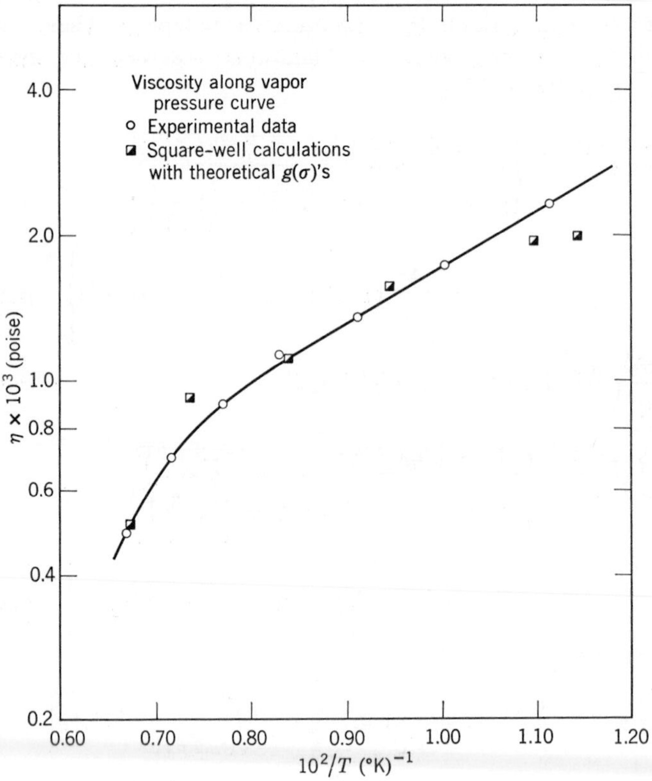

Figure 6.C.1.

the analytic solutions of the Percus-Yevick equation to provide the unperturbed function. Only the first-order correction to the unperturbed function need be retained.

The values of the parameters in the intermolecular potential for Ar were obtained from second virial coefficient data. Shear viscosities and thermal conductivities for liquid argon computed from equations (6.C.2) and (6.C.4) are displayed in Table 6.C.1 and Figures 6.C.1 and

6.C.2. The fluid conditions refer to the saturated vapor pressure line. As is clearly seen, the agreement between calculation and observation is very good, differing by only a few per cent (0–15%) except for the thermal conductivity at 45.5 atm. and 149.4°K. At this point argon is near to its critical point, and special considerations are required because of the long range correlations which exist in the critical region.

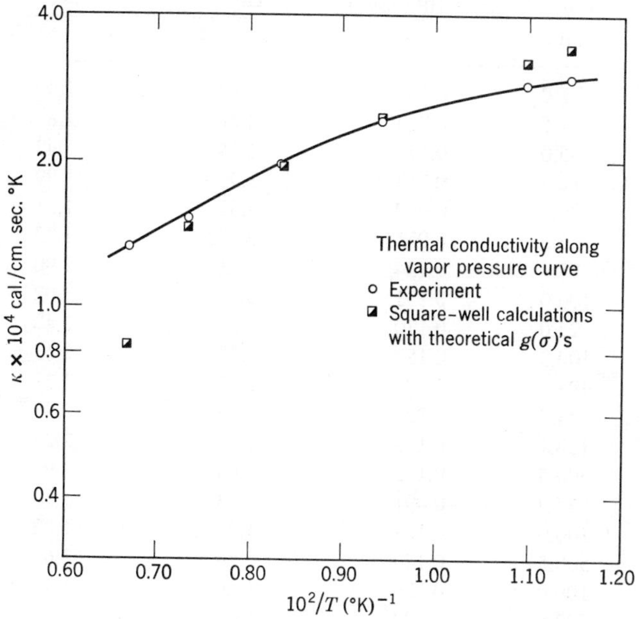

Figure 6.C.2.

A detailed examination of the theoretical calculations reveals that in this model fluid the primary role of the attractive region of the potential is to modify the pair correlation function, while the dominant fraction of the momentum and energy is transferred during rigid core encounters. That is, of the order of 70% of the contribution to the viscosity results from modified rigid core encounters. In this sense, the square well fluid does not represent a good model of a real fluid, since the rigid core contribution to the transport coefficients of argon when the potential is taken to be of the rigid core plus Lennard-Jones type, is smaller. However, examination of the calculations of Chapter 6 shows

TABLE 6.C.1

Calculated values of the shear viscosity, η, and calculated and observed values of the thermal conductivity, κ, for liquid argon at various temperatures and pressures. $g^{(2)}(\sigma_1)$ and $g^{(2)}(\sigma_2)$ were obtained theoretically using the perturbation method described in Section 2.5.C

T °K	p atm.	$\eta \times 10^2$ (calc.) poise	$\varkappa \times 10^2$ (calc.) $\frac{\text{cal.}}{\text{cm. sec.°K}}$	$\varkappa \times 10^2$ (obs.) $\frac{\text{cal.}}{\text{cm. sec.°K}}$
87.5	1.0	0.241	3.43	2.92
91.0	1.5	0.223	3.21	2.85
105.6	5.0	0.171	2.54	2.43
120.3	12.3	0.113	1.96	1.99
136.3	26.8	0.090	1.42	1.51
149.4	45.5	0.0515	0.832	1.32
91.04	23.9	0.224	3.21	2.90
91.27	100.0	0.231	3.31	3.02
105.57	25.0	0.170	2.56	2.49
105.47	100.3	0.183	2.72	2.65
105.35	498.1	0.186	2.82	3.28
120.25	24.7	0.127	1.95	2.03
120.46	100.1	0.138	2.12	2.23
120.48	500.8	0.173	2.68	2.97
136.26	27.9	0.091	1.43	1.50
135.78	100.0	0.108	1.70	1.82
135.87	500.5	0.140	2.26	2.65
149.63	100.0	0.080	1.29	1.78
149.60	500.8	0.124	2.03	2.40

that, in all cases, the dominant contribution to the transport coefficients arises from integration over the range $1.0 \leqslant x \leqslant 1.2$, so that we may conclude that it is the repulsive branch of the potential which is most important. Indeed, if we broaden our interpretation somewhat, it may be deduced from the two sets of calculations that the full potential is required to define accurately the statistical geometry of the liquid, but that the dominant mechanism of dissipation of energy or momentum arises from repulsive interactions between the molecules. The reader should note that this conclusion is consistent with the conclusion reached in the analysis of the extra dissipation due to electrostriction about an ion in a liquid.

REFERENCES

1. Irving, J. H., and J. G. Kirkwood, *J. Chem. Phys.*, **18,** 17 (1950).
2. Eisenschitz, R. K., *Phys. Rev.*, **99,** 1059 (1955).
3. Lowry, B. A., S. A. Rice, and P. Gray, *J. Chem. Phys.*, **40,** 3673 (1964).
4. Rice, S. A., and A. R. Allnatt, *J. Chem. Phys.*, **34,** 2144 (1961).
5. Allnatt, A. R., and S. A. Rice, *J. Chem. Phys.*, **34,** 2156 (1961).
6. Gray, P., and S. A. Rice, *J. Chem. Phys.*, **41,** 3689 (1961).
7. Kirkwood, J. G., F. P. Buff, and M. S. Green, *J. Chem. Phys.*, **17,** 988 (1949).
8. Zwanzig, R. W., J. G. Kirkwood, K. Stripp, and I. Oppenheim, *J. Chem. Phys.*, **21,** 2050 (1953).
9. Ikenberry, L. D., and S. A. Rice, *J. Chem. Phys.*, **39,** 1561 (1963).
10. Zwanzig, R. W., J. G. Kirkwood, I. Oppenheim, and B. J. Alder, *J. Chem. Phys.*, **22,** 783 (1954).
11. Naghizadeh, J., and S. A. Rice, *J. Chem. Phys.*, **36,** 2710 (1962).
12. Kirkwood, J. G., V. A. Lewinson, and B. J. Alder, *J. Chem. Phys.*, **19,** 139 (1951).
13. Berne, B., and S. A. Rice, *J. Chem. Phys.*, **40,** 1336 (1964).
14. Whittaker, E. T., and G. Robinson, *Calculus of Observations*, Blackie, London, p. 290 (1944); Spencer's formula reproduces a smooth function correctly up to third differences.
15. Rudenko, N. S., and L. Schubnikow, *Physik Z. Sowjetunion*, **6,** 470 (1934).
16. Zhdanowa, N. F., *Zh. Eksperim. i Teor Fiz.*, **31,** 724 (1956); *Soviet Phys. JETP* (*English Transl.*), **4,** 749 (1957).
17. Scott, R., Ph.D. Thesis, Queen Mary College, University of London, unpublished. *Program. Kam. Onnes Conf. Ion Temp. Phys.*, Leiden, 1958, p. 80.
18. Uhlir, A., *J. Chem. Phys.*, **20,** 463 (1952).
19. Ziebland, H., and J. T. A. Burton, *Brit. J. Appl. Phys.*, **9,** 52 (1958).
20. Keyes, F., *Trans. ASME*, **77,** 1395 (1955).
21. Sengers, J. V., *Thermal Conductivity Measurements at Elevated Gas Densities*, (Ph.D. Thesis, University of Amsterdam, 1962).
22. Davis, H. T., S. A. Rice, and L. Meyer, *J. Chem. Phys.*, **37,** 947 (1962).
23. Kihara, T., *Rev. Mod. Phys.*, **25,** 844 (1953).
24. Bearman, R. J., J. G. Kirkwood, and M. Fixman, in *Advances in Chemical Physics*, Vol. 1, I. Prigogine, ed., Interscience, New York, 1958, p. 1.
25. Rice, S. A., *Trans. Faraday Soc.*, **58,** 499 (1962).
26. Berne, B., and S. A. Rice, *J. Chem. Phys.*, **40,** 1347 (1964); see ref. 6 for errata.
27. Bearman, R. J., and J. G. Kirkwood, *J. Chem. Phys.*, **28,** 136 (1958).
28. Bockris, J. O'M., and G. W. Hooper, *Discussions Faraday Soc.*, **32,** 218 (1961).
29. Berne, B., and P. Gray, *J. Chem. Phys.*, **40,** 1582 (1964).
30. Longuet-Higgins, H. C., and J. A. Pople, *J. Chem. Phys.*, **25,** 884 (1956).
31. Davis, H. T., S. A. Rice, and J. V. Sengers, *J. Chem. Phys.*, **35,** 2210 (1961).
32. Rice, S. A., and J. G. Kirkwood, *J. Chem. Phys.*, **31,** 901 (1959).
33. Rice, S. A., *J. Chem. Phys.*, **31,** 901 (1959).
34. Collins, F. C., and H. Raffel, *J. Chem. Phys.*, **29,** 699 (1958).
35. Rice, S. A., *Mol. Phys.*, **4,** 305 (1961).
36. Gray, P., and S. A. Rice, *J. Chem. Phys.*, **40,** 3671 (1964).

37. Friedmann, H., and W. A. Steele, *J. Chem. Phys.*, **40,** 3669 (1964).
38. Boato, G., G. Casanova, and A. Levi, *J. Chem. Phys.*, **40,** 2419 (1964).
39. Sneddon, I. N., *Elements of Partial Differential Equations*, McGraw-Hill, New York, 1957.
40. Gray, P., *Mol. Phys.*, **7,** 235 (1964).
41. Boato, G., G. Casanova, and A. Levi, *J. Chem. Phys.*, **37,** 201 (1962); **60,** 44 (1963).
42. Rahman, A., *Phys. Rev.*, **136,** A405 (1964).
43. Atkins, K. R., *Phys. Rev.*, **116,** 1339 (1959).
44. Hirschfelder, J. O., C. F. Curtiss, and R. B. Bird, *Molecular Theory of Gases and Liquids*, Wiley, New York, 1954.
45. Cook, C. A., *Argon, Helium and the Rare Gases*, Vol. 1, Interscience, New York, 1961.
46. Davis, H. T., S. A. Rice, and L. Meyer, *J. Chem. Phys.*, **37,** 2470 (1962).
47. Green, M. S., *J. Chem. Phys.*, **19,** 1036 (1951).
48. O'Toole, J., and J. S. Dahler, *J. Chem. Phys.*, **33,** 1496 (1960).
49. Helfand, E., *Phys. Fluids*, **4,** 1 (1961).

CHAPTER 7

Comments on the General Theory of Irreversible Phenomena

7.1. INTRODUCTION

In the preceding chapters of this book we have constructed and tested a kinetic theory of liquids. Of particular importance in our analysis is the method of defining a dynamical event and of introducing the element of irreversibility which transforms the description of the system in terms of time reversible microscopic equations of motion into a description in terms of time irreversible macroscopic flow equations. Although time smoothing has proved useful and successful, it is by no means the only manner (nor the most elegant) of treating transport phenomena. It is not our purpose to make an elaborate comparison of the various theoretical approaches that have been proposed. For our purposes it is sufficient to remark that in the steady state all the extant statistical theories of transport lead to the same cluster expansion (1–5) of the integrodifferential equation defining the behavior of $f^{(n)}$, and also to the same autocorrelation function definitions of the transport coefficients (6–9) (see Section 7.3). It is our opinion that at present the only analysis which can be *practically* applied to the study of liquids is that discussed in this book. Nevertheless, there remain a number of questions of importance which cannot be answered within the framework of the formalism we have used: these include the nature of the approach to equilibrium, the possible role of non-Markovian effects, verification and clarification of the time coarse-graining hypothesis, etc.

Recent theoretical advances in the statistical mechanics of non-equilibrium systems are dominated by the studies of Prigogine and co-workers (10–12). In our opinion the work of the Prigogine school represents a generalization of statistical mechanics of comparable importance to the contributions of Gibbs. Any discussion of the approach to equilibrium must make some mention of this work even though the formalism, at the present time, is useful only for dilute systems. This statement does not imply anything more than that the formalism is hard to use for strongly interacting systems (such as a liquid).*

It is the purpose of this chapter to establish some formal connections between the general theory of non-equilibrium statistical mechanics and the more specific techniques and concepts employed in this book. To achieve this end, it is necessary to examine two different formalisms: the autocorrelation function approach of Green (6), Kubo (7), and others, and the approach of Prigogine and co-workers based on solution of the Liouville equation using the techniques of infinite order perturbation theory (10–12). These two formalisms may be demonstrated to be equivalent for the purpose of calculating transport coefficients (8).

The basic idea of the autocorrelation function analysis is that transport coefficients may be expressed as generalized susceptibilities defining the response of the system to some macroscopic constraint (such as a temperature gradient). The various published derivations all lead to the same formal expressions for the transport coefficients associated with the various fluxes. Unlike the kinetic analysis, wherein a quasi-stationary distribution function results from the balance between streaming in phase space and molecular interaction processes, in the autocorrelation function formalism the transport process arises from the decay of fluctuations in an equilibrium ensemble. Of course, the analysis is purely formal in the sense that it leads to expressions requiring solutions of the N-body problem before evaluation can be completed. At present, the autocorrelation function method cannot be used (practically) to describe strongly interacting systems, such as the liquid phase, without auxiliary consideration of kinetic equations defining the behavior of the distribution function.

The basis of the analysis of Prigogine and co-workers lies in the Fourier decomposition of the N-body distribution function, $f^{(N)}$, and the classification of terms which appear in the decomposition according to powers of t, N/V, and λ, where λ is the coupling constant of the intermolecular potential energy. In this formalism the Liouville equation takes a form which describes the transitions between different distributions of wave vectors; the transitions are generated by the interactions between the molecules, and the distributions of wave

* Because the Prigogine theory is treated in detail in the books by Prigogine (10), Balescu (11), and Résibois (12), our description will be brief and focus attention on only a few points.

vectors are the respective Fourier space representations of the distribution function. The equations are naturally ordered in a sequence which counts the number of nonzero wave vectors. To evaluate the terms in this representation, Prigogine and Balescu have invented a diagrammatic notation (10–12).

The general technique used to obtain a kinetic equation (i.e., an integro-differential equation describing the evolution of a reduced distribution function) is to sum classes of diagrams ordered in part according to the number of nonzero wave vectors. (A function of the coordinates of n molecules is expressed in terms of a Fourier transform, which is a function of n wave vectors, denoted by ρ_n.) Successively higher approximations are obtained by summing the contributions of terms with successively larger numbers of nonzero wave vectors and more complicated sequences of nonvanishing sets. This procedure of diagram selection and subsequent construction of reduced asymptotic equations constitutes the most elegant discussion of the approach to equilibrium yet devised. The salient features are the following. First, the asymptotic evaluation of the matrix elements by summing diagrams is only valid for large systems for which $N \to \infty$, $V \to \infty$, but N/V remains constant. Second, the approach to equilibrium appears in this formalism as a cascade mechanism by which the time dependence of a given Fourier component of the distribution function is related to different order Fourier components (i.e., different numbers of nonzero wave vectors). In general, the rate of change of any ρ_n is expressed in terms of the initial correlations $\rho_{n'}$, and is a sum over all transitions giving as a final outcome the transition $n' \to n$. In particular, the rate of change of ρ_0 (which is the velocity distribution function) depends upon ρ_0 through all possible sequences of transitions $0 \to n \to n' \to \cdots \to 0$, and upon the initial correlations $\rho_{n'}$, through all possible sequences $n' \to n'' \to \cdots \to 0$. The operator representing the former set of transitions is called the *diagonal* fragment, and that representing the latter set is called the *destruction* fragment. The kinetic equations so derived are strictly irreversible in the sense that the Poincaré recurrence time is rejected to infinity by the process of taking the limit $N \to \infty$, $V \to \infty$, N/V constant. However, the equations are mechanically reversible. Although the destruction fragment tends to zero rapidly compared to the approach to equilibrium, if at any time t all the velocities are reversed, then at time $2t$ the destruction fragment reattains its initial value.

7.2. THE KINETIC THEORY OF PRIGOGINE AND CO-WORKERS (10–12)

7.2.A. *The Development of the Kinetic Equations*

The very brief sketch given in the Introduction is not sufficient to form a basis for discussion of the relationship between various theories. In this section we present just enough of the detailed structure of the analysis of Prigogine and co-workers to permit discussion of transport equations and the nature of the approach to equilibrium.

The starting point of the analysis is, as usual, the Liouville equation defining the behavior of the complete distribution function $f^{(N)}$, written in the form

$$\frac{\partial f^{(N)}}{\partial t} = -i\mathscr{L} f^{(N)}, \tag{7.2.1}$$

where we have multiplied the usual Liouville operator by i for convenience. Because equation (7.2.1) is linear, the solutions of the equation are superposable, i.e., if $f_1^{(N)}$, and $f_2^{(N)}$ are special solutions of (7.2.1), then every combination $c_1 f_1^{(N)} + c_2 f_2^{(N)}$ is also a solution. It is easily shown that the operator $\mathscr{L}$ is Hermitean. Therefore, the eigenvalues λ_k corresponding to the eigenfunctions ψ_k of $\mathscr{L}$,

$$\mathscr{L}\psi_k = \lambda_k \psi_k, \tag{7.2.2}$$

are all real, and the eigenfunctions define a complete orthonormal set. The proof that the set of eigenfunctions is complete cannot be carried through in general: we shall assume this to be the case here and expand $f^{(N)}$ in terms of the set ψ_k. The result is

$$f^{(N)}(t) = \sum_k a_k(t)\psi_k(\{N\},\mathbf{p}^{(N)}). \tag{7.2.3}$$

Since

$$i \sum_k \left(\frac{da_k}{dt}\right) \psi_k = \sum_k \lambda_k a_k \psi_k, \tag{7.2.4}$$

from which it is readily found that

$$a_k(t) = c_k e^{-i\lambda_k t}, \tag{7.2.5}$$

and the formal solution of the Liouville equation becomes

$$f^{(N)}(\{N\},\mathbf{p}^{(N)};t) = \sum_k c_k e^{-i\lambda_k t}\psi_k(\{N\},\mathbf{p}^{(N)}). \tag{7.2.6}$$

Now, the eigenfunctions of $\mathscr{L}$ are complex. This follows immediately from the observation that the complex conjugate of $\mathscr{L}$ is

$$\mathscr{L}^* = -\mathscr{L}, \tag{7.2.7}$$

whereupon

$$\begin{aligned}\mathscr{L}^*\psi_k^* &= \lambda_k\psi_k^*,\\ \mathscr{L}\psi_k^* &= -\lambda_k\psi_k^*.\end{aligned} \tag{7.2.8}$$

The existence of the paired eigenvalues, λ_k and $-\lambda_k$, is a direct consequence of the reversibility of mechanics, since the transformation $\lambda_k \to -\lambda_k$ is equivalent to the time inversion $t \to -t$.

To justify the particular eigenfunction expansion we shall later use, consider the separation of ψ_k into real and imaginary parts:

$$\psi_k = \Phi_k + i\Xi_k. \tag{7.2.9}$$

It is then easy to see that

$$\mathscr{L}^2\psi_k = \mathscr{L}(\lambda_k\psi_k) = \lambda_k^2\psi_k = \lambda_k^2\Phi_k + i\lambda_k^2\Xi_k, \tag{7.2.10}$$

and since the operator $\mathscr{L}^2$ is real

$$\begin{aligned}\mathscr{L}^2\Phi_k &= \lambda_k^2\Phi_k,\\ \mathscr{L}^2\Xi_k &= \lambda_k^2\Xi_k.\end{aligned} \tag{7.2.11}$$

The expansion (7.2.6) is similar to an expansion in running waves, while (7.2.11) resembles the decomposition of this running wave into standing waves.

For the case of N free particles, the Hamiltonian function is just

$$\sum_j (p_j^2/2m),$$

to which corresponds the Liouville operator

$$\mathscr{L}_0 = -i\sum_j \frac{\mathbf{p}_j}{m}\cdot\nabla_j, \tag{7.2.12}$$

whereupon the eigenfunctions and eigenvalues become

$$\psi_{\{\mathbf{k}\}} = L^{-3N/2}\exp\left(i\sum_j \mathbf{k}_j\cdot\mathbf{R}_j\right), \tag{7.2.13}$$

$$\lambda_{\{\mathbf{k}\}} = \sum_j \mathbf{k}_j\cdot\frac{\mathbf{p}_j}{m}. \tag{7.2.14}$$

In writing equations (7.2.13) and (7.2.14) we have assumed the system to be confined to a cubic box with sides of length L. If periodic boundary conditions are imposed,

$$\mathbf{k}_j = \frac{2\pi}{L}\mathbf{n}_j, \tag{7.2.15}$$

where $\mathbf{n}_j$ is a vector whose components are integers.

Let the eigenfunctions be normalized as follows:

$$\psi_{\mathbf{k}_j} = L^{-3/2} e^{i\mathbf{k}_j\cdot\mathbf{R}_j}. \tag{7.2.16}$$

From the expansion (7.2.3), using the eigenfunctions of $\mathscr{L}_0$ as the basis set, we find the multiple Fourier series

$$\begin{aligned} f^{(N)}(\{N\},\mathbf{p}^{(N)};t) &= \sum_{\{\mathbf{k}\}} a_{\{\mathbf{k}\}}(\mathbf{p}^{(N)})\psi_{\{\mathbf{k}\}}(\{N\}) \\ &= \left(\frac{2\pi}{L}\right)^{3N} \sum_{\{\mathbf{k}\}} \rho_{\{\mathbf{k}\}}(\mathbf{p}^{(N)}) \exp\left[i\sum_j \mathbf{k}_j\cdot\left(\mathbf{R}_j - \frac{\mathbf{p}_j}{m}t\right)\right], \end{aligned} \tag{7.2.17}$$

where $(\rho_{\mathbf{k}}/a_{\mathbf{k}}) = (L^{3/2}/8\pi^3)$, and $\rho_{\{\mathbf{k}\}}$ is related to $a_{\{\mathbf{k}\}}$ by the Nth power of this quantity.

We now proceed to the study of a real system with pairwise interactions between the molecules. Let the volume of the system be $V = 8\pi^3\Omega$. Further, we rewrite the Fourier expansion (7.2.17) in groups of components having only one wave vector non-zero, two wave vectors nonzero, etc. Then,

$$\begin{aligned} f^{(N)} = \frac{1}{V^N}\Bigg\{&\rho_0 + \frac{1}{\Omega}\sum_j \sum_{\mathbf{k}_j}{}' \rho_{\mathbf{k}_j}{}^{j} \exp\left[i\mathbf{k}_j\cdot\left(\mathbf{R}_j - \frac{\mathbf{p}_j}{m}t\right)\right] \\ &+ \frac{1}{\Omega^2}\sum_{j<l}\sum_{\mathbf{k}_j}{}'\sum_{\mathbf{k}_l}{}' [\rho^{jl}_{\mathbf{k}_j\mathbf{k}_l} + \Omega\,\delta^{\mathrm{Kr}}_{\mathbf{k}_j+\mathbf{k}_l}\rho^{jl}_{\mathbf{k}_j\mathbf{k}_l}] \\ &\qquad \times \exp\left[i\mathbf{k}_j\cdot\left(\mathbf{R}_j - \frac{\mathbf{p}_j}{m}t\right)\right] \exp\left[i\mathbf{k}_l\cdot\left(\mathbf{R}_l - \frac{\mathbf{p}_l}{m}t\right)\right] \\ &+ \frac{1}{\Omega^3}\sum_{j<l<m}\sum_{\mathbf{k}_j}{}'\sum_{\mathbf{k}_l}{}'\sum_{\mathbf{k}_m}{}' [\rho^{jlm}_{\mathbf{k}_j\mathbf{k}_l\mathbf{k}_m} + \Omega\,\delta^{\mathrm{Kr}}_{\mathbf{k}_j+\mathbf{k}_l}\rho^{jlm}_{\mathbf{k}_j\mathbf{k}_l\mathbf{k}_m} \\ &\qquad + \Omega\,\delta^{\mathrm{Kr}}_{\mathbf{k}_j+\mathbf{k}_m}\rho^{jlm}_{\mathbf{k}_j\mathbf{k}_l\mathbf{k}_m} + \Omega\,\delta^{\mathrm{Kr}}_{\mathbf{k}_l+\mathbf{k}_m}\rho^{jlm}_{\mathbf{k}_j\mathbf{k}_l\mathbf{k}_m}] \\ &\qquad \times \exp\left[i\mathbf{k}_j\cdot\left(\mathbf{R}_j - \frac{\mathbf{p}_j}{m}t\right)\right] \exp\left[i\mathbf{k}_l\cdot\left(\mathbf{R}_l - \frac{\mathbf{p}_l}{m}t\right)\right] \\ &\qquad \times \exp\left[i\mathbf{k}_m\cdot\left(\mathbf{R}_m - \frac{\mathbf{p}_m}{m}t\right)\right] + \cdots\Bigg\}, \end{aligned} \tag{7.2.18}$$

where, of course, ρ_0, $\rho_{\mathbf{k}_j}{}^j$, $\rho_{\mathbf{k}_j\mathbf{k}_l}^{jl}$, $\cdots$ are functions of $\mathbf{p}^{(N)}$ and t, and $\delta_{\mathbf{k}_j+\cdots+\mathbf{k}_m}^{\mathrm{Kr}}$ is the Kronecker delta, which has the value unity when its argument vanishes, and is zero otherwise. The prime on the summation indicates the exclusion of $\mathbf{k} = 0$. We are interested in the limiting dependence of the terms in equation (7.2.18) on N, V, t, and λ as

$$\begin{aligned} N &\to \infty, \\ \Omega &\to \infty, \\ \frac{N}{8\pi^3\Omega} &= \rho = \text{constant}, \\ t &\to \infty. \end{aligned} \tag{7.2.19}$$

In this limit, we replace

$$\begin{aligned} &\frac{1}{\Omega}\sum_{\mathbf{k}}{}' \to \qquad \text{Principal value of} \int d\mathbf{k}, \\ &\Omega\, \delta_{\mathbf{k}}{}^{\mathrm{Kr}} \to \Omega\, \delta_{\mathbf{k}_x}{}^{\mathrm{Kr}}\, \delta_{\mathbf{k}_y}{}^{\mathrm{Kr}}\, \delta_{\mathbf{k}_z}{}^{\mathrm{Kr}} \to \delta(\mathbf{k}), \\ &\sum_{\mathbf{k}} \delta_{\mathbf{k}}{}^{\mathrm{Kr}} \to \int \delta(\mathbf{k})\, d\mathbf{k}. \end{aligned} \tag{7.2.20}$$

What meaning is to be attached to the Fourier components ρ_0, $\rho_{\mathbf{k}_j}{}^j$, $\cdots$? If equation (7.2.18) is integrated over $d\{N-1\}$ and $d\{N-2\}$ it is found that (taking the time factors into ρ for convenience)

$$\rho_0(\mathbf{p}^{(N)};t) = \int f^{(N)}\, d\{N\} = \varphi^{(N)}(\mathbf{p}^{(N)};t), \tag{7.2.21}$$

$$\frac{1}{\Omega}\sum_{\mathbf{k}_j}{}' \rho_{\mathbf{k}_j}{}^j e^{i\mathbf{k}_j\cdot\mathbf{R}_j} = V \int f^{(N)}\, d\{N-1\} - \rho_0, \tag{7.2.22}$$

$$\begin{aligned} \frac{1}{\Omega^2}\sum_{\mathbf{k}_j}{}'\sum_{\mathbf{k}_l}{}' \rho_{\mathbf{k}_j\mathbf{k}_l}^{jl} e^{i(\mathbf{k}_j\cdot\mathbf{R}_j+\mathbf{k}_l\cdot\mathbf{R}_l)} + \frac{1}{\Omega}\sum_{\mathbf{k}_j}{}' \rho_{\mathbf{k}_j,-\mathbf{k}_j}^{jl} e^{i\mathbf{k}_j\cdot(\mathbf{R}_j-\mathbf{R}_l)} \\ = \frac{1}{\rho^2} F_{2,N}(\mathbf{R}_j,\mathbf{R}_l,\mathbf{p}^{(N)};t) - \left[\frac{1}{\rho} F_{1,N}(\mathbf{R}_j,\mathbf{p}^{(N)};t) - \varphi^{(N)}\right] \\ - \left[\frac{1}{\rho} F_{1,N}(\mathbf{R}_l,\mathbf{p}^{(N)};t) - \varphi^{(N)}\right] - \varphi^{(N)}, \end{aligned} \tag{7.2.23}$$

where we have introduced the momentum distribution function

$$\varphi^{(s)} = \frac{(N-s)!}{N!}\int f^{(s)}\, d\{s\}, \tag{7.2.24}$$

and the mixed asymmetric momentum-coordinate distribution function

$$F_{s,r}(\{s\},\mathbf{p}^{(r)};t) = \frac{N!}{(N-s)!}\int f^{(N)}\, d\{N-s\}\, d\mathbf{p}^{(N-r)}. \tag{7.2.25}$$

The normalization of the reduced distribution functions is as introduced in Chapter 2. Now, from equations (7.2.22) and (7.2.25),

$$\frac{1}{\Omega}\sum_{\mathbf{k}_j}{}' \rho_{\mathbf{k}_j}{}^j e^{i\mathbf{k}_j\cdot\mathbf{R}_j} = \frac{1}{\rho}F_{1,N} - \varphi^{(N)}. \tag{7.2.26}$$

On integration over $d\mathbf{p}^{(N)}$, noting that

$$\begin{aligned}\int F_{1,N}\, d\mathbf{p}^{(N)} &= N\int f^{(N)}\, d\{N-1\}\, d\mathbf{p}^{(N-1)}\, d\mathbf{p}_j \\ &= \rho^{(1)}(\mathbf{R};t),\end{aligned} \tag{7.2.27}$$

and passing to the limit (7.2.19), we find*

$$\int d\mathbf{k}_j \bar{\rho}^j(\mathbf{k}_j;t) e^{i\mathbf{k}_j\cdot\mathbf{R}_j} = \frac{\rho^{(1)}(\mathbf{R}_j;t)-\rho}{\rho}, \tag{7.2.28}$$

$$\bar{\rho}^j(\mathbf{k}_j;t) = \int \rho_{k_j}{}^j(\mathbf{p}^{(N)};t)\, d\mathbf{p}^{(N)}. \tag{7.2.29}$$

Thus, $\bar{\rho}^j(\mathbf{k}_j;t)$ is the Fourier transform of the relative deviation of the number density from the mean value $\rho = N/V$. Similarly, on integration of (7.2.23) over $d\mathbf{p}^{(N)}$, using

$$\int F_{2,N}\, d\mathbf{p}^{(N)} = \rho^{(2)}(\mathbf{R}_j,\mathbf{R}_l;t), \tag{7.2.30}$$

and setting

$$\bar{\rho}^{jl}(\mathbf{k}_j,\mathbf{k}_l;t) = \int \rho^{jl}_{\mathbf{k}_j\mathbf{k}_l}(\mathbf{p}^{(N)};t)\, d\mathbf{p}^{(N)}, \tag{7.2.31}$$

* It is not necessary to include the principal value restriction on the integral here, since the integrand has no singularity at the origin.

it is found that

$$\int d\mathbf{k}_j\, d\mathbf{k}_l \bar{\rho}^{jl}(\mathbf{k}_j,\mathbf{k}_l;t) e^{i(\mathbf{k}_j\cdot\mathbf{R}_j+\mathbf{k}_l\cdot\mathbf{R}_l)} + \int d\mathbf{k}_j \bar{\rho}^{jl}(\mathbf{k}_j, -\mathbf{k}_j;t) e^{i\mathbf{k}_j\cdot(\mathbf{R}_j-\mathbf{R}_l)}$$

$$= \frac{\rho^{(2)}(\mathbf{R}_j,\mathbf{R}_l;t)}{\rho^2} - \left[\frac{\rho^{(1)}(\mathbf{R}_j;t)}{\rho} - 1\right] - \left[\frac{\rho^{(1)}(\mathbf{R}_l;t)}{\rho} - 1\right]. \quad (7.2.32)$$

The meaning of these deviation terms becomes clearer in the special case of a homogeneous system. Then, the distribution function is invariant under an arbitrary displacement of the system in space:

$$f^{(N)}(\{N + a\}, \mathbf{p}^{(N)};t) = f^{(N)}(\{N\},\mathbf{p}^{(N)};t),$$
$$\{N + a\} = (\mathbf{R}_1 + \mathbf{a}, \mathbf{R}_2 + \mathbf{a}, \cdots, \mathbf{R}_N + \mathbf{a}). \quad (7.2.33)$$

In this case

$$\rho^{(1)} = \rho,$$
$$\rho^{(2)}(\mathbf{R}_j,\mathbf{R}_l) = \rho^{(2)}(|\mathbf{R}_j - \mathbf{R}_l|), \quad (7.2.34)$$

and it follows that

$$\rho^{jl}_{\mathbf{k}_j\mathbf{k}_l} = 0 \qquad \text{for all} \qquad \mathbf{k}_j + \mathbf{k}_l \neq 0. \quad (7.2.35)$$

The invariance property defined in equation (7.2.33) when taken together with equation (7.2.18) implies that for homogeneous systems

$$\rho^{jlm\cdots}_{\mathbf{k}_j\mathbf{k}_l\mathbf{k}_m\cdots} = 0 \qquad \text{for} \qquad \sum_s \mathbf{k}_s \neq 0. \quad (7.2.36)$$

Using equation (7.2.34) leads to

$$\int d\mathbf{k} \bar{\rho}^{jl}(\mathbf{k},-\mathbf{k};t) e^{i\mathbf{k}\cdot(\mathbf{R}_j-\mathbf{R}_l)} = \frac{\rho^{(2)}(|\mathbf{R}_j - \mathbf{R}_l|) - \rho^2}{\rho^2}, \quad (7.2.37)$$

and in a similar fashion higher components

$$\rho^{jlm\cdots}_{\mathbf{k}_j\mathbf{k}_l\mathbf{k}_m\cdots}$$

can be correlated with higher order distribution functions.

If the total interaction energy, $\lambda U(\{N\})$, is represented as the sum of pairwise additive potentials,

$$\frac{\partial f^{(N)}}{\partial t} + \sum_j \frac{\mathbf{p}_j}{m} \cdot \nabla_j f^{(N)} = \lambda \sum_{j<m} \nabla_j u(j,m) \cdot \left(\frac{\partial}{\partial \mathbf{p}_j} - \frac{\partial}{\partial \mathbf{p}_m}\right) f^{(N)}. \quad (7.2.38)$$

Let $u(j,m)$ be expanded in a Fourier series,

$$u(j,m) = \frac{1}{\Omega}\sum_{\mathbf{l}} \tilde{u}(l) e^{i\mathbf{l}\cdot(\mathbf{R}_j-\mathbf{R}_m)}. \tag{7.2.39}$$

Using equation (7.2.18) together with (7.2.39) in equation (7.2.38), followed by multiplication with

$$\exp\left[-i\left\{\mathbf{k}_\alpha\cdot\left(\mathbf{R}_\alpha-\frac{\mathbf{p}_\alpha}{m}t\right)+\cdots+\mathbf{k}_\nu\cdot\left(\mathbf{R}_\nu-\frac{\mathbf{p}_\nu}{m}t\right)\right\}\right]$$

and integration over $d\{N\}$ leads to the following infinite system of equations:

$$\begin{aligned}
\Omega^{-r}\frac{\partial}{\partial t}\rho^{\alpha\cdots\nu}_{\mathbf{k}_\alpha\cdots\mathbf{k}_\nu} &= -\frac{i\lambda}{\Omega}e^{i(\mathbf{k}_\alpha\cdot\mathbf{p}_\alpha+\cdots+\mathbf{k}_\nu\cdot\mathbf{p}_\nu)(t/m)} \\
&\times\sum_{m<n}\Big\{\langle\mathbf{k}_\alpha\cdots\mathbf{k}_\nu|\delta\mathscr{L}_{mn}|\,0\rangle\rho_0 \\
&+\frac{1}{\Omega}\sum_j\sum_{\mathbf{k}_j}{}'\langle\mathbf{k}_\alpha\cdots\mathbf{k}_\nu|\delta\mathscr{L}_{mn}|\,\mathbf{k}_j\rangle\rho^{\;j}_{\mathbf{k}_j}e^{-i\mathbf{k}_j\cdot\mathbf{p}_j(t/m)} \\
&+\frac{1}{\Omega^2}\sum_{j<s}\sum_{\mathbf{k}_j}{}'\sum_{\mathbf{k}_s}{}'\langle\mathbf{k}_\alpha\cdots\mathbf{k}_\nu|\delta\mathscr{L}_{mn}|\,\mathbf{k}_j\mathbf{k}_s\rangle\rho^{js}_{\mathbf{k}_j\mathbf{k}_s}e^{-i(\mathbf{k}_j\cdot\mathbf{p}_j+\mathbf{k}_s\cdot\mathbf{p}_s)(t/m)} \\
&+\frac{1}{\Omega^2}\sum_{j<s}\sum_{\mathbf{k}_j}\langle\mathbf{k}_\alpha\cdots\mathbf{k}_\nu|\delta\mathscr{L}_{mn}|\,\mathbf{k}_j,-\mathbf{k}_j\rangle\rho^{js}_{\mathbf{k}_j,-\mathbf{k}_j}e^{-i\mathbf{k}_j\cdot(\mathbf{R}_j-\mathbf{R}_s)(t/m)}+\cdots\Big\},
\end{aligned} \tag{7.2.40}$$

where

$$\begin{aligned}
\langle\mathbf{k}_\alpha\cdots\mathbf{k}_\nu|\delta\mathscr{L}_{mn}|\,\mathbf{k}_j\cdots\mathbf{k}_s\rangle &= \\
&\frac{8\pi^3}{V}i\sum_{\mathbf{l}}\left(\frac{1}{8\pi^3\Omega}\right)^N\int d\{N\}\tilde{u}(l)e^{-i(\mathbf{k}_\alpha\cdot\mathbf{R}_\alpha+\cdots+\mathbf{k}_\nu\cdot\mathbf{R}_\nu)} \\
&\times i\mathbf{l}\cdot\left(\frac{\partial}{\partial\mathbf{p}_m}-\frac{\partial}{\partial\mathbf{p}_n}\right)e^{i\mathbf{l}\cdot(\mathbf{R}_m-\mathbf{R}_n)}e^{i(\mathbf{k}_j\cdot\mathbf{R}_j+\cdots+\mathbf{k}_s\cdot\mathbf{R}_s)}.
\end{aligned} \tag{7.2.41}$$

In equation (7.2.40), the exponent r of Ω is the number of wave vectors $\mathbf{k}_\alpha\cdots\mathbf{k}_\nu$ less the number of relations of the type $\mathbf{k}_\alpha+\mathbf{k}_\beta=0$ among the vectors of the set. The matrix elements $\langle \cdots | \delta \mathscr{L}_{mn} | \cdots \rangle$ are operators. In order that the matrix element $\langle \cdots | \delta \mathscr{L}_{mn} | \cdots \rangle$ does not vanish it is necessary that the molecule indices m, n be in the set $\alpha \cdots \nu, j \cdots s$. In fact, either

$$\left.\begin{aligned} \alpha = m = j \\ -\mathbf{k}_\alpha + \mathbf{l} + \mathbf{k}_j = 0 \end{aligned}\right\}$$

$$\left.\begin{aligned} \beta = n = s \\ -\mathbf{k}_\beta - \mathbf{l} + \mathbf{k}_s = 0 \end{aligned}\right\}$$

$$\mathbf{k}_\gamma = \mathbf{k}_t, \qquad \text{all other } \gamma, t, \tag{7.2.42}$$

or

$$\left.\begin{aligned} \alpha = m \\ -\mathbf{k}_\alpha + \mathbf{l} = 0 \end{aligned}\right\}$$

$$\left.\begin{aligned} n = j \\ -\mathbf{l} + \mathbf{k}_j = 0 \end{aligned}\right\}$$

$$\left.\begin{aligned} \beta = s \\ -\mathbf{k}_\beta + \mathbf{k}_s = 0 \end{aligned}\right\}$$

$$\mathbf{k}_\gamma = \mathbf{k}_t, \qquad \text{all other } \gamma, t. \tag{7.2.43}$$

In either case,

$$\mathbf{k}_\alpha + \mathbf{k}_\beta = \mathbf{k}_j + \mathbf{k}_s, \tag{7.2.44}$$

$$\mathbf{k}_\alpha + \mathbf{k}_\beta + \cdots + \mathbf{k}_\nu = \mathbf{k}_j + \cdots + \mathbf{k}_s, \tag{7.2.45}$$

for the matrix element to be non-vanishing. It is an important consequence that since all matrix elements $\langle \mathbf{k}_\alpha \cdots \mathbf{k}_\nu | \delta \mathscr{L}_{mn} | \mathbf{k}_j \cdots \mathbf{k}_s \rangle$ vanish unless equation (7.2.44) is satisfied, the system of equations displayed in equation (7.2.40) splits into two, independent, infinite sets of equations, one coupling all $\rho^{jlm\cdots}_{\mathbf{k}_j\mathbf{k}_l\mathbf{k}_m\cdots}$ with $\mathbf{k}_j + \mathbf{k}_l + \mathbf{k}_m + \cdots = 0$, and one coupling all $\rho^{jlm\cdots}_{\mathbf{k}_j\mathbf{k}_l\mathbf{k}_m\cdots}$ with $\mathbf{k}_j + \mathbf{k}_l + \mathbf{k}_m + \cdots \neq 0$. Let

$$\mathbf{D}_{jm} \equiv \left(\frac{\partial}{\partial \mathbf{p}_j} - \frac{\partial}{\partial \mathbf{p}_m}\right),$$

$$\mathbf{g}_{jm} \equiv \frac{1}{m}(\mathbf{p}_j - \mathbf{p}_m), \tag{7.2.46}$$

whereupon equation (7.2.40) becomes

$$\frac{\partial \rho_0}{\partial t} = \frac{\lambda}{\Omega^2} \sum_{j<m} \sum_{\mathbf{l}} \tilde{u}(l) i(\mathbf{l} \cdot \mathbf{D}_{jm}) e^{i\mathbf{l} \cdot \mathbf{g}_{jm}t} \rho^{jm}_{-\mathbf{l},\mathbf{l}}, \tag{7.2.47}$$

$$\begin{aligned} \frac{1}{\Omega} \frac{\partial \rho^{jm}_{-\mathbf{l},\mathbf{l}}}{\partial t} = &- \frac{\lambda}{\Omega} e^{-i\mathbf{l} \cdot \mathbf{g}_{jm}t} \tilde{u}(l) i(\mathbf{l} \cdot \mathbf{D}_{jm}) \rho_0 \\ &- \frac{\lambda}{\Omega^2} e^{-i\mathbf{l} \cdot \mathbf{g}_{jm}t} \sum_{r} \tilde{u}(l) i(\mathbf{l} \cdot \mathbf{D}_{jr}) e^{i\mathbf{l} \cdot \mathbf{g}_{rm}t} \rho^{rm}_{-\mathbf{l},\mathbf{l}} \\ &+ \frac{\lambda}{\Omega^2} e^{-i\mathbf{l} \cdot \mathbf{g}_{jm}t} \sum_{\mathbf{l}'} \tilde{u}(l') i(\mathbf{l}' \cdot \mathbf{D}_{jm}) e^{i(\mathbf{l}+\mathbf{l}') \cdot \mathbf{g}_{jm}t} \rho^{jm}_{-(\mathbf{l}+\mathbf{l}'),(\mathbf{l}+\mathbf{l}')} \\ &+ \cdots \rho^{jmn}_{\mathbf{k}_j\mathbf{k}_m\mathbf{k}_n} + \cdots \rho^{jmnr}_{\mathbf{k}_j\mathbf{k}_m\mathbf{k}_n\mathbf{k}_r}, \end{aligned} \tag{7.2.48}$$

where

$$\begin{aligned} &\mathbf{k}_j + \mathbf{k}_m + \mathbf{k}_n = 0, \\ &\mathbf{k}_j + \mathbf{k}_m + \mathbf{k}_n + \mathbf{k}_r = 0. \end{aligned} \tag{7.2.49}$$

The remaining members of the set of equations defining the time dependence of the Fourier coefficients are similar in form to equation (7.2.49) but ever increasing in complexity.

Thus far the analysis has been formal and we have done nothing more than re-express the Liouville equation in terms of the Fourier components of $f^{(N)}$. The system of equations is, therefore, equivalent to the usual hierarchy [Eqs. (5.3.3)] of integrodifferential equations derived from the Liouville equation.

We now digress to discuss briefly the nature of the correlations described by the $\rho^{jlm\cdots}_{\mathbf{k}_j\mathbf{k}_l\mathbf{k}_m\cdots}$: Corresponding to the Ursell-Mayer expansion of the equilibrium distribution function, we may introduce a cluster expansion of the non-equilibrium distribution function. Let

$$\varphi^{(s)}(\mathbf{p}^{(s)};t) = \prod_{i=1}^{s} \varphi^{(1)}(\mathbf{p}_i;t), \tag{7.2.50}$$

$$F_{s,r}(\{s\},\mathbf{p}^{(r)};t) = f^{(s)}(\{s\},\mathbf{p}^{(s)};t) \prod_{i=s+1}^{r} \varphi^{(1)}(\mathbf{p}_i;t). \tag{7.2.51}$$

What does factorization of the momentum distribution function imply? Consider the case of a homogeneous system. If $\varphi^{(s)}$ could not be expressed as a product of s one-particle momentum functions, there would be a correlation in momentum space between sets of molecules. Indeed, since $\varphi^{(s)}$ is independent of the molecular coordinates, such a momentum correlation would extend over the entire configuration space of the system, whatever the separation of the molecules. This is a physically unlikely situation since elementary considerations lead to the expectation that any correlation tends to vanish as the distance between particles tends to become infinitely large. Thus, it is a necessary condition that $\varphi^{(s)}$ be factorizable, i.e., that the velocity correlations and space correlations be of finite range. Indeed, it is fundamental to the theory of homogeneous systems that there exist no velocity correlations.

Consider now the definitions:

$$\mathscr{F}^{(s)} = \rho^{-s} f^{(s)}, \tag{7.2.52}$$

$$\mathscr{F}^{(1)}(1) = \mathscr{U}(1) + \varphi(1), \tag{7.2.53}$$

$$\mathscr{F}^{(2)}(1,2) = \mathscr{U}(1,2) + \mathscr{U}(1)\varphi(2) + \mathscr{U}(2)\varphi(1) + \varphi(1)\varphi(2), \tag{7.2.54}$$

$$\begin{aligned}\mathscr{F}^{(3)}(1,2,3) = {} & \mathscr{U}(1,2,3) + \mathscr{U}(1,2)\varphi(3) + \mathscr{U}(2,3)\varphi(1) + \mathscr{U}(1,3)\varphi(2) \\ & + \mathscr{U}(1)\varphi(2)\varphi(3) + \mathscr{U}(2)\varphi(1)\varphi(3) + \mathscr{U}(3)\varphi(1)\varphi(2) \\ & + \varphi(1)\varphi(2)\varphi(3).\end{aligned} \tag{7.2.55}$$

Proceeding as in Chapter 2, these definitions may be inverted to find the functions $\mathscr{U}$ in terms of the φ's and $\mathscr{F}$'s:

$$\mathscr{U}(1) = \mathscr{F}^{(1)}(1) - \varphi(1), \tag{7.2.56}$$

$$\mathscr{U}(1,2) = \mathscr{F}^{(2)}(1,2) - \mathscr{F}^{(1)}(1)\varphi(2) - \mathscr{F}^{(1)}(2)\varphi(1) + \varphi(1)\varphi(2), \tag{7.2.57}$$

$$\begin{aligned}\mathscr{U}(1,2,3) = {} & \mathscr{F}^{(3)}(1,2,3) - \mathscr{F}^{(2)}(1,2)\varphi(3) - \mathscr{F}^{(2)}(1,3)\varphi(2) \\ & - \mathscr{F}^{(2)}(2,3)\varphi(1) + \mathscr{F}^{(1)}(1)\varphi(2)\varphi(3) + \mathscr{F}^{(1)}(2)\varphi(1)\varphi(3) \\ & + \mathscr{F}^{(1)}(3)\varphi(1)\varphi(2) - \varphi(1)\varphi(2)\varphi(3).\end{aligned} \tag{7.2.58}$$

The functions $\mathscr{U}$ have two properties of interest:

(*a*) If

$$\mathscr{F}^{(s)}(\{s\}) = \mathscr{F}^{(r)}(\{r\})\mathscr{F}^{(s-r)}(\{s-r\}), \tag{7.2.59}$$

then

$$\mathscr{U}(\{s\}) = \mathscr{U}(\{r\})\mathscr{U}(\{s-r\}). \tag{7.2.60}$$

(*b*) If the set of particles s is divided into two independent subgroups, and the system is homogeneous, then $\mathscr{U}(\{s\})$ vanishes identically. For example, for two independent particles,

$$\begin{aligned}\mathscr{U}(1,2) & = \mathscr{F}^{(1)}(1)\mathscr{F}^{(1)}(2) - \mathscr{F}^{(1)}(1)\varphi(2) - \mathscr{F}^{(1)}(2)\varphi(1) + \varphi(1)\varphi(2) \\ & = [\mathscr{U}(1) + \varphi(1)][\mathscr{U}(2) + \varphi(2)] - [\mathscr{U}(1) + \varphi(1)]\varphi(2) \\ & \quad - [\mathscr{U}(2) + \varphi(2)]\varphi(1) + \varphi(1)\varphi(2) = \mathscr{U}(1)\mathscr{U}(2).\end{aligned} \tag{7.2.61}$$

Now, for a homogeneous system

$$\mathscr{F}^{(1)}(1) = \frac{1}{\rho} f^{(1)}(1) = \varphi^{(1)}(1), \tag{7.2.62}$$

so that

$$\mathscr{U}(1) = 0. \tag{7.2.63}$$

Similar demonstrations can be made when factorization occurs at a higher level.

It is clear that the $\mathscr{U}$ functions are related to the correlations between the molecules. For example, integration of equation (7.2.22) over $d\mathbf{p}^{(N-1)}$ leads to

$$\frac{1}{\Omega}\int \sum_{\mathbf{k}_j}{}' \rho_{k_j}^{j} e^{i\mathbf{k}_j\cdot\mathbf{R}_j}\, d\mathbf{p}^{(N-1)} = V\int f^{(N)}\, d\{N-1\}\, d\mathbf{p}^{(N-1)} - \int \varphi^{(N)}\, d\mathbf{p}^{(N-1)}$$

$$= \mathscr{F}^{(1)}(j) - \varphi^{(1)}(j), \tag{7.2.64}$$

and so forth. Thus, the functions $\mathscr{U}(\{s\})$ are the Fourier transforms of the sum of all coefficients $\rho_{\mathbf{k}_j\mathbf{k}_l\cdots}^{jl\cdots}$ with nonzero wave vectors corresponding to particles j, l, $\cdots$. Note that in the limit as $N \to \infty$ and $\Omega \to \infty$ with N/Ω constant, all Fourier coefficients are made to depend on N and Ω only through the ratio ρ.

It is also clear that $\rho_{\mathbf{k}_j,-\mathbf{k}_j}^{jl}$ is simply the Fourier transform of the binary correlation function $\mathscr{U}(j,l)$,

$$\mathscr{U}(j,l) = \frac{1}{\Omega}\sum_{\mathbf{k}_j\mathbf{k}_l}{}' \delta_{\mathbf{k}_j+\mathbf{k}_l}^{\mathrm{Kr}} \rho_{\mathbf{k}_j\mathbf{k}_l}^{jl} e^{i(\mathbf{k}_j\cdot\mathbf{R}_j+\mathbf{k}_l\cdot\mathbf{R}_l)}, \tag{7.2.65}$$

and so forth. In general, the only contributions to $\rho_{\mathbf{k}_j\mathbf{k}_l\mathbf{k}_m\cdots}^{jlm\cdots}$ arise from situations wherein all the molecules are simultaneously correlated. (More correctly, each molecule is correlated with at least one other molecule.) For all other configurations, the relevant $\mathscr{U}$ function vanishes. It is therefore possible to introduce a diagrammatic mapping similar to that used in the equilibrium analysis. The simplest diagrams are

$\rho_{\mathbf{k}_j,-\mathbf{k}_j}^{jl} \rightarrow$

(7.2.66)

$\rho_{\mathbf{k}_j,\mathbf{k}_l,-\mathbf{k}_j-\mathbf{k}_l}^{jlm} \rightarrow$

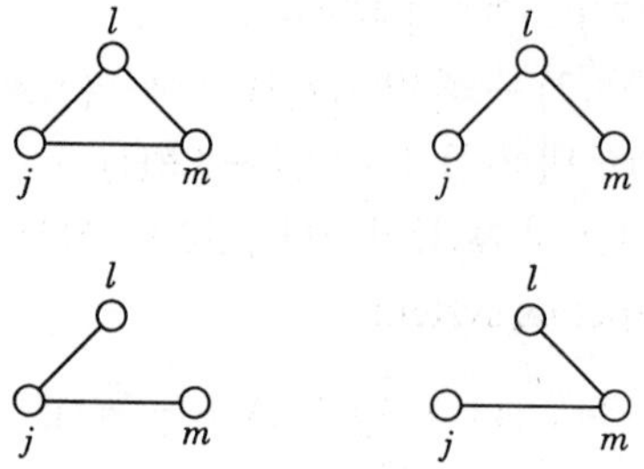

(7.2.67)

and so forth. Note that we have written equation (7.2.65) for $\mathscr{U}(j,l)$ for a homogeneous system, and the preceding diagrams also correspond to this case. In a sense, then, the Prigogine development describes a statistical mechanics of correlations. We now turn to a detailed examination of the time dependence of the distribution function.

The behavior of the N-body system is of interest both in the limit of infinite time and the limit of short time. From the long time behavior we extract information about the approach to equilibrium; from the short time behavior we extract information about the influence of finite interaction times on the molecular dynamics.

Consider first the asymptotic time dependence. This will be analyzed by examining the properties of the Fourier coefficients in the limit $t \to \infty$. Now the Liouville equation in Fourier analyzed form is to be solved by iteration, i.e., by the use of infinite order perturbation theory. The analysis takes advantage of the remarkable feature of the Fourier expansion in which ρ_0 is completely separated from the space dependent terms represented by the other Fourier coefficients. In this case, ρ_0 may be considered to correspond to a "ground state" of correlation and the space dependent terms to "excitations," where we employ an analogy to quantum mechanical problems. Now, each $\dfrac{\partial}{\partial t}\rho^{jm\cdots}_{\mathbf{k}_j\mathbf{k}_m\cdots}$ is given by a power series of the operator

$$\langle \mathbf{k}_\alpha \cdots \mathbf{k}_\nu \,|\delta\mathscr{L}_{mn}|\, \mathbf{k}_j \cdots \mathbf{k}_s\rangle.$$

To obtain the asymptotic behavior of the $\rho^{jm\cdots}_{\mathbf{k}_j\mathbf{k}_m\cdots}$ in the limits $N \to \infty$, $V \to \infty$, $N/V = \rho$, each term in the series is investigated (to each order in λ) with respect to the asymptotic dependence on N, Ω, and t. In each case only the dominant term to that order in λ is retained.

It is convenient for the subsequent analysis to represent the operators $\langle \mathbf{k}_\alpha \cdots \mathbf{k}_\nu \,|\delta\mathscr{L}_{mn}|\, \mathbf{k}_j \cdots \mathbf{k}_s\rangle$ defined in equation (7.2.41) by diagrams. In order that the integration over $\{N\}$ should not cause the operator to vanish it is immediately clear that the sets $(\alpha, \cdots, \nu)$ and $(j, \cdots, s)$ are identical and include (m,n). We shall therefore redefine the operator, in order to display this property, as $\langle \mathbf{k}_j \cdots \mathbf{k}_s \,|\delta\mathscr{L}_{mn}|\, \mathbf{k}_j' \cdots \mathbf{k}_s'\rangle$. It is now easy to see that the operator vanishes unless

$$\mathbf{k}_p = \mathbf{k}_p'; \qquad p \neq m, n$$

$$\left.\begin{aligned} \mathbf{k}_m' - \mathbf{k}_m + \mathbf{l} &= 0 \\ \mathbf{k}_n' - \mathbf{k}_n - \mathbf{l} &= 0 \end{aligned}\right\} \quad \text{or} \quad \mathbf{k}_n' + \mathbf{k}_m' = \mathbf{k}_n + \mathbf{k}_m'. \tag{7.2.68}$$

The second member of equation (7.4.68) is known as the *law of conservation of wave vectors*, and is due to the fact that the potential energy of two molecules depends on the distance between them, and is invariant to a translation of their center of mass.

The law of conservation of wave vectors gives rise to six fundamentally different types of interaction. Each type is represented by a diagram the lines of which represent only the nonzero wave vectors.

$$(a)\ \mathbf{k}_j, \mathbf{k}_n' \neq 0, \mathbf{k}_j', \quad \mathbf{k}_n = 0 \tag{7.2.69}$$

$$(b)\ \mathbf{k}_j', \mathbf{k}_n', \mathbf{k}_j, \mathbf{k}_n \neq 0 \tag{7.2.70}$$

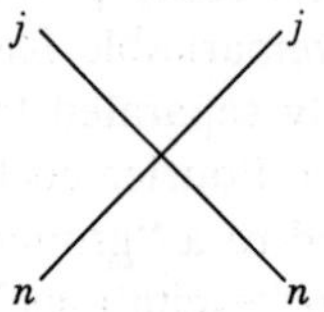

In equations (7.2.69) and (7.2.70) the number of nonzero wave vectors before (i.e., on the right of) the interaction (loop or vertex) is the same as that after. These diagrams, therefore, represent the *propagation of correlations*.

$$(c)\ \mathbf{k}_j', \mathbf{k}_n' \neq 0, \mathbf{k}_j, \quad \mathbf{k}_n = 0 \tag{7.2.71}$$

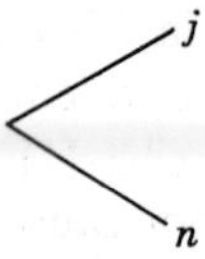

$$(d)\ \mathbf{k}_j', \mathbf{k}_n', \mathbf{k}_j \neq 0, \quad \mathbf{k}_n = 0 \tag{7.2.72}$$

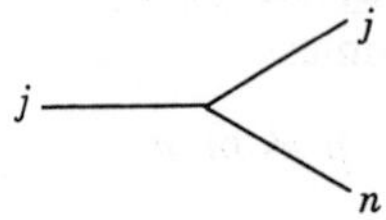

Equations (7.2.71) and (7.2.72) represent the *destruction of correlations*, because the number of nonzero wave vectors decreases, as a result of interaction.

(*e*) $\mathbf{k}_j, \mathbf{k}_n \neq 0, \mathbf{k}_j', \quad \mathbf{k}_n' = 0$ (7.2.73)

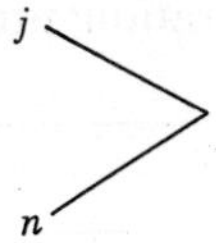

(*f*) $\mathbf{k}_j', \mathbf{k}_j, \mathbf{k}_n \neq 0, \quad \mathbf{k}_n' = 0$ (7.2.74)

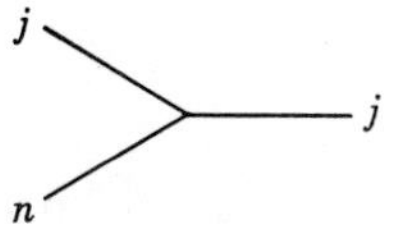

Equations (7.2.73) and (7.2.74) represent the *creation of correlations.* It should be noted that the indices on the vertices denote the molecules, not the wave vectors.

We now introduce the notation that Greek indices denote particular molecules, and Roman indices are dummies over which a summation is performed. In terms of the diagrams (7.2.69)–(7.2.74), the equations for

$$\frac{\partial \rho_0}{\partial t}, \qquad \frac{\partial \rho^{\alpha\beta}_{\mathbf{1},-\mathbf{1}}}{\partial t}, \qquad \text{etc.,}$$

take the form

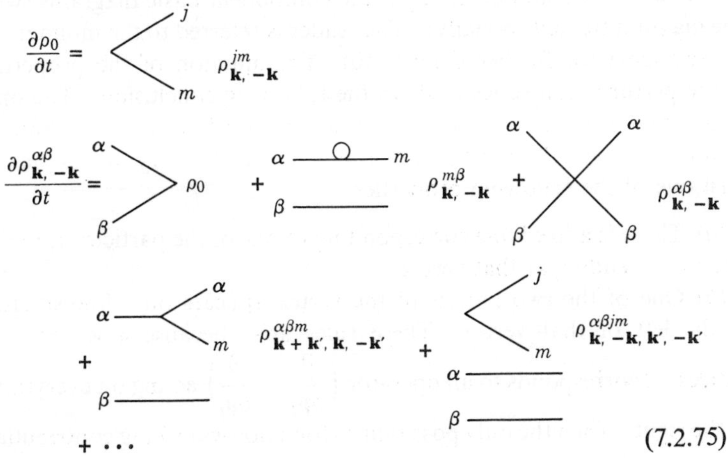

(7.2.75)

It would take us too far afield to compute the asymptotic dependence of the diagrams (i.e., the terms they represent) herein. Instead we quote the results shown in (7.2.76). [We use the notation R for the number of distinct Roman letters (dummy variables) and T for the kind of vertex, independent of R.] In the iteration procedure, the

	Diagram	Asymptotic dependence on λ, N, ρ	T
(a)		$\lambda\rho$	-1
(b)		$\lambda N\rho$	-1
(c)		λ	0
(d)	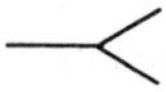	$\lambda\rho$	-1
(e)	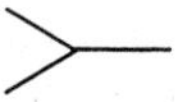	λ	0
(f)		λ	0

(7.2.76)

$\lambda^n N^R \Omega^{\Sigma T_i}$ dependence of a composite diagram can be obtained from those of the basic diagrams: n is the number of vertices (i.e., the order in λu), ΣT_i is the sum of the T_i of the component basic diagrams (with one diagram treated specially). The reader is referred to the monograph by Prigogine for further details (10). Examination of the properties of the perturbation series leads to the following conclusion: The only diagrams (terms) which give non-vanishing contributions to the Fourier components of $f^{(s)}(\{s\},\mathbf{p}^{(s)};t)$ are those in which every vertex has at least one of the following properties:

(*a*) There is a fixed line corresponding to one of the particles $1, \cdots, s$ starting or ending at that vertex.

(*b*) One of the two indices of the vertex appears on a line situated at the left of that vertex. These rules arise because a vertex with indices j, l corresponds to an operator $\left(\frac{\partial}{\partial \mathbf{p}_j} - \frac{\partial}{\partial \mathbf{p}_l}\right)$ acting on everything to the right. Then the only possibilities for a non-vanishing contribution are that integration over $\mathbf{p}_j$ or $\mathbf{p}_l$ is not to be performed, or that the operator is preceded (on the left) by a function of $\mathbf{p}_j$ or $\mathbf{p}_l$.

To describe the approach to equilibrium it suffices to derive a kinetic equation corresponding to given, well-defined, physical conditions. Obviously, different kinetic equations correspond to different physical situations. We choose, as an example, the derivation of the master equation for the case of a weakly interacting homogeneous gas. The derivation of other kinetic equations can be found in the monograph by Prigogine and in the original literature.

In the weakly interacting gas, the coupling parameter is, by definition, small. Of course, there is no real system for which λ is small for all interparticle separations. Nevertheless, the transport equation characteristic of this case displays all of the properties required for our general study of irreversible behavior.

In order to solve the Liouville equation it is necessary to specify, as a boundary condition, the initial state of the system. In the analysis of Prigogine and Balescu it is *assumed** that the order of magnitude of the Fourier components in N and λ is the same as that in the equilibrium state. Then

$$\rho_0(0) \sim \mathcal{O}[(2\pi mkT)^{-3N/2}], \tag{7.2.77}$$

$$\rho^{\alpha\beta}_{\mathbf{k}'\mathbf{k}''}(0) \sim \mathcal{O}[\lambda(2\pi mkT)^{-3N/2}], \tag{7.2.78}$$

$$\rho^{\alpha\beta\gamma}_{\mathbf{k}'\mathbf{k}''\mathbf{k}'''}(0) \sim \mathcal{O}[\lambda^2(2\pi mkT)^{-3N/2}], \tag{7.2.79}$$

for the case that

$$\mathbf{k}' + \mathbf{k}'' + \mathbf{k}''' = 0.$$

For the nonwave vector conserving components,

$$\rho^{\alpha\beta\gamma\delta}_{\mathbf{k}\mathbf{k}'\mathbf{k}''\mathbf{k}'''}(0) \sim \mathcal{O}[\lambda^2(2\pi mkT)^{-3N/2}]; \qquad \mathbf{k} + \mathbf{k}' = \mathbf{0}, \quad \mathbf{k}'' + \mathbf{k}''' = \mathbf{0}, \tag{7.2.80}$$

and

$$\rho^{\alpha\beta\gamma\delta}_{\mathbf{k}\mathbf{k}'\mathbf{k}''\mathbf{k}'''}(0) \sim \mathcal{O}[\lambda^3(2\pi mkT)^{-3N/2}] \tag{7.2.81}$$

* Such an assumption is not necessary in the more general approach described by Prigogine and Résibois (13). In particular, the Fokker-Planck master equation (7.2.84) remains valid for $\lambda^2 t$ finite, $\lambda \to 0$, $t \to \infty$, whatever the form of the correlations in $\rho_{\{\mathbf{k}\}}(0)$ (but with the general Ω and N dependence as quoted above). As will be seen later in this chapter, this independence of the Markovian master equation of the form of $\rho_{\{\mathbf{k}\}}(0)$ arises from the fact that the destruction terms (see (7.2.118)) do not grow in time. More precisely, under the limiting conditions cited, the exact master equation (7.2.129) approaches the Markovian form (7.2.84) to terms of order λ^3.

with

$$\mathbf{k} + \mathbf{k}' + \cdots \neq 0.$$

Consider now the limit $N \to \infty$, $V \to \infty$, $t \to \infty$ with (N/V) constant. What are the dominant contributions to ρ_0 in the iteration solution of the Liouville equation? Of the six basic diagrams, (*b*) is of largest magnitude in N. From equation (7.2.74) it is seen that equation (7.2.71) operates on $\rho_{\mathbf{k},-\mathbf{k}}^{\alpha\beta}(0)$, which is itself of the order of $\lambda(2\pi mkT)^{-3N/2}$, so that the total order of this contribution is $\lambda^2 N\rho(2\pi mkT)^{-3N/2}$. In general, the order of magnitude of a diagram consisting of n disconnected diagrams of the type (*c*) is of the order of $(\lambda^2 N\rho)^n(2\pi mkT)^{-3N/2}$, and this is the dominant order of magnitude in λ and N. Now consider the cycle

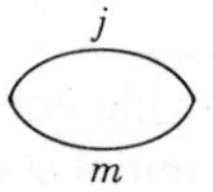

which is also of the order of magnitude of $\lambda^2 N\rho(2\pi mkT)^{-3N/2}$ [by combination of (*c*) and (*e*)]. In the limit of longtimes, which of these contributions will be dominant?

The time dependence of $f^{(N)}$ is in general very complicated. However, in the limit $\lambda = 0$ the system traverses free particle trajectories. Prigogine and Balescu have analyzed the long-time behavior of the diagrams and shown that:

(*a*) Time factors appearing in the combination $it\mathbf{k}$ do not lead to a systematic difference in the time dependence of $f^{(N)}$ and the distribution function in the free particle limit ($\lambda = 0$).

(*b*) Time factors appearing through an asymptotic integration over a long time, and which are not associated with a factor $i\mathbf{k}$, express a systematic deviation of the time dependence of $f^{(N)}$ from the distribution function in the free particle limit.

Now the cycle diagram is said to be diagonal in the sense that the correlations which are created are also destroyed, whereas the non-cyclic diagrams, such as (*c*), are said to be non-diagonal. We shall show that in the limit $t \to \infty$, the cycle is of the order of $\lambda^2 N\rho t(2\pi mkT)^{-3N/2}$ whereas (*c*), which is representative of a non-diagonal transition, contains no factor of t. Clearly, in the limit which we consider, the dominant contributions come from diagrams with a maximum number of factors t. That set of diagrams which fulfills this condition is the set of disconnected cycles,

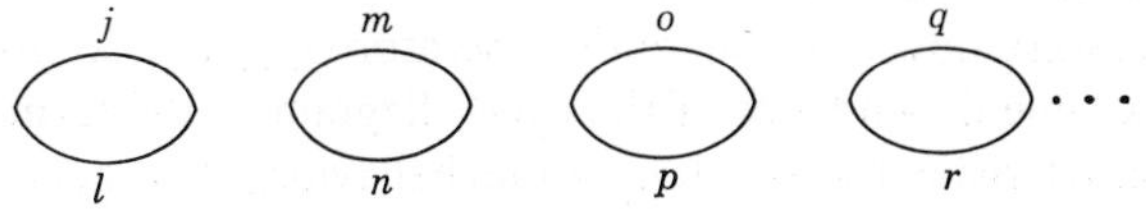

which is of the order of magnitude of $(\lambda^2 N\rho t)^n(2\pi mkT)^{-3N/2}$ for n cycles. Indeed, any non-diagonal transition will introduce at least one factor of λ without a compensating factor of t. Therefore, in the first approximation, in the limit $N \to \infty$, $V \to \infty$, $\lambda \to 0$, $t \to \infty$, with (N/V) and $\lambda^2 t$ constant, all contributions to ρ_0 other than the set of disconnected cycles may be neglected. Since there are never more than two lines in any intermediate state (correlations created or annihilated pairwise only) the Liouville equation reduces to a closed set of two equations:

$$\frac{\partial \rho_0}{\partial t} = \Big\langle_{m}^{j} \; \rho^{jm}_{\mathbf{k}_j, -\mathbf{k}_j},$$

$$\frac{\partial \rho^{\alpha\beta}_{\mathbf{k},-\mathbf{k}}}{\partial t} = {}_{\beta}^{\alpha}\Big\rangle \rho_0. \qquad (7.2.82)$$

This is a consequence of the fact that the intermolecular potential is between pairs of molecules. Thus, in the limit of large N, large t, and small λ, only binary correlations are of importance. These binary correlations, which are created by binary interactions, do not feed back information because in the limit $N \to \infty$, $V \to \infty$, (N/V) constant, the number of particles scattered by any given particle grows linearly in time and is not reflected back from any wall (infinite system). In this approximation, the dynamical description corresponds to independent binary encounters.

In the limit of long time, the dominant contribution to ρ_0 corresponds to the following:

$$\rho_0(t) = \sum_{n=0}^{\infty} \left[\int_0^t dt_n \int_0^{t_n} dt_{n-1} \cdots \int_0^{t_2} dt_1 \left(\sum_{j<m} \Theta_{2,jm} \right)^n \right] \rho_0(0), \qquad (7.2.83)$$

where $\Theta_{2,jm}$ is the asymptotic value of the operator corresponding to one cycle. By differentiation

$$\frac{\partial \rho_0(t)}{\partial t} = \sum_{j<m} \Theta_{2,jm} \rho_0(t), \qquad (7.2.84)$$

which is easily recognized to be a form of the master equation. The appearance of the sum in equations (7.2.83) and (7.2.84) derives from the independent binary encounters.

It is necessary now to evaluate the operator $\Theta_{2,jm}$ and to display the asymptotic time dependence of the cycle diagram in the form asserted to be characteristic for the long time behavior. Consider a single cycle (term in λ^2),

$$\frac{\partial \rho_0}{\partial t} =$$  $$\rho_0 \tag{7.2.85}$$

or in the expanded form of equation (7.2.82)

$$\frac{\partial \rho_0}{\partial t} = \frac{\lambda}{\Omega^2} \sum_{j<m} \sum_{\mathbf{l}} \tilde{u}(l) i(\mathbf{l} \cdot \mathbf{D}_{jm}) e^{i\mathbf{l} \cdot \mathbf{g}_{jm} t} \rho_{-\mathbf{l},\mathbf{l}}^{jm}, \tag{7.2.86}$$

$$\frac{\partial \rho_{-\mathbf{l},\mathbf{l}}^{\alpha\beta}}{\partial t} = -\lambda e^{-i\mathbf{l} \cdot \mathbf{g}_{\alpha\beta} t} \tilde{u}(l) i(\mathbf{l} \cdot \mathbf{D}_{\alpha\beta}) \rho_0. \tag{7.2.87}$$

This set of equations is solved by iteration: The solution of equation (7.2.87) is

$$\rho_{-\mathbf{l},\mathbf{l}}^{\alpha\beta}(t) = -\lambda \int_0^t dt_1 e^{-i\mathbf{l} \cdot \mathbf{g}_{\alpha\beta} t_1} \tilde{u}(l) i(\mathbf{l} \cdot \mathbf{D}_{\alpha\beta}) \rho_0(t_1), \tag{7.2.88}$$

and this may be substituted in equation (7.2.86) to give

$$\frac{\partial \rho_0}{\partial t} = \frac{\lambda^2}{\Omega} \sum_{j<m} \int d\mathbf{l}\, |\tilde{u}(l)|^2 (\mathbf{l} \cdot \mathbf{D}_{jm}) e^{i\mathbf{l} \cdot \mathbf{g}_{jm} t} \int_0^{t_1} e^{-i\mathbf{l} \cdot \mathbf{g}_{jm} t_1} (\mathbf{l} \cdot \mathbf{D}_{jm}) \rho_0(t_1)\, dt_1. \tag{7.2.89}$$

By integration of equation (7.2.89), we obtain

$$\rho_0(t) - \rho_0(0) = \mathcal{O}(\lambda^2), \tag{7.2.90}$$

so that, using the definition of the delta function

$$\begin{aligned} \pi\delta_+(\alpha) &= \lim_{t\to\infty} \int_0^t e^{i\alpha\tau}\, d\tau \\ &= \lim_{t\to\infty} \int_0^t e^{i\alpha(t-t_1)}\, dt_1 \\ &= \pi\, \delta(\alpha) + i\mathscr{P}\left(\frac{1}{\alpha}\right), \end{aligned} \tag{7.2.91}$$

which was introduced in Chapter 5, the contribution of order λ^2 to $\frac{\partial\rho_0}{\partial t}$ becomes, in the limit $t \to \infty$,

$$\frac{\partial\rho_0}{\partial t} = \frac{\pi\lambda^2}{\Omega} \sum_{j<m} \int d\mathbf{l}\, |\tilde{u}(l)|^2 \mathbf{l} \cdot \mathbf{D}_{jm}\, \delta_+(\mathbf{l} \cdot \mathbf{g}_{jm})\mathbf{l} \cdot \mathbf{D}_{jm}\rho_0(0), \quad (7.2.92)$$

where we have also set $\rho_0(t_1) = \rho_0(0)$ by virtue of equation (7.2.90). Similarly, the contribution of order λ^2 to ρ_0 is, from (7.2.89),

$$\rho_0(t) = \lim_{t\to\infty} \frac{\pi\lambda^2}{\Omega} \sum_{j<m} \int d\mathbf{l}\, |\tilde{u}(l)|^2 \mathbf{l} \cdot \mathbf{D}_{jm} \int_0^t e^{i\mathbf{l}\cdot\mathbf{g}_{jm}t_1'}\, dt_1' \times \int_0^{t_1'} e^{-i\mathbf{l}\cdot\mathbf{g}_{jm}t_1}\, dt_1 \mathbf{l} \cdot \mathbf{D}_{jm}\rho_0(0)$$

$$= \frac{\lambda^2}{\Omega} \sum_{j<m} \int d\mathbf{l}\, |\tilde{u}(l)|^2 \mathbf{l} \cdot \mathbf{D}_{jm} \int_0^t dt\, \delta_+(\mathbf{l} \cdot \mathbf{g}_{jm})(\mathbf{l} \cdot \mathbf{D}_{jm})\rho_0(0)$$

$$= \pi t \frac{\lambda^2}{\Omega} \sum_{j<m} \int d\mathbf{l}\, |\tilde{u}(l)|^2 \mathbf{l} \cdot \mathbf{D}_{jm}\, \delta(\mathbf{l} \cdot \mathbf{g}_{jm})(\mathbf{l} \cdot \mathbf{D}_{jm})\rho_0(0). \quad (7.2.93)$$

The reader should note that only the δ-function term of (7.2.91) gives a non-vanishing contribution to the cycle operator because the integrand is an even function of $\mathbf{l}$, whereas the principal part is an odd function of $\mathbf{l}$. Also note that we have first replaced the internal integral by its asymptotic value and then integrated with respect to t. As promised, the cycle diagram leads to a contribution linear in $\lambda^2 t$.

To calculate the contribution of two disconnected cycles, which is of order λ^4, we use (7.2.93) in (7.2.88) to find

$$\frac{\partial\rho_0}{\partial t} = \pi t \frac{\lambda^2}{\Omega} \sum_{j<m} \int d\mathbf{l}\, |\tilde{u}(l)|^2 \mathbf{l} \cdot \mathbf{D}_{jm}\, \delta(\mathbf{l} \cdot \mathbf{g}_{jm})\mathbf{l} \cdot \mathbf{D}_{jm} \times \frac{\lambda^2}{\Omega} \sum_{r<s} \int d\mathbf{l}\, |\tilde{u}(l)|^2 \mathbf{l} \cdot \mathbf{D}_{rs}\, \delta(\mathbf{l} \cdot \mathbf{g}_{rs})\mathbf{l} \cdot \mathbf{D}_{rs}\rho_0(0), \quad (7.2.94)$$

from which we find that the contribution of order λ^4 is

$$\frac{t^2}{2!}\left[\frac{\pi\lambda^2}{\Omega} \sum_{j<m} \int d\mathbf{l}\, |\tilde{u}(l)|^2 (\mathbf{l} \cdot \mathbf{D}_{jm})\, \delta(\mathbf{l} \cdot \mathbf{g}_{jm})\mathbf{l} \cdot \mathbf{D}_{jm}\right]^2 \rho_0(0), \quad (7.2.95)$$

and clearly the whole series becomes

$$\rho_0(t) = \exp\left(t \sum_{j<m} \Theta_{2,jm}\right) \rho_0(0), \quad (7.2.96)$$

which leads to equation (7.2.84) as stated. If we recall that ρ_0 is just the N-body momentum distribution function [see Eq. (7.2.21)], integrate equation (7.2.96) over $d\mathbf{p}^{(N-1)}$ to obtain an equation for the one particle momentum distribution function, $\varphi^{(1)}$, and then use the factorization condition (7.2.50), we are led to the master equation

$$\frac{\partial \varphi^{(1)}(\alpha)}{\partial t} = 8\pi^4\lambda^2\rho \int d\mathbf{p}_j \int d\mathbf{l}\, |\tilde{u}(l)|^2 \mathbf{l} \cdot \frac{\partial}{\partial \mathbf{p}_\alpha}\, \delta(\mathbf{l} \cdot \mathbf{g}_{\alpha j}) \times \mathbf{l} \cdot \left(\frac{\partial}{\partial \mathbf{p}_\alpha} - \frac{\partial}{\partial \mathbf{p}_j}\right) \varphi^{(1)}(\mathbf{p}_\alpha)\varphi^{(1)}(\mathbf{p}_j). \quad (7.2.97)$$

Although (7.2.97) relates $\varphi^{(1)}$ to $\varphi^{(2)}$, the factorization condition (7.2.50) leads to a closed equation for $\varphi^{(1)}$. In contrast to the usual hierarchy in configuration space, the Prigogine theory leads to a hierarchy in momentum space, for which a natural (and rigorous) truncation procedure exists (factorization). Moreover, the chaos property of the momentum factorization is propagated by the master equation, so that even beyond the justification for factorization given earlier, chaos is maintained if it is realized at a given instant. Actually, the uses to which we put the master equation herein do not require the use of factorization and the existence of the approach to equilibrium is entirely independent of any relation of the form of (7.2.50).

It must be noted that the master equation we have derived results from iterating only between the pair of equations (7.2.82) after neglecting other terms from the general system of equations. Moreover, the equation is only valid in the long time limit, which means

$$t \gg \frac{m}{\mathbf{l} \cdot (\mathbf{p}_j - \mathbf{p}_m)}, \quad (7.2.98)$$

where l^{-1} is of the order of the range of the pair interaction. Then $(\mathbf{l} \cdot \mathbf{g}_{jm})^{-1}$ is of the order of the collision time, τ_c, so that (7.2.98) becomes the condition

$$t \gg \tau_c. \quad (7.2.99)$$

Finally, we note that the series (7.2.96) is basically an expansion in powers of $\lambda^2 t$ and is formally meaningful only if $\lambda^2 t\Theta_{2,jm}$ remains finite, or

$$\frac{\pi\lambda^2 t}{\Omega} \sum_{j<m} \int d\mathbf{l}\, |\tilde{u}(l)|^2 \mathbf{l} \cdot \mathbf{D}_{jm}\, \delta(\mathbf{l} \cdot \mathbf{g}_{jm})\mathbf{l} \cdot \mathbf{D}_{jm} \ll (\mathbf{l} \cdot \mathbf{g}_{jm})t = \frac{t}{\tau_c}. \quad (7.2.100)$$

This condition implies that the interaction be both weak and short ranged for the theory to be valid.

7.2.B. *Comments on the Nature of Irreversibility*

It has already been shown in Section 3.3.A that once a master equation is obtained it then follows that an entropy function can be defined which increases in time. Here we have, from the definition

$$H^{(N)} = k \int d\mathbf{p}^{(N)} \rho_0 \ln \rho_0, \tag{7.2.101}$$

using equations (7.2.84) and (7.2.93), that

$$\begin{aligned} \frac{d}{dt} \int d\mathbf{p}^{(N)} \rho_0 \ln \rho_0 \\ &= \frac{\pi\lambda^2}{\Omega} \sum_{j<m} \int d\mathbf{l}\, |\tilde{u}(l)|^2 \int d\mathbf{p}^{(N)} (1 + \ln \rho_0) \mathbf{l} \cdot \mathbf{D}_{jm}\, \delta(\mathbf{l} \cdot \mathbf{g}_{jm}) \mathbf{l} \cdot \mathbf{D}_{jm} \rho_0 \\ &= -\frac{\pi\lambda^2}{\Omega} \sum_{j<m} \int d\mathbf{l}\, |\tilde{u}(l)|^2 \int d\mathbf{p}^{(N)} \frac{1}{\rho_0}\, \delta(\mathbf{l} \cdot \mathbf{g}_{jm}) (\mathbf{l} \cdot \mathbf{D}_{jm} \rho_0)^2 \\ &\leqslant 0. \end{aligned} \tag{7.2.102}$$

Just as in the discussion of Chapter 3, this result implies that ρ_0 approaches some function of the Hamiltonian only, and because of the assumption of weak coupling the relevant Hamiltonian is that of the unperturbed system.

It is also of interest to remark that the master equation derived is only for the special case of weak short range forces, and therefore differs from the usual master equation in detail. Indeed, examination of the operator $\Theta_{2,jm}$ shows that only the component of the force perpendicular to $(\mathbf{p}_j - \mathbf{p}_m)$ influences the motion of the pair of molecules. This approximation corresponds to the calculation, in classical mechanics, of the cross section for small angle scattering.

Of course, the chief objective of the work of Prigogine and coworkers is to provide an understanding of the nature of irreversibility. Now, the infinite set of equations arising from the Fourier analysis of the Liouville equation is time reversible. On the other hand, when in the limit $N \to \infty$, $V \to \infty$, $t \to \infty$, $N/V =$ constant, only the dominant contributions are retained, it is found that the set of equations becomes partially decoupled, and more important, the symmetry in time is destroyed. Consider the pair of equations (7.2.82).* In this approximation (as $t \to \infty$) $\rho^{jm}_{\mathbf{k},-\mathbf{k}}$ contributes to ρ_0 and $\rho^{jlm}_{\mathbf{kk'k''}}, \rho^{jlmn}_{\mathbf{kk'k''k'''}}, \cdots$, but only ρ_0 contributes $\rho^{jm}_{\mathbf{k},-\mathbf{k}}$. Schematically, the flow of coupling in the full set of equations can be displayed in the form

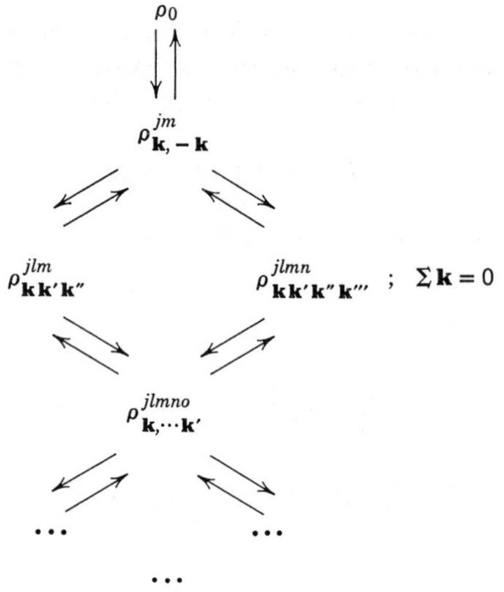

(7.2.103)

whereas the asymptotic behavior of the reduced system is of the form

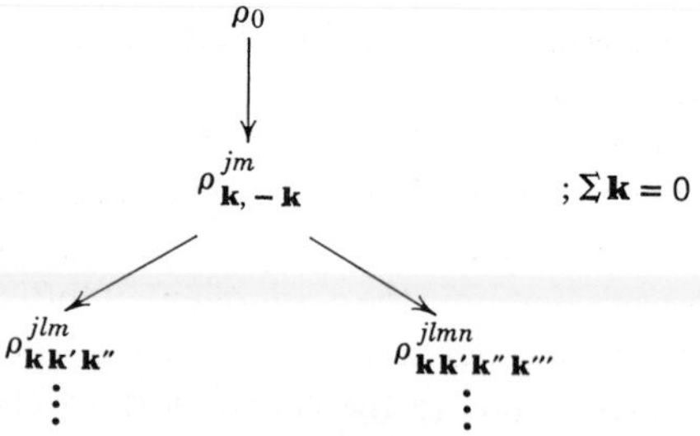

(7.2.104)

In this approximation, the fact that $\rho^{jlm}_{\mathbf{kk'k''}}, \rho^{jlmn}_{\mathbf{kk'k''k'''}}$ do not contribute to $\rho^{jm}_{\mathbf{k},-\mathbf{k}}$ clearly results in a definition of the direction of time. In somewhat picturesque language, the information contained in ρ_0 flows into higher and higher Fourier coefficients, but the reverse is not true.

* Equations (7.2.82) are essentially short time equations. For long times, ρ_0 satisfies a closed equation and $\rho_{\mathbf{k},-\mathbf{k}}$ is determined only by ρ_0 (creation fragment).

The changes of ρ_0 are not related to the changes of $\rho^{jlm}_{\mathbf{kk'k''}}$, $\rho^{jlmn}_{\mathbf{kk'k''k'''}}$, $\cdots$. The reader will realize that this passage of information into ever more complex correlations is exactly the same interpretation of irreversibility as derived from Mayer's theorem (cf. Section 3.3.C).

In the present case the approach to equilibrium [decrease of the H function, Eq. (7.2.101)] has been assured at the expense of neglecting the effect of initial correlations. It can be shown, however, that under quite general assumptions about the analytic properties of the operator representing the initial correlations (destruction fragment), the velocity distribution function still approaches equilibrium. The only feature of the general kinetic equation that is lost by neglecting the destruction fragment is mechanical reversibility.

7.2.C. *Short-Time Behavior and General Kinetic Equations* (13)

The simplicity of the theory of irreversible processes presented in Section 7.2.A arises from the neglect of all effects due to the finite duration of binary encounters. For the dilute weakly interacting gas, the correct asymptotic behavior in the limit $t \to \infty$ is obtained by treating all interactions as instantaneous, but for more general interactions or higher concentrations, this limiting condition of zero collision time cannot be used. In order to remove this restriction on the analysis, Prigogine and Résibois (13) have reformulated the solution of the Liouville equation using operator techniques. The chief advantage of the new technique is compactness.

Let $\mathfrak{P}(s)$ be the Laplace transform of the N-body specific distribution function,

$$\mathfrak{P}(s) = \int_0^\infty dt\, e^{-st} f^{(N)}(t). \tag{7.2.105}$$

If the Liouville equation is multiplied by $\exp(-st)$ and integrated from $t = 0$, to $t = \infty$, the following equation is obtained:

$$-if^{(N)}(0) + is\mathfrak{P} = \mathscr{L}\mathfrak{P}. \tag{7.2.106}$$

Equation (7.2.106) has the formal solution

$$\mathfrak{P}(s) = -i\left(\frac{1}{\mathscr{L} - is}\right) f^{(N)}(0). \tag{7.2.107}$$

The inverse of the Laplace transform requires evaluation of

$$f^{(N)}(t) = \frac{1}{2\pi i}\int_{\gamma-i\infty}^{\gamma+i\infty} ds\, e^{ts}\mathfrak{P}(s)$$
$$= -\frac{1}{2\pi}\int_{\gamma-i\infty}^{\gamma+i\infty} ds\, e^{ts}\left(\frac{1}{\mathscr{L} - is}\right) f^{(N)}(0), \qquad (7.2.108)$$

where the contour of integration is chosen such that $f^{(N)}(t) = 0$ for $t < 0$. This contour is a straight line parallel to the imaginary axis with all the singularities of $(\mathscr{L} - is)^{-1}$ to the left of the line. It is usual to define the resolvent operator, $\mathscr{R}(z)$, corresponding to the Liouville operator, $\mathscr{L}$, by

$$\mathscr{R}(z) = \frac{1}{\mathscr{L} - z}. \qquad (7.2.109)$$

Since $\mathscr{L}$ is Hermitian and has only real eigenvalues, $\mathscr{R}$ exists and is bounded for all non-real z, and the only singularities of $\mathscr{R}$ are on the real axis. Incidentally, because all the singularities of $\mathscr{R}$ are on the real axis and the exponential factor $\exp(-izt)$ appears in equation (7.2.108), any contour enclosing the real axis consisting of a line parallel to the real axis and a closed path in the lower half plane may be used.

From the operator identity

$$\mathscr{A}^{-1} - \mathscr{B}^{-1} = \mathscr{A}^{-1}(\mathscr{B} - \mathscr{A})\mathscr{B}^{-1}, \qquad (7.2.110)$$

the resolvent operator corresponding to the unperturbed Liouville operator $\mathscr{L}_0$ can be written in the form

$$(\mathscr{L} - z)^{-1} - (\mathscr{L}_0 - z)^{-1} = -\lambda(\mathscr{L} - z)^{-1}\delta\mathscr{L}(\mathscr{L}_0 - z)^{-1}, \qquad (7.2.111)$$

which may be formally solved by iteration to yield

$$(\mathscr{L} - z)^{-1} = \sum_{n=0}^{\infty}(-\lambda)^n(\mathscr{L}_0 - z)^{-1}[\delta\mathscr{L}(\mathscr{L}_0 - z)^{-1}]^n. \qquad (7.2.112)$$

As in the preceding sections, we expand $f^{(N)}$ in the basis set of the eigenfunctions of $\mathscr{L}_0$, with the result

$$\rho_{\{\mathbf{k}\}}(t) = -\frac{1}{2\pi i}\oint_c e^{-izt}dz$$
$$\times \sum_{\{\mathbf{k}'\}}\sum_{n=0}^{\infty}\langle\{\mathbf{k}\}\,|(\mathscr{L}_0 - z)^{-1}[-\lambda\,\delta\mathscr{L}(\mathscr{L}_0 - z)^{-1}]^n|\,\{\mathbf{k}'\}\rangle\rho_{\{\mathbf{k}'\}}(0),$$
$$(7.2.113)$$

where we have used equations (7.2.108), (7.2.112), and

$$\rho_{\{\mathbf{k}\}} \equiv \langle\{\mathbf{k}\} \mid f^{(N)}\rangle = \int d\{N\}\psi^{*}_{\{\mathbf{k}\}}(\{N\})f^{(N)}. \qquad (7.2.114)$$

Equation (7.2.113) is a purely formal (and therefore exact) result which in principle permits the calculation of $f^{(N)}(t)$ if $f^{(N)}(0)$ is known. The formula is convenient because $(\mathscr{L}_0 - z)^{-1}$ is simple in the Fourier representation,

$$\langle\{\mathbf{k}\}|\,(\mathscr{L}_0 - z)^{-1}\,|\{\mathbf{k}'\}\rangle = \left[\left(\sum_j \mathbf{k}_j \cdot \frac{\mathbf{p}_j}{m} - z\right)\right]^{-1} \delta^{\mathrm{Kr}}_{\{\mathbf{k}\},\{\mathbf{k}'\}}, \qquad (7.2.115)$$

i.e., the unperturbed resolvent leads to only diagonal terms. Also, the matrix elements of $\lambda\,\delta\mathscr{L}$ are subject to restrictions if nonvanishing contributions are to be obtained. For example,

$$\langle\{\mathbf{k}\}\,|\delta\mathscr{L}|\,\{\mathbf{k}'\}\rangle = \sum_{i<j}\langle\{\mathbf{k}\}|\,\delta\mathscr{L}_{ij}\,|\{\mathbf{k}'\}\rangle \qquad (7.2.116)$$

$$\begin{aligned}
&\langle\{\mathbf{k}\}\,|\delta\mathscr{L}_{ij}|\,\{\mathbf{k}'\}\rangle \\
&= \frac{i}{\Omega^N}\int d\{N\}\exp\left(-i\sum_l \mathbf{k}_l\cdot\mathbf{R}_l\right)\frac{\partial u_{ij}}{\partial \mathbf{R}_{ij}}\cdot\left(\frac{\partial}{\partial \mathbf{p}_i} - \frac{\partial}{\partial \mathbf{p}_j}\right)\exp\left(i\sum_l \mathbf{k}_l'\cdot\mathbf{R}_l\right) \\
&= -\frac{1}{\Omega}\,\tilde{u}(|\mathbf{k}_i - \mathbf{k}_i'|)(\mathbf{k}_i - \mathbf{k}_i')\cdot\left(\frac{\partial}{\partial \mathbf{p}_i} - \frac{\partial}{\partial \mathbf{p}_j}\right) \\
&\qquad\qquad \times\, \delta^{\mathrm{Kr}}_{\mathbf{k}_i+\mathbf{k}_j-\mathbf{k}_i'-\mathbf{k}_j'}\prod_{l\neq i,j}\delta^{\mathrm{Kr}}_{\mathbf{k}_l-\mathbf{k}_l'}. \qquad (7.2.117)
\end{aligned}$$

Just as in the preceding analysis, the only transitions induced by the binary interactions are those which simultaneously change two wave vectors subject to the conservation condition (7.2.68). Indeed, a corollary of this result is that $\Sigma_i\,\mathbf{k}_i$ is conserved at each interaction. Thus, the totality of Fourier coefficients with a given value of this sum evolve amongst themselves. In particular, for a homogeneous system, $\Sigma_i\,\mathbf{k}_i = 0$, and the Fourier coefficients corresponding to the homogeneous case evolve separately from those describing any inhomogeneities. It should be remarked that the use of infinite-order perturbation theory is questionable if u_{ij} has an attractive portion, since the resonances which correspond to bound states can probably not then be described. We shall not mention this problem again, but it underlies the entire analysis based on the use of the resolvent operator. Provided that there are no bound states of the potential we can proceed to discuss the approach to equilibrium.

Just as in the preceding analysis, to every term in the expansion (7.2.113) there is associated a diagram built up from the six basic vertices displayed in equation (7.2.69)–(7.2.74). To aid in the topological analysis of complex diagrams it is convenient to introduce two new definitions. Prigogine and Resibois define a destruction vertex, D, to be:

(a) Any vertex involving the interaction of two initially excited lines, and resulting in only one excited line, i.e.,

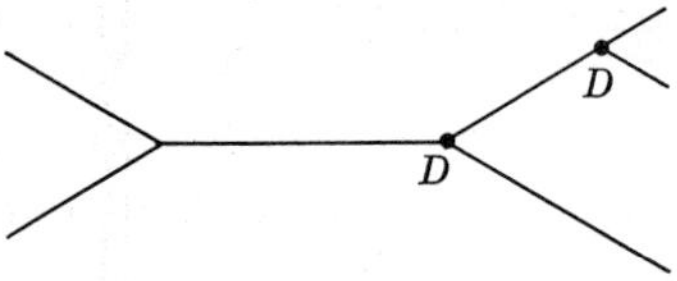

(7.2.118)

(recall that time increases from right to left),

(b) The last vertex in a set of transitions where an initially excited particle transfers its total wave vector to another particle, i.e.,

(7.2.119)

An arbitrary diagram may then be divided into two regions, the reducible region and the destruction region. The reducible region is defined to be that part of the diagram to the left (later in time) of the last destruction vertex. In the case of a set of connected successive transitions, i.e., joined cycles,  · · · , which occurs at the same time as the last destruction vertex, the entire sequence is defined to be part of the destruction region.

The topological classification just made is designed to describe the short time behavior of the system. Let it be assumed that in the initial state all correlations are of finite extension in configuration space. Then, after a finite time, particles which were initially correlated tend to separate and become uncorrelated. By definition, the destruction region corresponds to the part of the diagram where these initial correlations change in time. If it is assumed that the correlations in the initial state are limited in spatial extension to molecular dimensions, then the destruction region corresponds to events taking place during a time of the order of magnitude of a collision time. Therefore, only the reducible region can give an asymptotically growing contribution in the limit $t \to \infty$.

Let a diagonal fragment be defined as the representation of any set of transitions $\{\mathbf{k}'\} \to \{\mathbf{k}'\}$ with no intermediate state identical to $\{\mathbf{k}'\}$, and a creation fragment as the representation of any set of transitions $\{\mathbf{k}'\} \to \{\mathbf{k}\}$ in the reducible region with no intermediate state identical to $\{\mathbf{k}'\}$ and such that the number of non-zero elements of $\{\mathbf{k}\}$ exceeds those of $\{\mathbf{k}'\}$. Then the most general reducible region decomposes into either m ($m \geqslant 0$) diagonal fragments if $\{\mathbf{k}'\} \equiv \{\mathbf{k}\}$, or m ($m \geqslant 0$) diagonal fragments $\{\mathbf{k}'\} \to \{\mathbf{k}'\}$ followed by one creation fragment $\{\mathbf{k}'\} \to \{\mathbf{k}\}$ (with $\{\mathbf{k}'\} \neq \{\mathbf{k}\}$). The preceding statement needs amplification. Starting from a state $\{\mathbf{k}'\}$, the final state $\{\mathbf{k}\}$ is reached, in general, as follows. First, there may be an arbitrary number of diagonal transitions bringing the system to the same intermediate state, $\{\mathbf{k}'\}$, and then if $\{\mathbf{k}'\}$ is different from $\{\mathbf{k}\}$, there follows a creation transition $\{\mathbf{k}'\} \to \{\mathbf{k}\}$. The last transition is necessarily a creation transition, bringing the system to a state of greater correlation, because we have included all possible destruction transitions in the destruction region. Using these definitions and topological arguments it is now possible to establish the equations of evolution for $f^{(N)}$ for arbitrary time.

Consider the operators

$$\Psi_{\{\mathbf{k}\},\{\mathbf{k}\}}(z) = \sum_{n=2}^{\infty} (-\lambda)^n \left\langle \{\mathbf{k}\} \middle| \delta\mathscr{L} \left[\frac{1}{\mathscr{L}_0 - z} \delta\mathscr{L} \right]^n \middle| \{\mathbf{k}\} \right\rangle, \quad (7.2.120)$$

which is clearly the sum of all possible diagonal fragments ($\{\mathbf{k}\} \to \{\mathbf{k}\}$),

$$C_{\{\mathbf{k}\},\{\mathbf{k}'\}}(z) = \sum_{n=1}^{\infty} (-\lambda)^n \left\langle \{\mathbf{k}\} \middle| \left[\frac{1}{\mathscr{L}_0 - z} \delta\mathscr{L} \right]^n \middle| \{\mathbf{k}'\} \right\rangle, \quad (7.2.121)$$

which is the sum of all possible creation fragments ($\{\mathbf{k}'\} \to \{\mathbf{k}\}$), and

$$\mathscr{D}_{\{\mathbf{k}'\},\{\mathbf{k}''\}}(z) = \sum_{n=1}^{\infty} (-\lambda)^n \left\langle \{\mathbf{k}'\} \middle| \left[\delta\mathscr{L} \frac{1}{\mathscr{L}_0 - z} \right]^n \middle| \{\mathbf{k}''\} \right\rangle, \quad (7.2.122)$$

which is the sum of all possible destruction fragments. (In the latter case the number of non-zero elements of $\{\mathbf{k}'\}$ is always less than those of $\{\mathbf{k}''\}$.) It would take us too far afield to examine the analytic properties of these operators* so that we merely cite the properties to be used. These are:

(*a*) $\Psi_{\{\mathbf{k}\},\{\mathbf{k}\}}(z)$, $C_{\{\mathbf{k}\},\{\mathbf{k}'\}}(z)$, and $\sum_{\{\mathbf{k}''\}} \mathscr{D}_{\{\mathbf{k}'\},\{\mathbf{k}''\}}(z) \rho_{\{\mathbf{k}''\}}(0)$

* See Reference 10.

are analytic functions of z in the whole complex plane except for a finite discontinuity on the real axis. Corresponding to $\mathscr{I}m\, z > 0$ and $\mathscr{I}m\, z < 0$, the two sets of functions

$$C^{+}_{\{\mathbf{k}\},\{\mathbf{k}'\}}(z), \quad C^{-}_{\{\mathbf{k}\},\{\mathbf{k}'\}}(z); \quad \sum_{\{\mathbf{k}''\}} \mathscr{D}^{+}_{\{\mathbf{k}'\},\{\mathbf{k}''\}}(z)\rho_{\{\mathbf{k}''\}}, \quad \sum_{\{\mathbf{k}''\}} \mathscr{D}^{-}_{\{\mathbf{k}'\},\{\mathbf{k}''\}}\rho_{\{\mathbf{k}''\}},$$

are defined to be analytic in the upper half plane and the lower half plane, respectively.

(*b*) The functions defined in the upper half plane (+) and analytic in the upper half plane, have analytic continuations in the lower half plane. It is also assumed that these continuations are regular except for poles removed a finite distance from the real axis.

While the first of these conditions is an exact mathematical consequence of the definitions, the second need not hold under all conditions. For the purposes of our discussion, condition (*b*) is assumed, and thereby represents a sufficient condition on the following analysis. Of course, the particular properties of Ψ^{+}, C^{+}, and $\mathscr{D}^{+}$ depend on the particular form of the pair potential, but we shall not need such detailed information for our purposes.

We consider as the simplest case the time evolution of the velocity distribution function, $\rho_0(t)$. Clearly, there can be no possible creation fragment ending with $\{\mathbf{k}\} = 0$. Therefore, the most general contribution to $\rho_0(t)$ consists of some destruction region followed by an arbitrary number of diagonal fragments:

$$\rho_0(t) = -\frac{1}{2\pi i}\oint_c dz\, e^{-izt} \sum_{n=0}^{\infty} \left\{ -\frac{1}{z}\left[\Psi_{00}{}^{+}(z)\left(-\frac{1}{z}\right)\right]^n \right\}$$
$$\times \left[\rho_0(0) + \sum_{\{\mathbf{k}''\}\neq 0} \mathscr{D}^{+}_{0,\{\mathbf{k}''\}}(z)\rho_{\{\mathbf{k}''\}}(0)\right], \qquad (7.2.123)$$

where we have used equation (7.2.115) in the $\mathbf{k} = 0$ limit. Of course, since all terms have been included, equation (7.2.123) can also be taken as a definition of the Laplace transform of $\rho_0(t)$. Now consider an operator related to the integrand of equation (7.2.123) and defined by

$$D_{00}{}^{+}(z) = \sum_{n=0}^{\infty}\left(-\frac{1}{z}\right)\left[\Psi_{00}{}^{+}(z)\left(-\frac{1}{z}\right)\right]^n, \qquad (7.2.124)$$

which may be manipulated into the form

$$D_{00}{}^{+}(z) = -\frac{1}{z} - \frac{1}{z}\Psi_{00}{}^{+}(z)\, D_{00}{}^{+}(z). \qquad (7.2.125)$$

Substitution of equations (7.2.124) and (7.2.125) into equation (7.2.123), followed by differentiation with respect to time gives

$$\frac{\partial \rho_0}{\partial t} = -\frac{1}{2\pi}\oint_c dz\, e^{-izt} \sum_{\{\mathbf{k}''\}\neq 0} \mathscr{D}^{+}_{0,\{\mathbf{k}''\}}(z)\rho_{\{\mathbf{k}''\}}(0)$$
$$-\frac{1}{2\pi}\oint_c dz\, e^{-izt}\Psi_{00}{}^{+}(z)\, D_{00}{}^{+}(z)\left[\rho_0(0) + \sum_{\{\mathbf{k}''\}\neq 0} \mathscr{D}^{+}_{0,\{\mathbf{k}''\}}\rho_{\{\mathbf{k}''\}}(0)\right]. \tag{7.2.126}$$

Finally, use of the two Laplace transforms

$$\mathfrak{D}_0(t, \rho_{\{\mathbf{k}''\}}(0)) = -\frac{1}{2\pi}\oint_c dz\, e^{-izt} \sum_{\{\mathbf{k}''\}\neq 0} \mathscr{D}^{+}_{0,\{\mathbf{k}''\}}(z)\rho_{\{\mathbf{k}''\}}(0), \tag{7.2.127}$$

$$G_{00}(\tau) = \frac{1}{2\pi i}\oint_c dz\, e^{-iz\tau}\Psi_{00}^{+}(z), \tag{7.2.128}$$

and of the convolution theorem of the Laplace transform on the second term of the right-hand side of equation (7.2.126) leads to the equation

$$\frac{\partial \rho_0(t)}{\partial t} = \mathfrak{D}_0(t, \rho_{\{\mathbf{k}''\}}(0)) + \int_0^t G_{00}(t - t')\rho_0(t')\, dt'. \tag{7.2.129}$$

The exact master equation (7.2.129) describes the time evolution of ρ_0 for all time. The structure of the equation is very simple: the inhomogeneous term $\mathfrak{D}_0$ gives the contribution, at time t, of the initially excited Fourier components which through interaction decay towards a state with no correlations; the second term has a non-Markovian structure so that $\dfrac{\partial \rho_0}{\partial t}$ depends upon $\rho_0(t')$ for times $t' < t$, and is representative of the fact that ρ_0 in general changes *during* a collision. Note that all the effects of the initial correlations and initial conditions appear in the term $\mathfrak{D}_0$, while for the case we are considering G_{00} refers only to diagonal fragments. A kinetic equation for the nondiagonal Fourier components, $\rho_{\{\mathbf{k}\}}(t)$, may be obtained by methods similar to those used above. For this and other applications the reader is referred to the monograph by Prigogine and the original literature.

The first use to which the general master equation can be put is the examination of kinetic equations in the limit $t \to \infty$. It may be shown that in this limit, for the case of the weakly coupled homogeneous gas, the kinetic equation becomes just equation (7.2.84). In the transition to the limit it is seen that not only do all the effects contained in

$\mathfrak{D}_0$ wash out, but also that all effects arising from the finite duration of the binary encounters still do not prevent the kinetic equation being Markovian in the limit $t \to \infty$. For example, the phenomenological transport coefficients involve only the asymptotic cross sections defined by $\Psi^+(0)$, and no terms appear which are related to the duration of an encounter.*

To demonstrate this we consider a simple system in which only pairwise interactions need be considered. Then, neglecting $\mathfrak{D}_0$ (see later comments),

$$\frac{\partial \rho_0(t)}{\partial t} = \int_0^t G_{00}(t - t')\rho_0(t')\, dt', \tag{7.2.130}$$

and to order of terms referring only to binary interactions,

$$G_{00}(\tau) = \frac{1}{2\pi i} \oint_c e^{-iz\tau} \Psi_{00}^{+(2)}(z)\, dz, \tag{7.2.131}$$

$$\Psi_{00}^{+(2)}(z) = \left\langle \mathbf{0} \middle| \delta\mathscr{L} \frac{1}{\mathscr{L}_0 - z} \delta\mathscr{L} \middle| \mathbf{0} \right\rangle. \tag{7.2.132}$$

The operator $\Psi_{00}^{+(2)}(z)$ corresponds to all possible disjoint binary encounters, i.e., to the series of disjoint but successive cycle diagrams. Now, by a change of variable,

$$\frac{\partial \rho_0(t)}{\partial t} = \int_0^t G_{00}(\tau)\rho_0(t - \tau)\, d\tau \tag{7.2.133}$$

and expanding $\rho_0(t - \tau)$ in a Taylor's series,

$$\rho_0(t - \tau) = \rho_0(t) - \tau\left(\frac{\partial \rho_0}{\partial t}\right) + \frac{\tau^2}{2}\left(\frac{\partial^2 \rho_0}{\partial t^2}\right) + \cdots, \tag{7.2.134}$$

whereupon

$$\frac{\partial \rho_0(t)}{\partial t} = \int_0^t G_{00}(\tau)\rho_0(t)\, d\tau - \int_0^t G_{00}(\tau)\tau\left(\frac{\partial \rho_0(t)}{\partial t}\right) d\tau + \cdots. \tag{7.2.135}$$

In the long time limit, $\dfrac{\partial \rho_0}{\partial t}$ is given by equation (7.2.84), showing that the term in $\dfrac{\partial \rho_0}{\partial t}$ leads to a contribution of order λ^2 higher than the first term. To lowest order,

$$\frac{\partial \rho_0(t)}{\partial t} = \int_0^\infty G_{00}(\tau)\rho_0(t)\, d\tau = i\Psi_{00}^{+(2)}(+i0)\rho_0(t), \tag{7.2.136}$$

* The bulk viscosity must be considered separately.

where the last line of equation (7.2.136) is obtained by integrating equation (7.2.131) over $d\tau$ and evaluating the residue at $z = +i0$. Corrections to equation (7.2.136) appear first in the term proportional to $\left(\frac{\partial \rho_0}{\partial t}\right)$. This term contains

$$\int_0^\infty G_{00}(\tau)\tau\, d\tau = \frac{\partial}{\partial z} \Psi_{00}^{+(2)}(z)\bigg|_{z=+i0,} \tag{7.2.137}$$

again using equation (7.2.131) and the residue theorem. Limiting attention to the term linear in τ, we may make the approximation

$$\begin{aligned}\frac{\partial \rho_0(t)}{\partial t} &= \left[\int_0^\infty G_{00}(\tau)\, d\tau\right]\rho_0(t) - \left[\int_0^\infty G_{00}(\tau)\tau\, d\tau\right]\left(\frac{\partial \rho_0}{\partial t}\right) + \cdots \\ &\cong \left[\int_0^\infty G_{00}(\tau)\, d\tau - \int_0^\infty G_{00}(\tau)\tau\, d\tau \int_0^\infty G_{00}(\tau')\, d\tau' + \cdots\right]\rho_0(t) \\ &= \left[1 + \left[\frac{\partial}{\partial z}\Psi_{00}^{+(2)}(z)\right]_{z=+i0} + \cdots\right] i\Psi_{00}^{+(2)}(+i0)\rho_0(t).\end{aligned} \tag{7.2.138}$$

Now, $\Psi_{00}^{+(2)}$ represents the asymptotic binary cross section. Since

$$\left[\frac{\partial}{\partial z}\Psi_{00}^{+(2)}(z)\right]_{z=+i0}$$

arises from the term in $\frac{\partial \rho_0}{\partial t}$ it is readily seen that in a stationary state only the asymptotic cross section enters the kinetic equation, and all effects of the finite duration of a collision disappear.

The appearance of the time convolution in the generalized master equation (7.2.129) specifically includes contributions to $(\partial\rho_0(t)/\partial t)$ from $\rho_0(t')$ for $t' \leqslant t$, with a weight $G_{00}(t - t')$. The behavior of $G_{00}(t - t')$ is determined by the poles of $\Psi_{00}{}^{+}(z)$, which are themselves determined by the intermolecular forces, density, etc., but *not* by the initial state of the system. Thus, the role of the convolution as such will only be important for times of the order of the interaction time τ_c, giving rise to what we have previously called transient effects. For $t \gg \tau_c$, the velocity distribution will vary only a little during τ_c, and the operator

$$\int_0^t G_{00}(t - t')\, dt'$$

will be approximately independent of t. The kinetic equation (7.2.129) will then have the Markovian form

$$\frac{\partial \rho_0}{\partial t} = \mathscr{G}_{00}\rho_0, \tag{7.2.139}$$

where the operator $\mathscr{G}_{00}$ is given by

$$\mathscr{G}_{00} = \int_0^\infty G_{00}(t - t')\, dt'. \tag{7.2.140}$$

At this stage, correlations over distances of the order $(p/m\tau_c)$ will have been destroyed and the system will be evolving in the kinetic regime.

This description bears a considerable resemblance to the role which was assigned to the time coarse graining in Section 5.2, where, in order to develop an explicit representation of $\mathscr{G}_{00}$, a mechanism for the interactions was proposed. Equally important is the difference between the coarse graining proposed by Kirkwood and the way in which $\mathscr{G}_{00}$ is reached. The simple form of coarse graining used in Chapter 5 involves an unweighted time average, while $\mathscr{G}_{00}$ is the result of a complex weighting determined by the poles of $\Psi_{00}^{+}(z)$. It is possible that a more penetrating analysis than that given in Section 5.2 of the way in which a Markovian process can be extracted from a high order, non-Markovian process would throw some light upon the problems we have encountered.

The method used to obtain a master equation for the velocity distribution function may also be used, with slight extension, to describe the time evolution of the molecular correlations. Again, a non-Markovian equation is found to hold for all t, reducing to a Markovian equation in the limit $t \to \infty$.

In brief, then:

(*a*) The general kinetic equation is non-Markovian.

(*b*) For times long compared to the duration of an encounter (and to other characteristic times in more general cases) it reduces to a Markovian equation, which may or may not require correction for effects due to the finite duration of an encounter.

(*c*) For quasi-stationary situations, only the asymptotic form of the diagonal fragment enters the collision operator.

Thus, the form of the kinetic equation depends on the type of process being described and on the time scale of interest. The reader should compare this remark with the discussion of Chapters 3 and 4, especially those comments concerning the spin–echo experiment and the probability after effect.

It is interesting to compare the Kirkwood coarse graining hypothesis with the neglect of the initial correlations described by $\mathfrak{D}_0$ and the transition to Markovian behavior. First, it should be noted that $\mathfrak{D}_0$ tends to zero as t increases for the reason that correlations of finite extent in the initial state can only interact for a finite time. Indeed, if the range of the correlations is of molecular dimensions, then the lifetime of the initial correlations is of the order of an interaction time.* Second, the effect of the non-Markovian kernel is to connect the distribution function to itself over times of the order of the duration of an encounter. Now the fundamental idea involved in the use of coarse graining is that the dynamical event in τ is independent of prior dynamical events. This means that on the time scale chosen, $\mathfrak{D}_0$ must vanish and that the time integral involving $G_{00}(\tau)$ must approach a limit independent of τ.

Consider the first requirement. In Chapter 5 we remarked that if the distribution function returned to the form characteristic of the local environment on a time scale short compared to τ, then the process defined by time smoothing became a Markov process. Moreover, for the case of a perturbation in momentum space, it was shown that the singlet kinetic equation is consistent with this condition. It is clear that, in effect, the calculation of the relaxation time for a perturbation in momentum space is equivalent to the calculation of the lifetime of the correlations in a specified initial state. The consistency in this regard shows that $\mathscr{D}_0$ can be neglected under the conditions described by the Rice-Allnatt equation and that the use of time coarse graining does lead, as expected, to $\mathfrak{D}_0 = 0$. Of course this is shown only for a special case, but the physical description is clear enough that the argument can be extended. For some states $\mathfrak{D}_0$ cannot be neglected (spin–echo experiment) and each situation must be separately analyzed. It may be concluded, however, that for the liquids studied in this book coarse graining does lead to an equation from which all information about the initial correlations has been removed.

Consider now the second requirement. For the case of a stationary state, such as is characteristic of the study of steady state transport phenomena, it has been shown that the effects of finite duration of an

* The lifetime of the correlations is, in fact, of the order of a relaxation time. Nevertheless, the destruction term vanishes in an interaction time.

interaction do not appear and only the asymptotic form of the interaction operator is required.* The general theorem is proved using a Taylor expansion of the distribution function about some origin in time and noting that the correction to the asymptotic zero duration collision operator arises from the first time derivative of the distribution function [see Eq. 7.2.138)]. Under conditions characterizing a stationary state the derivative term may be neglected, leading to the result cited.

There are many other general theorems which may be proven within the formalism outlined. For example, it may be shown that the Maxwell-Boltzmann distribution is a stationary solution of the asymptotic master equation, that the time dependent correlations approach the Mayer equilibrium correlations described in Chapter 2, etc. (10). In addition, connections between the general theory and other theories are established through demonstrating the identity of all terms in the cluster expansion of the integrodifferential equation defining the properties of $f^{(1)}$, and by showing that the autocorrelation function formulas for the transport coefficients are consistent with the general theory. For these and other results the reader is referred to the literature.

We conclude our discussion of the theory of Prigogine and coworkers by a discussion on the relationship of this theory to the classic paradoxes stated in Chapter 3. The Poincaré recurrence paradox is easily eliminated. For, the recurrence time becomes extremely large when the number of degrees of freedom of the system becomes itself large. In the Prigogine analysis, only the limit of an infinite system is considered, thereby rejecting the Poincaré recurrence time to infinity so that it plays no role. Incidentally, the passage to the limit $N \to \infty$, $V \to \infty$, $N/V = \rho$ is fundamental to the analysis, for the analytic behavior of the resolvent operator depends critically on the existence

* More precisely, the effects of the finite duration of a collision do not appear in the collision operator, Ψ_{00}^{+}. Résibois and Davis (*J. Chem. Phys.*, **40,** 3276 (1964)), in an incisive and elegant study of the electrical conductivity of a weakly coupled system of charged particles, show that the appropriate Fokker-Planck equation contains a contribution describing the long range interactions between the ions (which leads to the limiting laws of electrolyte behavior) which clearly corresponds to an effect of the external field during the finite duration of a collision. It is clear that this is the expected result when the pair interaction is of such long range that particles are effectively in collision over a very large spatial domain and for a very long time. In the Résibois-Davis analysis, the short-range interactions, described by Ψ_{00}^{+}, do not contain any effects of the finite (but now very short) duration of encounters at small distances of approach of the pair of particles.

of a continuous spectrum for $\mathscr{L}$. It is only in this limit that sums of the form

$$\sum_{\{\mathbf{k}\}} \langle \mathbf{0}| \, \delta\mathscr{L}_{mn} \, |\{\mathbf{k}\}\rangle(\mathbf{k}\cdot\mathbf{g}_{mn} - z)^{-1}\langle\{\mathbf{k}\}| \, \delta\mathscr{L}_{mn} \, |\mathbf{0}\rangle$$

can be replaced by integrals over $d\mathbf{k}$. In the case of a discrete spectrum, such as would correspond to a finite volume, the resolvent would only have isolated singularities on the real axis, and there would be no discontinuity on crossing the real axis (except at isolated singularities).

Far more interesting than the recurrence time paradox is the reversibility paradox, also discussed in Chapter 3. In the analysis discussed here the effect of all initial correlations is contained in $\mathfrak{D}_0$. If the trajectories of all particles are reversed and the resultant motion described by the equation containing $\mathfrak{D}_0$ (7.2.129), then reversibility is preserved. But it may be shown that

$$\lim_{\tau\to\infty} C_{\{\mathbf{k}\},\{\mathbf{k}'\}}(\tau) \to 0, \tag{7.2.141}$$

because initial correlations are dissipated by interactions, and the newly created correlations are then in turn dissipated by new interactions, etc. Also,

$$\lim_{\tau\to\infty} G_{\{\mathbf{k}\},\{\mathbf{k}'\}}(\tau) \to 0, \tag{7.2.142}$$

because the duration of an encounter is always finite, and

$$\lim_{\tau\to\infty} \mathfrak{D}_{\{\mathbf{k}\}}(\tau) \to 0, \tag{7.2.143}$$

because when the correlations in the initial state are of finite extent in configuration space, initially excited states can only interact for a finite time. On the other hand, it is precisely the neglect of the destruction term $\mathfrak{D}_0$ which is the important step in deriving an irreversible equation. Thus, the time reversed states defined by a time reversed kinetic equation in which the term $\mathfrak{D}_0$ is omitted are of a completely different nature from the states which were initially present. For this case, then, time reversibility is not obtained. Once again, the reader should compare this argument with the comments made in Chapter 3, especially with reference to the length and complexity of the correlation history, which it is necessary to know before time reversibility may be attained.

We therefore see that the general theory of irreversibility quantifies and clarifies our understanding of the nature of dissipative processes, but otherwise confirms the qualitative notions introduced earlier. The enormous advantage of the general theory lies in the quantification scheme, as it now appears possible to describe the time evolution of distribution functions (and thereby both microscopic and macroscopic properties of matter) for all times. It is to be expected that thereby many new phenomena will be discovered, and many well known phenomena will be better understood and more fundamentally interpreted.

7.3. THE CORRELATION FUNCTION FORMALISM

An alternative to the analysis described in the first part of this chapter has developed concurrently with it. Stimulated perhaps by the expression for the friction coefficient* obtained by Kirkwood (14) (see Sections 4.5.B and 5.6), which is essentially the time integral of a force autocorrelation function, the essential features of this formalism were first proposed by M. S. Green (6). The transport coefficients which appear in the correlation function formalism fall into two distinct classes. Namely, those which are associated with the response of a system to externally applied conservative forces, and those which cannot be so associated. Of the former type, rigorous expressions for the transport coefficients were first obtained by Kubo (7).† An obvious example is the electrical conductivity. The latter class includes transport processes which result from non-uniformities in a system, of which an example is the transport of momentum in a non-uniform velocity field (viscosity coefficient). In this case, the difficulty of representing non-mechanical disturbances in terms of some sort of perturbation to the system Hamiltonian has led to a number of alternative formulations of the problem (6,9,15–23) and no rigorous derivation of the expressions for the transport coefficients has yet been given. In the subsequent sections of this chapter we shall attempt to display the essential features of both classes of transport coefficients.

* In the present context the friction coefficient should be regarded as a diffusion (i.e., transport) coefficient in momentum space.

† Expressions for transport coefficients of *both* types are often referred to as Kubo coefficients.

7.3.A. *The Response of a System to a Mechanical Disturbance*

A system subjected to a mechanical disturbance is supposed to be one whose Hamiltonian, H', may be expressed as the sum of an equilibrium (undisturbed) part, $H(\Gamma_N)$, and a small (possibly time dependent) part, $\delta H(\Gamma_N;t)$, due to an externally applied conservative force. Thus the Hamiltonian, $H'(\Gamma_N;t)$, of the system is

$$H'(\Gamma_N;t) = H(\Gamma_N) + \delta H(\Gamma_N;t). \tag{7.3.1}$$

It is assumed that the perturbation δH has the form

$$\delta H = -A(\Gamma_N)F_A(t), \tag{7.3.2}$$

where $A(\Gamma_N)$ is a function of the phase only, and $F_A(t)$ is a function of time only. As an example consider the coupling of an electric field to the charges in a system. The assumption (7.3.2) applies only if the field is uniform in space and if the rapidity with which the field changes is not so great that retardation effects become important. Let e_i be the charge on molecule i. Then

$$A(\Gamma_N) = \sum_{i=1}^{N} e_i\mathbf{R}_i,$$

and

$$\delta H = -\sum_{i=1}^{N} e_i\mathbf{R}_i \cdot \mathbf{E},$$

where

$$F_A(t) = \mathbf{E}$$

is the electric field strength. The time dependence of $F_A(t)$ is usually regarded as containing a "switching-on" factor, $\exp(\epsilon t)$ (with $\epsilon > 0$ and $\epsilon \to 0$), so that at some time in the remote past the system is assumed to have been undisturbed.

In analogy to equation (7.3.1) we define a Liouville operator, $\mathscr{L}'$, for the system as

$$\mathscr{L}' = \mathscr{L} + \delta\mathscr{L}(t), \tag{7.3.3}$$

where $\mathscr{L}$ describes the evolution of the undisturbed system and $\delta\mathscr{L}(t)$ the effect of the external field. It is convenient to specify the structure of $\delta\mathscr{L}(t)$ more precisely. Corresponding to the definition (7.3.2) of δH, therefore, we set

$$\mathscr{L}_A = i[A, \cdots], \tag{7.3.4}$$

so that

$$\begin{aligned}\delta\mathscr{L}(t) &= i[\delta H, \cdots] \\ &= -\mathscr{L}_A F_A(t),\end{aligned} \tag{7.3.5}$$

where the square bracket denotes a Poisson bracket as used, for instance, in equation (3.2.19).

We now seek a formal solution, $f^{(N)}$, of the Liouville equation (7.2.1) which may be expressed in the form

$$f^{(N)} = f_0^{(N)} + \delta f^{(N)}, \tag{7.3.6}$$

where $f_0^{(N)}$ is the solution for the undisturbed system:

$$\mathscr{L} f_0^{(N)} = 0. \tag{7.3.7}$$

Substitution of equations (7.3.3)–(7.3.7) in equation (7.2.1) immediately yields the equation

$$\left(\frac{\partial}{\partial t} + i\mathscr{L}\right) \delta f^{(N)} = i\mathscr{L}_A(f_0^{(N)} + \delta f^{(N)})F_A(t), \tag{7.3.8}$$

of which it is clear that $\exp(it\mathscr{L})$ is an integrating factor. Thus, after multiplication on the left by $\exp(it\mathscr{L})$ and an integration over t, use of the boundary condition $\delta f^{(N)}(\Gamma_N; -\infty) = 0$ leads to

$$\delta f^{(N)}(t) = i\int_{-\infty}^{t} \exp[i(s-t)\mathscr{L}]\mathscr{L}_A(f_0^{(N)} + \delta f^{(N)}(s))F_A(s)\, ds \tag{7.3.9}$$

for the solution of equation (7.3.8). Since $\delta f^{(N)}$ is assumed to be small, depending essentially on the presence of the driving force $F_A(t)$, it can be isolated on the left-hand side of equation (7.3.9) by iteration. We are only concerned here with the linear response; that is, the first-order term in $F_A(t)$. To this order,

$$\delta f^{(N)}(t) = i\int_{-\infty}^{t} \exp[i(s-t)\mathscr{L}]\mathscr{L}_A f_0^{(N)} F_A(s)\, ds + \mathscr{O}(F_A{}^2). \tag{7.3.10}$$

Now, $f_0^{(N)}$ is the distribution function of the undisturbed (equilibrium) system, and consequently is of the form

$$f_0^{(N)} = \exp[\beta(A_N - H)], \tag{7.3.11}$$

where A_N is the Helmholtz free energy of the system. It is found, therefore, that

$$\begin{aligned}\mathscr{L}_A f_0^{(N)} &= i[A, f_0^{(N)}] \\ &= -i\beta[A, H] f_0^{(N)} \\ &= -i\beta\dot{A} f_0^{(N)},\end{aligned}$$

from equation (6.A.3). $\dot{A}$ is called the current operator, J_A, for A. In the example previously cited, J_A is seen to be the *total* electric current in the system. If we denote $A(\Gamma_N)$ by $A(t = 0)$ then it follows from equation (6.A.3) that*

$$\exp\,[i(s - t)\mathscr{L}]A(t = 0) = A(s - t) \tag{7.3.12}$$

so that equation (7.3.10) becomes

$$\delta f^{(N)}(t) = \beta \int_{-\infty}^{t} \dot{A}(s - t) f_0^{(N)} F_A(s)\, ds. \tag{7.3.13}$$

We now wish to use the perturbation function (7.3.13) to calculate the average value of the flux density, j_B of type B in response to a force of type A. For simplicity we shall assume that in equilibrium j_B is zero. Of course, for a uniform system j_B is related to the B-current operator, J_B, by $j_B = V^{-1}J_B$, where V is the volume of the system. Using the definition

$$\langle j_B \rangle = \int j_B f^{(N)}\, d\Gamma_N, \tag{7.3.14}$$

it is found from equation (7.3.13) that

$$\langle j_B \rangle = \frac{1}{VkT} \int_{-\infty}^{t} \langle J_B J_A(s - t) \rangle_0 F_A(s)\, ds, \tag{7.3.15}$$

where

$$\langle J_B J_A(s - t) \rangle_0 = \int J_B J_A(s - t) f_0^{(N)}\, d\Gamma_N$$
$$= \phi_{AB}(t - s) \tag{7.3.16}$$

is the *equilibrium* temporal correlation function of the flows of A and B.

Equation (7.3.15) is a particular example of a general non-Markovian relation between the B response, $R_B(t)$, to an A force:

$$R_B(t) = C \int_{-\infty}^{t} \phi_{AB}(t - s) F_A(s)\, ds. \tag{7.3.17}$$

The corresponding response *function*, defined as the response of the system to a unit impulse $F_A(s) = F_{A,0}\delta(s - t_0)$, is, from equation (7.3.17), clearly proportional to $\phi_{AB}(t - t_0)$.

The transport coefficient associated with the process just discussed, is called a *linear* transport coefficient because only the first order term

* Since A is only a function of the phase Γ_N at any instant, it follows that $A(s) = A(\Gamma_N;s)$ where $(\Gamma_N;s)$ is the phase at time s, and so on.

in the driving force is considered. It is denoted by $L_{AB}(\omega)$, and is defined as the ratio of the response $\langle j_B(\omega)\rangle$ of frequency ω to the force $F_A(\omega)$ of frequency ω:

$$\langle j_B(\omega)\rangle = L_{AB}(\omega)F_A(\omega). \tag{7.3.18}$$

The quantities $\langle j_B(\omega)\rangle$ and $F_A(\omega)$ introduced in equation (7.3.18) are, respectively, the response to a monochromatic driving force F_A exp $(i\omega t)$. Substitution of this form for the force in equation (7.3.18) leads to*

$$L_{AB}(\omega) = \lim_{\epsilon\to 0}\frac{1}{VkT}\int_0^\infty e^{(i\omega-\epsilon)t}\phi_{AB}(t)\,dt. \tag{7.3.19}$$

That is, $L_{AB}(\omega)$ is proportional to the Fourier transform of the correlation function $\phi_{AB}(t)$.

Consider now the special case that the driving force $F_A(t)$ is steady, so that $F_A(\omega) = 0$ for $\omega \neq 0$. From equation (7.3.18) we now obtain the static transport coefficient

$$L_{AB}(0) = \frac{1}{VkT}\int_0^\infty \phi_{AB}(t)\,dt, \tag{7.3.20}$$

assuming that ϕ_{AB} is integrable in the interval $0 \leqslant t \leqslant \infty$.

The A response of the system to a steady B force may be obtained immediately from the preceding formalism by interchanging A and B. Thus,

$$L_{BA}(0) = \frac{1}{VkT}\int_0^\infty \phi_{BA}(t)\,dt. \tag{7.3.21}$$

Now, from equation (7.3.16) it is immediately seen that

$$\phi_{AB}(t) = \phi_{BA}(-t) \tag{7.3.22}$$

since the time displacement operator can be transferred from J_A to J_B by applying a succession of partial integrations to each term of its series expansion, with a resulting change in the sign of t. If A and B, and hence J_A and J_B, are both either even or odd in the momenta, then

* The change in the limits of integration between equations (7.3.15) and (7.3.19) is easily achieved by the substitution in equation (7.3.15) of the new variable $t' = t - s$. The explicit introduction of the factor exp $(-\epsilon t)$ in equation (7.3.19) is due to the necessity of introducing the gradual "switching-on" process previously discussed.

by reversing the momenta we find*

$$\phi_{AB}(t) = \phi_{AB}(-t). \tag{7.3.23}$$

Substitution of equations (7.3.22) and (7.3.23) in equation (7.3.21) now leads to

$$L_{AB} = L_{BA}. \tag{7.3.24}$$

Equation (7.3.24) is a special case of the reciprocal relations of Onsager, which relations assert that the flux of B per unit A force is equal to the flux of A per unit B force. The reciprocal relations are a consequence of the reversibility of the microscopic laws of motion.

In deriving equation (7.3.24) explicit use is made of the fact that reversal of the molecular momenta replaces the Liouville operator by its negative:

$$\mathbf{p}_i \to -\mathbf{p}_i \text{ (all } i) \qquad \text{implies} \qquad \mathscr{L} \to -\mathscr{L}$$

if the forces are conservative. On the other hand, if charged particles in the system are also subjected to a magnetic field $\mathbf{B}$, then each experiences an additional force of the form $(mc)^{-1}\mathbf{p}_i \times \mathbf{B}$. The Liouville operator in this case contains an extra term:

$$i\mathscr{L}(\mathbf{B}) = \sum_i \left(\frac{\mathbf{p}_i}{m} \cdot \nabla_i + \sum_{j>i} \mathbf{F}_{ij} \cdot \nabla_{p_i} + \frac{1}{mc} (\mathbf{p}_i \times \mathbf{B}) \cdot \nabla_{pi} \right). \tag{7.3.25}$$

If, now, the momenta are reversed, the magnetic field must also be reversed:

$$\begin{matrix} \mathbf{p}_i \to -\mathbf{p}_i \\ \mathbf{B} \to -\mathbf{B} \end{matrix} \text{ (all } i) \qquad \text{implies} \qquad \mathscr{L}(\mathbf{B}) \to -\mathscr{L}(-\mathbf{B}),$$

so that the generalization of equation (7.3.24) to the case of magnetic fields is

$$L_{AB}(\mathbf{B}) = L_{BA}(-\mathbf{B}). \tag{7.3.26}$$

* If A and B are of different parity in the momenta, it is found that those forms of A and B of interest in the discussion of transport processes are then tensors of different rank (i.e., scalar, vector, second rank tensor, etc.). It then follows from the Curie principle, which is discussed in detail in the book by de Groot and Mazur (25), that the cross-coefficients L_{AB} vanish.

7.3.B. *The Non-Equilibrium Thermodynamics of Uniform Systems* (24,26–28)

In this section we discuss briefly the conventional formulation of non-equilibrium thermodynamics, in order to prepare the reader for the extension to non-uniform systems in the next section, and to bring out certain difficulties regarding the limits of time integrations. Consider a system, in equilibrium, immersed in a reservoir (for example, one replica system of a Grand Canonical Ensemble, or a massive particle suspended in a fluid.) The state of this system may be described by a set of functions A_i ($i = 1, \cdots, s$). The set may include, for instance, the energy, composition, linear and angular momenta. It is assumed that the system is sufficiently large that the equilibrium state may be defined operationally in terms of the A_i and that fluctuations of the functions A_i are small. An entropy function S may then be defined in terms of the A_i:

$$S = S(A_1, \cdots, A_s). \tag{7.3.27}$$

Since the entropy at equilibrium is a maximum (constant E,V), the entropy at any instant is not greater than the equilibrium entropy S_0, where

$$S_0 = S_0(\langle A_1\rangle, \cdots, \langle A_s\rangle) \tag{7.3.28}$$

is regarded as a function of the equilibrium values $\langle A_i\rangle$ of the functions A_i. Also, since the fluctuations are assumed small, S may be expanded about S_0 in a Taylor series in powers of the deviations

$$a_i = A_i - \langle A_i\rangle, \tag{7.3.29}$$

with the result

$$\begin{aligned} S &= S_0 - \frac{1}{2}\sum_{i,j=1}^{s} g_{ij}a_ia_j + \mathcal{O}(a^3) \\ &= S_0 - \tfrac{1}{2}\mathbf{g}:\mathbf{aa} + \mathcal{O}(a^3), \end{aligned} \tag{7.3.30}$$

where

$$g_{ij} = \left(\frac{\partial^2 S}{\partial A_i\,\partial A_j}\right)_{[\mathbf{A}=\langle\mathbf{A}\rangle]} \tag{7.3.31}$$

is a positive definite matrix, and a vector notation has been introduced in an obvious way. Note that the average values of the deviations defined in equation (7.3.29) vanish.

The probability distribution of the a_i is taken to be

$$f(a_1, \cdots, a_s) = C \exp\left(\frac{S - S_0}{k}\right), \tag{7.3.32}$$

where C is a normalization constant, given by

$$\frac{1}{C} = \int \exp\left(\frac{S - S_0}{k}\right) da_1 \cdots da_s \tag{7.3.33}$$

so that

$$\int f(a_1, \cdots, a_s)\, da_1 \cdots da_s = 1, \tag{7.3.34}$$

and k is, as usual, the Boltzmann constant. It follows now from equations (7.3.30), (7.3.32), (7.3.34), and (4.3.19) that the correlation matrix is

$$\langle \mathbf{a}\tilde{\mathbf{a}} \rangle = k\mathbf{g}^{-1}. \tag{7.3.35}$$

The average value of the entropy is found to be less than the value when each A_i assumes its average value. From equations (7.3.30) and (7.3.35) we obtain

$$\begin{aligned}\langle S \rangle &= S_0 - \tfrac{1}{2}\mathbf{g}\mathbf{:}\langle \mathbf{aa} \rangle \\ &= S_0 - \tfrac{1}{2}ks,\end{aligned} \tag{7.3.36}$$

where, it will be remembered, s is the order of the matrix $\mathbf{g}$, that is, the number of functions A_i in the set. The result (7.3.36) may be interpreted by appealing to the concepts of information theory. Broadly speaking, the entropy of a given (statistical) description of a system is less, and the information content greater, the more completely the state of the system is defined. In the present case, the amount by which the "equilibrium" entropy S_0 exceeds the average entropy $\langle S \rangle$ is directly proportional to the number s of functions in the set.

We come now to the treatment of time-dependence. Defining fluxes J_i by

$$J_i = \dot{a}_i \tag{7.3.37}$$

as in the previous section, we obtain by differentiation of equation (7.3.30) the expression

$$\frac{dS}{dt} = \sum_{i=1}^{s} J_i X_i, \tag{7.3.38}$$

where

$$X_i = \frac{\partial}{\partial a_i}(S - S_0) \tag{7.3.39}$$

is the thermodynamic force conjugate to a_i. It is an *axiom* of the theory that the average value of (dS/dt) is positive semidefinite. At this stage in the development of the theory some relation between the J_i and the X_i is assumed. It is sufficient for present purposes to introduce the linear relation

$$J_i = \sum_{j=1}^{s} L_{ij} X_j. \tag{7.3.40}$$

Equation (7.3.40) is essentially a macroscopic law as it is introduced here. That is, it presupposes that the values of the A_i can be controlled, so that if they are changed, the flow J_i results. Onsager proposed that equation (7.3.40) should apply also to the regression of fluctuations, which are not controllable. With equation (7.3.37), (7.3.40) may then be written as

$$\frac{da_i}{dt} = \sum_{j=1}^{s} L_{ij} X_j, \tag{7.3.41}$$

and this form of equation (7.3.40) is known as the *linear regression law*.

The meaning of the terms in equation (7.3.41) requires careful analysis, for, while equation (7.3.41) must imply the macroscopic relations (7.3.40), it cannot simultaneously describe a process occurring at the microscopic level. The regression is, in fact, interpreted as some sort of average behavior of the fluctuations. This difficulty is most clearly seen when one raises the question of the precise meaning of the time derivative in equation (7.3.41). Since, from equations (7.3.30) and (7.3.39), the forces are linear functions of the a_i, it is clear that the regressions have an exponential character, so that the behavior at $t = 0$ does not satisfy the arguments of Section 6.5.C and equation (6.A.20). The difficulty may be put another way. Taken at face value, equation (7.3.41) implies that fluxes appear *instantaneously* in response to fluctuations. This is clearly an oversimplification; there must occur a transient stage during which the flux builds up. [See, for instance, Fixman (29) and Longuet-Higgins (30).] It is these transients which are involved in the flat top of the correlation function discussed in Section 6.5.C and proved in equation (6.A.20). The solution of the problem is the interpretation of the time derivative as a coarse grained derivative

$$\frac{d\bar{a}_i}{dt} = \frac{1}{\tau} [\langle a_i(t + \tau)\rangle_1 - a_i(t)], \tag{7.3.42}$$

where $a_i(t)$ denotes the initial value of a_i, and $\langle a_i(t+\tau)\rangle_1$ denotes the average value of a_i at time τ later subject to the condition that the initial values of the a_i were $a_i(t)$. The coarse graining time, τ, must be short on a macroscopic scale, so that equation (7.3.41) appears as a macroscopic law on the one hand, but long enough on a microscopic scale to smooth over the transients. Equations (7.3.42) are now inserted in equation (7.3.41) in which the forces X_i are regarded as functions of the $a_j(t)$, and we obtain as transport equations the relations

$$\frac{1}{\tau}[\langle a_i(t+\tau)\rangle_1 - a_i(t)] = \sum_{j=1}^{s} L_{ij} X_j(\mathbf{a}(t)). \tag{7.3.43}$$

Explicit expressions for the L_{ij} may now be obtained by first multiplying both sides of equations (7.3.43) by $a_l(t)$ and averaging over all $\mathbf{a}(t)$ with the result

$$\frac{1}{\tau}[\langle a_i(t)a_l\rangle - \langle a_i a_l\rangle] = \sum_{j=1}^{s} L_{ij}\langle X_j(\mathbf{a})a_l\rangle, \tag{7.3.44}$$

where the time correlation function of a_i and a_l has been introduced through equation (6.5.107). In writing a_l for $a_l(t)$ in equation (7.3.44), we mean $a_l(0)$, and assume that the a_i are stationary random variables. Substitution of the identity

$$a_i(\tau) = \int_0^\tau dt'\,\dot{a}_i(t') + a_i(0) \tag{7.3.45}$$

in equation (7.3.44) now converts the left-hand side to

$$\frac{1}{\tau}\int_0^\tau dt'\,\langle \dot{a}_i(t')a_l\rangle \tag{7.3.46}$$

in combination with equation (6.5.54) or (6.A.20). The integrand of equation (7.3.46) is now transformed again, using the invariance of $\langle \dot{a}_i(t')a_l\rangle$ to a displacement of the origin of time t [cf. Eq. (6.5.53) or (6.A.20)]. Thus,

$$\langle \dot{a}_i(t')a_l(0)\rangle = -\langle a_i(t')\dot{a}_l(0)\rangle, \tag{7.3.47}$$

and from equations (7.3.45) and (6.5.54), this becomes

$$\langle \dot{a}_i(t')a_l(0)\rangle = -\int_0^{t'} dt''\,\langle \dot{a}_i(t'')\dot{a}_l(0)\rangle. \tag{7.3.48}$$

As a final step, the right-hand side of equation (7.3.44) is easily evaluated from equations (7.3.32)–(7.3.34) and (7.3.39), and is found to be

$$\langle X_j(\mathbf{a})a_l\rangle = -k\delta_{jl}. \tag{7.3.49}$$

The substitution of equations (7.3.46), (7.3.48), and (7.3.49) in equation (7.3.44) now yields

$$L_{il} = \frac{1}{k\tau}\int_0^{\tau}\int_0^{t'} \langle \dot{a}_i(t'')\dot{a}_l(0)\rangle \, dt''\, dt'. \tag{7.3.50}$$

Equation (7.3.50) may be transformed into a relation similar to that for the mechanical transport coefficient, equation (7.3.20), by a rotation of the axes of integration (see, for instance, Section 4.5.A). Indeed, (7.3.50) becomes

$$L_{il} = \frac{1}{k}\int_0^{\tau}\left(1 - \frac{t''}{\tau}\right)\langle \dot{a}_i(t'')\dot{a}_l(0)\rangle \, dt''. \tag{7.3.51}$$

If the correlation of the fluxes drops quickly to zero within the coarse graining time τ, so that

$$\begin{aligned} \langle \dot{a}_i(t'')\dot{a}_l(0)\rangle &\neq 0 \qquad \text{if} \quad t'' < \tau_1 \ll \tau \\ &= 0 \qquad \text{otherwise,} \end{aligned} \tag{7.3.52}$$

then equation (7.3.51) may be rewritten in the form

$$L_{il} = \frac{1}{k}\int_0^{\tau_1}\langle \dot{a}_i(t'')\dot{a}_l(0)\rangle \, dt''. \tag{7.3.53}$$

The foregoing argument is very similar to that given in the introduction to Section 6.5.C, equations (6.5.59) and (6.5.62). In fact, it is a generalization of that discussion to *general Brownian-type motions*. The essential point here is that starting with the set of generalized Langevin equations (7.3.41) we would naturally find that the correlation functions are exponential decays. The introduction of the coarse graining in equation (7.3.42) is designed to avoid the contradiction between this cusp, and the rigorous proof of the flat top of the correlation function. If, however, the temporal extent of the flat top, τ_c, is short compared to the relaxation time, τ_{rel}, of $\langle a_i(t)a_l(0)\rangle$, then $\langle \dot{a}_i(0)\dot{a}_l(0)\rangle$ is large and the normalized flux correlation falls from unity to near zero within τ_c, remaining small and negative for times of the order of τ_{rel}. This is precisely the situation of which a particular example is discussed in Section 4.5.B and 6.5.C.

These arguments have been confirmed *a priori* by Hashitsume (31), who replaced equations (7.3.41) by their stochastic equivalents, and calculated the "friction coefficients," L_{ij}, by an extension of the methods of Section 4.5. As might be expected, he obtained the result

$$L_{il} = \frac{1}{2k\tau} \langle \Delta a_i(\tau)\, \Delta a_l(\tau) \rangle, \tag{7.3.54}$$

where $\Delta a_i(\tau) = [a_i(\tau) - a_i(0)]$. Equation (7.3.54) can be reduced to equations (7.3.50)–(7.3.53) by the methods already described.

Finally, the reader's attention is drawn to the fact that, according to the formalism developed in this section, the upper limit of integration, τ, is *finite*. Indeed, we have seen that τ must be short on a macroscopic scale. There is some confusion in the literature on this point since it is known intuitively that in the case of, for instance, the self-diffusion coefficient, the integration should be carried to infinity (see again the introduction of Section 6.5.C). This point is resolved by remarking that the (random) variables a_i of this section are stationary, while those important for diffusion are not. In the latter case nonstationarity is established by the time dependent variance [see Eq. (4.4.16) and the next section].

7.3.C. *Non-Equilibrium Thermodynamics of Non-Uniform Systems*

The previous section was devoted to the discussion of systems described *as a whole* by functions $a_1, a_2, \cdots, a_s$. Such a formulation is not immediately appropriate to the discussion of systems in terms of internal non-uniformities. Standard treatments of non-uniform systems are deficient in adopting the equations (7.3.27)–(7.3.40) as they stand, and then writing down the Navier-Stokes equations, for instance, without displaying the means by which the transition is accomplished.

Consider a macroscopic fluid system occupying a volume V. This system will presumably have fixed total energy, composition, etc., but we shall not use these facts. Imagine that the volume V is divided into cells of fixed volume v, which are also fixed in space. The size, v, of the cells is chosen in such a way that there is a sufficient number of fluid molecules in each, on average, that local thermodynamic variables can be defined. In addition, v must be small enough that the changes of local variables, due to macroscopic gradients, on passing from one side of a cell to the opposite side, are negligible. Cells defined in this way should correspond to the volume elements of hydrodynamics.

The discussion of Section 3.4.C (Table 3.4 in particular) indicates that such a choice is usually possible.

The cells are labeled by superscripts chosen from the set $1, 2, \cdots, s'$, and the state of the fluid in each cell is specified by a set of s functions A_i ($i = 1, 2, \cdots, s$). The formalism of the preceding section is modified in an obvious way to read

$$S = S(A_1^{\ 1}, \cdots, A_s^{\ s'}), \tag{7.3.55}$$

$$a_i^{\ k} = A_i^{\ k} - \langle A_i^{\ k} \rangle, \tag{7.3.56}$$

$$S - S_0 = -\frac{1}{2} \sum_{i,j=1}^{s} \sum_{k,l=1}^{s'} g_{ij}^{\ kl} a_i^{\ k} a_j^{\ l} + \cdots, \tag{7.3.57}$$

$$g_{ij}^{\ kl} = \left(\frac{\partial^2 S}{\partial a_i^{\ k}\, \partial a_j^{\ l}} \right)_{[\mathbf{A}=\langle \mathbf{A} \rangle]}. \tag{7.3.58}$$

Note that equation (7.3.57) contains the possibility that interactions occur between the $a_i^{\ k}$ for different cells, although we shall not make use of this feature here. The probability distribution of the $a_i^{\ k}$ is defined analogously to equations (7.3.32)–(7.3.34), and the correlation matrix is found to be

$$\langle a_i^{\ k} a_j^{\ l} \rangle = k(\mathbf{g}^{-1})_{ij}^{\ kl}, \tag{7.3.59}$$

so that the mean entropy is

$$\begin{aligned} \langle S \rangle &= S_0 - \tfrac{1}{2} k \sum_{i,j=1}^{s} \sum_{k,l=1}^{s'} g_{ij}^{\ kl} (\mathbf{g}^{-1})_{ij}^{\ kl} \\ &= S_0 - \tfrac{1}{2} kss', \end{aligned} \tag{7.3.60}$$

since $g_{ij}^{\ kl}$ is a matrix of order ss'.

Now, in most systems of physical interest the spatial correlations of the $a_i^{\ k}$, which extend for distances of the order of a few intermolecular spacings, are so short that they are often small compared to the linear dimensions of a cell.* Equation (7.3.59) then assumes the form

$$\langle a_i^{\ k} a_j^{\ l} \rangle = k(\mathbf{g}^{-1})_{ij}^{\ kk} \delta_{kl}, \tag{7.3.61}$$

and equation (7.3.60) is unaffected. Equation (7.3.61) may be incorporated into (7.3.57) with the result

$$S = S_0 - \frac{1}{2} \sum_{i,j=1}^{s} \sum_{k=1}^{s'} g_{ij}^{\ kk} a_i^{\ k} a_j^{\ k}, \tag{7.3.62}$$

* In this case we would also expect the contribution due to interactions across cell boundaries to be small. An important exception to this assumption occurs in and near the critical region, but we shall not discuss that problem herein.

which is slightly simpler than (7.3.57), having now the explicit form of a coarse grained volume integration. We now introduce microscopic densities, α_i^k, defined by

$$\alpha_i^k v = a_i^k \tag{7.3.63}$$

and, further, define a new coupling matrix, h_{ij}^{kk}, related to g_{ij}^{kk} by

$$h_{ij}^{kk} = g_{ij}^{kk} v. \tag{7.3.64}$$

Using equations (7.3.63) and (7.3.64), the resemblance of equation (7.3.62) to a volume integral is exploited to yield

$$\begin{aligned} S &= S_0 - \frac{1}{2} \sum_{i,j=1}^{s} \sum_{k=1}^{s'} h_{ij}^{kk} \alpha_i^k \alpha_j^k v \\ &= S_0 - \frac{1}{2} \int \mathbf{h}(\mathbf{r}) \mathbin{:} \boldsymbol{\alpha}(\mathbf{r}) \boldsymbol{\alpha}(\mathbf{r}) \, d\mathbf{r}, \end{aligned} \tag{7.3.65}$$

where the cell number k has been replaced by the position variable $\mathbf{r}$, and the vector notation has been introduced, as in the previous section, to represent sets of functions. Thus,

$$(\alpha_1^k, \cdots, \alpha_s^k) \equiv \boldsymbol{\alpha}(\mathbf{r}).$$

Equation (7.3.65) requires some examination. The transition to infinitesimal volume elements is clearly not allowable under all circumstances, or for all problems. For instance, the average entropy calculated from the second member of equation (7.3.65) is negative infinite, a result to be expected since the system is, in effect, specified by an infinite number of variables in this case. Thus, calculation of the entropy is not a proper application of equation (7.3.65). We shall restrict use of the continuum representation to cases where no obvious difficulty of this kind appears. Secondly, it is not obvious that $\mathbf{h}(\mathbf{r})$ rather than $\mathbf{g}(\mathbf{r})$ should be independent of v in equation (7.3.64), but this may be established qualitatively as follows. As we have already pointed out, the fluid system in a cell may be treated as a replica member of a Grand Canonical Ensemble. Therefore, the quantity $\langle a_i^k a_j^k \rangle$ is proportional to the mean square deviation of the number, n, of molecules in v:

$$\langle a_i^k a_j^k \rangle \propto \langle (n - \langle n \rangle)^2 \rangle.$$

But if $\langle n \rangle$ is sufficiently large,

$$\begin{aligned} \langle (n - \langle n \rangle)^2 \rangle &= \mathcal{O}(\langle n \rangle) \\ &\propto \rho v. \end{aligned}$$

Hence, from equation (7.3.61), $(\mathbf{g}^{-1})_{ij}^{kk}$ is proportional to v, so that $\mathbf{g}(\mathbf{r})v$, and, therefore, $\mathbf{h}(\mathbf{r})$ is independent of v.

The functions a_i are in all cases chosen from the set of conserved quantities (mass, momentum, energy) so that the densities $\alpha_i(\mathbf{r})$ satisfy equations of continuity:

$$\frac{\partial}{\partial t}\alpha_i(\mathbf{r}) = -\nabla \cdot \mathbf{J}_i(\mathbf{r}), \tag{7.3.66}$$

where the $\mathbf{J}_i(\mathbf{r})$ are fluxes analogous to those defined in equation (7.3.37). The rate of change of entropy is, therefore, from equations (7.3.65) and (7.3.66),

$$\begin{aligned}\frac{dS}{dt} &= -\sum_{i,j=1}^{s}\int h_{ij}(\mathbf{r})\alpha_i(\mathbf{r})\frac{\partial\alpha_j(\mathbf{r})}{\partial t}\,d\mathbf{r}\\ &= \sum_{i,j=1}^{s}\int h_{ij}(\mathbf{r})\alpha_i(\mathbf{r})\nabla\cdot\mathbf{J}_j(\mathbf{r})\,d\mathbf{r}.\end{aligned} \tag{7.3.67}$$

After a partial integration, equation (7.3.67) yields a surface flow term and a source term:

$$\frac{dS}{dt} = \sum_{i,j=1}^{s}\int h_{ij}(\mathbf{r})\alpha_i(\mathbf{r})\mathbf{J}_j(\mathbf{r})\cdot d\Sigma - \sum_{i,j=1}^{s}\int \mathbf{J}_j(\mathbf{r})\cdot\nabla(h_{ij}(\mathbf{r})\alpha_i(\mathbf{r}))\,d\mathbf{r}. \tag{7.3.68}$$

The first term on the right-hand side of equation (7.3.68) is the flow of entropy through the external surface of the system. The second term represents internal entropy production, analogous to equation (7.3.38). We now define force densities $\mathbf{X}_i(\mathbf{r})$ by

$$\left(\frac{dS}{dt}\right)_{\text{internal}} = \sum_{i=1}^{s}\int \mathbf{J}_i(\mathbf{r})\cdot\mathbf{X}_i(\mathbf{r})\,d\mathbf{r}, \tag{7.3.69}$$

and comparison of equations (7.3.68) and (7.3.69) yields

$$\mathbf{X}_i(\mathbf{r}) = -\sum_{j=1}^{s}\nabla(h_{ij}(\mathbf{r})\alpha_j(\mathbf{r})). \tag{7.3.70}$$

If one of the A_i is a component of a vector (e.g., momentum), then the subscripts in equation (7.3.70) refer to vector components and the forces and fluxes are second rank tensors. The transport equation analogous to equation (7.3.40) is then seen to be

$$\mathbf{J}_i(\mathbf{r}) = \sum_{j=1}^{s} L_{ij}(\mathbf{r})\, \mathbf{X}_j(\mathbf{r}) + \mathbf{u}\alpha_i, \tag{7.3.71}$$

with the extra term $\mathbf{u}\alpha_i$ giving the contribution to the flow of a_i due to a fluid velocity $\mathbf{u}$. The most general form of the transport coefficients when the forces and fluxes are second rank tensors is a fourth rank tensor. Application of the Curie principle (25) shows that the structure of the tensor is such that equation (7.3.71) has (in the case of momentum transport) the form of the Newtonian stress tensor, displayed in equation (6.2.21). Combining equations (7.3.66), (7.3.70), and (7.3.71) we obtain generalized diffusion equations for the densities $\alpha_i(\mathbf{r})$:

$$\frac{\partial}{\partial t}\alpha_i(\mathbf{r}) = \sum_{m,j=1}^{s} \nabla \cdot [L_{ij}(\mathbf{r})\, \nabla\{h_{jm}(\mathbf{r})\alpha_m(\mathbf{r})\}] - \nabla \cdot [\mathbf{u}\alpha_i(\mathbf{r})]. \tag{7.3.72}$$

Equations (7.3.72) cannot be solved unless the dependence of $L_{ij}(\mathbf{r})$, $h_{jm}(\mathbf{r})$ and $\mathbf{u}$ upon $\mathbf{r}$ is known. In most cases, the spatial variation of L_{ij} and h_{jm} can be easily found. Owing to the coarse grained nature of the measurement of position, $h_{jm}(\mathbf{r})$ is expected to be independent of position except possibly near the boundaries of the system. The transport coefficients will be independent of position only if the fluctuations giving rise to transport are small enough. Thus, in the case of energy transport, the transport coefficient can only be regarded as independent of position if the temperature gradient is so small that only an insignificant change in the coefficient occurs in distances of the order of those for which the diffusion process must be followed. Under these conditions equation (7.3.72) becomes

$$\frac{\partial \alpha_i}{\partial t} = \sum_{m,j=1}^{s} L_{ij} h_{jm}\, \nabla^2 \alpha_m - \nabla \cdot (\mathbf{u}\alpha_i), \tag{7.3.73}$$

or, in matrix notation,

$$\frac{\partial \boldsymbol{\alpha}}{\partial t} = \mathbf{M} \cdot \nabla^2 \boldsymbol{\alpha} - \nabla \cdot (\mathbf{u}\boldsymbol{\alpha}), \tag{7.3.74}$$

where the

$$M_{ij} = \sum_{k=1}^{s} L_{ik} h_{kj} \tag{7.3.75}$$

are known as the phenomenological coefficients.

The diffusion equations (7.3.74) are usually solved for the case of zero fluid velocity.* The solutions are subject to the boundary conditions for diffusion beginning at $t = 0$ as a coarse grained delta function centered at some $\mathbf{r}_0$,

$$\begin{aligned} \boldsymbol{\alpha}(\mathbf{r};0) &= v^{-1}\mathbf{a}_0, \qquad \text{if} \quad \mathbf{r} \in v \text{ (at } \mathbf{r}_0) \\ &= \mathbf{0}, \qquad \text{if} \quad \mathbf{r} \notin v \text{ (at } \mathbf{r}_0) \end{aligned} \tag{7.3.76}$$

and having a finite range for finite time:

$$\boldsymbol{\alpha}(\infty;t) = \mathbf{0}, \qquad 0 < t < \infty. \tag{7.3.77}$$

If the vector $\boldsymbol{\alpha}$ is transformed by a matrix $\mathbf{C}$ to the form

$$\boldsymbol{\alpha}' = \mathbf{C}^{-1} \cdot \boldsymbol{\alpha}, \tag{7.3.78}$$

then equation (7.3.74) becomes

$$\begin{aligned} \frac{\partial}{\partial t}\boldsymbol{\alpha}' &= \mathbf{C}^{-1} \cdot \mathbf{M} \cdot \mathbf{C}\, \nabla^2 \boldsymbol{\alpha}' \\ &= \boldsymbol{\Lambda} \cdot \nabla^2 \boldsymbol{\alpha}', \end{aligned} \tag{7.3.79}$$

where $\mathbf{C}$ has been chosen to diagonalize $\mathbf{M}$ to $\boldsymbol{\Lambda} = \text{diag}\,(\lambda_1, \cdots, \lambda_s)$. The solutions of equation (7.3.79), subject to the boundary conditions

* Alternatively, we may appeal to a mildly circular argument, and apply the equation of continuity (not yet demonstrated within the framework of this formalism), after introducing new variables β_i defined by

$$\rho\beta_i = \alpha_i.$$

Equation (7.3.74) then becomes

$$\frac{\partial \boldsymbol{\beta}}{\partial t} = \frac{1}{\rho}\mathbf{M} \cdot \nabla^2 \rho\boldsymbol{\beta} - \mathbf{u} \cdot \nabla\boldsymbol{\beta}.$$

If we now introduce the Galilean transformation

$$\mathbf{r} \rightarrow \mathbf{r}' = \mathbf{r} - \mathbf{u}t; \qquad t \rightarrow t' = t,$$

this equation becomes

$$\frac{\partial \boldsymbol{\beta}}{\partial t} = \frac{1}{\rho}\mathbf{M} \cdot \nabla^2 \rho\boldsymbol{\beta},$$

and may be solved by the method described, *if the position and time dependence of* $\mathbf{u}$ *is neglected.* This is valid if the macroscopic distance required for the diffusion processes to reach their asymptotic forms is sufficiently short. The use of this transformation then replaces $\mathbf{p}_n$ by $\mathbf{p}_n' = \mathbf{p}_n - m\mathbf{u}$ in equations (7.3.103), (7.3.110), (7.3.112), and (7.3.114).

(7.3.76) and (7.3.77), are

$$\alpha_i'(\mathbf{r};t) = a_{i0}'[2(\pi\lambda_i t)^{1/2}]^{-3} \exp\left[-\frac{(\mathbf{r}-\mathbf{r}_0)^2}{4\lambda_i t}\right]; \qquad i = 1, \cdots, s,$$

for times t such that $2\lambda_i t \gg v^{2/3}$. (7.3.80)

The mean square spreads of the density distributions α_i' are defined by

$$\delta_i' = \int (\mathbf{r}-\mathbf{r}_0)^2 \alpha_i'(\mathbf{r};t)\, d\mathbf{r}, \tag{7.3.81}$$

so that the mean square vector spread is

$$\boldsymbol{\delta}' = 6t\boldsymbol{\Lambda} \cdot \mathbf{a}_0'. \tag{7.3.82}$$

The mean square spread of the original set $\boldsymbol{\alpha}$ is obtained by using the inverse transformation corresponding to equation (7.3.78):

$$\begin{aligned} \boldsymbol{\delta} &= \mathbf{C} \cdot \boldsymbol{\delta}' \\ &= 6t\mathbf{C} \cdot \boldsymbol{\Lambda} \cdot \mathbf{C}^{-1}\mathbf{a}_0 \\ &= 6t\mathbf{M} \cdot \mathbf{a}_0. \end{aligned} \tag{7.3.83}$$

Equation (7.3.83) is now multiplied on the right by $\mathbf{a}_0$ and averaged over $\mathbf{a}_0$. From equations (7.3.61), (7.3.64), and (7.3.75) it follows that

$$\mathbf{L} = (6kvt)^{-1}\langle \boldsymbol{\delta}\mathbf{a}_0 \rangle. \tag{7.3.84}$$

Equation (7.3.84) is a relation for the transport coefficients of the same form as equation (4.4.16) defining the diffusion coefficient. Indeed, if we are considering the transport of molecules, we write $a_1 = 1$, and retrieve equation (4.4.16). The most important feature of equation (7.3.84) is that no upper limit is placed upon t except insofar as the diffusion process becomes sensitive to the boundaries of the macroscopic system. The reason for this is, as we remarked at the end of the previous section, that the *diffusion process in space is not stationary*: $\boldsymbol{\delta}$ in equation (7.3.83) is a function of t.

We now seek a statistical mechanical expression corresponding to equation (7.3.84); in obtaining this expression we shall follow the method of Helfand. Let us consider the transport of a property denoted by $a_1 = a$ due to an initial fluctuation of a property $a_2 = b$. Equation (7.3.84) may be written for this case as

$$\begin{aligned} L_{ab} &= (6kvt)^{-1}\langle \delta_a b \rangle \\ &= (6kvt)^{-1}\int (\mathbf{r}-\mathbf{r}_0)^2 \alpha(\mathbf{r}; t \mid \mathbf{b}, \mathbf{r}_0; 0) b f(b,\mathbf{r}_0;0)\, db\, d\mathbf{r}, \end{aligned} \tag{7.3.85}$$

where $\alpha(\mathbf{r}; t \mid b, \mathbf{r}_0; 0)$ is the density of property a at $\mathbf{r}$ at t if a fluctuation of b within a volume v at $\mathbf{r}_0$ occurred at $t = 0$, and $f(b,\mathbf{r}_0;0)$ is the probability distribution of the magnitude of b. A statistical mechanical expression for $\alpha(\mathbf{r}; t \mid b, \mathbf{r}_0; 0)f(b,\mathbf{r}_0)$ is easily obtained in the following way: If $f_0^{(N)}(\Gamma_N;0)$ is the equilibrium phase space distribution function for the system as a function of the phase of the system at time $t = 0$, $(\Gamma_{N,0})$, then the quantity

$$\sum_{i,j=1}^{N}\left[\int \delta(a_{it} - a)\,\delta(\mathbf{R}_{it} - \mathbf{r})\,\delta(b_{j0} - b)\,\delta(\mathbf{R}_{j0} - \mathbf{r}_0) f_0^{(N)}(\Gamma_{N,0})\,d\Gamma_{N,0}\right] \times da\,db\,d\mathbf{r}\,d\mathbf{r}_0 \quad (7.3.86)$$

is the product of the number of molecules in the singlet phase volume element $da\,d\mathbf{r}$ at t, and the number of molecules in the singlet phase volume element $db\,d\mathbf{r}_0$ at $t = 0$. In equation (7.3.86) the notation a_{it} denotes the property a appropriate to molecule i at time t, while b_{j0} denotes the property b appropriate to molecule j at $t = 0$. Integration of equation (7.3.86) with respect to $\mathbf{r}_0$ over the small volume v now introduces the probability distribution of a fluctuation of b for the molecules in v at $t = 0; f(b,\mathbf{r}_0;0)$. Multiplication by a and integration with respect to a then introduces the density of a at $\mathbf{r}$ at t, conditional on the initial fluctuation of b. Thus, we find

$$\alpha(\mathbf{r}; t \mid b, \mathbf{r}_0; 0)f(b,\mathbf{r}_0;0) = \sum_{i,j=1}^{N} \int da \int_v d\mathbf{r}_0 \int d\Gamma_{N,0}\,\delta(a_{it} - a)\,\delta(\mathbf{R}_{it} - \mathbf{r})\,\delta(b_{j0} - b) \times \delta(\mathbf{R}_{j0} - \mathbf{r}_0) f_0^{(N)}(\Gamma_{N,0}). \quad (7.3.87)$$

After substitution of equation (7.3.87) in equation (7.3.85), the integrations over a, b, $\mathbf{r}$, and $\mathbf{r}_0$ may be performed explicitly because of the delta functions. The result is

$$L_{ab} = (6kvt)^{-1}\left\langle \sum_{i=1}^{N} \sum_{j=1}^{n} (\mathbf{R}_{it} - \mathbf{R}_{j0})^2 a_{it} b_{j0} \right\rangle, \quad (7.3.88)$$

where the brackets $\langle \cdots \rangle$ *now imply a full phase average*. The sum over j, which includes molecules in v at $t = 0$, runs from 1 to n, where n is the number of molecules in v at $t = 0$. Strictly speaking, a final step of averaging over n should be introduced. However, the problem has already been defined in such a way that values of n deviating from the average value $\langle n \rangle$ are extremely unlikely. Since deviations from overall uniformity are assumed to be small, we have, to a good approximation

$$\frac{n}{v} = \rho = \frac{N}{V} \tag{7.3.89}$$

where ρ is the average number density. Equation (7.3.88) finally becomes, therefore,

$$L_{ab} = (6kVt)^{-1}\left\langle \sum_{i,j=1}^{N} (\mathbf{R}_{it} - \mathbf{R}_{j0})^2 a_{it} b_{j0} \right\rangle. \tag{7.3.90}$$

Equation (7.3.90) can be put into a much more suggestive form in the following manner: Upon expanding the factor $(\mathbf{R}_{it} - \mathbf{R}_{j0})^2$ a set of three terms is obtained. Now, since the A_i are conserved quantities, we have, for instance,

$$\sum_{j=1}^{N} b_{j0} = \sum_{j=1}^{N} b_{jt}, \tag{7.3.91}$$

whereupon the term $\langle \sum_{i,j=1}^{N} R_{it}{}^2 a_{it} b_{j0} \rangle$ may be transformed to read

$$\begin{aligned} \left\langle \sum_{i,j=1}^{N} R_{it}{}^2 a_{it} b_{j0} \right\rangle &= \left\langle \sum_{i,j=1}^{N} R_{it}{}^2 a_{it} b_{jt} \right\rangle \\ &= \left\langle \sum_{i,j=1}^{N} R_{i0}{}^2 a_{i0} b_{j0} \right\rangle \\ &= \left\langle \sum_{i=1}^{N} R_{i0}{}^2 a_{i0} b_{i0} \right\rangle. \end{aligned} \tag{7.3.92}$$

The first member of equation (7.3.92) follows from equation (7.3.91). The second and third members follow from a canonical transformation from time t to time 0, and from the initial independence of a_i and b_j for $i \neq j$, and the result $\langle b_{j0} \rangle = 0$, respectively. The term

$$\left\langle \sum_{i,j=1}^{N} \mathbf{R}_{it} \cdot \mathbf{R}_{jt} a_{it} b_{jt} \right\rangle$$

may also be reduced, using similar arguments, to the last member of equation (7.3.92). In the same way it can be established that

$$\left\langle \sum_{i,j=1}^{N} R_{j0}{}^2 a_{it} b_{j0} \right\rangle = \left\langle \sum_{i,j=1}^{N} \mathbf{R}_{i0} \cdot \mathbf{R}_{j0} a_{i0} b_{j0} \right\rangle, \tag{7.3.93}$$

so that equation (7.3.90) becomes

$$L_{ab} = (6kVt)^{-1}\left\langle \left[\sum_{i=1}^{N} (\mathbf{R}_{it} a_{it} - \mathbf{R}_{i0} a_{i0})\right] \cdot \left[\sum_{j=1}^{N} (\mathbf{R}_{jt} b_{jt} - \mathbf{R}_{j0} b_{j0})\right] \right\rangle. \tag{7.3.94}$$

Equation (7.3.94) establishes that the transport coefficient L_{ab} is a measure of the correlation in the shifts of the centers of gravity of a- and b-distributions.

While equation (7.3.94) has the simple interpretation just given, it does not yet resemble the relations (7.3.53) of the previous section. It is easy to demonstrate that they are indeed similar. The identity

$$\mathbf{R}_{it}a_{it} - \mathbf{R}_{i0}a_{i0} = \int_0^t \frac{d}{dt'}[\mathbf{R}_i a_i]\, dt' \tag{7.3.95}$$

allows us to define a flux $\mathbf{J}_a$ by

$$\mathbf{J}_a = \sum_{i=1}^{N} \frac{d}{dt}[\mathbf{R}_i a_i]. \tag{7.3.96}$$

Substitution of equations (7.3.95) and (7.3.96) in equation (7.3.94) yields, after a transformation using the stationary property

$$\langle \mathbf{J}_a(t') \cdot \mathbf{J}_b(t'') \rangle = \langle \mathbf{J}_a(0) \cdot \mathbf{J}_b(t'' - t') \rangle,$$

$$L_{ab} = \frac{1}{3kV}\int_0^t \left(1 - \frac{s}{t}\right) \langle \mathbf{J}_a(0) \cdot \mathbf{J}_b(s) \rangle\, ds. \tag{7.3.97}$$

The value of t to be taken in equation (7.3.97) is one which is sufficiently large that $\delta \propto t$ (i.e., the linear extent of diffusion must be much larger than the dimensions of a cell), but not so large that the diffusion process becomes affected by the boundaries of the system. Thus, the value of t is limited by strictly macroscopic considerations in the present case, while in the relations (7.3.53), the value of τ is limited by considerations of relaxation at a microscopic level. Finally, then, the coefficients associated with transport in an inhomogeneous medium are given by

$$L_{ab} = \frac{1}{3kV}\int_0^\infty \langle \mathbf{J}_a(0) \cdot \mathbf{J}_b(s) \rangle\, ds. \tag{7.3.98}$$

We shall consider two examples of these coefficients; diffusion and heat conduction. For these two processes the entropy for a cell is defined in terms of the number of molecules n, and the energy E, within the cell.

A diffusion process cannot be observed unless the diffusing molecules are labeled in some way. We therefore apply the formalism to the case of tracer diffusion, against an effectively constant background, as in Section 6.5.A. The property transported is the molecule itself, and so $a = b = 1$. If the tracer is sufficiently dilute, the tracer molecules are independent of one another. Therefore, the flux density of tracer molecules is divergenceless. Also,

$$\langle \mathbf{J}_1(0) \cdot \mathbf{J}_1(s) \rangle = \frac{N}{m^2} \langle \mathbf{p}_i(0) \cdot \mathbf{p}_i(s) \rangle. \tag{7.3.99}$$

It is not necessary to evaluate the derivative, $(\partial^2 S/\partial n^2)_{E,V} = g$, directly. From equation (7.3.61) we have

$$\begin{aligned} \frac{k}{g(n)} &= \langle (n - \langle n \rangle)^2 \rangle \\ &= n\rho kT\kappa_T \\ &= n, \end{aligned} \tag{7.3.100}$$

from standard fluctuation theory in the G.C.E. applied to a dilute gas. It follows from equation (7.3.64) and (7.3.100) that

$$h(n) = \frac{kv}{n}. \tag{7.3.101}$$

Substitution of equation (7.3.99) in equation (7.3.98), and use of equation (7.3.89) yields

$$L_{11} = \frac{n}{3kvm^2} \int_0^\infty \langle \mathbf{p}_i(0) \cdot \mathbf{p}_i(s) \rangle \, ds. \tag{7.3.102}$$

From equation (7.3.73) and the definition of the self-diffusion coefficient [see Eq. (4.4.17)] it follows that

$$\begin{aligned} D &= h(n)L_{11} \\ &= \frac{1}{3m^2} \int_0^\infty \langle \mathbf{p}_i(0) \cdot \mathbf{p}_i(s) \rangle \, ds, \end{aligned} \tag{7.3.103}$$

a result which was established in equation (6.5.63). It is possible to develop this example further and to study heat conduction *by the tracer molecules*. Also, since both the transport of molecules and energy involve scalar properties, we would be led to study thermal diffusion (i.e., a cross effect in which a temperature gradient induces diffusion). However, we shall not do this, but rather shall study ordinary thermal conduction directly. In accordance with the assumptions introduced earlier, that L_{ij} and h_{jm} are independent of position, we have for the mean-square energy fluctuations in a cell, the relationship

$$\langle E^2 \rangle - \langle E \rangle^2 = kT^2 vc_V = \textit{constant}, \tag{7.3.104}$$

where c_V is the heat capacity at constant volume per unit volume. It is found, from equations (7.3.64) and (7.3.104), that

$$h(\mathscr{E}) = g(\mathscr{E})v = (c_V T^2)^{-1} = \textit{constant}. \tag{7.3.105}$$

It also follows that the Fourier law (6.2.33) may be expressed as

$$\mathbf{q} = -\frac{\varkappa}{C_V}\nabla\mathscr{E}. \tag{7.3.106}$$

The final form of $\varkappa$ is found by substitution of equations (7.3.105) and (7.3.106) in the general diffusion equation (7.3.73) with α replaced by $\mathscr{E}$. After some manipulation it is found that

$$\varkappa = \frac{1}{3kVT^2}\int_0^\infty \langle \mathbf{J}_E(0)\cdot\mathbf{J}_E(s)\rangle\, ds, \tag{7.3.107}$$

with $\mathbf{J}_E$ found to be

$$\mathbf{J}_E = \frac{d}{dt}\sum_{i=1}^N \mathbf{R}_i e_i, \tag{7.3.108}$$

and

$$e_i = E_i - \langle E_i\rangle,$$
$$E_i = \frac{p_i^2}{2m} + \frac{1}{2}\sum_{j\neq i=1}^N u(i,j). \tag{7.3.109}$$

Explicit differentiation of equation (7.3.108) yields

$$\mathbf{J}_E = \sum_{i=1}^N \left[\frac{p_i^2}{2m}\mathsf{I} + \frac{1}{2}\sum_{j\neq i=1}^N (u(i,j)\mathsf{I} - \mathbf{R}_{ij}\mathbf{F}_{ij})\right]\cdot\frac{\mathbf{p}_i}{m}, \tag{7.3.110}$$

where $\mathbf{F}_{ij} = \nabla_{ij}u(i,j)$. Equation (7.3.110) differs slightly from the form obtained by Helfand and other workers but agrees with equation (6.2.80) in that no contribution arises from $\langle E_i\rangle$ or from external forces. This can be proved easily by returning briefly to equation (7.3.94). From this equation we have

$$\begin{aligned} L_{EE} &= (6kVt)^{-1}\left\langle\left[\sum_{i=1}^N (\mathbf{R}_{it}e_{it} - \mathbf{R}_{i0}e_{i0})\right]^2\right\rangle \\ &= (6kVt)^{-1}\left\langle\left[\sum_{i=1}^N \{\mathbf{R}_{it}E_{it} - \mathbf{R}_{i0}E_{i0} - \langle E_i\rangle(\mathbf{R}_{it} - \mathbf{R}_{i0})\}\right]^2\right\rangle. \end{aligned} \tag{7.3.111}$$

The problem of heat conduction as we have formulated it explicitly excludes the possibility of non-vanishing fluid motion $\mathbf{u}(\mathbf{r})$. Thus, the state about which the energy fluctuations occur is one of true equilibrium. Consequently, $\langle E_i\rangle = N^{-1}\langle E\rangle$ is the same for each molecule.

We now see that the second term on the right-hand side of equation (7.3.111) contains the factor $[\sum_{i=1}^{N} (\mathbf{R}_{it} - \mathbf{R}_{i0})]$ squared. For a one-component system, this factor is obviously the shift of the center of gravity, and vanishes for an isolated system. Incidentally, it is for precisely this reason that the generalized diffusion equation for the number density does not contain a dissipative term in a one-component system.

In conclusion, we quote relations which may be obtained from the fluctuation–dissipation formalism, discussed in this section, when applied to momentum transfer. For shear viscosity it is found that

$$\eta = \frac{1}{VkT} \int_0^\infty \langle J_p{}^{xy}(0) J_p{}^{xy}(s) \rangle \, ds, \tag{7.3.106}$$

where

$$\begin{aligned} \mathbf{J}_p &= \frac{d}{dt}\left(\sum_{i=1}^{N} \mathbf{p}_i \mathbf{R}_i\right) \\ &= \sum_i \left(\frac{1}{m}\,\mathbf{p}_i \mathbf{p}_i - \frac{1}{2}\sum_j \mathbf{R}_{ij}\,\nabla_{ij} u(i,j)\right) + \sum_i \mathbf{R}_i \mathbf{X}_i \\ &= \sum_i \left(\frac{1}{m}\,\mathbf{p}_i \mathbf{p}_i - \frac{1}{2}\sum_j \mathbf{R}_{ij}\,\nabla_{ij} u(i,j)\right) - pV\mathbf{I}. \end{aligned} \tag{7.3.113}$$

In defining the momentum flux, or pressure tensor, $\mathbf{J}_p$, we find that the external forces $\mathbf{X}_i$ on molecule i are important. We shall assume that the relaxation time of $\sum_i \mathbf{R}_i \mathbf{X}_i$ is so short that it may be replaced by its average value, $-pV$, which is determined from the virial theorem. Thus $\mathbf{J}_p$ is indeed the non-equilibrium, or fluctuation, part of the pressure tensor. The bulk viscosity is found, as expected, to depend upon only the diagonal elements of $\mathbf{J}_p$:

$$\phi = \frac{1}{VkT} \int_0^\infty \langle J_p{}^{xx}(0) J_p{}^{xx}(s) \rangle \, ds. \tag{7.3.114}$$

7.3.D. *Non-Equilibrium Solutions of the Liouville Equation* (9,15–18,20,21,23)

The most direct way in which the correlation function relations for the transport coefficients may be derived is by constructing an appropriate solution of the Liouville equation. This method emphasizes the statistical mechanical argument which was subordinated to the phenomenological considerations in the previous section.

Techniques for treating the response of a system to internal inhomogeneities have been developed by several workers. Although individual methods differ in detail, all are based upon what is essentially an extension of the Chapman-Enskog method of solving the Boltzmann equation. The ensemble of systems is supposed initially constrained to local equilibrium,* a situation in which convective flow, but no dissipative flow, occurs. Upon removal of the constraints, dissipative flows build up and the system evolves towards equilibrium.

To begin with, it is necessary to choose for the distribution function of the constrained system one which yields the correct values of the local fluid velocity and temperature. The function

$$f_L^{(N)} = \exp\left[\Psi - \sum_{i=1}^{N} \beta_i \left(\frac{(\mathbf{p}_i - m\mathbf{u}_i)^2}{2m} + \frac{1}{2}\sum_j u(i,j)\right)\right], \qquad (7.3.115)$$

where $\beta_i = [kT(\mathbf{R}_i;t)]^{-1}$, $\mathbf{u}_i = \mathbf{u}(\mathbf{R}_i;t)$, and Ψ is a normalization factor, is an obvious choice. One then supposes that the correct distribution function is given by

$$f^{(N)} = f_L^{(N)} \exp \Theta \qquad (7.3.116)$$

and satisfies the Liouville equation for the isolated system†; thus,

$$\left(\frac{\partial}{\partial t} + i\mathscr{L}\right)\Theta = -\left(\frac{\partial}{\partial t} + i\mathscr{L}\right) \ln f_L^{(N)}. \qquad (7.3.117)$$

The right-hand side of equation (7.3.117) contains derivatives of the dynamical variables and both space and time derivatives of the thermodynamic variables. These latter are replaced by means of zeroth order equations calculated as moments of the Liouville equation (see Sections 5.4.A, and 6.2.B). As a result of the changes of the local variables, the normalization factor Ψ also changes, and its time derivative can be calculated by applying the condition that $f_L^{(N)}$ is always normalized. The possibility that the local variables change in the microscopic time scale of the buildup of dissipative flows may be extended to treat the existence of non-linear dissipative laws. However, we shall assume that the flux correlations decay rapidly compared to the rate at which the

* It is easily established that the local equilibrium distribution function does not satisfy the Liouville equation.

† A system interacting with reservoirs may also be treated.

local variables change, thereby restricting attention to the Markovian linear laws.

It is convenient, before considering explicit calculations, to introduce microscopic densities. Thus, the Hamiltonian function for the system

$$H = \sum_i \left[\frac{p_i^2}{2m} + \frac{1}{2}\sum_j u(i,j)\right], \tag{7.3.118}$$

and the Hamiltonian density,

$$H(\mathbf{r}) = \sum_i \left[\frac{p_i^2}{2m} + \frac{1}{2}\sum_j u(i,j)\right] \delta(\mathbf{R}_i - \mathbf{r}), \tag{7.3.119}$$

are related by

$$H = \int_V H(\mathbf{r})\, d\mathbf{r}, \tag{7.3.120}$$

where V is the volume of the system. It follows that the internal energy density $E(\mathbf{r})$ is given by

$$\begin{aligned} E(\mathbf{r}) &= \sum_i \left[\frac{(\mathbf{p}_i - m\mathbf{u}_i)^2}{2m} + \frac{1}{2}\sum_j u(i,j)\right] \delta(\mathbf{R}_i - \mathbf{r}) \\ &= H(\mathbf{r}) - \mathbf{j}_p(\mathbf{r}) \cdot \mathbf{u}(\mathbf{r}) + \tfrac{1}{2}\rho_m(\mathbf{r}) u^2(\mathbf{r}), \end{aligned} \tag{7.3.121}$$

where $\mathbf{j}_p$ is the microscopic momentum density

$$\mathbf{j}_p(\mathbf{r}) = \sum_i \mathbf{p}_i\, \delta(\mathbf{R}_i - \mathbf{r}). \tag{7.3.122}$$

The reader will recall that the fluid velocity $\mathbf{u}$ is defined by

$$\left\langle \sum_i m\, \delta(\mathbf{R}_i - \mathbf{r}) \right\rangle_L \mathbf{u}(\mathbf{r}) = \left\langle \sum_i \mathbf{p}_i\, \delta(\mathbf{R}_i - \mathbf{r}) \right\rangle_L,$$

where $\langle \cdots \rangle_L$ denotes the *local equilibrium* average, and $\rho_m(\mathbf{r})$ is the microscopic mass density

$$\rho_m(\mathbf{r}) = \sum_i \rho m \delta(\mathbf{R}_i - \mathbf{r}). \tag{7.3.123}$$

The zeroth-order, macroscopic-flow equations may be obtained directly from Section 6.2 simply by taking the ordinary equations without the dissipative terms. They are

$$\frac{\partial}{\partial t}\mathbf{u} + \mathbf{u} \cdot \nabla \mathbf{u} = -\frac{1}{\rho_m} \nabla p, \tag{7.3.124}$$

$$\left(\frac{\partial}{\partial t} + \mathbf{u} \cdot \nabla\right) T = 0, \tag{7.3.125}$$

$$(\mathscr{E} + p)\nabla \cdot \mathbf{u} + \left(\frac{\partial}{\partial t} + \mathbf{u} \cdot \nabla\right)\mathscr{E} = 0. \tag{7.3.126}$$

The normalization condition

$$\int d\Gamma_N \exp\left[\Psi(t) - \int \beta(\mathbf{r})E(\mathbf{r})\, d\mathbf{r}\right] = 1 \qquad (7.3.127)$$

yields, upon differentiation with respect to t, the equation

$$\frac{d}{dt}\Psi(t) = \int \frac{\partial}{\partial t}[\beta(\mathbf{r})\mathscr{E}(\mathbf{r})]\, d\mathbf{r}, \qquad (7.3.128)$$

where we have used the result

$$\mathscr{E}(\mathbf{r}) = \langle E(\mathbf{r})\rangle_L. \qquad (7.3.129)$$

With use of equations (7.3.124)–(7.3.126), equation (7.3.128) now becomes

$$\frac{d}{dt}\Psi(t) = -\int \beta p\, \nabla \cdot \mathbf{u}\, d\mathbf{r}, \qquad (7.3.130)$$

where the dependence of β, p, and $\mathbf{u}$ upon $\mathbf{r}$ is understood and not displayed.

Equations (7.3.115) and (7.3.130) are now substituted in equation (7.3.117). The operator $(\partial/\partial t)$ affects the local variables $\beta, \mathbf{u}$, and $\Psi(t)$, while the operator $i\mathscr{L}$ affects the microscopic variables. It may be shown by explicit calculation, similar to that described in Section 6.2.B, that

$$i\mathscr{L}H = \dot{H} = -\nabla \cdot \mathbf{j}_H, \qquad (7.3.131)$$

where

$$\mathbf{j}_H = \sum_i \left[\left(\frac{p_i^2}{2m} + \frac{1}{2}\sum_j u(i,j)\right)\mathsf{I} - \frac{1}{2}\sum_j \mathbf{R}_{ij}\, \nabla_{ij} u(i,j)\right] \cdot \frac{\mathbf{p}_i}{m}\, \delta(\mathbf{R}_i - \mathbf{r}) \qquad (7.3.132)$$

is the energy flux density. Similarly, it is found that

$$i\mathscr{L}\mathbf{j}_p = -\nabla \cdot \mathsf{P}, \qquad (7.3.133)$$

where

$$\mathsf{P} = \sum_i \left(\frac{1}{m}\mathbf{p}_i\mathbf{p}_i - \frac{1}{2}\sum_j \mathbf{R}_{ij}\, \nabla_{ij} u(i,j)\right) \delta(\mathbf{R}_i - \mathbf{r}) \qquad (7.3.134)$$

is the microscopic pressure tensor. Also, of course,

$$i\mathscr{L}_m = -\nabla \cdot \mathbf{j}_p. \qquad (7.3.135)$$

The gradients of the microscopic flows are removed by partial integration, to yield gradients of $\beta, \mathbf{u}$, etc. The resulting surface terms vanish in an isolated system; in a system interacting with reservoirs they can be shown to cancel with a term $i\mathscr{L}_R$ representing the reservoirs in the Liouville operator. Denoting the result of this operation by $F(\mathbf{r})$, where

$$\int F(\mathbf{r})\,d\mathbf{r} = \left(\frac{\partial}{\partial t} + i\mathscr{L}\right)\left(\Psi(t) - \int \beta E\,d\mathbf{r}\right), \qquad (7.3.136)$$

it is found that

$$F(\mathbf{r}) = -\beta p \nabla \cdot \mathbf{u} + E\mathbf{u} \cdot \nabla\beta - \mathbf{j}_H \cdot \nabla\beta + \mathbf{P} : \nabla(\mathbf{u}\beta) - (\mathbf{j}_p - \rho_m \mathbf{u}) \cdot (\nabla \mathbf{u}) \cdot \mathbf{u} - \tfrac{1}{2}\mathbf{j}_p \cdot \nabla(\beta u^2), \qquad (7.3.137)$$

where a term $(\mathbf{j}_p - \rho_m\mathbf{u}) \cdot \nabla p$ has been neglected.

Upon expansion of the multiple gradient terms, equation (7.3.137) may be separated into two parts, depending upon the (inverse) temperature gradient and velocity gradient, respectively:

$$\begin{aligned} F(\mathbf{r}) &= \left(E\mathbf{u} - \mathbf{j}_H + \mathbf{u} \cdot \mathbf{P} - \frac{u^2}{2}\mathbf{j}_p\right) \cdot \nabla\beta \\ &\quad + \beta(-p\mathbf{I} + \mathbf{P} - \mathbf{j}_p\mathbf{u} - \mathbf{u}\mathbf{j}_p + \rho_m \mathbf{u}\mathbf{u}) : \nabla\mathbf{u} \\ &= -\hat{\mathbf{j}}_E \cdot \nabla\beta + \beta\,\hat{\mathbf{P}} : \nabla\mathbf{u}. \end{aligned} \qquad (7.3.138)$$

In (7.3.138),

$$\hat{\mathbf{j}}_E = \sum_i \left[\left(\frac{(\mathbf{p}_i - m\mathbf{u}_i)^2}{2m} + \frac{1}{2}\sum_j u(i,j)\right)\mathbf{I} - \frac{1}{2}\sum_j \mathbf{R}_{ij}\,\nabla_{ij} u(i,j)\right] \cdot \frac{(\mathbf{p}_i - m\mathbf{u}_i)}{m}\,\delta(\mathbf{R}_i - \mathbf{r}) \qquad (7.3.139)$$

is the local *internal* energy conduction current (compare Eq. (6.2.80)), and

$$\hat{\mathbf{P}} = \sum_i \left[\frac{1}{m}(\mathbf{p}_i - m\mathbf{u}_i)(\mathbf{p}_i - m\mathbf{u}_i) - \frac{1}{2}\sum_j \mathbf{R}_{ij}\,\nabla_{ij} u(i,j)\right]\delta(\mathbf{R}_i - \mathbf{r}) - p\mathbf{I}, \qquad (7.3.140)$$

is the non-equilibrium part of the pressure tensor [compare to the stress tensor, Eq. (6.2.60)].

It is convenient, before solving equation (7.3.117), to perform the volume integration of equation (7.3.136) explicitly, thereby reintroducing the absolute fluxes. In doing so, we impose the condition that the velocity and temperature gradients are constant. Introducing the definitions

$$\hat{\mathbf{J}}_E = \int \hat{\mathbf{j}}_E \, d\mathbf{r}$$
$$= \sum_i \left[\left(\frac{(\mathbf{p}_i - m\mathbf{u}_i)^2}{2m} + \frac{1}{2} \sum_j u(i,j) \right) \mathbf{I} - \frac{1}{2} \sum_j \mathbf{R}_{ij} \nabla_{ij} u(i,j) \right] \cdot \left(\frac{\mathbf{p}_i - m\mathbf{u}_i}{m} \right) \quad (7.3.141)$$

and

$$\hat{\mathbf{J}}_p = \sum_i \left[\frac{1}{m} (\mathbf{p}_i - m\mathbf{u}_i)(\mathbf{p}_i - m\mathbf{u}_i) - \frac{1}{2} \sum_j \mathbf{R}_{ij} \nabla_{ij} u(i,j) \right] - pV\mathbf{I}, \quad (7.3.142)$$

which are similar to the quantities $\mathbf{J}_E, \mathbf{J}_p$ defined in equations (7.3.110) and (7.3.113), being defined in this case in a frame of reference moving with the fluid. It is found that

$$\int F(\mathbf{r}) \, d\mathbf{r} = \frac{1}{kT^2} \hat{\mathbf{J}}_E \cdot \nabla T + \frac{1}{kT} \hat{\mathbf{J}}_p : \nabla \mathbf{u}. \quad (7.3.143)$$

The solution of equation (7.3.117) is now determined by the same method as was used to solve equation (7.3.8). In the approximation employed here, the space and time dependence of the temperature, temperature gradient, and velocity gradient are now neglected since they are related to nonlinear phenomena. The result is

$$\Theta(t) = -\int_0^t ds \left[\frac{1}{kT^2} \hat{\mathbf{J}}_E(s - t) \cdot \nabla T + \frac{1}{kT} \hat{\mathbf{J}}_p(s - t) : \nabla \mathbf{u} \right], \quad (7.3.144)$$

and the time dependence of Θ, $\hat{\mathbf{J}}_E$, and $\hat{\mathbf{J}}_p$ denotes, as in equation (7.3.12), a dependence on the phase at the corresponding time.

In the linear approximation, equation (7.3.116) becomes

$$f^{(N)} = f_L^{(N)}(1 + \Theta), \quad (7.3.145)$$

and equation (7.3.145) is used to calculate the average values of the internal energy flux density and non-equilibrium pressure tensor, $\hat{\mathbf{P}}$. We are not interested in the position dependence of these fluxes, and, therefore, use rather their volume averages, obtained by integrating over and dividing by the volume. The fluxes then become

$$\frac{1}{V} \int \hat{\mathbf{j}}_E \, d\mathbf{r} = V^{-1} \hat{\mathbf{J}}_E$$
$$\frac{1}{V} \int \hat{\mathbf{P}} \, d\mathbf{r} = V^{-1} \hat{\mathbf{J}}_p. \quad (7.3.146)$$

Using the phenomenological relations defining the coefficients of thermal conductivity, shear and bulk viscosity, and microscopic reversibility, we find that

$$\varkappa = \frac{1}{3VkT^2}\int_0^\infty \langle \hat{\mathbf{J}}_E(0)\cdot\hat{\mathbf{J}}_E(s)\rangle_L\, ds, \tag{7.3.147}$$

$$\eta = \frac{1}{VkT}\int_0^\infty \langle \hat{\mathbf{J}}_p^{xy}(0)\hat{\mathbf{J}}_p^{xy}(s)\rangle_L\, ds, \tag{7.3.148}$$

$$\phi = \frac{1}{VkT}\int_0^\infty \langle \hat{\mathbf{J}}_p^{xx}(0)\hat{\mathbf{J}}_p^{xx}(s)\rangle_L\, ds. \tag{7.3.149}$$

The justification for extending the upper limits of the time integrals to infinity is not so clear cut in the present case as it was in the discussion of the fluctuation–dissipation process of the previous section. In this case we see that it is necessary to assert that the dominant contributions to the correlation integrals arise before sufficient time has elapsed that the thermodynamic forces (i.e., the temperature and velocity gradients) have changed due to the dissipative fluxes. This assertion is, in fact, *implicit* in the fluctuation–dissipation discussion.

7.3.E. *The Relation of the Correlation-Function Formalism with Kinetic Theory* (8,12)

The principal virtue of the relations for transport coefficients developed in the preceding sections is their elegance. The clarity of the physical interpretation of these relations is, however, marred by the incomplete prescription given for the explicit calculation of the coefficients for any particular substance and physical state.

Consider the meaning of a correlation function. As we pointed out in Appendix 6.A, the autocorrelation function $\psi_{AA}(t)$ of a dynamical variable $A(\Gamma_N;t) = A(t)$, which is defined by

$$\psi_{AA}(\tau) = \langle A(t)A(t+\tau)\rangle \qquad \text{(stationary case)}, \tag{7.3.150}$$

in reality involves two averages. The first average is the average of $A(t+\tau)$ subject to the given initial value $A(t)$, while the second average is over all possible initial values $A(t)$. It is the first average which contains the essential feature of the temporal correlation. To calculate it requires, in principle, the complete solution of the N-body problem; that is, it requires all the results of the kinetic theory of Prigogine and co-workers described in Section 7.2. To put this another way, one may say that the correlation function formalism does not, *per se*, contain the element of irreversibility. The relations for the transport coefficients are identified only after one has assumed the existence of (linear) dissipative laws. Having arrived at the relations it still remains to prove the convergence of the time integral.

A proof (8,12) of the equivalence of the correlation function formalism and the general kinetic theory has been given for both the cases of the formula for the electrical conductivity of a homogeneous system first derived by Kubo and for the thermal transport coefficients (i.e., arising from inhomogeneities in the system). Proof of the equivalence for the case of thermal transport coefficients requires the extension of the general kinetic theory to inhomogeneous systems, an analysis which has just been completed (32).

The equivalence of the formalisms for transport induced by a mechanical disturbance may be demonstrated in the following way: Consider the case of the electrical conductivity. The current operator for a system of N charge carriers of charge e_i ($i = 1, \cdots, N$) and mass m, is

$$\mathbf{J} = \sum_i \frac{e_i}{m} \mathbf{p}_i. \tag{7.3.151}$$

Now, equation (7.3.20) may be written in the form

$$\boldsymbol{\sigma} = \frac{1}{VkT} \lim_{T\to\infty} \frac{\displaystyle\int_0^T dt \int d\Gamma_N \mathbf{J} \exp(-it\mathscr{L})\mathbf{J} \exp(-\beta H)}{\displaystyle\int d\Gamma_N \exp(-\beta H)}, \tag{7.3.152}$$

where $\boldsymbol{\sigma}$ is here the conductivity tensor. Upon introducing the resolvant operator (7.2.115), and the Fourier decomposition of $f_{eq}^{(N)}$, described in Section 7.2, equation (7.3.152) becomes

$$\boldsymbol{\sigma} = \frac{1}{VkT} \lim_{T\to\infty} \int_0^T dt \sum_{\{\mathbf{k}\}} \int d\mathbf{p}^{(N)} \mathbf{J} \left(-\frac{1}{2\pi i}\right) \oint_c \exp(-izt)\, dz$$
$$\times \langle \mathbf{0} | (\mathscr{L} - z) | \{\mathbf{k}\} \rangle \mathbf{J} \rho_{\{\mathbf{k}\}}^{eq}, \tag{7.3.153}$$

where the contour c is that described in Section 7.2. From equations

(7.2.116), (7.2.121), and (7.2.126), it follows that

$$\langle \mathbf{0} | (\mathscr{L} - z) | \{\mathbf{k}\} \rangle = \sum_{n=0}^{\infty} \left(-\frac{1}{z}\right) \left[\Psi_{00}^{+} \left(-\frac{1}{z}\right)\right]^{n} \times [\delta^{Kr}_{\mathbf{0},\{\mathbf{k}\}} + \mathscr{D}^{+}_{\mathbf{0},\{\mathbf{k}\}}(z)] \quad (7.3.154)$$

and from equation (7.2.116) it follows that the inverse collision operator is formally defined by

$$\sum_{n=0}^{\infty} \left(-\frac{1}{z}\right) \left[\Psi_{00}^{+} \left(-\frac{1}{z}\right)\right]^{n} = \frac{1}{z - \Psi_{00}^{+}(z)}. \quad (7.3.155)$$

Using now the theorem (33)

$$\lim_{T\to\infty} \int_0^T dt \oint_c dz\, e^{-izt} f(z) = \oint_c dz \frac{e^{-izt} f(z)}{-iz} = -2\pi f(0), \quad (7.3.156)$$

we may write equation (7.3.153) in the form

$$\boldsymbol{\sigma} = -\frac{1}{VkT} \sum_{\{\mathbf{k}\}} \int d\mathbf{p}^{(N)} \mathbf{J} \frac{1}{i\Psi_{00}^{+}(0)} [\delta^{Kr}_{\mathbf{0},\{\mathbf{k}\}} + \mathscr{D}^{+}_{\mathbf{0},\{\mathbf{k}\}}(0)] \mathbf{J} \rho^{eq}_{\{\mathbf{k}\}}. \quad (7.3.157)$$

Equation (7.3.157) is the resolvent operator form of Kubo's formula (7.3.20) for the conductivity tensor, and was first given by Balescu (34).

Consider now an earlier stage in the derivation of equation (7.3.20), at which the equation for the correction $\delta f^{(N)}(t)$ to the distribution function for the undisturbed system is reached: equation (7.3.13). In the resolvent formalism we obtain an equation for $\delta\rho_0(\mathbf{p}^{(N)};t)$:

$$\delta\rho_0 = -\frac{1}{2\pi i} \oint_c e^{-izt} \sum_{\{\mathbf{k}\}} \sum_{n=0}^{\infty} \left(-\frac{1}{z}\right) \left[\Psi_{00}^{+} \left(-\frac{1}{z}\right)\right]^{n} \times [\delta^{Kr}_{\{\mathbf{k}\},\mathbf{0}} + \mathscr{D}^{+}_{\mathbf{0},\{\mathbf{k}\}}]\, \delta\mathscr{L} \left(\frac{1}{\omega - z}\right) \rho^{eq}_{\{\mathbf{k}\}}, \quad (7.3.158)$$

where $\delta\mathscr{L} = i\mathbf{E}_0 (\sum_i e_i \nabla_{p_i})$ and $\mathbf{E}(t) = \mathbf{E}_0 \exp(-i\omega t)$. Comparison of equation (7.2.123) and the formal solution of the Liouville equation (7.2.1),

$$f^{(N)}(t) = e^{-it\mathscr{L}} f^{(N)}(0),$$

immediately establishes that equation (7.3.158) is equivalent to equation (7.3.13). The point of the proof is that, by differentiation with respect to t, and rearrangement, $\delta\rho_0$ can be shown to satisfy a kinetic equation similar to equation (7.2.129). Explicitly, this equation is

$$\frac{\partial}{\partial t}\,\delta\rho_0 - i\,\delta\mathscr{L}e^{-i\omega t}\rho_0{}^{eq} - i\sum_{\{\mathbf{k}\}}\int_0^t \langle\mathbf{0}|\,\mathscr{D}(t-t')\,|\{\mathbf{k}\}\rangle\,\delta\mathscr{L}e^{-i\omega t'}\rho_{\{\mathbf{k}\}}^{eq}\,dt'$$

$$= \int_0^t G_{00}(t-t')\,\delta\rho_0\,(t')\,dt'. \qquad (7.3.159)$$

We now see two flow terms on the left-hand side, instead of the single term $-i\delta\mathscr{L}e^{-i\omega t}\rho_0{}^{eq}$ which appears in the simple kinetic equations discussed in Chapters 5 and 6. The old flow term describes the effect of the applied field upon the particles between collisions, while the new flow term, which involves the Laplace transform of the destruction operator $\mathscr{D}^{+}_{0,\{\mathbf{k}\}}(z)$, describes the effect of the field during collisions. If the collisions are instantaneous, the latter vanishes.

It is in general very difficult to obtain a solution of equation (7.3.159). However, in the long time limit Balescu has shown that equation (7.3.159) admits a solution of the form

$$\delta\rho_0 = \Delta\rho_0(\omega)e^{-i\omega t}. \qquad (7.3.160)$$

Bearing in mind that

$$\delta\mathscr{L}\rho^{eq} = -\frac{i}{mkT}\,\mathbf{E}_0\cdot\mathbf{J}\rho^{eq}, \qquad (7.3.161)$$

it is now a simple matter to obtain the result

$$\Delta\rho_0(0) = -\frac{1}{i\Psi_{00}{}^{+}(0)}\sum_{\{\mathbf{k}\}}[\delta^{Kr}_{0,\{\mathbf{k}\}} + \mathscr{D}^{+}_{0,\{\mathbf{k}\}}(0)]\rho^{eq}_{\{\mathbf{k}\}}, \qquad (7.3.162)$$

and equation (7.3.157) follows immediately upon substituting equation (7.3.162) in equation (7.3.14).

With these remarks we close this chapter. Many of the details of the comparison between the several formal theories and the approximate theory developed herein have been omitted. The reader is referred to References 1–4 for proof of the equivalence of the several cluster expansions in the steady state, and to Reference 9 for a derivation of the autocorrelation function formulas similar in spirit to that described herein, but based on the explicit use of time smoothing. It is our belief that the demonstration of the equivalence between the exact formalisms and the approximate theory for the computation of transport coefficients lends strong support to the analysis of liquids described in this book.

APPENDIX 7.A

Zwanzig's Derivation of the Master Equation

Zwanzig has presented a very clear and compact derivation of the weak coupling Master equation avoiding the use of infinite order many body perturbation theory. The general theory developed is not by any means restricted to the description of homogeneous weakly coupled systems, but we examine only that case herein so as to compare directly the results displayed in the text of Chapter 7 with those obtained in this Appendix.

At the outset we note that averages of functions of the momenta are completely defined by just the N-body momentum distribution function. Now, the N-body momentum distribution function may be obtained from the full N-body function, $f^{(N)}$, by application of the projection operator

$$\mathscr{P} \equiv V^{-N} \int d\{N\}. \tag{7.A.1}$$

That is,

$$V^N \varphi^{(N)}(\mathbf{p}^{(N)};t) = \mathscr{P} f^{(N)}. \tag{7.A.2}$$

Therefore, the time dependence of functions of the momenta is completely determined by the solutions of the kinetic equation for the function $V^N \varphi^{(N)} \equiv \tilde{\rho}_0$. Note that $\tilde{\rho}_0$ differs from ρ_0 defined in Section 7.2.A only by the normalization constant V^N.

In a sense, application of the operator $\mathscr{P}$ to the distribution function $f^{(N)}$ may be interpreted as a procedure for separating $f^{(N)}$ into a "relevant" part and an "irrelevant" part. By this we mean that the calculation of the average of any given function requires not the full distribution function $f^{(N)}$, but only its projection onto some relevant subspace. In the case cited (functions of momenta) we need only the projection of $f^{(N)}$ on the subspace of the functions of momenta, and hence choose $\mathscr{P}$ as that operator which removes position variables by integrating over the volume of the system. $\mathscr{P}$ is clearly a projection operator since it satisfies the condition

$$\mathscr{P}^2 = \mathscr{P}, \tag{7.A.3}$$

as can be established by considering the integration of a function independent of the momenta.

We first proceed in a formal manner to write

$$f_R^{(N)}(t) = \mathscr{P} f^{(N)}(t),$$
$$f_I^{(N)}(t) = (1 - \mathscr{P}) f^{(N)}(t). \tag{7.A.4}$$

Since $\mathscr{P}$ is a time independent linear operator,

$$\mathscr{P} i \frac{\partial f^{(N)}}{\partial t} = i \frac{\partial f_R^{(N)}}{\partial t} = \mathscr{P}\mathscr{L}[f_R^{(N)} + f_I^{(N)}], \tag{7.A.5}$$

and

$$(1 - \mathscr{P}) i \frac{\partial f^{(N)}}{\partial t} = i \frac{\partial f_I^{(N)}}{\partial t} = (1 - \mathscr{P})\mathscr{L}[f_R^{(N)} + f_I^{(N)}]. \tag{7.A.6}$$

The formal solution of equation (7.A.6) may be written in the form

$$f_I^{(N)}(t) = e^{-it(1-\mathscr{P})\mathscr{L}} f_I^{(N)}(0) - i \int_0^t e^{-is(1-\mathscr{P})\mathscr{L}} (1 - \mathscr{P})\mathscr{L} f_R^{(N)}(t - s)\, ds, \tag{7.A.7}$$

as is easily verified. The substitution of equation (7.A.7) into (7.A.5) leads to an equation for $f_R^{(N)}$ which has the form

$$i \frac{\partial f_R^{(N)}}{\partial t} = \mathscr{P}\mathscr{L} e^{it(1-\mathscr{P})\mathscr{L}} f_I^{(N)}(0) + \mathscr{P}\mathscr{L} f_R^{(N)}(t)$$
$$- i \int_0^t \mathscr{P}\mathscr{L} e^{-is(1-\mathscr{P})\mathscr{L}} (1 - \mathscr{P})\mathscr{L} f_R^{(N)}(t - s)\, ds. \tag{7.A.8}$$

We immediately note that $(\partial f_R^{(N)}/\partial t)$ depends on $f_I^{(N)}(0)$, which may be thought of as a dependence of the "relevant" component of the distribution function on the initial state of the system. Also, the integral term of equation (7.A.8) displays explicitly the dependence of $(\partial f_R^{(N)}/\partial t)$ on the history of the process, i.e., equation (7.A.8) is non-Markovian in form. The development thus far is exact. To proceed further new considerations must be introduced.

As an example, we study the homogeneous weakly coupled gas. For this case,

$$f_R^{(N)}(t) = \tilde{\rho}_0(t), \tag{7.A.9a}$$

and we assume that

$$f_I^{(N)}(0) = 0. \tag{7.A.9b}$$

If we again expand the Liouville operator in the form

$$\mathscr{L} = \mathscr{L}_0 + \lambda\, \delta\mathscr{L},$$

with $\mathscr{L}_0$ the free particle Liouville operator and $\lambda\,\delta\mathscr{L}$ the interaction operator, then

$$\mathscr{P}\mathscr{L}\tilde{\rho}_0 = 0 \tag{7.A.10}$$

because

$$\mathscr{L}_0\tilde{\rho}_0 = 0, \tag{7.A.11}$$

since $\tilde{\rho}_0$ is independent of the position coordinates. Moreover,

$$\mathscr{P}\,\delta\mathscr{L}\tilde{\rho}_0 = V^{-N}\int d\{N\}[i\lambda\,\nabla_j u_{jk}\cdot\mathbf{D}_{jk}]\tilde{\rho}_0 = 0, \tag{7.A.12}$$

since the integral of an odd vector function over all space vanishes. Alternatively, partial integration shows that $\mathscr{P}\,\delta\mathscr{L}\tilde{\rho}_0$ vanishes at infinity if u_{jk} falls off faster than $\mathbf{R}_{jk}^{-1}$ and is regular at the origin. Equation (7.A.8) thereupon reduces to

$$\begin{aligned}\frac{\partial\tilde{\rho}_0}{\partial t} &= -\int_0^t ds\,\mathscr{P}\mathscr{L}e^{-is(1-\mathscr{P})\mathscr{L}}\mathscr{L}\tilde{\rho}_0(t-s)\\ &= -\lambda\int_0^t ds\,\mathscr{P}\mathscr{L}e^{-is(1-\mathscr{P})\mathscr{L}}\,\delta\mathscr{L}\tilde{\rho}_0(t-s),\end{aligned} \tag{7.A.13}$$

again using equation (7.A.11). With the definition

$$K(s,\lambda) = -\mathscr{P}\,\delta\mathscr{L}e^{-is(1-\mathscr{P})\mathscr{L}}\,\delta\mathscr{L}, \tag{7.A.14}$$

we finally find

$$\frac{\partial\tilde{\rho}_0}{\partial t} = \lambda^2\int_0^t ds\,K(s,\lambda)\tilde{\rho}_0(t-s). \tag{7.A.15}$$

To introduce the weak coupling assumption, set

$$\begin{aligned}\theta &= \lambda^2 t,\\ \tilde{\rho}_0(t) &= w(\theta),\end{aligned} \tag{7.A.16}$$

so that equation (7.A.15) assumes the form

$$\frac{\partial w}{\partial\theta} = \int_0^{\theta/\lambda^2} ds\,K(s,\lambda)w(\theta-\lambda^2 s). \tag{7A.17}$$

The reader will note that equation (7A.15) is non-Markovian in form, and that the kernel $K(s,\lambda)$ plays the role of a memory function. If it be assumed that $K(s,\lambda) \to 0$ for $s > \tau$, then

$$\lim_{\substack{\lambda\to\infty \\ t\to\infty \\ \theta=\text{constant}}} \frac{\partial \tilde{\rho}_0}{\partial t} = \lambda^2 \int_0^\infty ds K(s,0)\tilde{\rho}_0(t)\, ds, \tag{7.A.18}$$

$$\lim_{\substack{\lambda\to\infty \\ t\to\infty \\ \theta=\text{constant}}} K(s,0) = -\mathscr{P}\,\delta\mathscr{L} e^{-is\mathscr{L}_0}\,\delta\mathscr{L}, \tag{7.A.19}$$

since in our particular problem $\mathscr{P}\mathscr{L}$ is replaceable by $\lambda\mathscr{P}\,\delta\mathscr{L}$. Equation (7.A.18) is just the weak coupling Master equation derived by Prigogine and Brout and discussed in detail in the main text of Chapter 7. The demonstration of the identity of equation (7.A.19) and equation (7.2.84) is straightforward but tedious. The interested reader is referred to the article by Zwanzig for the details of this proof.

To complete our discussion of the Zwanzig analysis, we seek to make some additional connections with the formal perturbation theory of Prigogine and co-workers. First note that if we *do not* assume that $f_I^{(N)}(0) = 0$, then although $\mathscr{P}\mathscr{L}f_R^{(N)}(t)$ still vanishes, equation (7.A.8) becomes

$$\begin{aligned}
\frac{\partial \tilde{\rho}_0}{\partial t} &= \int_0^t ds K(s)\tilde{\rho}_0(t-s) + \mathscr{D}(t) f_I^{(N)}(0), \\
\mathscr{D}(t) &= \mathscr{P}\mathscr{L}e^{it(1-\mathscr{P})\mathscr{L}}, \\
K(s) &= \mathscr{P}\mathscr{L}e^{-is(1-\mathscr{P})\mathscr{L}}(1-\mathscr{P})\mathscr{L},
\end{aligned} \tag{7.A.20}$$

where the term involving the operator $\mathscr{D}(t)$ expresses the effect of the initial correlations on the time evolution of the velocity distribution function. Since $\mathscr{D}(t)$ acts only on $f_I^{(N)}(0)$, if the correlations at $t = 0$ are of finite range, then $\mathscr{D}(t)f_I^{(N)}(0) \to 0$ as $t \to \infty$. The reader should compare this description of the loss of the influence of the initial conditions with the discussion of the destruction fragment in Section 7.2.C. Also, the first term on the right-hand side of equation (7.A.20) has been shown to have a form which is Markovian in the limit $t \to \infty$, $\lambda \to 0$, $\theta = \text{constant}$ [see Eq. (7.A.18)], and this feature should be compared with the corresponding discussion in Section 7.2.C of the asymptotic time behavior of the general kinetic equation. Note that the restriction to long times used in the derivation of equation (7.A.18) implies that the Markovian kernel is valid only when times of the order of a collision times are not considered.

Thus, by the use of projection operators and related analytic tools, the results of the infinite order perturbation theory may be quickly reproduced. For any given problem, however, the choice of projection operator may be difficult. Also, the very detailed information inherent in the Fourier decomposition used in the perturbation theory is not examined in the projection operator analysis. While this information may not be necessary for the description of transport phenomena, its use does lead to a very deep and satisfying understanding of the nature of irreversibility.

REFERENCES

1. Bogolubov, N., *Studies in Statistical Mechanics*, **1**, 1 (1962); *J. Phys. U.S.S.R.*, **10**, 256, 265 (1946).
2. Rice, S. A., J. G. Kirkwood, and R. A. Harris, *Physica*, **27**, 717 (1961).
3. Green, M. S., *Physica*, **24**, 393 (1958); *J. Chem. Phys.*, **25**, 836 (1956).
4. Résibois, P., *J. Math. Phys.*, **4**, 166 (1963).
5. Stecki, J., *Phys. Fluids*, **7**, 33 (1964); *J. Chem. Phys.*, **40**, 1197 (1964); H. S. Taylor and J. Stecki, to be published; see also, ONR Technical Report No. Nonr228(23) NR 013-307.
6. Green, M. S., *J. Chem. Phys.*, **20**, 1281 (1952); *J. Chem. Phys.*, **22**, 398 (1954).
7. Kubo, R., *J. Phys. Soc. Japan*, **12**, 570, 1203 (1957).
8. Résibois, P., *Physica*, to be published.
9. Kirkwood, J. G., and D. D. Fitts, *J. Chem. Phys.*, **33**, 1317 (1960).
10. Prigogine, I., *Non-Equilibrium Statistical Mechanics*, Interscience, New York 1962.
11. Balescu, R., *Statistical Mechanics of Charged Particles*, Wiley, New York, 1964.
12. Résibois, P., *Kinetic Theory of Classical Gases*, Gordon and Breach, to be published.
13. Prigogine, I., and P. Résibois, *Physica*, **27**, 629 (1961).
14. Kirkwood, J. G., *J. Chem. Phys.*, **14**, 180 (1946).
15. Mori, H., *Phys. Rev.*, **111**, 694 (1958); *Phys. Rev.*, **112**, 1829 (1958).
16. Green, H. S., *J. Math. Phys.*, **2**, 344 (1961).
17. Green, H. S., and W. Storer, *Phys. Fluids*, **5**, 1212 (1962).
18. McLennan, J. A., *Phys. Rev.*, **115**, 1405 (1959); *Phys. Fluids*, **3**, 493 (1960); *Phys. Fluids*, **4**, 1319 (1961); *Advances in Chemical Physics*, Vol. 5, I. Prigogine, ed., Interscience, New York, 1963, p. 261.
19. Helfand, E., *Phys. Rev.*, **119**, 1 (1960).
20. Kirkwood, J. G., *Rend. Scuola Intern. Fis. "Enrico Fermi."* X, Societá Italiana di Fisica, Bologna, 1960, p. 205.
21. Zubarev, D. N., *Dokl. Akad. Nauk SSSR*, **140**, 92 (1961); *Sov. Phys. Doklady (English Transl.)*, **6**, 776 (1962).
22. Montroll, E. W., *Rend. Scuola Intern. Fis. "Enrico Fermi."* X, Societá Italiana di Fisica, Bologna, 1960, p. 217; *Lectures in Theoretical Physics*, Vol. 3, W. E. Brittin, W. B. Downs, and J. Downs, eds., Interscience, New York, 1961, p. 221.

23. Lebowitz., J. L., and A. Shimony, *Phys. Rev.*, **128,** 1945 (1962).
24. Kubo, R., *Lectures in Theoretical Physics*, Vol. 1, W. E. Brittin and L. S. Dunham, eds., Interscience, New York, 1959, p. 120.
25. de Groot, S. R., and P. Mazur, *Nonequilibrium Thermodynamics*, North Holland, Amsterdam, 1962.
26. Mori, H., *J. Phys. Soc. Japan*, **11,** 1029 (1956).
27. Kubo, R., M. Yokota, and S. Nakajima, *J. Phys. Soc. Japan*, **12,** 1203 (1957).
28. Zwanzig, R. W., *Phys. Rev.*, **124,** 983 (1961); *Lectures in Theoretical Physics*, Vol. 3, W. E. Brittin, W. B. Downs and J. Downs, eds., Interscience, New York, 1962, p. 106.
29. Fixman, M., *J. Chem. Phys.*, **26,** 1421 (1957).
30. Longuet-Higgins, H. C., *Mol. Phys.*, **6,** 65 (1963).
31. Hashitsume, *Prog. Theoret. Phys.* (*Kyoto*), **8,** 461 (1952); **15,** 369 (1956).
32. Résibois, P., *J. Chem. Phys.*, **41,** 2979 (1964); G. Severne, *Physica*, to be published.
33. Widder, D. W., *The Laplace Transform*, Princeton University Press, Princeton, N.J., 1946.
34. Balescu, R., *Physica*, **27,** 693 (1961).

A Summing Up

This book has been devoted to the development of a kinetic theory of simple liquids. Throughout, we have emphasized one particular approach to this problem, describing extensively the relationships between theory and experiment. In closing, it is pertinent to summarize the main feature of the analysis. We limit attention to the theory of non-equilibrium processes.

(*a*) The description of non-equilibrium processes in a strongly interacting system requires, as a first step, resolution of the difficulties introduced by the time reversibility of the classical equations of motion and of a set of apparent paradoxes related to other aspects of the analytic character of these equations. We have shown that an internally consistent theory of steady state phenomena in liquids can be based on the following hypothesis (due to Kirkwood): There exists a time τ such that the phase of a subsystem of 1, 2, $\cdots$, molecules changes significantly only through interaction with its environment, and that the behavior of the environment during a time τ is statistically independent of its behavior in preceding intervals of length τ. With this hypothesis, the kinetic equations assume a Markovian form. It has also been shown that:

(1) In the steady state limit, the general theory of irreversible processes leads to Markovian kinetic equations.

(2) In the steady state limit, the general cluster series development of the kinetic equation derived from the time coarse graining hypothesis is identical with that derived from both the general analysis of Prigogine and co-workers and that of Bogolubov and of Green.

(3) The coarse graining hypothesis leads to the same autocorrelation function relations defining the transport coefficients as do the theories of Green and of Kubo. We therefore accept the coarse graining hypothesis as valid for the description of steady state phenomena in the liquid phase.

(*b*) The mode of interaction between a molecule or molecules and its environment in the liquid phase, as introduced above, is assumed to be a strongly repulsive encounter between a pair of molecules, followed by a quasi-Brownian motion of the molecule or molecules in the rapidly fluctuating force field of all the other neighboring molecules. Of course, the binary encounter is also influenced by the surrounding force field. This type of interaction leads to a natural division of the time scale into two parts: a short time scale on which large momentum and energy transfers occur via binary encounters, and a long time scale on which frequent small momentum and energy transfers occur via fluctuations in the intermolecular force field. It has been shown that:

(1) The use of different dynamical approximations suitable, respectively, to large momentum and energy transfers during the binary encounters and small momentum and energy transfers during the quasi-Brownian motion leads to simple kinetic equations for the singlet, doublet, · · · distribution functions in the liquid.

(2) The relevant relaxation times corresponding to the two parts of the fundamental dynamical event satisfy the conditions required for the validity of the coarse graining and for the validity of the definition of the mode of interaction, thus establishing the internal consistency of the analysis.

(*c*) The kinetic equations described in (*b*) may be solved for the case of small deviations from the equilibrium state of the liquid. The perturbed distribution functions depend on the macroscopic parameters defining the non-equilibrium state of the liquid both through distortions in momentum space and distortions in configuration space. In the approximation in which a constant (momentum independent) friction coefficient is defined, thereby reducing the fundamental kinetic equations to a sum of a modified Enskog-Boltzmann term and a Fokker-Planck term, it is found that

(1) The thermal conductivity contains contributions from both the modified binary encounters and the quasi-Brownian motion, but no cross terms. Using experimental data to compute the friction coefficient, good agreement between theory and experiment is obtained. The largest contribution to the thermal conductivity arises from the configuration space distortion of the distribution function.

(2) In addition to contributions similar to those just described, both the shear viscosity and the bulk viscosity contain a cross term

arising from the non-vanishing distortion of the pair correlation function at the short distances characteristic of the strongly repulsive binary encounter. Again, the configuration space distortion of the distribution function leads to a large contribution to the viscosities. Using experimental data to compute the friction coefficient, the agreement between theoretical and experimental shear viscosities is good. Preliminary investigations suggest that the bulk viscosity is also satisfactorily computed in the framework described.

(3) Application of the theory to the description of the limiting ionic mobility in cases such as Ar_2^+ in liquid Argon, and also to the description of the behavior of molten salts, leads to both qualitative and quantitative agreement between theory and experiment wherever such agreement may be tested.

(4) The analysis of the friction coefficient is the least adequate part of the kinetic theory developed. Nonetheless, semiquantitative agreement between theory and experiment is obtained when the effects of recoil (negative correlation) are included in the autocorrelation function for momentum. The general properties of the momentum autocorrelation function, as deduced from computer experiments, are well reproduced by simple arguments based on the notion that the average diffusive displacement in the liquid is a small fraction of the intermolecular spacing. This notion is supported by the available experimental data.

Having displayed the accomplishments of our analysis of transport processes in liquids, we now examine the inherent approximations in the theory, its shortcomings, and the directions in which improvements are needed. We note that

(*a*) The theory, as developed, is inapplicable to the description of transient phenomena. Because of the importance of non-Markovian effects in transient phenomena, it appears unlikely that any simple extension of the theory presented here will be useful in that regime.

(*b*) The general theory, as presented in Chapter 5, leads to a set of kinetic equations with momentum dependent friction coefficients. We have used the simplest possible approximation to this set of equations, in which the friction coefficients are assumed independent of momentum. Clearly, a more accurate description of liquids than that developed requires solution of the unapproximated kinetic equations. Experience gained from the analysis of the behavior of gases leads us to believe that no significant changes of interpretation will occur as a result of using the complete kinetic equations, but small quantitative changes in the predicted transport coefficients are to be expected.

A more far reaching improvement of the steady state theory will be achieved by the development of a systematic method for truncating the coupled hierarchy of integrodifferential equations for the distribution functions. The time coarse graining used here is, *a priori*, a hypothesis, and it is likely that an analysis of the process by which a non-Markovian equation may be reduced to a Markovian equation will facilitate the correct treatment of multiple collisions, render the assumption that the limit $\tau \to \infty$ is valid for calculating the Fokker-Planck term unnecessary, and allow explicit calculation of the interference between the strongly repulsive encounters and the quasi-Brownian motion.

(*c*) The theory of molecular friction, and especially of the momentum autocorrelation function, requires improvement. It is of particular importance to examine the role of non-Markovian effects in the autocorrelation function.

(*d*) The establishment of a direct connection between the general theory of irreversible processes developed by Prigogine and co-workers and the analysis described in this book is needed. Although we have shown that there is consistency at all points between these theories, and it is known that in the steady state they lead to the same formal cluster expansion, the theory presented here represents an unknown very highly summed form of the Prigogine perturbation series. It would be desirable to known which terms in the perturbation analysis have been omitted, and what perturbation theoretic meaning is to be attached to the notion of local equilibrium.

(*e*) The analysis presented has been entirely within the framework of classical mechanics. Extension of the theory to the description of quantum fluids is obviously desirable.

In this book we have presented what we believe to be a good first-order approximation to the description of non-equilibrium processes in the liquid phase. It is our hope that the theory developed can aid in the understanding of the properties of the liquid state in a manner analogous to the understanding of the gaseous state obtained from the mean free path theory of transport in gases. That is, we believe that all important physical phenomena have been included in our analysis, and that the numerical predictions of the theory are reasonably accurate. Whether or not the theory presented will play the role indicated depends upon its assimilation into the general corpus of the kinetic theory of matter. If the theory of liquids presented herein serves as a stimulus for further research on the many body problem, the efforts put forth in the preparation of the text will have been rewarded.

Author Index*

* *Italic* numbers refer to reference pages.

Subject Index